ELECTRONIC
CIRCUITS,
SIGNALS,
AND SYSTEMS

P9-BZS-836

S. Haykin

ELECTRONIC CIRCUITS, SIGNALS, AND SYSTEMS

SAMUEL J. MASON
Professor of Electrical Engineering

HENRY J. ZIMMERMANN
Professor of Electrical Engineering

Department of Electrical Engineering
and Research Laboratory of Electronics

Massachusetts Institute of Technology

JOHN WILEY & SONS, INC.
New York · London

Copyright © 1960 by John Wiley & Sons, Inc.

All rights reserved. This book or any part
thereof must not be reproduced in any form
without the written permission of the publisher.

Library of Congress Catalog Card Number: 60–5601

Printed in the United States of America

TO

JEANIE AND PRISCILLA

F O R E W O R D

This book is one of several resulting from a recent revision of the Electrical Engineering Course at The Massachusetts Institute of Technology. The books have the general format of texts and are being used as such. However, they might well be described as reports on a research program aimed at the evolution of an undergraduate core curriculum in Electrical Engineering that will form a basis for a continuing career in a field that is ever-changing.

The development of an educational program in Electrical Engineering to keep pace with the changes in technology is not a new endeavor at The Massachusetts Institute of Technology. In the early 1930's, the Faculty of the Department undertook a major review and reassessment of its program. By 1940, a series of new courses had been evolved, and resulted in the publication of four related books.

The new technology that appeared during World War II brought great changes to the field of Electrical Engineering. In recognition of this fact, the Faculty of the Department undertook another reassessment of its program. By about 1952, a pattern for a curriculum had been evolved and its implementation was initiated with a high degree of enthusiasm and vigor.

The new curriculum subordinates option structures built around areas of industrial practice in favor of a common core that provides a broad base for the engineering applications of the sciences. This core structure includes a newly developed laboratory program which stresses the role of experimentation and its relation to theoretical model-making in the solution of engineering problems. Faced with the time limitation of a four-year program for the Bachelor's degree, the entire core curriculum gives priority to basic principles and methods of analysis rather than to the presentation of current technology.

J. A. STRATTON

P R E F A C E

The study of electronic circuits, signals, and systems is based on a variety of models, each devised to facilitate the application of mathematical methods to engineering problems. The laws of physics provide basic models of charge motion, in terms of which we explain the observed terminal behavior of elementary components and devices, such as resistors, inductors, capacitors, diodes, transistors, and vacuum tubes. From physical models and observed terminal characteristics, we make circuit models that lead to simple circuits capable of performing basic operations or functions. These operations, such as amplification, addition, multiplication, and time delay, serve as the elementary building blocks or models with which we can construct models of more general systems. By a system, we mean a model of a signal transmission or processing operation, usually an interconnection of elementary models performing basic operations.

In the companion volume to this book, *Electronic Circuit Theory*, elementary linear circuit theory is extended to electronic circuits by adding the controlled source as one of the basic circuit elements. To cope with nonlinear problems, the ideal diode is introduced as a circuit element. These two elements, plus resistance, inductance, capacitance, and independent sources, permit the synthesis of models for electronic devices and circuits. In the first book the basic circuits that can be devised from control valves (such as transistors, triodes, and pentodes) are then developed to perform basic operations or functions, namely, linear amplification, wave shaping, waveform generation, and modulation. In all cases, these functions involve analytically simple waveforms and structurally simple circuits. Nearly all of these circuit functions involve nonlinear operations which can be handled either by square-law or piecewise-linear approximations.

In this volume we present methods suitable for handling more general circuits, with more general signals applied. These methods form an introduction to system theory. More specifically, Chapters 2 through 5 are concerned with matrix, topological, and signal-flow-graph methods of circuit analysis. Chapter 6 introduces Fourier theory and applies it to the description of signals, including some random signals. Chapter 7 uses amplifier circuits to illustrate the transmission of signals through linear systems, with transform techniques and convolution providing the basic mathematical tools. Chapter 8 applies the foregoing material to nonlinear and time-varying linear systems. Chapter 9 brings both the analytical and the topological methods to bear upon simple systems that exploit the negative-feedback concept.

The material can be organized in a number of ways for classroom presentation. For a one-semester subject in the area of signals and systems, one of several possible sequences of material is the following: the first half of Chapter 4; the first part of Chapter 7, through the super-position integral; selected topics from Chapter 6; the remainder of Chapter 7, omitting Hilbert transforms and transmission lines; Chapters 8 and 9. For a one-semester circuit-analysis subject, to follow a basic electronic-circuits subject, a possible sequence consists of Chapters 2 through 5, followed by 9. The selection of text material and problems can provide considerable flexibility in the level at which the subject is taught.

For background, history, extensions, further detail, and general collateral reading in circuit analysis, signal analysis, system theory, and communications, the reader is referred to the following short bibliography:

H. S. Black, *Modulation Theory*, Van Nostrand, New York, 1953.

H. W. Bode, *Network Analysis and Feedback Amplifier Design*, Van Nostrand, New York, 1945.

W. Cauer, *Synthesis of Linear Communication Networks*, Vols. I and II, translated by G. E. Knausenberger and J. N. Warfield, McGraw-Hill, New York, 1958.

Colin Cherry, *On Human Communication*, Technology Press, Cambridge, and John Wiley, New York, 1957.

W. B. Davenport, Jr., and W. L. Root, *An Introduction to the Theory of Signals and Noise*, McGraw-Hill, New York, 1958.

William Feller, *An Introduction to Probability Theory and Its Applications*, Vol. I, John Wiley, New York, 2nd ed., 1957.

M. F. Gardner and J. L. Barnes, *Transients in Linear Systems*, Vol. I, John Wiley, New York, 1942.

E. A. Guillemin, *The Mathematics of Circuit Analysis*, John Wiley, New York, 1949.

G. E. Valley and H. Wallman, *Vacuum-Tube Amplifiers*, McGraw-Hill, New York, 1948.

B. Van Der Pol and H. Bremmer, *Operational Calculus, Based on the Two-sided Laplace Integral*, Cambridge University Press, 1955.

H. J. Zimmermann and S. J. Mason, *Electronic Circuit Theory, Devices, Models, and Circuits*, John Wiley, New York, 1959.

Cherry's book contains an extensive general bibliography in the areas of modern statistical communication theory, information theory, and the physiology, psychology, and linguistics of communications. Cauer's book carries an excellent bibliographical appendix, including references in the field of topological network analysis, which originated with Kirchhoff in 1847.

We wish to acknowledge our indebtedness to many of our colleagues on the teaching staff and staff members of the Research Laboratory of Electronics. In particular, personal communication with Godfrey T. Coate helped to set the initial direction of the material on circuit analysis. The continuing influence of Professors Murray F. Gardner, Ernst A. Guillemin, and Yuk-Wing Lee is clearly apparent in various parts of the text. We also wish to thank Professors Peter Elias, James W. Graham, Edward M. Hofstetter, and Doctor Albert H. Nuttall for valuable comments on portions of the manuscript, and Robert S. Cooper, David A. Chesler, Lester A. Gimpleson, and Frederick C. Hennie, III, for their careful and helpful reading of proof. Professors Campbell L. Searle and Richard D. Thornton also contributed significantly to the job in the early stages of notes and manuscript.

We express our thanks to Professor Gordon S. Brown for his leadership and support during his tenure as Head of the Electrical Engineering Department and for his continuing interest since becoming Dean of Engineering. We are also indebted to Professor Jerome B. Wiesner, Director of the Research Laboratory of Electronics and currently Acting Head of the Electrical Engineering Department, for his advice and encouragement. Our acknowledgments would be incomplete without thanks to the secretaries who typed rough draft, notes, and manuscript. They are Carolyn Bennett, Marjorie D'Amato, Margot Fuller, and Nancy Rhodenizer.

SAMUEL J. MASON
HENRY J. ZIMMERMANN

Cambridge, Massachusetts
January, 1960

C O N T E N T S

Chapter 1   Introduction   1

   1.1 Circuits, Signals, and Systems, 1
   1.2 Signal Transmission and Processing, 2
   1.3 System Models, 2
   1.4 Methods of Analysis, 3

      2   Matrix Circuit Analysis   6

   2.1 Introduction, 6
   2.2 Matrix Operations, 8
   2.3 Matrix Representation of Linear Simultaneous
        Equations, 13
   2.4 Some Properties of Determinants, 14
   2.5 Inversion of a Matrix, 17
   2.6 Formulation of the Nodal Admittance Matrix of
        a Branch Network, 20
   2.7 The Nodal Impedance Matrix, 24
   2.8 Voltage Ratios and Current Ratios, 26
   2.9 The Floating Nodal Admittance Matrix, 27
   2.10 Floating Admittance Matrices for Circuit Models
        of Electronic Devices, 31
   2.11 An Illustrative Example—the Cathode Fol-
        lower, 37
   2.12 Another Illustrative Example—the Miller In-
        tegrator, 38
   2.13 Other   Matrices   for   Three-Terminal-Device
        Models, 39
   2.14 Complex Power, 41

3 Topological Circuit Analysis   **54**

3.1 Introduction, 54
3.2 The Network Determinant, 55
3.3 Partial Factoring of Determinants, 56
3.4 The Topological Transmission Law for a Branch
     Network, 59
3.5 A Branchlike Model for the General Linear Net-
     work, 62
3.6 The Topological Transmission Law for a General
     Linear Network, 66
3.7 Analysis of a Simple Triode Circuit, 68
3.8 Analysis of a Triode Amplifier, 69
3.9 Analysis of a Transistor Amplifier, 69
3.10 The Gyristor and the Gyrator, 71
3.11 Outline of a Proof of the Topological Transmission
     Laws, 76
3.12 Absorption of a Node, 81

4 Linear Signal-Flow Graphs   **92**

4.1 Introduction, 92
4.2 The Linear Signal-Flow Graph, 93
4.3 Elementary Equivalences, 95
4.4 The Effect of a Self-Loop, 96
4.5 Absorption of a Node, 98
4.6 The Transmission of a Flow Graph, 99
4.7 The General Flow Graph, 100
4.8 Evaluation of a Graph Transmission by Identi-
     fication of Paths and Loops, 100
4.9 Node Splitting, 105
4.10 The Loop Transmission of a Node or a Branch, 105
4.11 The Determinant of a Flow Graph, 107
4.12 Expansion of the Determinant in Loops, 110
4.13 Factorable Determinants, 111
4.14 Expansion on a Node or on a Branch, 112
4.15 Outline of a Proof of the General Transmission
     Expression, 114
4.16 Inversion of a Path or Loop, 115
4.17 Normalization of Branch Transmissions, 120
4.18 Reversal of a Flow Graph, 122

5 Flow-Graph Circuit Analysis **127**

5.1 Introduction, 127
5.2 Two-Terminal-Pair Networks, 129
5.3 Cascaded Two-Terminal-Pair Networks, 137
5.4 The Primitive Flow Graph for a Branch Network, 140
5.5 Node-Voltage and Loop-Current Analysis, 145
5.6 Unilateral Constraints, 153
5.7 The Node-Voltage Flow Graph for a Unistor Network, 155
5.8 Basic Transistor and Vacuum-Triode Models, 157
5.9 The Cathode-Coupled Amplifier, 169
5.10 The Cascode Amplifier, 170
5.11 The Pentode Amplifier, 172

6 Signal Analysis **178**

6.1 Introduction, 178
6.2 Pulse Signals, 180
6.3 Periodic Signals, 182
6.4 Almost-Periodic Signals, 184
6.5 Random Signals, 185
6.6 Stationary Random Processes, 188
6.7 Direct and Alternating Components, 190
6.8 Even and Odd Components, 193
6.9 Real and Imaginary Components, 194
6.10 Comparison of Vectors, 195
6.11 Comparison of Signals, 197
6.12 The Correlation Function, 206
6.13 The Trigonometric Fourier Series for a Periodic Signal, 222
6.14 The Exponential Fourier Series, 227
6.15 Some Fundamental Properties of the Fourier Series, 231
6.16 Transition to the Fourier Integral of a Pulse Signal, 232
6.17 Some Fundamental Properties of Fourier Transforms, 235
6.18 Bounds on the Spectrum, 237
6.19 The Fourier Series as a Limiting Form of the Fourier Integral, 242

6.20 Comparison of Spectra, 247
6.21 Completeness of the Fourier Representation, 249
6.22 Some Pulse Signals and Their Spectra, 251
6.23 Some Periodic Signals and Their Spectra, 261
6.24 Some Random Power Signals and Their Spectra, 269
6.25 A Word About Random Pulse Signals, 278
6.26 Crosscorrelation of Spectra, 279
6.27 The Sampling Theorem, 281
6.28 More About Combinations of Signals, 282

7 Transmission of Signals Through Linear Systems   310

7.1 Introduction, 310
7.2 The Singularity Signals, 310
7.3 The Impulse Response of a Linear Transmission System, 318
7.4 The Superposition Integral, 320
7.5 Interpretation of the Superposition Integral as a Correlation Operation, 324
7.6 Convolution Algebra, 326
7.7 The Solution of Certain Convolution Equations, 330
7.8 Complex Exponential Signals, 335
7.9 The System Function $H(s)$, 340
7.10 Correlation of Input and Output Signals, 343
7.11 Signal Matching, 345
7.12 Real and Imaginary Parts of a Realizable Stable Frequency-Response Function, 350
7.13 The Real Part Integral, 354
7.14 Gain and Phase, 357
7.15 Carrier Delay and Envelope Delay, 366
7.16 Exponential Transforms, 369
7.17 Some Fundamental Properties of Exponential Transforms, 373
7.18 Contour Integration, 376
7.19 The One-Pole Transmission, 385
7.20 Circle Diagrams, 392
7.21 An Illustrative Example—a Feedback Integrator, 395
7.22 The Two-Pole Transmission, 399
7.23 The Resonant Two-Pole Transmission, 406

7.24 Resonance in an RC-Coupled Feedback Circuit, 418

7.25 The Basic Definition of Q in Terms of Energy, 420

7.26 The Flat Low-Pass Transmission, 422

7.27 The Flat Band-Pass Transmission, 428

7.28 Rational Transmissions, 432

7.29 The One-Pole All-Pass Transmission, 436

7.30 The Exponential Transmission—Ideal Delay, 440

7.31 Reflection of Waves, 444

7.32 Wave Launching, 449

7.33 A Lumped Attenuator, 450

7.34 Discontinuities in Characteristic Resistance, 451

7.35 Scattering Coefficients, 455

7.36 A System Containing Random-Phase Transmissions, 458

7.37 A "Pulse-Forming" Transmission-Line System, 460

7.38 A Potentially Unstable Transmission-Line System, 461

7.39 Some General Remarks About Systems Containing Ideal-Delay Elements, 464

7.40 The "Binomial" Delay System, 466

8 Nonlinear and Time-Varying Linear Systems   503

8.1 Introduction, 503

8.2 Multiplication of Signals in a Nonlinear System, 505

8.3 The Pentode as a Modulator, 508

8.4 Elementary Systems Containing Multipliers, 509

8.5 Power Amplification in a Time-Varying System, 511

8.6 General Representation of a Time-Varying Linear System, 514

8.7 Amplitude Modulation, 515

8.8 Suppressed-Carrier Modulation, 520

8.9 A Two-Channel Modulation System, 524

8.10 Illustrations of Different Types of Modulation in Terms of the Two-Channel System, 527

8.11 Phase and Frequency Modulation, 531

8.12 Frequency Multiplexing, 534

8.13 Pulse-Amplitude Modulation, 535

8.14 Time Multiplexing, 538
8.15 Pulse-Code Modulation, 543
8.16 Some General Remarks About Nonlinear Sys-
       tems, 549

9 The Negative-Feedback Concept   565

9.1   Introduction, 565
9.2   Automatic Control by Means of Negative Feed-
       back, 566
9.3   Control of a Nonlinear Transmission, 569
9.4   Control of a Linear Frequency-Dependent Trans-
       mission, 572
9.5   Control of a Nonlinear Frequency-Dependent
       Transmission, 575
9.6   Reduction of Noise and Distortion, 577
9.7   Sensitivity, 579
9.8   Control of Impedance, 583
9.9   Stability Considerations, 584
9.10 The Stability of an Arbitrary Linear Flow
       Graph, 592
9.11 Illustrative Examples of Feedback in Electronic
       Circuits, 595

Appendix A   Bessel Functions of the First Kind   612

Index   613

Introduction

1.1 Circuits, Signals, and Systems

Electronic systems can be defined broadly as combinations of circuits that process signals. The signals may be voltages or currents, but if energy transducers are part of the system, the signals may represent other physical variables. The distinction between circuits and systems depends more on the point of view than on complexity. For example, a simple RC circuit is an elementary signal processing system. The system viewpoint emphasizes operational functions or input-output relations. The circuit viewpoint is concerned with the determination of currents and voltages for branches or loops of a circuit. System theory is involved with signal transmission or signal processing, circuit theory with the realization of circuits to perform the necessary functions or carry out the processes.

Just as we build up a circuit theory based on ideal circuit elements that are similar to physical devices, we shall find it convenient to build up a system theory based on ideal elements that represent desired system functions. A knowledge of the capabilities and limitations of circuits is necessary for practical system design. However, it is possible to proceed with system studies, based on ideal elements, independent of how the counterpart of the ideal element is designed as a physical circuit.

1.2   Signal Transmission and Processing

Signals are the physical means of conveying messages, and since electrical signals are by far the most convenient to process or transmit they are used in nearly all branches of technology. A transmission system is one in which a signal must be preserved and eventually reproduced. Conventional communication systems are familiar examples.

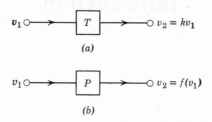

$$(a)$$

$$(b)$$

Fig. 1-1.   Signal transmission and processing systems.

A signal processing system is one that operates on a message signal to derive a new message. Thus, a digital computer combines a number of input signals in order to produce a result that is dependent on the inputs yet entirely different from any of them. It is apparent from Fig. 1-1 that transmission can be considered as a special case of processing since the former amounts to a proportional relation between input and output whereas the latter can be any functional relation. As we shall see, signal processing by a *linear* system is equivalent to transmission through a number of systems in parallel, each capable of carrying signals at a different frequency.

1.3   System Models

System analysis and design are facilitated by the use of models based upon ideal elements. In general, the elements represent functional operations on signals. Typical examples are amplification, integration, time delay, addition, and multiplication. These are ideal mathematical operations that can be approximated quite closely by physical circuits.

An audio amplifier is a transmission system which is performing only one function, namely, amplification. Representing the entire amplifier by a single block as in Fig. 1-1(a) is a higher level of abstraction than a complete circuit diagram. The circuit of a simple Miller integrator is shown in Fig. 1-2(a) while (b) denotes an ideal integrator followed by an ideal amplifier. Since a system element may be the idealization of any one of many circuits, the diagram in (b) is more general than the circuit in (a).

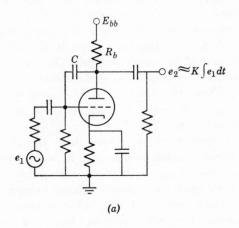

(a)

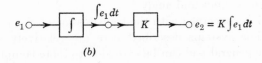

(b)

Fig. 1-2. Miller circuit and ideal integrator.

1.4 Methods of Analysis

Analysis and synthesis procedures useful for dealing with circuits, signals, and systems fall into a number of different categories. Although these methods are all somewhat related, they can be studied more or less independently of each other.

Chapter 2 introduces the methods of matrix algebra, which provide the formal procedure for handling linear equations. Although matrices are not heavily used in the remainder of the book, some knowledge of the subject is desirable as background.

Chapter 3 presents a topological method of circuit analysis that had its origin with Kirchhoff. This method provides considerable insight into circuit behavior. Its power lies in the fact that there are only two steps; formulation of a problem can be followed directly with the solution.

It is expected that the reader is already familiar with conventional methods of circuit analysis; the topological laws are offered for the value of another viewpoint. Proof of the laws is facilitated by the use of matrices.

Chapter 4 develops a topological method of analysis that sets forth the system concept explicitly. Each branch of a signal-flow graph designates a transmission or cause-and-effect relation between two variables. This corresponds to the input-output relation characteristic of a system element, hence a signal-flow graph is a system diagram. Like the topological method of circuit analysis, the signal-flow graph method provides a solution by inspection of the structure of the graph.

Chapter 5 provides illustrative examples of the use of flow graphs in solving electronic circuit problems. Any one of these circuits can be considered to be a small "system."

Chapter 6 treats Fourier methods, which form the core of signal analysis. The correlation concept is discussed at some length for the purpose of providing a unified approach to periodic, pulse, and random signals. Although signal analysis is closely related to circuit analysis, the mathematical methods presented here differ sharply from those in the previous chapters. One might say that Chapters 2 through 5 are "algebraic," whereas Chapter 6 and the remainder of the book draw heavily upon calculus and analysis.

Chapter 7 is concerned with the transmission of signals through linear systems. The systems described here are relatively simple but the methods are general and can be extended to more complicated systems. The calculation of system response for a given input signal is closely related to the mathematics of signal analysis.

Chapter 8 presents extensions of the linear methods to nonlinear and time-varying-linear systems. The modulation functions described here are quite general, yet the variety of specific examples indicates the many possibilities that exist for signal processing.

Chapter 9 gives a brief introduction to the negative-feedback concept, which is the basis for control system design. As in Chapter 8, linear methods are exploited in the quasi-linear analysis of systems that are actually nonlinear.

PROBLEMS

1.1 Devise a simple resistive circuit whose output voltage is the instantaneous average of two or more applied voltages.

1.2 A capacitance driven by an ideal current source develops a voltage proportional to the integral of the current. If the capacitance C is now shunted by a resistance R, determine suitable restrictions on the operation (the current waveform, the time of integration, and so forth) if e is to be within 1 per cent of the true integral.

1.3 Draw a block-diagram model for a pentode amplifier with parallel RLC plate load. Assume linear operation.

1.4 Sketch at least three physical systems that have the same block diagram as that obtained in Problem 1.3, that is, the same relationship between excitation and response variables.

1.5 Sketch the block diagram of a system for converting a sine wave to an approximate square wave.

1.6 Draw a block diagram indicating the functions involved in the operation of a radio transmitter and receiver.

1.7 Draw a block diagram representing the second-order linear differential equation

$$a \frac{d^2y}{dt^2} + b \frac{dy}{dt} + cy = f(t)$$

1.8 Draw a block diagram for the operations involved in calculating the value of a second-order determinant.

1.9 Draw a block diagram for a system that computes the product of two signals, using only linear system elements plus "squaring" elements. The output signal of a squaring element is the instantaneous square of the input. *Hint:* $(x + y)^2 - (x - y)^2 = 4xy$.

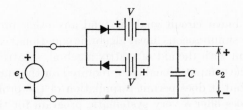

Fig. P1-1

1.10 The circuit in Fig. P1-1 is sometimes used to simulate electrically the relationship between the input and output shaft angles of a mechanical gear drive in which "backlash" is present. Explain. Draw a block diagram for the system.

Matrix Circuit Analysis

2.1   Introduction

Problems in linear circuit analysis (and any other problems describable in terms of simultaneous linear algebraic equations) can be organized in compact form with the aid of matrix algebra. Matrix notation does not eliminate the computational labor required for the numerical solution of a problem, but it does permit formulation of the problem in unified style, and it does offer a very systematic program for the arithmetical solutions. In this chapter we shall present the fundamentals of matrix algebra, and use them to describe and analyze the linear models of electric and electronic circuits.

A matrix is a rectangular array of elements. It can be expressed as a single symbol, which stands for the whole array, or the two-dimensional arrangement of elements can be shown in full. Various notations are used to set off the array, the most common being boxes, brackets, or large parentheses.

Matrix:

$$A = \begin{array}{|c|c|c|} \hline A_{11} & A_{12} & A_{13} \\ \hline A_{21} & A_{22} & A_{23} \\ \hline \end{array} = \begin{bmatrix} A_{11} & A_{12} & A_{13} \\ A_{21} & A_{22} & A_{23} \end{bmatrix} = \begin{pmatrix} A_{11} & A_{12} & A_{13} \\ A_{21} & A_{22} & A_{23} \end{pmatrix}$$

$$(2.1)$$

The size of a matrix is given by the number of rows and the number of columns.

$$\textit{Rectangular matrix:} \quad \left.\begin{pmatrix} A_{11} & A_{12} \\ A_{21} & A_{22} \\ A_{31} & A_{32} \end{pmatrix} \begin{matrix} \cdots \\ \cdots \\ \cdots \end{matrix} \right\} \; 3 \text{ rows} \qquad (2.2)$$

$$\underbrace{\phantom{2 \text{ columns}}}_{2 \text{ columns}}$$

The location of an element in the array is usually designated by double subscripts; the first subscript is the row number and the second subscript is the column number. The rows are numbered from the top of the matrix downward; the columns, from left to right.

Matrix element: $\quad A_{jk}$ = element in jth row and kth column $\quad$ (2.3)

A square matrix is one having the same number of rows and columns.

$$\textit{Square matrix:} \quad \begin{pmatrix} A_{11} & A_{12} \\ A_{21} & A_{22} \end{pmatrix} \qquad (2.4)$$

A diagonal matrix has nonzero elements only on the main diagonal. If a matrix is known to be diagonal, double-subscript notation becomes superfluous and, when convenient or desirable, a single subscript can be used.

$$\textit{Diagonal matrix:} \quad \begin{pmatrix} A_{11} & 0 & 0 \\ 0 & A_{22} & 0 \\ 0 & 0 & A_{33} \end{pmatrix} \quad \text{or} \quad \begin{pmatrix} A_1 & 0 & 0 \\ 0 & A_2 & 0 \\ 0 & 0 & A_3 \end{pmatrix} \quad (2.5)$$

A triangular matrix is empty either above or below the principal diagonal.

$$\textit{Triangular matrix:} \quad \begin{pmatrix} A_{11} & A_{12} & A_{13} \\ 0 & A_{22} & A_{23} \\ 0 & 0 & A_{33} \end{pmatrix} \quad \text{or} \quad \begin{pmatrix} A_{11} & 0 & 0 \\ A_{21} & A_{22} & 0 \\ A_{31} & A_{32} & A_{33} \end{pmatrix} \quad (2.6)$$

The row matrix has only one row,

Row matrix or *Row vector:*

$$(A_{11} \quad A_{12} \quad A_{13}) \quad \text{or} \quad (A_1 \quad A_2 \quad A_3) \qquad (2.7)$$

and the column matrix has only one column,

$$\textit{Column matrix or Column vector:} \quad \begin{pmatrix} A_{11} \\ A_{21} \\ A_{31} \end{pmatrix} \quad \text{or} \quad \begin{pmatrix} A_1 \\ A_2 \\ A_3 \end{pmatrix} \quad (2.8)$$

Row and column matrices are sometimes referred to as vectors because of the analogy between the elements of the matrix and the components of a vector. However, a vector is a special entity having certain properties arising from associated geometry. If we speak of a vector here it will be in the loose sense, and will denote only a one-dimensional array of arbitrary elements.

The unit matrix has unity elements on the main diagonal and zeros elsewhere.

$$\textit{Unit matrix or Identity matrix:} \quad I = \begin{pmatrix} 1 & 0 & 0 \\ 0 & 1 & 0 \\ 0 & 0 & 1 \end{pmatrix} \quad (2.9)$$

The null matrix is vacant, having zeros for each of its elements.

$$\textit{Null or zero matrix:} \quad 0 = \begin{pmatrix} 0 & 0 & 0 \\ 0 & 0 & 0 \\ 0 & 0 & 0 \end{pmatrix} \quad (2.10)$$

Formally, two matrices can be compared only if they have the same number of rows and the same number of columns. In order that matrices of different sizes may be compared, one or both of them can be filled out to the same dimensions as the other by adding columns of zeros on the right or rows of zeros on the bottom. This process is called completing the matrix.

$$\textit{Completion of a matrix:} \quad \begin{pmatrix} A_{11} \\ A_{21} \end{pmatrix} \rightarrow \begin{pmatrix} A_{11} & 0 \\ A_{21} & 0 \end{pmatrix} \quad (2.11)$$

or
$$(A_{11} \quad A_{12}) \rightarrow \begin{pmatrix} A_{11} & A_{12} \\ 0 & 0 \end{pmatrix} \quad (2.12)$$

or
$$\begin{pmatrix} A_{11} & A_{12} \\ A_{21} & A_{22} \end{pmatrix} \rightarrow \begin{pmatrix} A_{11} & A_{12} & 0 & 0 \\ A_{21} & A_{22} & 0 & 0 \\ 0 & 0 & 0 & 0 \end{pmatrix} \quad (2.13)$$

2.2 Matrix Operations

Having defined the fundamental matrix forms, we come next to the rules for operating with matrices. These are analogous to the laws of algebra which govern the manipulation of ordinary numbers or their symbols.

Two matrices are said to be equal if their corresponding elements are equal. Obviously, two matrices cannot be equal unless they have the same number of rows and columns, or unless they have been completed to the same size as illustrated above.

$$\text{Equality:} \quad A = B \text{ means } A_{jk} = B_{jk}, \text{ for all } j \text{ and } k \qquad (2.14)$$

The addition of two matrices is accomplished by adding their corresponding elements.

$$\text{Addition:} \quad A + B = C \text{ means } A_{jk} + B_{jk} = C_{jk} \qquad (2.15)$$

Multiplication of a matrix by a scalar is equivalent to multiplying each element of that matrix by that scalar. A scalar is an ordinary number (a matrix having only one row and one column).

$$\text{Multiplication by a scalar } \phi: \quad \phi A = B \text{ means } \phi A_{jk} = B_{jk} \qquad (2.16)$$

When matrices are being equated, added, or multiplied by a scalar, they have exactly the same properties as ordinary numbers. Multiplication of one matrix by another, however, follows special rules reflecting the properties of linear algebraic transformations. The product AB is another matrix C in which each element C_{jk} is defined as a sum of products of elements taken from the two matrices, A and B, as follows.

$$\text{Matrix multiplication:} \quad AB = C \text{ means } \sum_{m} A_{jm} B_{mk} = C_{jk} \qquad (2.17)$$

To find the element C_{jk} in the jth row and kth column of the product matrix C, lift the jth row from the first matrix and the kth column from the second. Place this row and this column alongside each other, multiply adjacent elements, and then add the resulting products, as indicated in Fig. 2-1(a). The dimensions of the product matrix can be seen clearly with the aid of the arrangement shown in Fig. 2-1(b). Observe that the product AB, formed by *premultiplying* B by A, or *postmultiplying* A by B, will have the same number of rows as A and the same number of columns as B. Moreover, the product has meaning only if the columns of A and the rows of B are equal in number. This last condition is known as compatibility. In terms of Fig. 2-1(b), matrices A and B may be interpreted as the side and top views of a box. The product C represents the front view. Matrices A and B are compatible with respect to the product AB if the box is the same length in both the side view and the top view.

It follows from (2.14) through (2.17) that matrices obey all the fundamental laws of elementary algebra with the exception of multiplicative commutation.

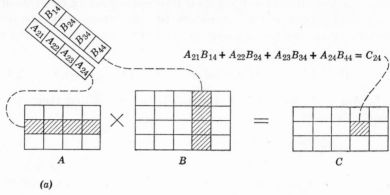

(a)

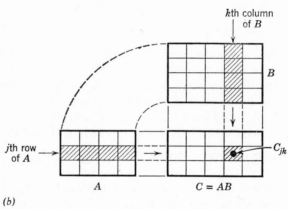

(b)

Fig. 2-1.   Matrix multiplication.

Additive association: $(A + B) + C \equiv A + (B + C)$ (2.18)

Additive commutation: $A + B \equiv B + A$ (2.19)

Distribution: $A(B + C) \equiv AB + AC$ (2.20)

Multiplicative association: $(AB)C \equiv A(BC)$ (2.21)

Multiplicative commutation: $AB \not\equiv BA$ (2.22)

Multiplication by unit matrix: $IA \equiv AI \equiv A$ (2.23)

The general failure of commutation can be deduced directly from (2.17), but a quick disproof is offered by the specific counterexample shown in Fig. 2-2. Postmultiplication of a column vector by a row vector gives a square multiplication table, whereas premultiplication by the row vector leads to a scalar which is sometimes called the *inner product* of the two vectors.

The associative law for multiplication, (2.21), needs some explanation since it may not be immediately obvious from (2.17). Relation (2.17) leads directly to the triple product

$$ABC = D \text{ means } \sum_{m,n} A_{jm}B_{mn}C_{nk} = D_{jk} \qquad (2.24)$$

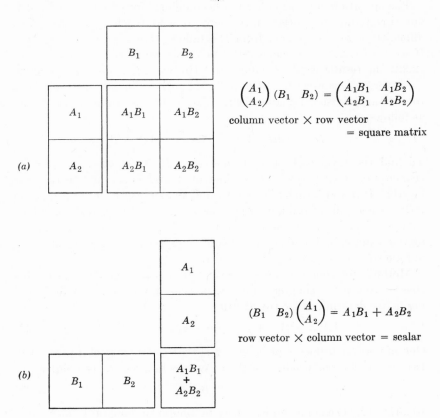

$$\begin{pmatrix} A_1 \\ A_2 \end{pmatrix} (B_1 \quad B_2) = \begin{pmatrix} A_1B_1 & A_1B_2 \\ A_2B_1 & A_2B_2 \end{pmatrix}$$

column vector $\times$ row vector
$\qquad\qquad = $ square matrix

$$(B_1 \quad B_2)\begin{pmatrix} A_1 \\ A_2 \end{pmatrix} = A_1B_1 + A_2B_2$$

row vector $\times$ column vector = scalar

Fig. 2-2. An example which illustrates $AB \neq BA$.

and the associative law then results from the observation that it does not matter whether we sum first over the index m or over the index n.

The transposition of a matrix is accomplished by interchanging those pairs of elements which are mirror images about the main diagonal. In short, the matrix is flipped about the main diagonal.

$$\textit{Transposition:} \quad A = B_t \text{ means } A_{jk} = B_{kj} \qquad (2.25)$$

In transposing a nonsquare matrix, we tacitly assume that the matrix is first completed to a square by means of (2.11) or (2.12). A small amount of subscript manipulation in (2.17) shows that the transposition of a product of two matrices is the product of their transpositions taken in reverse order,

$$(AB)_t \equiv B_t A_t \tag{2.26}$$

The operation of division has not been defined for matrices, and much notational difficulty arises if we try to work with quotients. The difficulty arises, of course, from the failure of the commutation law. If we say A/B, do we mean AB^{-1} or do we mean $B^{-1}A$? In view of (2.22) the results would be different. However, it is possible to define the inverse of a matrix B^{-1} so that the sequence of operations equivalent to ordinary division remains clear. The inverse of a matrix is defined as follows,

$$Inversion: \quad A = B^{-1} \text{ means } AB = I \tag{2.27}$$

To find the inverse A of a given matrix B, we must determine the elements of A such that the product of A and B is equal to the unit matrix. If A and B each have n rows and n columns, the matrix equation $AB = I$ contains n^2 ordinary equations which can (in general) be solved for the n^2 unknown element values A_{jk}. The inverse of a nonsquare matrix cannot be found, as we should soon see if we tried to obtain a unique solution of the associated equations.

Methods for constructing the inverse of a square matrix will be discussed later in the chapter. For the present, the inverse is defined and implicitly determined by the identity

$$AA^{-1} \equiv A^{-1}A \equiv I, \text{ for a square matrix } A \tag{2.28}$$

One important property of inversion is that the inverse of a product of two matrices is the product of their inverses taken in reverse order.

$$(AB)^{-1} \equiv B^{-1}A^{-1} \tag{2.29}$$

Relation (2.29) can be verified easily by premultiplying both sides of the identity by AB. The left side then reduces immediately to the unit matrix, as does the right side of the identity after recognition of (2.21) and (2.23).

The diagonal matrix is a special case in which the inverse is very easy to construct, since the product of two diagonal matrices is obtained merely by multiplying the corresponding elements. It follows that

$$Inversion \ of \ a \ diagonal \ matrix: \quad A = B^{-1} \text{ means } A_{jj} = 1/B_{jj} \tag{2.30}$$

As we shall see later, one very useful way of inverting a general square matrix is to reduce it first to diagonal form with the aid of certain elementary transformations.

2.3 Matrix Representation of Linear Simultaneous Equations

Figure 2-3 shows two sets of simultaneous linear equations. The first pair of equations expresses variables z_1 and z_2 in terms of the variables y_1 and y_2. Given the values of the coefficients a_{11}, a_{12}, a_{21}, and a_{22}, we can calculate z_1 and z_2 explicitly for any assigned values of

$$z_1 = a_{11}y_1 + a_{12}y_2, \qquad y_1 = b_{11}x_1 + b_{12}x_2$$

$$z_2 = a_{21}y_1 + a_{22}y_2, \qquad y_2 = b_{21}x_1 + b_{22}x_2$$

$$\begin{pmatrix} z_1 \\ z_2 \end{pmatrix} = \begin{pmatrix} a_{11} & a_{12} \\ a_{21} & a_{22} \end{pmatrix} \begin{pmatrix} y_1 \\ y_2 \end{pmatrix}, \qquad \begin{pmatrix} y_1 \\ y_2 \end{pmatrix} = \begin{pmatrix} b_{11} & b_{12} \\ b_{21} & b_{22} \end{pmatrix} \begin{pmatrix} x_1 \\ x_2 \end{pmatrix}$$

$$z = ay, \qquad y = bx$$

$$z = a(bx) = (ab)x$$

or

$$z = cx, \text{ where } c = ab$$

Fig. 2-3. Linear transformations.

y_1 and y_2. In mathematical language we can say that the square matrix a *transforms* the vector y into a new vector z. Similarly, the second set of equations shown in Fig. 2-3 represents the transformation of vector x into vector y.

Matrix notation offers a very convenient way of handling a succession of such transformations. The transformations from x to y and thence to z can be combined as a single transformation c relating x to z, as indicated in Fig. 2-3. The operation involved is matrix multiplication.

Now consider a single set of simultaneous linear equations which can be written as the single matrix equation

$$y = ax \tag{2.31}$$

Matrix a is assumed to be known, whereas vectors x and y are variables related by the matrix equation. Given x, we can calculate y directly by matrix multiplication. Suppose, instead, that y is given and the corresponding value of x is desired. In other words, it is desired to solve a set of simultaneous linear algebraic equations for the unknown values

$x_1, x_2, \cdots, x_n$ in terms of the given quantities $y_1, y_2, \cdots, y_n$ and the known coefficients a_{jk}. Here again, matrix notation is a great convenience. Premultiplication of both sides of (2.31) by the inverse of the coefficient matrix yields

$$a^{-1}y = a^{-1}(ax) = (a^{-1}a)x = Ix = x \qquad (2.32)$$

Hence the desired value of x is given explicitly by the matrix equation

$$x = a^{-1}y \qquad (2.33)$$

The operation involved is inversion of a matrix. In short, the solution of simultaneous linear algebraic equations and the inversion of a matrix are identical problems. Matrices permit us to express large sets of linear simultaneous algebraic equations in a very simple symbolic form. Thus the numerical calculations can be put off until the very end of the problem, at which point the matrix expressions serve as a systematic and efficient program for the required arithmetic.

2.4 Some Properties of Determinants

The inverse of a matrix can be calculated by combining the elements of that matrix in a specified way to give the elements of the inverse matrix. Instead of jumping directly to the formulas which give the elements of the inverse in terms of the elements of the original matrix, it is more instructive to introduce a quantity called the determinant of a matrix. The inverse matrix can then be expressed rather simply in terms of the determinant and other quantities derived from the determinant. The determinant of a matrix is usually denoted by placing vertical bars on each side of the array of matrix elements.

$$\text{Determinant of matrix } a: \quad \Delta = \begin{vmatrix} a_{11} & a_{12} & a_{13} \\ a_{21} & a_{22} & a_{23} \\ a_{31} & a_{32} & a_{33} \end{vmatrix} \qquad (2.34)$$

These bars mean that the matrix elements are to be combined in a certain way to yield a single scalar quantity or number Δ which is called the determinant of that matrix. The determinant of matrix a is defined as:

$\Delta = \sum a_{1i}a_{2j}a_{3k} \cdots a_{nr}$, summed over all permutations of the column subscripts $i, j, k \cdots r$, with the sign of each term being positive (negative) for an even (odd) number of ad-

jacent interchanges required to produce that permutation
from the original column-subscript order 1, 2, 3 $\cdots n$ (2.35)

For example,

$$\begin{vmatrix} a_{11} & a_{12} \\ a_{21} & a_{22} \end{vmatrix} = a_{11}a_{22} - a_{12}a_{21} \qquad (2.36)$$

and

$$\begin{vmatrix} a_{11} & a_{12} & a_{13} \\ a_{21} & a_{22} & a_{23} \\ a_{31} & a_{32} & a_{33} \end{vmatrix} = \begin{aligned} & a_{11}a_{22}a_{33} - a_{11}a_{23}a_{32} + a_{13}a_{21}a_{32} \\ & - a_{13}a_{22}a_{31} + a_{12}a_{23}a_{31} - a_{12}a_{21}a_{33} \end{aligned} \quad (2.37)$$

In (2.37) the successive column-subscript permutations are 123, 132,
312, 321, 231, 213, and each permutation differs from its predecessor by
a single interchange of adjacent column numbers.

The cofactor of any element a_{jk} is defined as

$$Cofactor\ of\ element\ a_{jk}\colon \quad \Delta_{jk} = \frac{\partial \Delta}{\partial a_{jk}} \qquad (2.38)$$

An equivalent definition of the cofactor is

Δ_{jk} = the Δ obtained by collapsing the jth row and kth column

multiplied by $(-1)^{j+k}$ (2.39)

For example, the cofactor of element a_{33} in (2.37) is just equal to the
determinant (2.36). Further examples are given in Fig. 2-4.

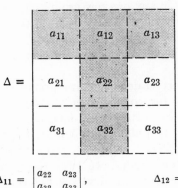

$$\Delta = \begin{vmatrix} a_{11} & a_{12} & a_{13} \\ a_{21} & a_{22} & a_{23} \\ a_{31} & a_{32} & a_{33} \end{vmatrix}$$

Collapsing first
row and second
column (shaded)
leaves Δ_{12}. Negative sign is
associated since
$1 + 2$ is odd.

$$\Delta_{11} = \begin{vmatrix} a_{22} & a_{23} \\ a_{32} & a_{33} \end{vmatrix}, \qquad \Delta_{12} = (-1)\begin{vmatrix} a_{21} & a_{23} \\ a_{31} & a_{33} \end{vmatrix}$$

$$\Delta_{21} = (-1)\begin{vmatrix} a_{12} & a_{13} \\ a_{32} & a_{33} \end{vmatrix}, \qquad \Delta_{22} = \begin{vmatrix} a_{11} & a_{13} \\ a_{31} & a_{33} \end{vmatrix}$$

Fig. 2-4. A determinant and four of its cofactors.

The cofactor concept provides a convenient way of grouping the terms in the complete expression for the determinant. Such grouping is called a cofactor expansion of the determinant

$$\Delta = \sum_j a_{jk}\Delta_{jk} = \sum_k a_{jk}\Delta_{jk} \qquad (2.40)$$

Equation (2.40) tells us that the determinant of a matrix is equal to a weighted sum of the elements along any row (or column), the weighting factor for each element being the cofactor of that element. Since the cofactors are themselves determinantal quantities, each cofactor may be expanded, in turn, along one of its own rows or columns in exactly the same way. Such expansions are convenient for numerical calculation of the determinant, since they group and factor the terms of (2.35) and thereby reduce the number of arithmetic operations required. For example, expansion of (2.37) along the second column yields

$$\begin{vmatrix} a_{11} & a_{12} & a_{13} \\ a_{21} & a_{22} & a_{23} \\ a_{31} & a_{32} & a_{33} \end{vmatrix} = - a_{12}(a_{21}a_{33} - a_{31}a_{23}) + a_{22}(a_{11}a_{33} - a_{31}a_{13}) - a_{32}(a_{11}a_{23} - a_{21}a_{13}) \qquad (2.41)$$

A comparison of (2.37) and (2.41) shows that, although the number of additions and subtractions is the same, the required number of multiplications has been reduced from twelve to nine. As the number of rows and columns in the matrix becomes larger, the saving in arithmetical labor afforded by cofactor expansion becomes very much greater.

Results of considerable interest can be deduced from relation (2.40). For instance, multiplication of a determinant by a scalar is equivalent to multiplication of the elements in any one row or any one column of the matrix by that scalar. It also follows directly from (2.40), and from the fact that the expansion process applies to a cofactor as well as to a determinant, that the determinant of a triangular matrix is the product of its diagonal elements.

A study of (2.35) leads to further determinantal properties of interest. Interchanging any two rows (or columns) in a matrix changes the algebraic sign of its determinant. Hence the determinant of a matrix having two identical rows (or two identical columns) must be its own negative. The only two numbers having this property are zero and infinity. Ruling out the value infinity, we have the result that the determinant vanishes whenever any two rows (or two columns) in the matrix are identical. The same result holds if two rows or columns have elements which are correspondingly proportional, since identical rows or columns can be changed into proportional rows or columns through multiplication of the determinant by a scalar.

Now consider the determinantal identity

$$\begin{vmatrix} a + kb & b \\ c + kd & d \end{vmatrix} \equiv \begin{vmatrix} a & b \\ c & d \end{vmatrix} \tag{2.42}$$

in which the second column of the right-hand matrix has been multiplied by a constant k and added to the first column to obtain the matrix on the left. The cofactor expansion taken along the first column of the left-hand matrix will contain two sets of terms: those involving k, and those not involving k. It is evident from (2.40) that the terms involving k represent the cofactor expansion for a matrix with two proportional columns. Hence the terms involving k contribute nothing to the value of the determinant. In other words, the determinant shown in (2.42) is independent of the value of k, and we may set k equal to zero to obtain the identity indicated. This result, of course, is general and may be stated as follows: The determinant is unchanged if any row (column) in the matrix is multiplied by a scalar and added to any other row (column).

The addition of rows and columns may be used to produce zeros in the determinant. For example, multiplication of the second column by the negative of c/d and algebraic addition of the result to the first column yields

$$\begin{vmatrix} a & b \\ c & d \end{vmatrix} = \begin{vmatrix} a - \left(\dfrac{bc}{d}\right) & b \\ 0 & d \end{vmatrix} = ad - bc \tag{2.43}$$

The zero element so produced makes the matrix triangular; thus its value is given by the product of the elements on the main diagonal. Triangularization is a useful method of evaluating the determinants of large matrices.

2.5 Inversion of a Matrix

Determinantal notation makes it possible to formulate the inverse of a matrix in a straightforward manner.

If $\Delta = $ determinant of a

and $b = a^{-1}$

then $b_{jk} = \Delta_{kj}/\Delta \tag{2.44}$

The inverse of a matrix is its transposed cofactor matrix divided by its determinant.   The cofactor matrix is a square array composed of elements Δ_{jk}, and transposition corresponds to the subscript reversal shown in relation (2.44).

For verification of the inversion formula (2.44), it is only necessary to multiply matrix a by its inverse b.

$$(ab)_{jk} = \sum_m a_{jm}b_{mk} = \frac{1}{\Delta} \sum_m a_{jm}\Delta_{km} = \begin{cases} 1, \text{ for } j = k \\ 0, \text{ for } j \neq k \end{cases} \qquad (2.45)$$

For j equal to k, the resulting summation is recognizable as the cofactor expansion of Δ.   When j is not equal to k, the summation is identifiable as the expansion of a determinant in which rows j and k are identical. Hence the matrix elements of the product ab have unity value on the main diagonal and zero value elsewhere.   Thus the product of matrix a and matrix b is the unit matrix, which establishes the inverse relationship between a and b.

As an illustration, consider the inversion of a two-by-two matrix having elements a, b, c, and d:

$$\begin{pmatrix} a & b \\ c & d \end{pmatrix}^{-1} = \begin{pmatrix} \dfrac{d}{ad-bc} & \dfrac{-b}{ad-bc} \\ \dfrac{-c}{ad-bc} & \dfrac{a}{ad-bc} \end{pmatrix} = \frac{1}{ad-bc}\begin{pmatrix} d & -b \\ -c & a \end{pmatrix} \qquad (2.46)$$

Notice that it is not the cofactor of element b but rather the cofactor of its transposition c which appears in the upper right-hand corner of the inverse matrix.

Certain matrices of special form are very easy to invert by inspection. Among these are the elementary matrix

$$\begin{pmatrix} 1 & a & b \\ 0 & 1 & 0 \\ 0 & 0 & 1 \end{pmatrix}^{-1} = \begin{pmatrix} 1 & -a & -b \\ 0 & 1 & 0 \\ 0 & 0 & 1 \end{pmatrix} \qquad (2.47)$$

composed of a unit matrix plus additional elements in one row or in one column, and the diagonal matrix

$$\begin{pmatrix} a & 0 & 0 \\ 0 & b & 0 \\ 0 & 0 & c \end{pmatrix}^{-1} = \begin{pmatrix} \dfrac{1}{a} & 0 & 0 \\ 0 & \dfrac{1}{b} & 0 \\ 0 & 0 & \dfrac{1}{c} \end{pmatrix} \qquad (2.48)$$

whose inverse is obtained simply by inverting the elements on the diagonal.

The ease of inverting a diagonal matrix suggests that an arbitrary (square) matrix can be inverted easily by reducing it first to diagonal form. Consider an arbitrary matrix A, and a set of properly chosen elementary matrices $M_1, M_2, \cdots, M_m$, such that premultiplication and postmultiplication of A by the elementary matrices yield a diagonal matrix D. Each elementary matrix has unity elements on its diagonal and, apart from the diagonal, nonzero elements in only one row or one column. As it turns out, for a matrix A with n rows and n columns, we shall need $n - 1$ elementary premultipliers and $n - 1$ postmultipliers for the desired reduction to diagonal form. In particular, for $n = 3$,

$$M_1 M_2 A M_3 M_4 = D$$
$$M_4^{-1} M_3^{-1} A^{-1} M_2^{-1} M_1^{-1} = D^{-1}$$

(2.49)

where the second form follows from (2.29). The inverse of A is given by

$$A^{-1} = M_3 M_4 D^{-1} M_1 M_2 \tag{2.50}$$

Construction of the elementary matrices is illustrated by the following example.

$$\begin{pmatrix} 1 & 0 \\ -\dfrac{c}{a} & 1 \end{pmatrix} \begin{pmatrix} a & b \\ c & d \end{pmatrix} \begin{pmatrix} 1 & -\dfrac{b}{a} \\ 0 & 1 \end{pmatrix} = \begin{pmatrix} a & 0 \\ 0 & \dfrac{ad - bc}{a} \end{pmatrix} \tag{2.51}$$

$$\begin{pmatrix} a & b \\ c & d \end{pmatrix}^{-1} = \begin{pmatrix} 1 & -\dfrac{b}{a} \\ 0 & 1 \end{pmatrix} \begin{pmatrix} \dfrac{1}{a} & 0 \\ 0 & \dfrac{a}{ad - bc} \end{pmatrix} \begin{pmatrix} 1 & 0 \\ -\dfrac{c}{a} & 1 \end{pmatrix} \tag{2.52}$$

Here only one elementary premultiplier and one elementary postmultiplier are required for the diagonalization (2.51). The premultiplier produces a zero in the lower left-hand corner, and the postmultiplier produces a zero in the upper right-hand corner. In effect, the elementary premultiplier multiplies the first row of the matrix by the negative of c/a and adds the result to the bottom row. The postmultiplier then multiplies the first column of the result by the negative of b/a and adds this to the second column. By a proper choice of element values in the elementary matrices, it is a simple matter to produce zero values of the nondiagonal elements of the product. Inversion can then be completed by carrying out the matrix multiplication indicated in (2.52). The result will be the same as that given in (2.46).

As mentioned above, the elementary matrices may be thought of as operators which multiply some row or column of a matrix by a scale factor, and then add the result to some other row or column. Hence the product of an elementary matrix and an arbitrary matrix has the same determinant as the arbitrary matrix itself. Moreover, the determinant of an elementary matrix is unity. Since any matrix can be represented as the product of a diagonal matrix and a set of elementary matrices, it follows that the determinant of a product of matrices is equal to the product of their determinants. This fact is so important and so useful that we shall state it again in concise form.

$$\text{determinant of } AB = (\text{determinant of } A) \cdot (\text{determinant of } B) \qquad (2.53)$$

The rule need be given only for a product of two matrices, since the associative law extends it to any number of matrices.

2.6 Formulation of the Nodal Admittance Matrix of a Branch Network

We come now to the main business of this chapter, the application of matrix methods to electric and electronic circuit analysis. Our attention will be confined to formulation of the circuit equations on the node basis. Nodal formulation is convenient for electronic circuit analysis, especially at high frequencies where interterminal capacitance becomes important. The loop basis of analysis is discussed in Chapter 5.

Figure 2-5(a) represents a simple electric circuit or network. This particular network has three nodes, one of them taken as ground or datum, and three branch elements whose admittances are a, b, and c. The branch elements are shown here as simple line segments without any special symbol to tell whether that branch is actually a resistance, a capacitance, an inductance, or some combination of such elements. Whatever the nature of the branch, we assume that it can be characterized by a single complex admittance, which is here designated by a letter. Such a schematic representation of a network is usually called a *linear graph*.

Various parts of the network are shown separately in Fig. 2-5(b), (c), and (d), together with the associated nodal admittance equations, which give the currents i_1 and i_2 entering the network as explicit functions of the voltages v_1 and v_2 present at the ungrounded terminals. The voltage v_1 applied across the single branch in Fig. 2-5(b) causes a current i_1 to flow into the terminal, and the value of this current is just equal to av_1. Current i_2 is obviously zero for all finite values of the applied voltages v_1 and v_2. Thus the admittance matrix in Fig. 2-5(b) has only one nonzero element.

When a single branch is "floating" between two ungrounded terminals, as in Fig. 2-5(d), the admittance of that branch appears in four different

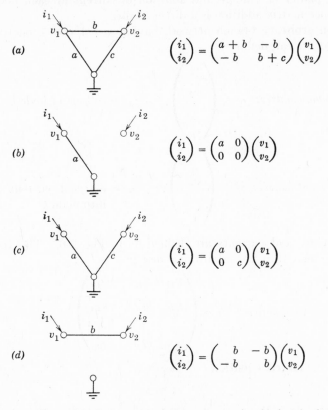

(a) $$\begin{pmatrix} i_1 \\ i_2 \end{pmatrix} = \begin{pmatrix} a+b & -b \\ -b & b+c \end{pmatrix} \begin{pmatrix} v_1 \\ v_2 \end{pmatrix}$$

(b) $$\begin{pmatrix} i_1 \\ i_2 \end{pmatrix} = \begin{pmatrix} a & 0 \\ 0 & 0 \end{pmatrix} \begin{pmatrix} v_1 \\ v_2 \end{pmatrix}$$

(c) $$\begin{pmatrix} i_1 \\ i_2 \end{pmatrix} = \begin{pmatrix} a & 0 \\ 0 & c \end{pmatrix} \begin{pmatrix} v_1 \\ v_2 \end{pmatrix}$$

(d) $$\begin{pmatrix} i_1 \\ i_2 \end{pmatrix} = \begin{pmatrix} b & -b \\ -b & b \end{pmatrix} \begin{pmatrix} v_1 \\ v_2 \end{pmatrix}$$

Fig. 2-5. The nodal admittance equations of some simple electric circuits.

elements of the admittance matrix, since a change in either one of the applied voltages v_1 or v_2 will affect the values of both i_1 and i_2.

The network in Fig. 2-5(a) can be obtained by connecting networks (c) and (d) in parallel (that is, by coalescing correspondingly numbered nodes). Current i_1 in network (a) is the sum of the currents i_1 appearing in networks (c) and (d), and the same is true for i_2. If the corresponding voltages are the same and the corresponding currents are additive, the admittance matrix in Fig. 2-5(a) should be the sum of the admittance matrices in Fig. 2-5(c) and (d); and such is the case. Thus the admittance matrix of a branch network is the sum of the admittance matrices of each of the parts of that network. This is true whether the parts are individual branch elements or larger subnetworks which form the complete network when combined in parallel by connecting together their corresponding nodes. To summarize, parallel connection means equality of voltage and addition of current at each node, and admittance matrix addition is a direct result.

For an arbitrary branch network having $n + 1$ nodes, one of them grounded, we can define

$$\text{Node voltage matrix:} \quad v = \begin{pmatrix} v_1 \\ v_2 \\ \vdots \\ v_n \end{pmatrix}, \qquad v_k = \text{voltage of node } k \quad (2.54)$$

$$\text{Node current matrix:} \quad i = \begin{pmatrix} i_1 \\ i_2 \\ \vdots \\ i_n \end{pmatrix}, \qquad \begin{aligned} i_k &= \text{external current} \\ &\quad \text{into node } k \end{aligned} \quad (2.55)$$

The voltages and currents are defined as in Fig. 2-6. The vectors v and i are related by the admittance matrix

$$\text{Node admittance matrix:} \quad y = \begin{pmatrix} y_{11} & y_{12} & \cdots & y_{1n} \\ y_{21} & y_{22} & \cdots & y_{2n} \\ \vdots & \vdots & & \vdots \\ y_{n1} & y_{n2} & \cdots & y_{nn} \end{pmatrix} \quad (2.56)$$

through the matrix equation

$$i = yv \quad (2.57)$$

so that

$$i_j = \sum_k y_{jk} v_k, \qquad \text{for each } j \quad (2.58)$$

In other words, each current i_j is a superposition of the effects due to each of the applied voltages v_k acting alone. Hence each admittance y_{jk} can be interpreted as a result of an experiment in which all but one of the applied voltages are set equal to zero (short-circuited). Under these conditions, admittance y_{jk} is numerically equal to the quotient of the measured current i_j and the applied voltage v_k.

$$y_{jk} = \frac{\partial i_j}{\partial v_k} = \left(\frac{i_j}{v_k} \right)_{\text{only } v_k \neq 0} \quad (2.59)$$

Relation (2.59) can be taken as a basic definition of the nodal admittances y_{jk}. These quantities are sometimes called short-circuit admittances, since each is measured with all but one of the node voltages short-circuited to ground. For j equal to k, we speak of a driving-point admittance, since the current is measured at the same terminal where the voltage is applied. For j not equal to k, we speak of a transfer admittance, since the measured ratio involves the applied voltage at one terminal and the current flowing in a short circuit connecting some other terminal to the ground point.

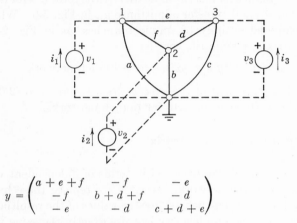

$$y = \begin{pmatrix} a+e+f & -f & -e \\ -f & b+d+f & -d \\ -e & -d & c+d+e \end{pmatrix}$$

$y_{jj} = \sum$ branch admittances connected to node j

y_{jk} = negative of branch admittance connected between two different nodes j and k

Fig. 2-6. The nodal admittance matrix of a branch network.

As a specific example, consider the evaluation of admittances y_{11} and y_{21} in the circuit of Fig. 2-6. For both of these measurements we shall set v_1 equal to unity and both v_2 and v_3 equal to zero, so that voltage sources v_2 and v_3 become short circuits connecting nodes 2 and 3 to ground. With nodes 2 and 3 grounded, branches a, f, and e are connected in parallel between node 1 and ground. Hence, with a unit voltage v_1 applied, the current i_1 will be numerically equal to the admittance sum $a + e + f$. This establishes the value of y_{11} in the upper left-hand corner of the admittance matrix. To find y_{21}, we need only determine the value of short-circuit current i_2. With a unit voltage v_1 applied, and with voltages v_2 and v_3 equal to zero, the current flowing from node 1 toward node 2 through branch f must be numerically equal to the branch admittance f. Since voltages v_2 and v_3 are both zero, no current can flow in either branch b or branch d. Hence the current entering node 2 through branch f must complete its journey to ground by flowing out node 2 and through the attached source v_2, which happens at the moment to be generating zero voltage. Since the direction of flow is opposed to the reference direction of current i_2, we see that the measured ratio of i_2 to v_1 is negative and equal in magnitude to the branch admittance f. This gives us the value of the element y_{21} in the first column and second row of the admittance matrix.

For branch networks, the branch admittances fit into the admittance matrix in a very systematic way, as indicated by the formulas for driving-point admittance y_{jj} and transfer admittance y_{jk} in Fig. 2-6. When the network is composed entirely of simple branches, as in Fig. 2-6, the admittance matrix is symmetric, that is:

$$y = y_t, \quad (y_{jk} = y_{kj}), \quad \text{for a branch network} \qquad (2.60)$$

Just as (2.58) is a statement of the *superposition* theorem, so (2.60) is a statement of the *reciprocity* theorem for branch networks.

2.7 The Nodal Impedance Matrix

In the preceding article we reasoned in terms of independent voltage sources connected to the network. What if we replace these by independent current sources and then ask for the values of the resulting node voltages? To solve this problem, we can use exactly the same voltage and current variables as before, except that now the currents will play the role of independent quantities. Given a network and the attached voltage sources $v_1, v_2, \cdots, v_n$, the problem is to adjust the values of the voltage sources to produce a preassigned set of values of the currents $i_1, i_2, \cdots, i_n$. The solution is a set of voltages; these are exactly the same as the voltages resulting when current sources having the aforementioned preassigned values are attached to the network. In other words, an electrical source or generator may be either a current source or a voltage source, depending upon what we ask it to do. (If we attach a voltage source to a network, and agree in advance that the voltage is always to be adjusted to produce a specified value of current, then the source is indistinguishable from a current source.)

Solution of the admittance equations for the voltages in terms of the currents leads to an impedance matrix.

$$\textit{Node impedance matrix:} \quad z = \begin{pmatrix} z_{11} & z_{12} & \cdots & z_{1n} \\ z_{21} & z_{22} & \cdots & z_{2n} \\ \vdots & \vdots & & \vdots \\ z_{n1} & z_{n2} & \cdots & z_{nn} \end{pmatrix} \qquad (2.61)$$

The impedance matrix equation expresses the voltages as explicit functions of the currents,

$$v = zi \tag{2.62}$$

In particular,

$$v_j = \sum_k z_{jk} i_k, \text{ for each } j \tag{2.63}$$

and

$$z_{jk} = \frac{\partial v_j}{\partial i_k} = \left(\frac{v_j}{i_k}\right)_{\text{only } i_k \neq 0} \tag{2.64}$$

A comparison of (2.57) and (2.62) shows that the so-called open-circuit impedance matrix z is the inverse of the short-circuit admittance matrix y,

$$z = y^{-1} \tag{2.65}$$

For networks of some complexity, the open-circuit impedances z_{jk} are more difficult to evaluate by inspection than are the short-circuit admittances y_{jk}. Hence it is convenient to evaluate z_{jk} directly in terms of the admittance determinant. Let

$$\Delta = \text{determinant of the } y \text{ matrix} \tag{2.66}$$

then

$$z_{jk} = \frac{\Delta_{kj}}{\Delta} \tag{2.67}$$

Since the y matrix of an ordinary branch network is symmetric, it follows that Δ_{kj} and Δ_{jk} are equal, and reciprocity therefore manifests

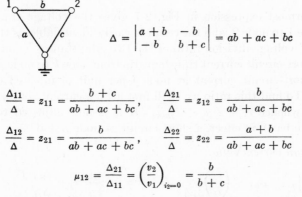

$$\Delta = \begin{vmatrix} a+b & -b \\ -b & b+c \end{vmatrix} = ab + ac + bc$$

$$\frac{\Delta_{11}}{\Delta} = z_{11} = \frac{b+c}{ab+ac+bc}, \qquad \frac{\Delta_{21}}{\Delta} = z_{12} = \frac{b}{ab+ac+bc}$$

$$\frac{\Delta_{12}}{\Delta} = z_{21} = \frac{b}{ab+ac+bc}, \qquad \frac{\Delta_{22}}{\Delta} = z_{22} = \frac{a+b}{ab+ac+bc}$$

$$\mu_{12} = \frac{\Delta_{21}}{\Delta_{11}} = \left(\frac{v_2}{v_1}\right)_{i_2=0} = \frac{b}{b+c}$$

Fig. 2-7. Nodal impedances and voltage ratio for a simple branch circuit.

itself in the same way for open-circuit impedances as it does for short-circuit admittances.

$$z = z_t, \ (z_{jk} = z_{kj}), \text{ for a branch network} \qquad (2.68)$$

Figure 2-7 shows a simple network, its admittance determinant Δ, and the four open-circuit impedances calculated from Δ and the co-factors of Δ.

2.8 Voltage Ratios and Current Ratios

In addition to short-circuit admittances and open-circuit impedances, it is often desirable to calculate the transfer voltage or current ratios from one point in a network to another. The open-circuit voltage transfer ratio from node k to node j is defined as the open-circuit voltage appearing at node j per unit of applied voltage at node k. Here we have another situation in which it does not really matter whether we think of the source connected to node k as a current source or as a voltage source. All we need is something which will create a voltage at node k and allow a current to flow into node k. In other words, the transfer voltage ratio will be the same no matter which type of electrical source is used to excite the input terminal. It is more convenient here to think in terms of a current source i_k which produces a voltage v_j at node j and a voltage v_k at node k. The desired voltage ratio is then obtainable as the ratio of two open-circuit impedances.

Open-circuit voltage ratio:

$$\mu_{kj} = \left(\frac{v_j}{v_k}\right)_{\text{only } i_k \neq 0} = \frac{(v_j/i_k)_{\text{only} i_k \neq 0}}{(v_k/i_k)_{\text{only} i_k \neq 0}} = \frac{z_{jk}}{z_{kk}} = \frac{\Delta_{kj}}{\Delta_{kk}} \qquad (2.69)$$

The lowermost expression in Fig. 2-7 gives the voltage transfer ratio from node 1 to node 2, and the result is easily identifiable as the "potentiometer" voltage-division ratio of the two admittances b and c.

The short-circuit current transfer ratio from node k to node j is defined as the short-circuit current at node j per unit of injected current at node k. To find this ratio we shall first attach current sources at nodes j and k, whence $v_j = z_{jj}i_j + z_{jk}i_k$. If i_j is now adjusted to make v_j vanish, we have, in effect, a short circuit at node j, and

Short-circuit current ratio:

$$\alpha_{kj} = \left(\frac{i_j}{i_k}\right)_{\substack{v_j = 0 \\ \text{only } i_j \text{ and } i_k \neq 0}} = -\frac{z_{jk}}{z_{jj}} = -\frac{\Delta_{kj}}{\Delta_{jj}} \qquad (2.70)$$

For reciprocal networks (those which obey reciprocity) the admittance matrix is symmetric and Δ_{kj} is equal to Δ_{jk}. Hence it follows from (2.69) and (2.70) that for such networks the open-circuit voltage transfer ratio from one node to another is equal to the negative of the short-circuit current transfer ratio in the opposite direction between those two nodes. Specifically, for a reciprocal network the open-circuit voltage ratio from k to j is the negative of the short-circuit current ratio from j to k. This is another manifestation of reciprocity. The statements, short-circuit admittances in opposite directions are equal, open-circuit impedances in opposite directions are equal, and the open-circuit voltage ratio in one direction is the negative of the short-circuit current ratio in the opposite direction, are three different ways of saying the same thing. If one of these three statements is known, the other two must follow. The third form of reciprocity makes its appearance in the treatment of mutual inductance. When a magnetic transformer is idealized by making the winding reactance infinite and the flux coupling coefficient unity, the transformer can be described by a single real number representing the ratio of primary to secondary turns. The short-circuit current transfer ratio in a magnetic transformer is just equal to the open-circuit voltage transfer ratio in the other direction.

2.9 The Floating Nodal Admittance Matrix

Since, by the conservation of charge, the current entering all the nodes of an isolated network must add up to zero, and since these currents are dependent upon voltage differences between various node pairs rather than upon the absolute potential of the environment, there is no loss of generality in taking one of the nodes of the network as a datum or ground reference. The voltage of the reference node is set equal to zero, and the current entering the reference node from ground may be ignored, since it can always be calculated as the negative sum of the currents entering the remaining ungrounded nodes. However, there are some significant advantages to be gained by a formulation in which no ground node is chosen and the entire network is allowed to float free in insulated electrical space.

Figure 2-8 shows the formulation on this basis for the network previously considered in Fig. 2-6. Elements in the admittance matrix are still defined by relation (2.59), but now a fourth row and fourth column appear in the admittance matrix because the fourth node is no longer fixed permanently at ground potential. Each column of the floating

admittance matrix has an algebraic sum equal to zero, as a direct consequence of the fact that the external currents entering the network
must have an algebraic sum equal to zero. Similarly, each row must
add to zero. This is a consequence of the obvious physical fact that
the currents remain invariant when all of the applied node voltages are

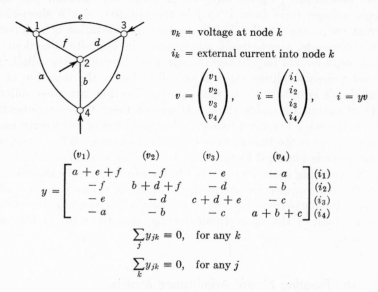

v_k = voltage at node k

i_k = external current into node k

$$v = \begin{pmatrix} v_1 \\ v_2 \\ v_3 \\ v_4 \end{pmatrix}, \qquad i = \begin{pmatrix} i_1 \\ i_2 \\ i_3 \\ i_4 \end{pmatrix}, \qquad i = yv$$

$$y = \begin{array}{c} \\ \\ \\ \\ \end{array} \overset{\displaystyle (v_1) \qquad\quad (v_2) \qquad\quad (v_3) \qquad\quad (v_4)}{\left[\begin{array}{cccc} a+e+f & -f & -e & -a \\ -f & b+d+f & -d & -b \\ -e & -d & c+d+e & -c \\ -a & -b & -c & a+b+c \end{array} \right]} \begin{array}{c} (i_1) \\ (i_2) \\ (i_3) \\ (i_4) \end{array}$$

$$\sum_j y_{jk} \equiv 0, \quad \text{for any } k$$

$$\sum_k y_{jk} \equiv 0, \quad \text{for any } j$$

Fig. 2-8. The floating nodal admittance matrix of a four-node branch network.

increased by the same constant increment. Currents anywhere in the
network are dependent only upon the differences between the terminal
voltages, and these differences are unchanged by the addition of a constant voltage increment to each of the node potentials.

When all but one row and one column of the floating admittance
matrix have been formulated, the remaining row and column can be
filled in forthwith, since each row and each column of the complete
matrix must add to zero. Hence the floating matrix, although it contains an extra row and an extra column, is really no more difficult to
write by inspection of the network than is the datum-node matrix. The
network branch admittances enter the floating matrix in a beautifully
symmetrical form. Each branch admittance appears in a square pattern
of four element positions centered about the main diagonal. The two
rows and two columns associated with the square pattern have the
same numbers as the nodes to which the branch in question is connected
in the network. The branch admittance enters with a positive sign

on the main diagonal and with a negative sign in the off-diagonal corners of the square pattern. (We shall find that a nonreciprocal element, such as the transconductance of a vacuum tube, will also enter the floating matrix in a rectangular pattern of four element positions, but the pattern will no longer be centered on the main diagonal.)

The usefulness of the floating admittance matrix lies in the fact that it facilitates the formulation of the transfer impedance from *any* pair of nodes in the network to *any* other pair. More specifically, suppose that a current source is connected between any two nodes r and k so that a current i_r is injected into the rth node and at the same time is extracted from the kth node. Suppose also that an ideal voltmeter is connected from node j to node m so that it indicates the potential rise from m to j. The transfer impedance so defined is:

$$z_{jk,mr} = \frac{v_j - v_m}{i_k}, \qquad \text{with } i_r = -i_k, \text{ and only } i_k \text{ and } i_r \neq 0 \quad (2.71)$$

Now let

$$Y = \text{determinant of the floating matrix} \qquad (2.72)$$

$$Y_{jk} = \text{first-order cofactor obtained by}$$
$$\text{collapsing } j\text{th row and } k\text{th column} \qquad (2.73)$$

$$Y_{jk,mr} = \text{second-order cofactor obtained by collapsing}$$
$$\text{rows } j \text{ and } m \text{ and columns } k \text{ and } r \qquad (2.74)$$

The determinant of the floating matrix is of course identically equal to zero, since all of its rows and columns add to zero. However, the transfer impedance is a function only of the first-order and second-order cofactors of the floating matrix,

$$z_{jk,mr} = \frac{Y_{kj,rm}}{Y_{rm}} = \frac{Y_{rm,kj}}{Y_{rm}} \qquad (2.75)$$

In calculating the value of a second-order cofactor, we must be careful to apply the algebraic-sign rule correctly. The algebraic sign associated with a first-order cofactor Y_{kj} is plus (minus) if the sum of the row and column numbers is even (odd). The algebraic sign of a second-order cofactor $Y_{kj,rm}$ is $(-1)^{j+k+r'+m'}$, where r' and m' are the *new* row and column *positions* occupied by r and m *after* j and k have been *collapsed*. In short, the second-order cofactor is a first-order cofactor of some element in a first-order cofactor, and the sign rule must be applied in two successive steps. In Fig. 2-4, for example, $\Delta_{12,21} = -a_{33}$, whereas $\Delta_{11,22} = a_{23}$.

We shall now give a plausibility argument for the form of (2.75).

First, purely for orientation, let us use (2.75) to calculate the transfer impedance $z_{31,44}$ for the network of Fig. 2-8. A comparison of Figs. 2-6 and 2-8 shows that z_{31}, Δ_{13}, and Δ in Fig. 2-6 will be, respectively, identical with $z_{31,44}$, $Y_{13,44}$, and Y_{44} in Fig. 2-8. The underlying plan of relation (2.75) now begins to emerge. *Collapsing the mth column of the floating matrix is equivalent to setting voltage v_m equal to zero*, which effectively designates node m as the voltage-datum node. On the other hand, *collapsing the rth row of the floating matrix is equivalent to ignoring the equation for current i_r* in terms of the various node voltages. With voltage v_m set equal to zero and current i_r ignored, we are left with a set of *independent algebraic equations* from which the desired open-circuit impedance is obtainable as the quotient of a cofactor and the determinant of those equations.

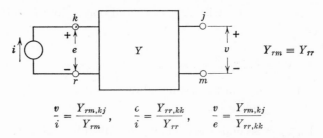

$$\frac{v}{i} = \frac{Y_{rm,kj}}{Y_{rm}}, \qquad \frac{c}{i} = \frac{Y_{rr,kk}}{Y_{rr}}, \qquad \frac{v}{e} = \frac{Y_{rm,kj}}{Y_{rr,kk}}$$

Fig. 2-9. Impedance and voltage ratio in terms of cofactors of the floating admittance matrix.

Various calculations based upon the floating admittance matrix are summarized in Fig. 2-9. Expressions for transfer impedance, driving-point impedance, and voltage transfer ratio are given in the figure. In the numerator of the transfer impedance the subscript order is as follows: r, the current reference node; m, the voltage reference node; k, the current injection point; and j, the voltage measurement point. Nodes r and m form a sort of double datum, r for current and m for voltage; and nodes k and j then designate the input and output of the transfer measurement. It also helps to remember that, in any expression for impedance, the first subscript in a subscript pair has to do with current and the second subscript has to do with voltage. The formula for the transfer impedance v/i in Fig. 2-9 is all that one needs to carry in his head. The two remaining expressions, for driving-point impedance and voltage transfer ratio, can always be deduced rather easily from the first. The second formula is a special case of the first, in which node m becomes identical with node r, and node j becomes identical with node k. The third formula is simply the quotient of the first two.

The results given in Fig. 2-9 are, of course, quite general, since the letters r, m, k, and j may refer to the numbers of any four nodes in any network.

As yet, we have said nothing about the remarkable cofactor identity indicated in Fig. 2-9. As a matter of fact, the quantity Y_{jk} has exactly the same value for any choice of j or k. This is not true for the second-order cofactors $Y_{jk,mr}$. Equality of first-order cofactors is a property of any matrix each of whose rows and columns adds to zero. This property becomes somewhat less remarkable when we observe that any one of the first-order cofactors is obtainable from any other by means of elementary determinantal transformation involving addition of rows or columns. As we have seen previously, such transformations do not affect the value of a determinant.

As an illustration of the use of the floating matrix, suppose that nodes r, m, k, j in Fig. 2-9 are identified with nodes 1, 2, 3, 4, respectively, in the circuit of Fig. 2-8. The signal is applied across branch e in Fig. 2-8, and the response is measured across branch b. The circuit is therefore identifiable as a bridge. With the aid of the third formula given in Fig. 2-9 we find the voltage transfer ratio of the bridge to be

$$\frac{v}{e} = \frac{Y_{12,34}}{Y_{11,33}} = \frac{\begin{vmatrix} -f & -d \\ -a & -c \end{vmatrix}}{\begin{vmatrix} b+d+f & -b \\ -b & a+b+c \end{vmatrix}}$$

$$= \frac{cf - ad}{b(a + c + d + f) + (a + c)(d + f)} \tag{2.76}$$

Notice that, if the branch admittance product cf is equal to the product ab, the bridge is perfectly balanced and the voltage transfer ratio reduces to zero.

2.10 Floating Admittance Matrices for Circuit Models of Electronic Devices

The floating admittance matrix of a linear electronic circuit model may differ in some respects from the matrix of a reciprocal network, but it can be formulated in exactly the same fashion on the basis of relations (2.54), (2.55), and (2.59). Figure 2-10(a) shows the low-frequency linear incremental circuit model of a vacuum triode. Nodes 1, 2, and 3 correspond to the grid, plate, and cathode terminals, respectively.

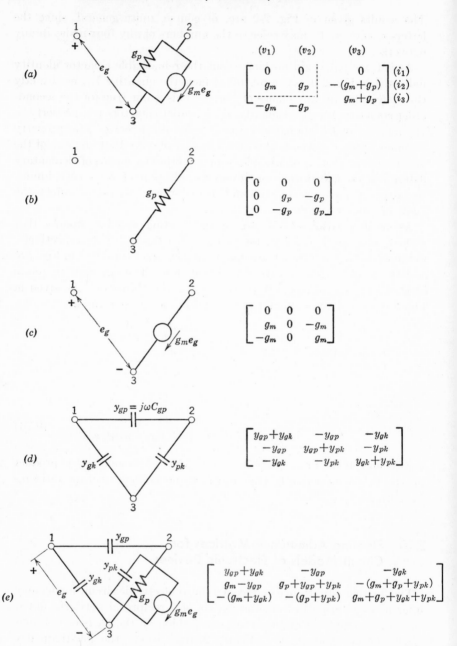

Fig. 2-10. The floating matrix for a vacuum-triode model.

Let us temporarily ground the cathode, which is equivalent to collapsing temporarily the third row and third column of the floating admittance matrix. With v_1 set equal to unity and v_2 and v_3 set equal to zero, no current can flow through the conductance g_p, and it follows that the external current entering node 2 must be numerically equal to the transconductance g_m. This establishes the value of the admittance element in the first column and second row of the matrix. Similarly, with v_1 and v_3 set equal to zero and v_2 taking the value unity, the external current flowing into node 2 must be numerically equal to the plate conductance g_p. This fixes the value of the admittance matrix element in the second row and the second column. It is also obvious by inspection of the circuit that no external current will flow into node 1 for any values of the applied voltages, so that the admittance elements in the top row of the matrix are all equal to zero. Having evaluated the four short-circuit admittance elements lying in the upper left-hand portion of the matrix, we can easily fill in the element values in the third row and the third column, since each row and each column must add to zero. Elements in the third row and column could, of course, be evaluated independently, but such labor is unnecessary once all but one row and one column are known.

As an alternate route to the floating admittance matrix, we can first break the circuit model into two parallel parts, as indicated in Fig. 2-10(b) and (c). Each of these parts has a simpler floating admittance matrix, and the matrix of the complete circuit is the sum of the matrices of the two parts. The single branch shown in Fig. 2-10(b) is a reciprocal circuit element. As mentioned earlier in the chapter, the branch admittance appears in the floating matrix in a square array centered upon the main diagonal of the matrix. The transconductance element shown in Fig. 2-10(c) is a unilateral circuit element. Its transfer admittance enters the floating matrix in a rectangular pattern which is not centered upon the main diagonal. This asymmetry is evidence of the violation of the reciprocity condition. Observe that the transconductance is actuated by the voltages at nodes 1 and 3 that correspond to the first and third columns of the matrix. Similarly, the transconductance affects the currents of nodes 2 and 3 which are associated with the second and third rows of the matrix.

Figure 2-10(d) shows the interelectrode capacitances of a triode and the associated floating matrix. At sufficiently high frequencies, these capacitances become important and their effect must be included in the admittance matrix of the triode. Figure 2-10(e) gives the complete high-frequency model together with its floating admittance matrix.

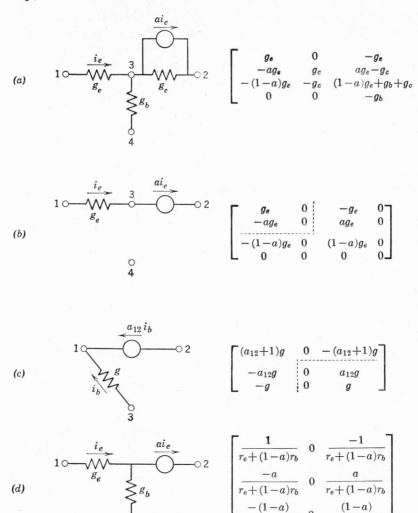

Fig. 2-11. Floating matrices for some transistor models.

Notice that each element in the circuit appears at four different places in the matrix.

One of the many different low-frequency incremental circuit models for a transistor is shown in Fig. 2-11(a). Nodes 1, 2, and 4 correspond to the emitter, collector, and base terminals of the transistor, respectively. As a convenient (though not necessary) step in the formulation of the matrix, first remove the base and collector conductance elements, leaving the circuit shown in Fig. 2-11(b). Let nodes 3 and 4 of this circuit be temporarily grounded so that we are dealing with only the upper left-hand quarter of the matrix. The elements in this portion of the matrix (set off by dashed lines in the figure) can be found very easily by inspection of the circuit. With nodes 3 and 4 once more disconnected from ground, we see that node 4 is isolated, so that the fourth row and fourth column of the matrix must be empty. The third row and third column can then be filled in, so as to make each row and column add to zero. Conductances g_b and g_c may now be reintroduced to give the complete floating matrix shown in Fig. 2-11(a).

A somewhat simpler transistor circuit model is given in Fig. 2-11(c). Nodes 1, 2, and 3 correspond to the emitter, collector, and base, respectively. In this model the collector admittance is assumed to be so small that it can be neglected. Moreover, the transistor transfer effect is here treated as a base-to-collector current amplification a_{12}. For evaluation of the matrix, it is convenient to ground node 1 temporarily; then the lower right-hand corner of the matrix is relatively easy to fill in by inspection of the circuit. The matrix may then be completed in the usual way.

Figure 2-11(d) shows still another model. Just as in the previous model, the collector admittance is assumed to be negligible. Models (c) and (d) are actually identical in character, the difference between them being only one of notation, as evidenced by the general form of their floating matrices. As a sample calculation we shall evaluate y_{11}. To find y_{11}, we first connect nodes 2 and 3 to ground and then apply a unit voltage at node 1. Current i_e enters the circuit at node 1, but only a fraction $(1 - a)$ of this current flows downward through the base conductance to ground. Hence the apparent resistance presented between terminals 1 and 3 is the series combination of the emitter resistance and $(1 - a)$ times the base resistance.

No matter how we choose to describe the transistor (or for that matter any other linear network or device having three external terminals), it can always be represented by a floating admittance matrix with three rows and three columns, in which, at most, four of the admittance elements are independent quantities. The point is that once the admittance matrix has been formulated, we can "plug the device into the remainder of the circuit" by simply adding the matrices of the device and the environmental circuitry.

Another element which frequently appears in the circuit models of electronic systems is the idealized mutual inductance, usually called an ideal transformer. Three ideal-transformer connections and their associ-

ated matrices are shown in Fig. 2-12. The ideal transformer is characterized by a single real constant n, which relates the currents and voltages
of the two windings, as indicated in Fig. 2-12(a). The ideal transformer
by itself has infinite short-circuit admittances and infinite open-circuit

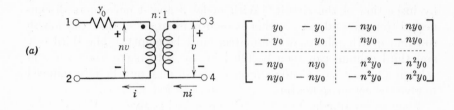

(a)

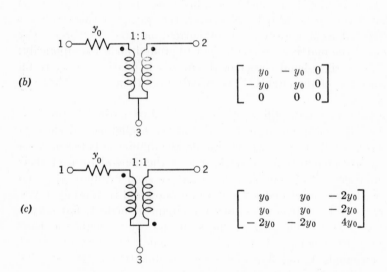

(b)

(c)

Fig. 2-12. Floating matrices for ideal-transformer models.

impedances, and hence cannot be formally characterized on the nodal
basis. However, in practice a transformer usually appears in series with
some other circuit element having a finite admittance. If we associate
this element, say y_0, with the transformer, then the floating admittance
matrix becomes finite and tractable.

The floating admittance matrix given in Fig. 2-12(a) can be parti-
tioned into four submatrices (set off by the dashed lines), in each of
which the columns and rows add to zero. This reflects the fact that
the two windings of the transformer have no direct connection between

them. Apart from the mutual inductive coupling, each winding floats free of the other in the electrical sense. For a transformer with a common ground and a turns ratio n equal to unity, the admittance matrix has the form shown in Fig. 2-12(b). This matrix is the same as that of a single branch admittance y_0 connected between nodes 1 and 2. Node 3 is effectively isolated because the current in the two windings is continuous and no current can flow into or out of node 3. For reverse winding polarity, the matrix takes a new form, indicated in Fig. 2-12(c).

2.11 An Illustrative Example—The Cathode Follower

The cathode-follower connection of a vacuum-triode amplifier is shown in Fig. 2-13(a) and the low-frequency linear incremental circuit model is given in (b). The evaluation of the floating admittance matrix is facilitated by temporarily grounding node 2. This permits us to identify the elements in the four corners of the matrix; the remaining admittances can then be filled in to yield zero sums for each row and column.

The voltage gain of the amplifier is just the voltage transfer ratio from node pair 13 to node pair 23. This can be evaluated as a ratio of two second-order cofactors, as shown.

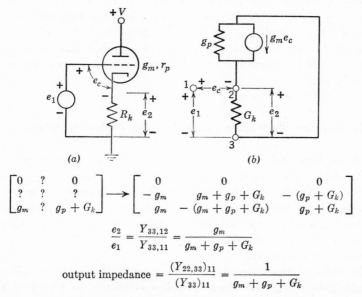

$$\begin{bmatrix} 0 & ? & 0 \\ ? & ? & ? \\ g_m & ? & g_p + G_k \end{bmatrix} \rightarrow \begin{bmatrix} 0 & 0 & 0 \\ -g_m & g_m + g_p + G_k & -(g_p + G_k) \\ g_m & -(g_m + g_p + G_k) & g_p + G_k \end{bmatrix}$$

$$\frac{e_2}{e_1} = \frac{Y_{33,12}}{Y_{33,11}} = \frac{g_m}{g_m + g_p + G_k}$$

$$\text{output impedance} = \frac{(Y_{22,33})_{11}}{(Y_{33})_{11}} = \frac{1}{g_m + g_p + G_k}$$

Fig. 2-13. Voltage gain and output impedance of a cathode-follower circuit model.

The output impedance of the amplifier is defined as the apparent impedance between the two output terminals across which e_2 is measured. The standard definition of the output impedance of an amplifier also states that the amplifier input voltage e_1 must be set equal to zero during the output impedance calculation or measurement. With e_1 set equal to zero in Fig. 2-13(b), node 1 effectively disappears from the circuit, and this disappearance is equivalent to a collapsing of the first row and the first column in the matrix. Accordingly, each of the cofactors entering the output-impedance expression carries the auxiliary double subscript 11, as shown in Fig. 2-13. The cofactor in the numerator of the output-impedance expression is obtained by collapsing all three of the rows and columns of the matrix. In general, the nth-order cofactor of an nth-order matrix is to be interpreted as having the value unity.

The special precautions to insure a zero value of voltage e_1 for the output-impedance calculation were necessary because of the fact that node 1 is completely isolated in Fig. 2-13(b). The voltage on a completely isolated node is indeterminate, and without our special precautions we would have arrived at an indeterminate value for the output impedance. An alternative method of circumventing the entire difficulty is first to connect some branch admittance, say y_0, between nodes 1 and 3 in Fig. 2-13(b). With a nonzero admittance connecting node 1 to node 3, voltage e_1 is no longer indeterminate; in fact, it takes the value zero whenever current is not being injected into node 1. The cofactors $Y_{22,33}$ and Y_{33} are both nonzero, and the auxiliary subscripts 11 become unnecessary. Admittance y_0 may then be allowed to approach zero to obtain the same output-impedance expression as that shown in Fig. 2-13.

2.12   Another Illustrative Example—the Miller Integrator

Another illustrative example of the use of the floating matrix is given in Fig. 2-14. The amplifier shown in (a) is sometimes called a Miller integrator. The linear incremental circuit model is given in Fig. 2-14(b). Temporarily grounding node 4, we identify the first nine elements of the floating admittance matrix by inspection of the circuit. The elements in the fourth row and column are then added to make each row and column have a zero sum.

The ratio of two properly chosen second-order cofactors gives the voltage gain e_2/e_1, and the expression simplifies to the final result shown in Fig. 2-14. The amplifier operates as an integrator at those frequencies for which the dominant term in both the numerator and the denominator of the voltage-gain expression is the term involving g_m. In this frequency range the voltage gain is inversely proportional to the complex frequency $j\omega$, so that the amplifier approximates an ideal integrator.

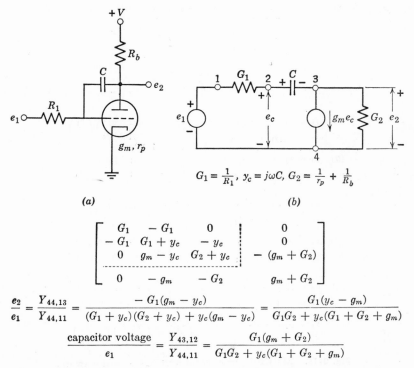

$$G_1 = \frac{1}{R_1}, \ y_c = j\omega C, \ G_2 = \frac{1}{r_p} + \frac{1}{R_b}$$

(a)   (b)

$$\begin{bmatrix} G_1 & -G_1 & 0 & \vdots & 0 \\ -G_1 & G_1 + y_c & -y_c & \vdots & 0 \\ 0 & g_m - y_c & G_2 + y_c & \vdots & -(g_m + G_2) \\ \hline 0 & -g_m & -G_2 & & g_m + G_2 \end{bmatrix}$$

$$\frac{e_2}{e_1} = \frac{Y_{44,13}}{Y_{44,11}} = \frac{-G_1(g_m - y_c)}{(G_1 + y_c)(G_2 + y_c) + y_c(g_m - y_c)} = \frac{G_1(y_c - g_m)}{G_1 G_2 + y_c(G_1 + G_2 + g_m)}$$

$$\frac{\text{capacitor voltage}}{e_1} = \frac{Y_{43,12}}{Y_{44,11}} = \frac{G_1(g_m + G_2)}{G_1 G_2 + y_c(G_1 + G_2 + g_m)}$$

Fig. 2-14. Voltage gain and capacitor-voltage response of a Miller integrator circuit model.

As a further illustration of the use of the floating admittance matrix and its cofactors, the transmission from input voltage to capacitance voltage is also evaluated in Fig. 2-14. Notice that this transmission approaches zero at high frequencies where the capacitor admittance y_c becomes very large.

2.13   Other Matrices for Three-Terminal-Device Models

Short-circuit admittances and open-circuit impedances are not the only parameters which can be used to describe an electric network or the circuit model of an electronic device. Many other sets of parameters are also convenient for certain calculations. Figure 2-15 shows the six possible ways in which the terminal voltages and currents of a three-terminal device can be related by a pair of linear equations. The

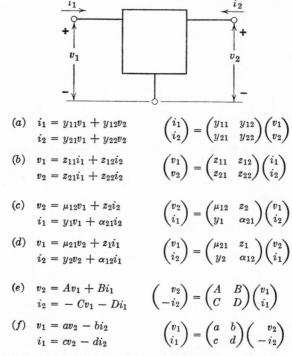

(a) $i_1 = y_{11}v_1 + y_{12}v_2$
$i_2 = y_{21}v_1 + y_{22}v_2$
$$\begin{pmatrix} i_1 \\ i_2 \end{pmatrix} = \begin{pmatrix} y_{11} & y_{12} \\ y_{21} & y_{22} \end{pmatrix} \begin{pmatrix} v_1 \\ v_2 \end{pmatrix}$$

(b) $v_1 = z_{11}i_1 + z_{12}i_2$
$v_2 = z_{21}i_1 + z_{22}i_2$
$$\begin{pmatrix} v_1 \\ v_2 \end{pmatrix} = \begin{pmatrix} z_{11} & z_{12} \\ z_{21} & z_{22} \end{pmatrix} \begin{pmatrix} i_1 \\ i_2 \end{pmatrix}$$

(c) $v_2 = \mu_{12}v_1 + z_2 i_2$
$i_1 = y_1 v_1 + \alpha_{21} i_2$
$$\begin{pmatrix} v_2 \\ i_1 \end{pmatrix} = \begin{pmatrix} \mu_{12} & z_2 \\ y_1 & \alpha_{21} \end{pmatrix} \begin{pmatrix} v_1 \\ i_2 \end{pmatrix}$$

(d) $v_1 = \mu_{21}v_2 + z_1 i_1$
$i_2 = y_2 v_2 + \alpha_{12} i_1$
$$\begin{pmatrix} v_1 \\ i_2 \end{pmatrix} = \begin{pmatrix} \mu_{21} & z_1 \\ y_2 & \alpha_{12} \end{pmatrix} \begin{pmatrix} v_2 \\ i_1 \end{pmatrix}$$

(e) $v_2 = A v_1 + B i_1$
$i_2 = - C v_1 - D i_1$
$$\begin{pmatrix} v_2 \\ -i_2 \end{pmatrix} = \begin{pmatrix} A & B \\ C & D \end{pmatrix} \begin{pmatrix} v_1 \\ i_1 \end{pmatrix}$$

(f) $v_1 = a v_2 - b i_2$
$i_1 = c v_2 - d i_2$
$$\begin{pmatrix} v_1 \\ i_1 \end{pmatrix} = \begin{pmatrix} a & b \\ c & d \end{pmatrix} \begin{pmatrix} v_2 \\ -i_2 \end{pmatrix}$$

Fig. 2-15. Matrix descriptions of a three-terminal network.

parameters shown in Fig. 2-15(a) and (b) are the short-circuit admittances and the open-circuit impedances about which we have already spoken.

The quantities A, B, C, and D of Fig. 2-15(e) are sometimes called the general circuit parameters. The inverse transformation is given in (f) and is here designated by the lower-case letters a, b, c, and d. The general circuit parameters are usually defined for an input current flowing into the network and an output current flowing out of the network. In other words, the reference polarity of current i_2 should be reversed in Fig. 2-15; or, to accomplish the same effect, we can talk in terms of the input-variable pair v_1 and i_1 and the output-variable pair v_2 and $-i_2$. The input-variable and output-variable pairs (v_1, i_1) and

(v_2, $-i_2$) carry power into one side of the network and out of the opposite side. Figure 2-16 illustrates the very convenient way in which the general circuit matrix lends itself to the analysis of cascaded networks. To find the input impedance of two networks in cascade, with a load impedance Z_3 attached to the output terminals of the second network, we need only multiply two matrices and then divide v_1 by i_1.

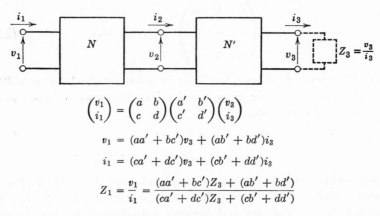

$$\begin{pmatrix} v_1 \\ i_1 \end{pmatrix} = \begin{pmatrix} a & b \\ c & d \end{pmatrix} \begin{pmatrix} a' & b' \\ c' & d' \end{pmatrix} \begin{pmatrix} v_3 \\ i_3 \end{pmatrix}$$

$$v_1 = (aa' + bc')v_3 + (ab' + bd')i_3$$

$$i_1 = (ca' + dc')v_3 + (cb' + dd')i_3$$

$$Z_1 = \frac{v_1}{i_1} = \frac{(aa' + bc')Z_3 + (ab' + bd')}{(ca' + dc')Z_3 + (cb' + dd')}$$

Fig. 2-16. Calculation of the input impedance of a chain by means of the N matrix.

Parts (c) and (d) of Fig. 2-15 represent the two remaining possibilities. Matrix (c) is suited to the description of a low-frequency vacuum-tube voltage amplifier, or any other device having high input impedance, high forward-voltage gain, low output impedance, and low reverse-current gain. Matrix (d), on the other hand, is useful for the description of most transistor amplifiers or any other devices having high input admittance, high forward-current gain, low output admittance, and low reverse-voltage gain. We shall see more of transformations (c) and (d) in Chapter 5.

2.14 Complex Power

Matrix notation offers a convenient means of expressing the power delivered to the terminals of a network. Since power is the product of voltage and current, we might expect that the total power input to a network could be formulated in terms of the column matrices representing the terminal voltages and currents. Two column matrices cannot be multiplied, of course. However, the transposition of a column matrix is a row matrix,

$$i = \begin{pmatrix} i_1 \\ i_2 \\ i_3 \end{pmatrix} \rightarrow \begin{pmatrix} i_1 & 0 & 0 \\ i_2 & 0 & 0 \\ i_3 & 0 & 0 \end{pmatrix} \tag{2.77}$$

and

$$i_t = \begin{pmatrix} i_1 & i_2 & i_3 \\ 0 & 0 & 0 \\ 0 & 0 & 0 \end{pmatrix} \rightarrow (i_1 \quad i_2 \quad i_3) \tag{2.78}$$

Now, a current (voltage) row matrix postmultiplied by a voltage (current) column matrix gives a scalar identifiable as the total power delivered to the network,

$$Complex\ power: \quad p = i_t{}^*v = v_t i^* \tag{2.79}$$

$$p = v_1 i_1{}^* + v_2 i_2{}^* + v_3 i_3{}^* + \cdots \tag{2.80}$$

In expression (2.80) the voltage and current symbols stand for effective or rms complex amplitudes of the sinusoidal voltage and current. It is assumed that all voltages and currents are sinusoids having the same frequency. The asterisk denotes the complex conjugate. Hence p is the net total complex power delivered to all the independent terminal pairs of the network. This power is supplied to the network by attached sources such as those shown in Fig. 2-6.

The complex power can be separated into its real and imaginary parts

$$p = p_r + jp_i \tag{2.81}$$

$$p_r = \tfrac{1}{2}(p + p^*) \tag{2.82}$$

$$jp_i = \tfrac{1}{2}(p - p^*) \tag{2.83}$$

and the real part can be expressed in the form

$$p_r = \tfrac{1}{2}(i_t{}^*v + v_t{}^*i) \tag{2.84}$$

Now, since $v = zi$, we can eliminate v to obtain an expression for the real or average power in terms of the terminal current i and the impedance matrix z.

$$p_r = \tfrac{1}{2}(i_t{}^*zi + i_t{}^*z_t{}^*i) \tag{2.85}$$

Alternatively, we could have eliminated the currents and expressed the real power in terms of the admittance matrix y and the terminal voltages v. From here on, the argument proceeds in exactly the same way no matter which choice we make.

An arbitrary impedance matrix (or any other matrix having complex elements) can always be resolved uniquely into two parts

$$z = \rho + j\xi \tag{2.86}$$

such that

$$\rho_t{}^* = \rho \tag{2.87}$$

and

$$\xi_t{}^* = \xi \tag{2.88}$$

A matrix having the property that its transpose equals its complex conjugate is said to be a *hermitian* matrix. Thus both ρ and ξ are hermitian but $j\xi$ is not. Hence we shall call ρ the *hermitian part* of z. Matrices ρ and ξ are, in general, complex. For a reciprocal network, however, both ρ and ξ are real and become identical to resistance r and reactance x, respectively. It follows from (2.86) through (2.88) that

$$\rho = \tfrac{1}{2}(z + z_t{}^*) \tag{2.89}$$

$$j\xi = \tfrac{1}{2}(z - z_t{}^*) \tag{2.90}$$

Now, expression (2.85) can be factored to obtain

$$p_r = i_t{}^* \rho i \tag{2.91}$$

Similarly,

$$p_i = i_t{}^* \xi i \tag{2.92}$$

Carrying out the matrix multiplication indicated in (2.91), we find, for a two-by-two impedance matrix,

$$p_r = i_1{}^* \rho_{11} i_1 + i_1{}^* \rho_{12} i_2 + i_2{}^* \rho_{21} i_1 + i_2{}^* \rho_{22} i_2 \tag{2.93}$$

Such an expression is called a *quadratic form*. The character of the quadratic form (2.93) is related to the properties of the *hermitian determinant*

$$\Delta^h = \text{determinant of } \rho \tag{2.94}$$

By a straightforward calculus minimization procedure, it can be shown that the real quadratic form p_r will be nonnegative for any choice of the complex currents i, if and only if the associated hermitian determinant and all of its principal cofactors (those cofactors obtained by collapsing one or more rows and at the same time collapsing the like-numbered columns) are nonnegative. In short, $p_r \geq 0$ for all possible choices of the currents, if and only if

$$\Delta^h, \quad \Delta^h_{jj}, \quad \Delta^h_{jj,kk}, \quad \Delta^h_{jj,kk,ii}, \quad \cdots, \quad \text{all} \geq 0 \tag{2.95}$$

However, it is not necessary to verify all of the inequalities (2.95). For a *hermitian* matrix, if the determinant and *one* principal cofactor of *each* order are nonnegative, then *all* principal cofactors are nonnegative. For example, if Δ^h, Δ^h_{11}, $\Delta^h_{11,22}$, $\Delta^h_{11,22,33}$, $\cdots$ are nonnegative, this is *sufficient* to insure a nonnegative p_r.

As an example, consider the two-by-two impedance matrix

$$z = \begin{pmatrix} r_{11} + jx_{11} & r_{12} + jx_{12} \\ r_{21} + jx_{21} & r_{22} + jx_{22} \end{pmatrix} = \begin{pmatrix} z_{11} & z_{12} \\ z_{21} & z_{22} \end{pmatrix} \tag{2.96}$$

whose hermitian part is

$$\rho = \begin{pmatrix} r_{11} & \frac{1}{2}(z_{12} + z_{21}{}^{*}) \\ \frac{1}{2}(z_{21} + z_{12}{}^{*}) & r_{22} \end{pmatrix} = \begin{pmatrix} \rho_{11} & \rho_{12} \\ \rho_{21} & \rho_{22} \end{pmatrix} \tag{2.97}$$

The associated hermitian determinant is given by

$$\Delta^h = r_{11}r_{22} - \left| \frac{z_{12} + z_{21}{}^{*}}{2} \right|^2 = \rho_{11}\rho_{22} - |\rho_{12}|^2 \tag{2.98}$$

and the two principal cofactors are

$$\Delta^h_{11} = r_{11} \tag{2.99}$$

$$\Delta^h_{22} = r_{22} \tag{2.100}$$

Now consider a three-terminal model characterized by the impedance matrix (2.96). Suppose that the model is connected to an environmental network in which all the electrical sources operate at a steady-state frequency ω. If (2.98), (2.99), and (2.100) are all nonnegative at that frequency, there is no possible way of designing the environmental network so as to draw net average power from the model at that frequency.

If a quadratic form is *nonnegative* for all possible choices of values of its variables, that quadratic form and the associated determinant are said to be *positive semidefinite*. (*Positive definite* means that the quadratic form is *positive*.) If the impedance or admittance matrix for an electronic device is "hermitian positive semidefinite" at a certain frequency, the device cannot be used to amplify the power of an input signal having that frequency. Hence the ability of a device to amplify signal power can be investigated by examining its hermitian determinant and a set of principal cofactors of that determinant. In order for a device to be an amplifier at a certain steady-state frequency ω, one or more of these determinantal quantities must be negative at that frequency.

Incidentally, if a model is open-circuit stable (that is, if spontaneous oscillations do not occur when the model is open-circuited; or, saying it another way, if excitation of the model leads to transient open-circuit terminal voltages which decay with time), and if the hermitian determinant of the impedance matrix is positive semidefinite at all steady-

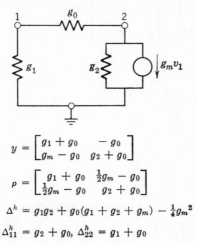

$$y = \begin{bmatrix} g_1 + g_0 & -g_0 \\ g_m - g_0 & g_2 + g_0 \end{bmatrix}$$

$$\rho = \begin{bmatrix} g_1 + g_0 & \tfrac{1}{2}g_m - g_0 \\ \tfrac{1}{2}g_m - g_0 & g_2 + g_0 \end{bmatrix}$$

$$\Delta^h = g_1 g_2 + g_0(g_1 + g_2 + g_m) - \tfrac{1}{4}g_m{}^2$$

$$\Delta_{11}^h = g_2 + g_0, \quad \Delta_{22}^h = g_1 + g_0$$

Fig. 2-17. The hermitian determinant and cofactors for a simple triode circuit model.

state frequencies ω, then the device can never be usefully employed as an oscillator or as an amplifier of signal power at any steady-state frequencies. Such a circuit model is said to be *passive*. On the other hand, if a model violates any of the passivity criteria, the device can always be connected to operate either as an amplifier or as an oscillator. Such models are said to be *active*.

Passivity criteria can be stated in the same way on the admittance basis. If a model is short-circuit stable, and if the hermitian determinant of its admittance matrix is positive semidefinite at all steady-state frequencies ω, that model is passive.

Figure 2-17 shows the hermitian determinant on the admittance basis for a simple triode model. It is apparent that a sufficiently large value of the transconductance g_m, or sufficiently small values of the other circuit conductances, will give a negative value of the hermitian determinant, in which case the circuit is usable as an amplifier or as an oscillator. These calculations do not tell us how to design the associated coupling network so as to produce the desired oscillator or amplifier, but they do give us the very important information as to whether or not such a design is possible.

PROBLEMS

2.1 Rewrite each of the following expressions as a single equivalent matrix.

(a) $\begin{bmatrix} 3 & 2 & 6 \\ 7 & 1 & -5 \\ 9 & -8 & 5 \end{bmatrix} + \begin{bmatrix} 1 & -8 & 8 \\ 4 & 1 & 2 \\ 6 & 3 & 4 \end{bmatrix}$

(b) $\begin{bmatrix} 1 & 1 \\ -1 & 1 \end{bmatrix}^8$

(c) $\begin{bmatrix} a_{11} & a_{12} & a_{13} \\ 0 & a_{22} & a_{23} \\ 0 & 0 & a_{33} \end{bmatrix}^{-1}$

(d) $[x_1 \quad x_2 \quad x_3][y_1 \quad y_2 \quad y_3]_t$

(e) $[x_1 \quad x_2 \quad x_3]_t[y_1 \quad y_2 \quad y_3]$

2.2 Carry out the indicated matrix multiplication.

(a) $\begin{bmatrix} 1 & 4 & 6 \\ 3 & 2 & 5 \\ 7 & 2 & 9 \end{bmatrix} \times \begin{bmatrix} 1 & 1 & 8 \\ 6 & 3 & 7 \\ 4 & 1 & 0 \end{bmatrix}$

(b) $\begin{bmatrix} a_{11} & a_{12} & a_{13} \\ a_{21} & a_{22} & a_{23} \\ a_{31} & a_{32} & a_{33} \end{bmatrix} \times \begin{bmatrix} b_{11} & 0 & 0 \\ 0 & b_{22} & 0 \\ 0 & 0 & b_{33} \end{bmatrix}$

2.3 For the matrix products in Problem 2.2, show by direct calculation that the determinant of the product is the product of the determinants.

2.4 Find the inverse of each of the following matrices:

$$\begin{pmatrix} 1 & 0 \\ 0 & 1 \end{pmatrix}, \quad \begin{pmatrix} 1 & 0 \\ 0 & -1 \end{pmatrix}, \quad \begin{pmatrix} 0 & 1 \\ 1 & 0 \end{pmatrix}, \quad \begin{pmatrix} 0 & 1 \\ -1 & 0 \end{pmatrix}$$

2.5 Find the inverse of

$$[a_1 \quad a_2 \quad a_3]\begin{bmatrix} b_{11} & b_{12} \\ b_{21} & b_{22} \\ b_{31} & b_{32} \end{bmatrix}\begin{bmatrix} c_1 \\ c_2 \end{bmatrix}$$

2.6 Evaluate the multiple product indicated.

$$\begin{bmatrix} 2 & 1 \\ 4 & 7 \end{bmatrix} \times \begin{bmatrix} 3 & 3 \\ 8 & 9 \end{bmatrix} \times \begin{bmatrix} 5 & 1 \\ 4 & 6 \end{bmatrix}$$

2.7 Given matrices A, B, and C as follows:

$$A = \begin{bmatrix} 1 & 0 & 1 \\ 3 & 1 & 2 \end{bmatrix}; \quad B = \begin{bmatrix} 1 & 0 & 0 \\ 1 & 1 & 1 \\ 2 & 0 & 2 \end{bmatrix}; \quad C = \begin{bmatrix} 4 & 1 & 1 \\ 0 & 0 & 2 \\ 3 & 1 & 0 \end{bmatrix}$$

(a) Calculate $A(B + C)$ and $AB + AC$. Are they equal?
(b) Calculate $(AB)C$ and $A(BC)$. Are they equal?
(c) Calculate BC and CB. Are they equal?

2.8 Consider the matrices A, B, and C of Problem 2.7.

(a) Compute BA. Does this product make sense?
     Compute BA_t. Does this product make sense?
(b) Show that $(BC)_t \equiv C_t B_t$.

2.9 Find the inverse of the following matrix:

$$A = \begin{pmatrix} 1 & 3 \\ -2 & 7 \end{pmatrix}$$

Compute AA^{-1} as a check.

2.10 Write the matrix representation for the following pair of equations:

$$v_1 = r_{11}i_1 + r_{12}i_2$$

$$v_2 = r_{21}i_1 + r_{22}i_2$$

2.11 Write the matrix representation for the following pair of equations:

$$i_1 = g_{11}v_1 + g_{12}v_2$$

$$i_2 = g_{21}v_1 + g_{22}v_2$$

2.12 Assume the equations of Problems 2.10 and 2.11 are alternative descriptions of the same two-terminal-pair network. Determine the relations between the two sets of circuit parameters.

2.13 The hybrid parameters, frequently used for incremental transistor models, relate the input and output variables for a two-terminal-pair circuit as follows:

$$v_1 = h_{11}i_1 + h_{12}v_2$$

$$i_2 = h_{21}i_1 + h_{22}v_2$$

For a transistor linear incremental model, relate the common-emitter h matrix and the common-base h matrix.

2.14 Let

$$x = [x_1 \quad x_2 \quad \cdots \quad x_n]$$

$$a = \begin{bmatrix} a_{11} & a_{12} & \cdots & a_{1n} \\ a_{21} & a_{22} & \cdots & a_{2n} \\ \vdots & \vdots & & \vdots \\ a_{n1} & a_{n2} & \cdots & a_{nn} \end{bmatrix}$$

$$\Delta = \text{determinant of } a$$
$$\Delta_{jk} = \text{cofactor of } a_{jk}$$

Show that if

$$ax_t = 0$$

then the only nontrivial solution for x occurs in the special case $\Delta = 0$, and that in this case

$$\frac{x_j}{x_k} = \frac{\Delta_{ij}}{\Delta_{ik}}$$

where i may be any number from 1 to n.

2.15 Consider the following matrix:

$$A = \begin{bmatrix} 3 & 4 & 0 & 1 & 5 \\ 1 & 0 & 0 & 1 & 3 \\ 2 & 2 & 2 & 1 & 0 \end{bmatrix}$$

Find a matrix P such that:

$$PA = C = \begin{bmatrix} 1 & 0 & 0 & a_{14} & a_{15} \\ 0 & 1 & 0 & a_{24} & a_{25} \\ 0 & 0 & 1 & a_{34} & a_{35} \end{bmatrix}$$

where $a_{14} \cdots a_{35}$ are unspecified.

2.16 Consider the following set of linear equations, in which $s = \sigma + j\omega$, and the admittance of a capacitance is therefore Cs.

$$(3s + 2)v_1 - v_2 - 5v_3 = i_1$$

$$-v_1 + 7sv_2 - sv_3 = i_2$$

$$-5v_1 - sv_3 + 0 = i_3$$

Draw an electric circuit described by the above nodal admittance equations. Does the circuit contain negative conductance or capacitance? Express this set of equations in matrix form, $I = YV$. Find the determinant Δ of the matrix Y. In the special case $i_1 = i_2 = i_3 = 0$, and with s chosen so that Δ vanishes, calculate v_2/v_1 and v_3/v_1. For $s = 1$ and $i_1 = i_2 = i_3 = 1$, find v_1, v_2, and v_3.

2.17 Diagonalize the following matrix by means of premultiplication and postmultiplication by elementary matrices.

$$A = \begin{bmatrix} 1 & 0 & 0 & 1 \\ 0 & 2 & 0 & 1 \\ 0 & 5 & 3 & 2 \\ 4 & 0 & 0 & 1 \end{bmatrix}$$

Now employ these elementary matrices and the diagonal form to invert A.

2.18 An arbitrary two-by-two matrix M can always be expressed as the weighted sum of four elementary matrices

$$M = aI + bJ + cK + dL$$

where a, b, c, d are scalar weighting factors, and

$$I = \begin{pmatrix} 1 & 0 \\ 0 & 1 \end{pmatrix}, \quad J = \begin{pmatrix} 1 & 0 \\ 0 & -1 \end{pmatrix}, \quad K = \begin{pmatrix} 0 & 1 \\ 1 & 0 \end{pmatrix}, \quad L = \begin{pmatrix} 0 & 1 \\ -1 & 0 \end{pmatrix}$$

are the four elementary matrices. Show that

$$M_1 M_2 \equiv M_2 M_1$$

if and only if

$$\frac{b_1}{b_2} = \frac{c_1}{c_2} = \frac{d_1}{d_2}$$

thus establishing a class of two-by-two matrices whose algebra is the same as that of scalars.

2.19 Let the complex number $z = x + jy$ be denoted by the matrix

$$z = \begin{pmatrix} x & y \\ -y & x \end{pmatrix}$$

and show that, with this notation, the matrix algebra of real numbers replaces the scalar algebra of complex numbers. In particular, show that

$$z_1 z_2 = z_2 z_1$$

and

$$|x + jy|^2 = (x + jy)(x - jy) = x^2 + y^2$$

Also give an interpretation to the polar form

$$re^{j\theta} = r \cos\theta + jr \sin\theta$$

2.20 For the matrices

$$x = \begin{pmatrix} 1 & 2 \\ 3 & 4 \end{pmatrix}, \quad y = \begin{pmatrix} 5 & 6 \\ 7 & 8 \end{pmatrix}, \quad z = \begin{pmatrix} 9 & 0 \\ 1 & 2 \end{pmatrix}$$

evaluate:
 (a) $x + y + z$.
 (b) $(x + y)(y + z)$.
 (c) xyz.
 (d) zyx.

2.21 If each scalar addition costs 1 cent and each scalar multiplication costs 10 cents, what is the approximate cost of inverting an n-by-n matrix (a) by cofactor expansions of the determinant, (b) by reduction to diagonal form with the aid of elementary premultiplier and postmultiplier matrices? Which method is less expensive for large matrices?

2.22 A "contact" or "switching" network has branches consisting of switches, each of which is either open or closed. Let x_{jk} be a number associated with the branch joining nodes j and k, and let

$$x_{jk} = \begin{cases} 1, & \text{if the switch is closed} \\ 0, & \text{if the switch is open} \end{cases}$$

The network is characterized by a symmetric matrix x whose elements are x_{jk}. (The diagonal elements x_{jj} are all unity since any node is inherently "connected" to itself.)

Suppose that in multiplying two contact matrices together, we carry out the indicated scalar operations according to the "Boolean" algebraic laws

$$0 \cdot 0 = 0 \qquad 0 + 0 = 0$$
$$0 \cdot 1 = 0 \qquad 0 + 1 = 1$$
$$1 \cdot 0 = 0 \qquad 1 + 0 = 1$$
$$1 \cdot 1 = 1 \qquad 1 + 1 = 1$$

$$\text{multiplication} \qquad \text{addition}$$

one of which $(1 + 1 = 1)$ is different from ordinary arithmetic.

(a) Show that the mth power x^m of the contact matrix has elements

$$(x^m)_{jk} = \begin{cases} 1, & \text{if the network contains at least one path} \\ & \text{of no more than } m \text{ branches between nodes } j \text{ and } k \\ 0, & \text{if there is no such path} \end{cases}$$

(b) Show that for a network of n nodes,

$$x^{n-1} \equiv x^{n-1+r}$$

where r is a nonnegative integer.

(c) Write the contact matrix for a network whose branches coincide with the edges of a cube and verify formally that the shortest path between diagonally opposite nodes contains three branches.

2.23 Formulate the floating admittance matrix of a bridge circuit (including both source and detector admittance) and from it compute the voltage-transfer ratio from the source to the detector.

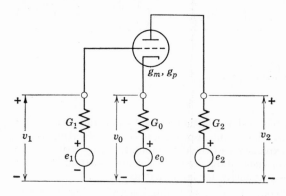

Fig. P2-1

2.24 For the low-frequency linear incremental model of the general triode amplifier circuit shown in Fig. P2-1,

(a) Formulate the floating admittance matrix.

(b) Find the elements A_{jk} of the matrix A relating the applied-voltage column matrix e and the electrode-potential column matrix v, as defined by the matrix equation

$$v = Ae$$

(c) Compute the voltage amplifications of the common-cathode, common-plate (cathode follower), and common-grid triode amplifier circuits, as special cases.

2.25 Using matrix methods, formulate the admittance between two terminals of a network whose branches coincide with the edges of a tetrahedron (bridge circuit).

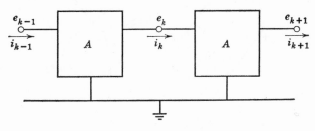

Fig. P2-2

2.26 Figure P2-2 shows a cascade connection of identical amplifiers A. Each amplifier can be characterized by the matrix equation

$$W_k = AW_{k+1}$$

where

$$A = \begin{pmatrix} a & b \\ c & d \end{pmatrix}, \qquad W_k = \begin{pmatrix} e_k \\ i_k \end{pmatrix}$$

(a) Find a suitable circuit model for the amplifier in the special case $a = b = c = d = r$, where r is a positive constant. Also calculate the voltage amplification of n stages, e_n/e_0 for $i_n = 0$.

(b) For an arbitrary A, show that the input impedance $z_0 = e_0/i_0$ and the load impedance $z_n = e_n/i_n$ of an n-stage cascade are related by

$$\left(\frac{z_0 - \alpha}{z_0 - \beta} \right) = \left(\frac{z^{oc} - \alpha}{z^{oc} - \beta} \right)^n \left(\frac{z_n - \alpha}{z_n - \beta} \right)$$

where z^{oc} is the input impedance of a stage as measured with the output of that stage open-circuited, and where α and β are the two values of x satisfying the quadratic equation

$$x = \frac{ax + b}{cx + d}$$

Quantities α and β are the two "image" values of load impedance, those values which yield an input impedance identical to the load impedance.

(c) By means of specific calculations, investigate the effect of grid-to-plate capacitance in an amplifier consisting of five identical triode stages terminating in a resistive load.

2.27 Using matrix methods, compute the current gain, input impedance, and output impedance of:

(a) A typical common-emitter transistor amplifier.

(b) A common-base amplifier.

(c) A common-collector amplifier.

2.28 Find the ranges of frequency ω and transconductance g_m within which the circuit of Fig. P2-3 is active. Passive.

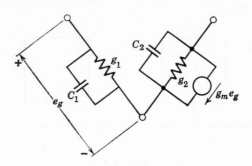

Fig. P2-3

2.29 (a) Find the ranges of frequency ω within which the device model in Fig. P2-4 is active. Passive. (The junction point between r_b and r_e is not an accessible terminal for connection of the model to its environment.) *Hint:* Formulate the problem on the impedance basis and consider the hermitian impedance matrix.

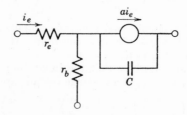

Fig. P2-4

(b) The model becomes a more accurate representation of a junction transistor at high frequencies if we replace the constant a ($a \approx 1$ at low ω) by sech $\sqrt{2j\omega/\omega_0}$ and the resistance r_e by $Z_e = R_e + jX_e$, where R_e is treated as a constant. Investigate activity and passivity for this modified model.

2.30 An antisymmetric square matrix A (that is, one for which $A_{jk} = -A_{kj}$) having an odd number of rows has a determinant identically equal to zero. Is this statement true or false?

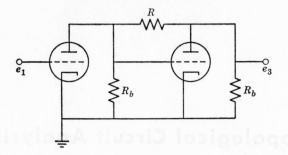

Fig. P2-5

2.31 For the incremental circuit (plate supply and grid bias not shown) in Fig. P2-5, construct the floating admittance matrix and find e_3/e_1 in terms of G ($G = 1/R$). Let $g_m = 5$, $r_p = R_b = 2$. Also find the current in R per unit of applied voltage e_1.

2.32 For a square matrix A, show that $AA^{-1} \equiv A^{-1}A$.

Topological Circuit Analysis

3.1   Introduction

A network transmission is the ratio of meter reading to source value for a meter and source attached to a network at two specified terminal pairs.   Topological circuit analysis, as we shall use the term here, is concerned with the relationship between a network transmission and the structure or "topology" of the network.   With the aid of topological methods, the transmission can be evaluated directly by inspection of the network.   The topological approach offers an alternative viewpoint which complements and enhances the more familiar methods of analysis.

Topology is a branch of mathematics which deals with certain properties of a geometric figure, structure, or object; in particular, those properties which are *invariant under a continuous one-to-one spatial transformation*.   The deformation of a rubber object is a physical interpretation of such a transformation, provided we are careful not to tear the rubber nor bring two parts together which originally did not touch. Continuity implies that any two neighboring points p and q on the original object *transform* or *map* into two neighboring points p' and q' on the new (transformed) object.   "One-to-one" means that p uniquely determines p' and vice versa, so that the transformation is single-valued and reversible.

The existence of a hole in a doughnut is a topological property of that doughnut, since no continuous one-to-one mapping of the doughnut can eliminate the hole. Similarly, the number of branches in an electric network is a topological property of that network, as are the number of nodes, the number of loops, and the number of different paths from one node to another. The topology of linear graphs is a vast subject. However, only a few elementary topological concepts are required in order to establish the intimate relationship between the structure of an electric network and the form of its transmission function.

3.2 The Network Determinant

The topological analysis of branch networks proceeds from the following definitions:

tree: a connected set of branches touching all nodes and not forming any loops (3.1)

tree value: product of the branch admittances in that tree (3.2)

network determinant (Δ): sum of the values of the different trees contained in the network (3.3)

In a network of n nodes, a tree (a) has $n - 1$ branches, (b) connects all node pairs, and (c) forms no loops. Any two of these three properties may be taken as the definition of a tree, whence the third property follows. We shall, for convenience and simplicity, often use the name "tree" interchangeably for both "tree" and "tree value," since the distinction is always clear from the usage.

Figure 3-1(g) shows a simple three-branch network whose branch admittances are a, b, and c. This network contains three different trees ab, ac, and bc, and the determinant is the sum of the trees. The other parts of the figure show several other networks and their determinants. *The determinant vanishes whenever a part or node is completely isolated from the remainder of the network,* as indicated in (c). *For a network having only one node,* either with or without an attached branch, *the determinant is identically equal to unity,* as illustrated in (e). Part (h) of Fig. 3-1 shows a network composed of *two connected parts having a single node in common.* For such networks *the determinant is expressible as the product of the determinants of those two parts.* This follows from the fact that a tree in each part is part of a tree in the complete network, and every tree in the complete network is a combination of such parts.

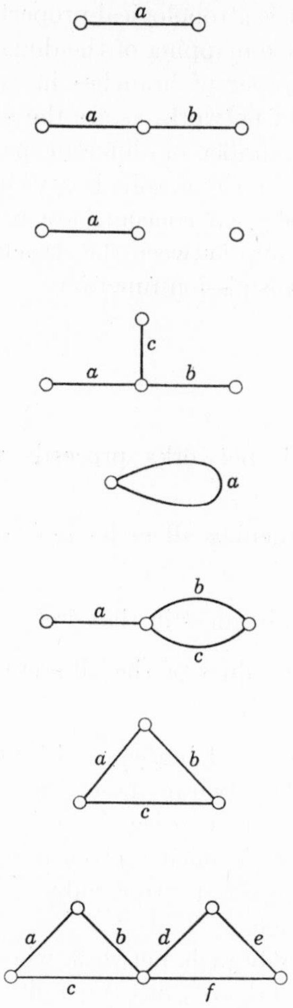

(a) $\Delta = a$

(b) $\Delta = ab$

(c) $\Delta = 0$

(d) $\Delta = abc$

(e) $\Delta = 1$

(f) $\Delta = ab + ac$

(g) $\Delta = ab + ac + bc$

(h) $\Delta = (ab + ac + bc)(de + df + ef)$

Fig. 3-1. Determinants of some elementary branch networks.

3.3 Partial Factoring of Determinants

As the network becomes more complicated, the search for all possible trees becomes more tedious. The job can be done systematically by alphabetically (or numerically) ordering the branches within each tree, and then searching through the entire "dictionary" to find all possible "tree words." For all but the simplest networks it is very convenient to condense the form of a determinantal expression by grouping those terms which contain some chosen set of branch admittances, and then writing that part of the determinant in factored form. This reduces the number of symbols in the expression and therefore simplifies the calculation of a numerical value. In Fig. 3-1(g), for example, the determinant Δ contains six symbols, whereas a partially factored form, $a(b + c) + bc$, has only five. In more complicated networks the saving is much greater. Fortunately, *we can write the determinant directly in a partially factored form* with the aid of the following definitions:

path: a simple (nonintersecting) string of branches terminating at two specified nodes. A simple string is a continuous succession of branches along which no node is encountered more than once (3.4)

path value (P_k): product of the branch admittances in path k (3.5)

path cofactor (Δ_k): the determinant of the network remaining when all the branches in path k are collapsed (short-circuited). The cofactor is unity if the path contains all nodes in the original network (3.6)

These definitions lead to the useful result,

$$\Delta = \sum_k P_k \Delta_k \tag{3.7}$$

Relation (3.7) is called an *expansion in paths* or *expansion on a node pair*. Each cofactor Δ_k is itself a determinantal entity, and can therefore be expanded in a new set of paths. Such expansions may be continued until all remaining cofactors are unity. Thus the determinant can be evaluated entirely in terms of paths and subpaths. The amount of condensation of the determinantal expression achieved by an expansion in paths will depend, of course, upon the structure of the particular network under consideration and upon the choice of node pairs for the expansion and subexpansions.

The proof of the path expansion (3.7) follows from the facts that each tree contains one, and only one, path between two specified nodes, and that the product of a path with each term of its cofactor is a tree. The following examples clarify these facts.

Figure 3-2 illustrates the expansion of a determinant for two different choices of the expansion node pair. The chosen nodes are shown as solid circles. Observe that choice (a) accomplishes the greater amount of condensation, reducing the number of symbols from twenty-four (in the sum of the trees) to thirteen (in the expansion). In Fig. 3-2(b), the cofactor of path a appears as the bracketed expression. The cofactor is the determinant of the network remaining when branch a is collapsed, and subexpansion has been carried out with the new paths $d + c$ and be.

(Collapsing a places d and c in parallel, whence they are equivalent to a single branch $d + c$.)

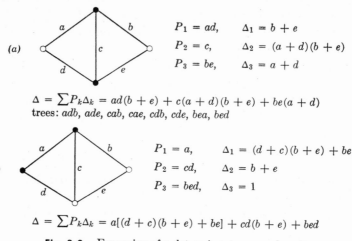

$$P_1 = ad, \quad \Delta_1 = b + e$$
$$P_2 = c, \quad \Delta_2 = (a + d)(b + e)$$
$$P_3 = be, \quad \Delta_3 = a + d$$

$\Delta = \sum P_k \Delta_k = ad(b + e) + c(a + d)(b + e) + be(a + d)$
trees: $adb, ade, cab, cae, cdb, cde, bea, bed$

$$P_1 = a, \quad \Delta_1 = (d + c)(b + e) + be$$
$$P_2 = cd, \quad \Delta_2 = b + e$$
$$P_3 = bed, \quad \Delta_3 = 1$$

$\Delta = \sum P_k \Delta_k = a[(d + c)(b + e) + be] + cd(b + e) + bed$

Fig. 3-2. Expansion of a determinant on a node pair.

Another useful grouping of terms is afforded by *node expansion* of the determinant. Suppose that three branches a, b, c terminate at a given node. The determinant can be written as

$$\Delta = a\Delta_a + b\Delta_b + c\Delta_c$$
$$+ ab\Delta_{ab} + ac\Delta_{ac} + bc\Delta_{bc} \qquad (3.8)$$
$$+ abc\Delta_{abc}$$

where Δ_a is the determinant of the network remaining after branch a is collapsed and branches b and c are erased. Similarly, Δ_{ab} is evaluated with a and b collapsed and c erased, and Δ_{abc} means that $a, b,$ and c are all collapsed. The generalization of (3.8), to accommodate four or more branches at the node, follows the same form. As it turns out, Δ_a, Δ_b, and Δ_c are equal, so that (3.8) becomes

$$\Delta = (a + b + c)\Delta_a$$
$$+ ab\Delta_{ab} + ac\Delta_{ac} + bc\Delta_{bc} \qquad (3.9)$$
$$+ abc\Delta_{abc}$$

Execution of this expansion at the uppermost node in Fig. 3-2 yields $\Delta = (a + b + c)de + ab(d + e) + ac(e) + bc(d) + abc$. For comparison, expansion at the left-hand node in Fig. 3-2 gives $(a + d)(bc + be + ce) + ad(b + e)$, a very compact result.

As a third determinantal identity, we shall mention *branch expansion*, or expansion on a branch. Let a be the chosen branch, whence

$$\Delta = \Delta_o + a\Delta_a \qquad (3.10)$$

wherein Δ_o is to be evaluated with branch a erased and Δ_a with branch a collapsed. Using Fig. 3-2 once more as an example, we find $\Delta_o = d(bc + be + ce)$ and $\Delta_a = (b + e)(d + c) + be$, so that $\Delta = d[(b + e)c + be] + a[(b + e)(d + c) + be]$.

3.4   The Topological Transmission Law for a Branch Network

The transmission of a branch network can be measured by attaching or inserting a source branch (s) and a meter branch (m). If several sources and meters are present, only one pair need be considered at a time, since in a linear network the effects of sources are superposable and meters are independent. A few more definitions will complete the picture and give us a topological formulation of the transmission.

transmission (T): ratio of meter reading to source value   (3.11)

transmission path: a path *containing* the meter branch and terminating at the two nodes where the source is attached to the network   (3.12)

transmission path value (P_k'): product of the branch admittances in the kth transmission path, with the meter *here* treated as a *unity* admittance. The associated algebraic sign is plus (minus) if current, circulating through the kth path in the positive source direction, would tend to make the meter reading positive (negative)   (3.13)

transmission path cofactor (Δ_k'): determinant of the network remaining when the kth transmission path, *including* the meter branch, is collapsed   (3.14)

The final result, for which a proof will be given later, is

$$T = \frac{\sum P_k'\Delta_k'}{\Delta} \qquad (3.15)$$

For the evaluation of Δ in (3.15), *voltage sources* and *current meters* are *collapsed*, whereas *current sources* and *voltmeters* are *erased*. In view of (3.7), the transmission may be expressed in the alternate form

$$T = \frac{\sum P_k'\Delta_k'}{\sum P_k\Delta_k} \qquad (3.16)$$

Figure 3-3 illustrates the application of this formula to the calculation of impedance or admittance at a pair of terminals. In Fig. 3-3(a) the transmission path consists of the voltmeter branch alone. With the voltmeter collapsed, the transmission path cofactor is recognizable as the determinant of branches b and c in parallel. In Fig. 3-3(b) there are

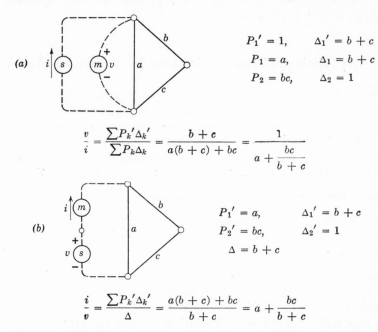

(a)

$$P_1' = 1, \qquad \Delta_1' = b + c$$
$$P_1 = a, \qquad \Delta_1 = b + c$$
$$P_2 = bc, \qquad \Delta_2 = 1$$

$$\frac{v}{i} = \frac{\sum P_k' \Delta_k'}{\sum P_k \Delta_k} = \frac{b+c}{a(b+c)+bc} = \frac{1}{a + \dfrac{bc}{b+c}}$$

(b)

$$P_1' = a, \qquad \Delta_1' = b + c$$
$$P_2' = bc, \qquad \Delta_2' = 1$$
$$\Delta = b + c$$

$$\frac{i}{v} = \frac{\sum P_k' \Delta_k'}{\Delta} = \frac{a(b+c)+bc}{b+c} = a + \frac{bc}{b+c}$$

Fig. 3-3. Calculation of (a) input impedance and (b) input admittance.

two different transmission paths to be considered in evaluating the numerator of the transmission expression. For the denominator, collapsing both the meter and the source leaves a two-node network consisting of b and c in parallel.

Further examples are given in Fig. 3-4. Notice that path P_2' in Fig. 3-4(a) has an associated negative sign, because the source current flowing through the meter via that path would tend to make the meter reading negative. In the circuit of Fig. 3-4(b) the current meter is in series with branch d and no special meter symbol has been shown. With the voltage source collapsed in Fig. 3-4(b), the network reduces to a triangle whose three sides have the admittances c, $a + d$, and $b + e$. Hence the path values P_1 and P_2 are those given in the figure.

A final example is offered in Fig. 3-5. The ladder network has but one transmission path, for the source and meter shown, and that path con-

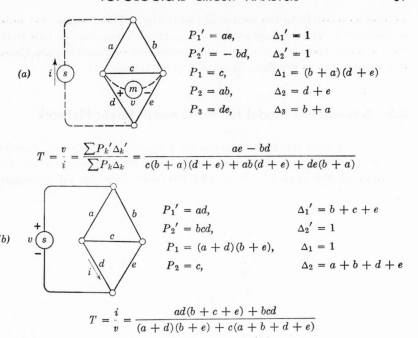

$$P_1' = ae, \qquad \Delta_1' = 1$$
$$P_2' = -bd, \qquad \Delta_2' = 1$$
(a) $\qquad\qquad P_1 = c, \qquad \Delta_1 = (b + a)(d + e)$
$$P_2 = ab, \qquad \Delta_2 = d + e$$
$$P_3 = de, \qquad \Delta_3 = b + a$$

$$T = \frac{v}{i} = \frac{\sum P_k' \Delta_k'}{\sum P_k \Delta_k} = \frac{ae - bd}{c(b + a)(d + e) + ab(d + e) + de(b + a)}$$

$$P_1' = ad, \qquad\qquad \Delta_1' = b + c + e$$
$$P_2' = bcd, \qquad\qquad \Delta_2' = 1$$
(b) $\qquad\qquad P_1 = (a + d)(b + e), \qquad \Delta_1 = 1$
$$P_2 = c, \qquad\qquad \Delta_2 = a + b + d + e$$

$$T = \frac{i}{v} = \frac{ad(b + c + e) + bcd}{(a + d)(b + e) + c(a + b + d + e)}$$

Fig. 3-4. Bridge-circuit transmissions. (a) A transfer impedance. (b) A transfer admittance.

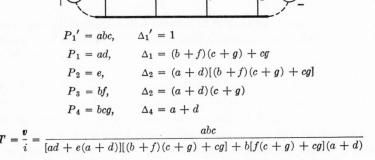

$$P_1' = abc, \qquad \Delta_1' = 1$$
$$P_1 = ad, \qquad \Delta_1 = (b + f)(c + g) + cg$$
$$P_2 = e, \qquad \Delta_2 = (a + d)[(b + f)(c + g) + cg]$$
$$P_3 = bf, \qquad \Delta_2 = (a + d)(c + g)$$
$$P_4 = bcg, \qquad \Delta_4 = a + d$$

$$T = \frac{v}{i} = \frac{abc}{[ad + e(a + d)][(b + f)(c + g) + cg] + b[f(c + g) + cg](a + d)}$$

Fig. 3-5. The transfer impedance of an unbalanced ladder network.

tains all the nodes of the network, with the result that the numerator of the transfer impedance is particularly simple. The denominator Δ can be greatly compacted by choosing, for the expansion node pair, the bottom node (shown as a heavy line in the figure) and an upper node as near as possible to the center of the ladder. This insures that most of the paths, when collapsed, leave a network consisting of two parts with a single node in common. The associated cofactors Δ_k are therefore identifiable as products of simpler subdeterminants.

3.5   A Branchlike Model for the General Linear Network

In a reciprocal network a measured transfer impedance (a current source-to-voltmeter transmission ratio) remains the same when the locations of the current source and the voltmeter are interchanged.

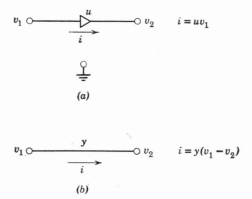

(a)

(b)

Fig. 3-6.   Basic linear circuit elements. (a) The unistor, a unilateral branchlike element. (b) The ordinary branch, a reciprocal element.

An arbitrary linear network is in general nonreciprocal, having unequal transfer impedances in opposite directions. The linear circuit models of vacuum-tube and transistor amplifiers are prime examples of nonreciprocal networks.

In order to extend the topological transmission law (3.15) to electronic circuits, we must first provide a circuit model. The model should be sufficiently general to permit characterization of an arbitrary linear circuit and, at the same time, sufficiently branchlike in character to afford a simple topological interpretation. Such a model can be constructed with the aid of a basic circuit element which we shall call a *unistor*. The unistor and the ordinary branch are defined and compared in Fig. 3-6(a) and (b), respectively. Both are branches, in the sense that the current in each element is determined by its terminal potentials, and each element is characterized by a single complex admittance, u or y. However, the unistor is not completely specified unless we also (1) indicate a branch reference direction and (2) designate the ground node with respect to which other node potentials are to be measured. The necessity of designating a ground node means that the unistor is, strictly speaking, a *three-terminal* element.

The unistor is, in effect, a current source controlled by the potential at one end of that source. Hence the unistor is analogous to the linear incremental circuit model of a special grounded-grid triode in which the plate conductance is small and the grid-to-plate transconductance is the only important parameter.

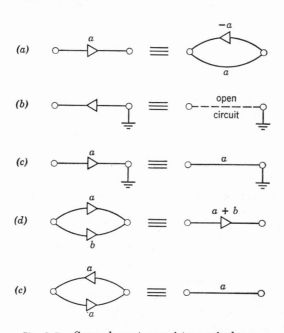

Fig. 3-7. Some elementary unistor equivalences.

A number of elementary equivalences, which follow directly from the definitions of the unistor and the reciprocal branch, are presented in Fig. 3-7. Figure 3-8(*a*) shows the unistor model of an arbitrary four-terminal network. By inspection of the associated admittance matrix, Fig. 3-8(*b*), we can see that

$$u_{jk} = -y_{kj}, \quad \text{for } k \neq 0, j \tag{3.17}$$

$$u_{j0} = \sum_{k=1}^{n} y_{kj} \tag{3.18}$$

$$u_{jj} = 0 \tag{3.19}$$

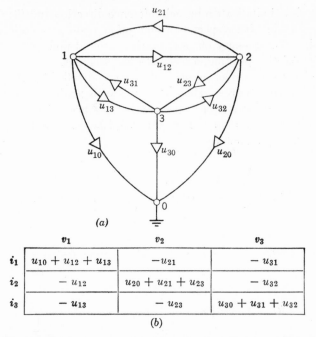

(a)

	v_1	v_2	v_3
i_1	$u_{10} + u_{12} + u_{13}$	$-u_{21}$	$-u_{31}$
i_2	$-u_{12}$	$u_{20} + u_{21} + u_{23}$	$-u_{32}$
i_3	$-u_{13}$	$-u_{23}$	$u_{30} + u_{31} + u_{32}$

(b)

Fig. 3-8. The general unistor model (a) and short-circuit admittance matrix (b) for a linear network.

where y_{kj} are the short-circuit admittances defined in the preceding chapter. We have reversed the subscript scheme for u, as compared with that for y, since a progression of subscripts in the direction of unistor orientation is more convenient for topological arguments. For example, the path from node 1 to node 2 to node 3 to ground in Fig. 3-8(a) has a path value $u_{12}u_{23}u_{30}$, in which the sequence of subscripts matches the succession of nodes along the path.

It is obvious from relations (3.17) through (3.19) that we can make a unistor model of an arbitrary linear network. Unistors u_{0j} need not be shown, because of the equivalence given in Fig. 3-7(b). For the special case $u_{jk} = u_{kj}$ the model reduces to that of a reciprocal branch network, as indicated by the equivalences in Fig. 3-7(c) and (e).

The unistor model of an electronic circuit can be constructed directly from the circuit diagram, without going through the admittance matrix as an intermediate step. A controlled-source unilateral transconductance, appearing in the conventional circuit representation of a vacuum tube, has the unistor model shown in Fig. 3-9(a). For a model of the transfer current effect in a transistor, we can reinterpret the effect as a transconductance, as indicated in Fig. 3-9(b). A grounded-grid triode circuit and a grounded-emitter transistor circuit have particularly simple unistor models, because two of the three unistors in the model become open circuits.

For network models containing unistor triplets such as those in Fig. 3-9 the choice of a ground node is arbitrary, since an equal change in all

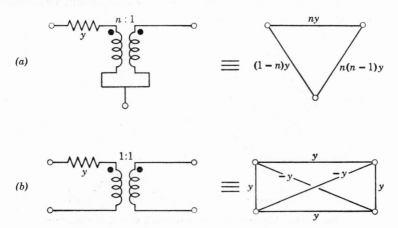

Fig. 3-9. Unistor models for (a) vacuum-tube transconductance and (b) transistor current amplification.

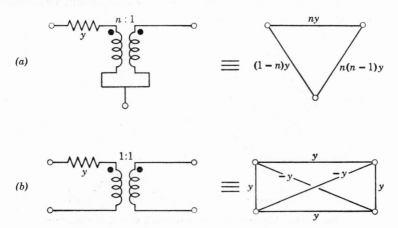

Fig. 3-10. Branch models for ideal transformers.

three of the node potentials changes the current circulating in the triangle of unistors but does not alter the flow of current from that triangle to the remainder of the network. Thus the three-unistor model of a transconductance is a *floating element* which may be "plugged" into any circuit, no matter where ground is located.

The ideal transformer is another circuit element that can be replaced by a branch model to facilitate topological interpretation of its properties. Figure 3-10 shows branch models for the ideal transformer. Unistors are not required here, since the ideal transformer is reciprocal. The equivalences follow from a comparison of the admittance matrices of the transformer (loaded with a series admittance y to make the short-circuit admittance description tractable) and the branch model.

3.6 The Topological Transmission Law for a General Linear Network

In order to extend the topological transmission law to networks containing unistors, only two modifications or restrictions are required:

The *ground* node must be located at one of the *meter* terminals   (3.20)

A tree or path is *improper* and is to be *ignored* if any unistor
points *away* from ground in that tree or path   (3.21)

A *proper* tree or path, therefore, is one in which all unistors point toward ground. The determinantal expansions (3.7), (3.9), and (3.10) can still be used, provided we drop any terms corresponding to improper trees in the network.

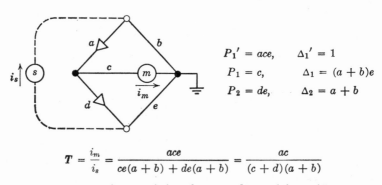

$$P_1' = ace, \qquad \Delta_1' = 1$$
$$P_1 = c, \qquad \Delta_1 = (a+b)e$$
$$P_2 = de, \qquad \Delta_2 = a+b$$

$$T = \frac{i_m}{i_s} = \frac{ace}{ce(a+b) + de(a+b)} = \frac{ac}{(c+d)(a+b)}$$

Fig. 3-11.   A transmission of a network containing unistors.

An example is given in Fig. 3-11. Observe that transmission path bcd (including the meter) is improper, since unistor d points away from ground *in that path*. Expansion of the determinant Δ is carried out on the two nodes shown solid in Fig. 3-11 and one of these is located at ground to insure that each path in the expansion shall contain the ground node. Otherwise rule (3.21) would be ambiguous. Path ab is improper, and is therefore ignored in computing Δ, because unistor a points away from ground in that path, just as it points away from ground in, for example, the improper tree abe. The unistor a appears, however, in the cofactors of paths c and de, since unistor a forms a proper tree in the network remaining after c or de is collapsed.

Rule (3.20) holds for the evaluation of all transmission paths involving unistors. In the evaluation of a network determinant, however, the

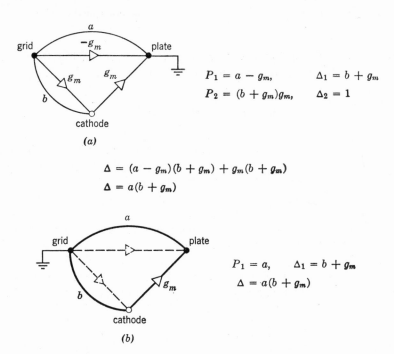

$$P_1 = a - g_m, \qquad \Delta_1 = b + g_m$$
$$P_2 = (b + g_m)g_m, \qquad \Delta_2 = 1$$

(a)

$$\Delta = (a - g_m)(b + g_m) + g_m(b + g_m)$$
$$\Delta = a(b + g_m)$$

$$P_1 = a, \qquad \Delta_1 = b + g_m$$
$$\Delta = a(b + g_m)$$

(b)

Fig. 3-12. The determinant of a network containing the unistor model of a transconductance.

choice of ground is arbitrary when the unistors appear in floating triplets. Figure 3-12(a) gives the path expansion for a simple network containing a floating transconductance model. Although the location of the ground node is arbitrary for a floating model, the path expansion can be made particularly simple by locating the ground node at the grid, as shown in Fig. 3-12(b), since only one of the three unistors then enters the calculation. It is apparent, therefore, that the determinant cannot involve the square of the transconductance g_m. Consideration of the various proper trees in a general network containing a transconductance shows that the determinant can be expanded as follows:

$$\Delta = \Delta'' + g_m \sum P_k'' \Delta_k'' \tag{3.22}$$

where

$P_k'' = k$th path between grid and plate, external to g_m and
not touching the cathode   (3.23)

$\Delta'' =$ value of Δ with g_m set equal to zero   (3.24)

$\Delta_k'' =$ cofactor of P_k'' with the cathode now collapsed to the
grid or plate   (3.25)

Application of this special expansion to the network in Fig. 3-12 yields
$\Delta'' = ab$, $P_1'' = a$, $\Delta_1'' = 1$, so that $\Delta = ab + g_m a$.

3.7   Analysis of a Simple Triode Circuit

The basic cathode-follower triode circuit is shown in Fig. 3-13(a).
Since the plate-supply potential is assumed to be fixed, the input voltage
source appears between plate and grid in the linear incremental model
(b). There is one proper transmission path since the grid-to-cathode
unistor points toward the meter in that path. To evaluate the determinant of the network, we first collapse the voltage source and the
current meter, which places the two positive unistors in parallel with
each other and in parallel with g_p and G_k. No matter which of the two
remaining nodes is chosen as ground, the determinant will be the same.
Another way of arriving at the same conclusion is to notice that when

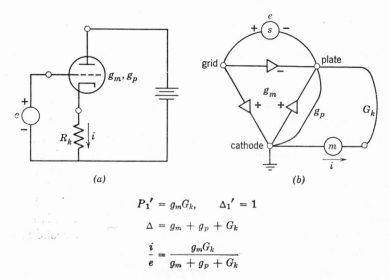

$$P_1' = g_m G_k, \qquad \Delta_1' = 1$$

$$\Delta = g_m + g_p + G_k$$

$$\frac{i}{e} = \frac{g_m G_k}{g_m + g_p + G_k}$$

Fig. 3-13. The transfer conductance of a cathode follower.

both the source and the meter are collapsed, the two unistors thereby placed in parallel are equivalent to a single reciprocal branch.

3.8 Analysis of a Triode Amplifier

A triode-amplifier circuit is shown in Fig. 3-14(a) and its linear incremental model in (b). Straightforward application of the topological rules yields the transmission expression. The denominator has been evaluated with the aid of the special expansion (3.22). Alternatively, we could have used the path expansion (3.7), with the grid chosen as the ground node for convenience.

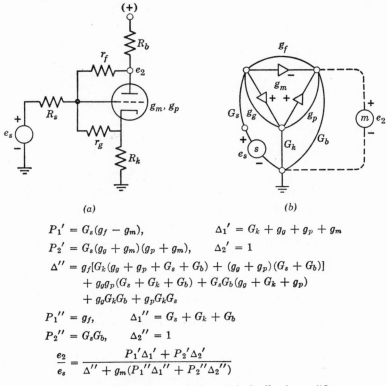

$$P_1' = G_s(g_f - g_m), \qquad \Delta_1' = G_k + g_g + g_p + g_m$$
$$P_2' = G_s(g_g + g_m)(g_p + g_m), \qquad \Delta_2' = 1$$
$$\Delta'' = g_f[G_k(g_g + g_p + G_s + G_b) + (g_g + g_p)(G_s + G_b)]$$
$$+ g_g g_p(G_s + G_k + G_b) + G_s G_b(g_g + G_k + g_p)$$
$$+ g_g G_k G_b + g_p G_k G_s$$
$$P_1'' = g_f, \qquad \Delta_1'' = G_s + G_k + G_b$$
$$P_2'' = G_s G_b, \qquad \Delta_2'' = 1$$
$$\frac{e_2}{e_s} = \frac{P_1'\Delta_1' + P_2'\Delta_2'}{\Delta'' + g_m(P_1''\Delta_1'' + P_2''\Delta_2'')}$$

Fig. 3-14. The voltage gain of a triode feedback amplifier.

3.9 Analysis of a Transistor Amplifier

Figure 3-15 shows a transistor amplifier (a) and its linear incremental model (b). The emitter-to-collector transconductance of the transistor is equal to ag_e, where a is the familiar emitter-to-collector current transfer factor of the transistor and g_e is the emitter conductance. Notice that the algebraic signs of the unistor admittances are opposite to those in a vacuum-triode transconductance model. The sign reversal accounts

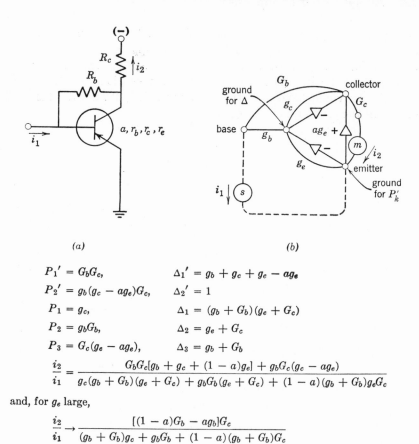

(a)   (b)

$$P_1' = G_b G_c,$$

$$P_2' = g_b(g_c - ag_e)G_c,$$

$$P_1 = g_c,$$

$$P_2 = g_b G_b,$$

$$P_3 = G_c(g_e - ag_e),$$

$$\Delta_1' = g_b + g_c + g_e - ag_e$$

$$\Delta_2' = 1$$

$$\Delta_1 = (g_b + G_b)(g_e + G_c)$$

$$\Delta_2 = g_e + G_c$$

$$\Delta_3 = g_b + G_b$$

$$\frac{i_2}{i_1} = \frac{G_b G_c[g_b + g_c + (1-a)g_e] + g_b G_c(g_c - ag_e)}{g_c(g_b + G_b)(g_e + G_c) + g_b G_b(g_e + G_c) + (1-a)(g_b + G_b)g_e G_c}$$

and, for g_e large,

$$\frac{i_2}{i_1} \rightarrow \frac{[(1-a)G_b - ag_b]G_c}{(g_b + G_b)g_c + g_b G_b + (1-a)(g_b + G_b)G_c}$$

Fig. 3-15.   The current gain of a transistor amplifier.

for the fact that the emitter-to-collector gain of a transistor is positive, whereas the grid-to-plate gain of a triode is negative.

If the emitter conductance g_e is assumed to be very large, the current gain of the amplifier approaches the form shown at the bottom of Fig. 3-15. This limiting form can be obtained directly, by agreeing to record a term in the expression only if the associated path or its cofactor contains g_e.

3.10 The Gyristor and the Gyrator

The unistor is a convenient branchlike model for unilateral transfer effects, such as those occurring in vacuum tubes and transistors. For general analytical work, however, another basic circuit element, called

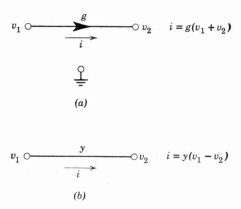

$$v_1 \xrightarrow[i]{g} \circ v_2 \qquad i = g(v_1 + v_2)$$

(a)

$$v_1 \xrightarrow[i]{y} \circ v_2 \qquad i = y(v_1 - v_2)$$

(b)

Fig. 3-16. Basic linear circuit elements. (a) The gyristor, an antireciprocal branch-like element. (b) The ordinary branch, a reciprocal element.

the gyristor, becomes useful. The gyristor is defined in Fig. 3-16(a) and compared with the ordinary branch (b). The gyristor current is influenced by *both* of its terminal potentials, but the effect is antisymmetric. An increase in v_1 sends current to the right, whereas a decrease in v_2 causes current to flow toward the left in Fig. 3-16(a).

Elementary gyristor equivalences are shown in Fig. 3-17. Since a gyristor is replaceable by two unistors, as indicated in Fig. 3-17(f), the topological transmission laws for networks containing gyristors can be deduced directly from the unistor laws already stated in (3.15), (3.16), (3.20), and (3.21). It follows that (3.15) and (3.16) apply, provided

the ground node is located at one of the meter terminals   (3.26)

and

a tree or path value is multiplied by -1 for each gyristor pointing *away* from ground in that tree or path   (3.27)

The symmetric triangular triplet of gyristors shown in Fig. 3-18(a) is called a *gyrator*. The gyrator, like the transconductance model in Fig. 3-9(a), is a floating element whose appearance in a network does not restrict the choice of a ground node. Using the transmission laws,

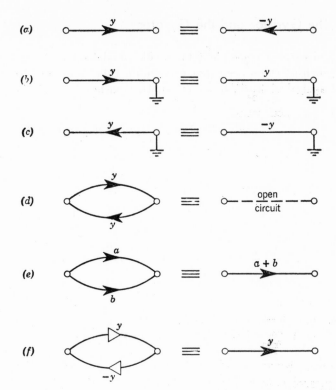

Fig. 3-17. Some elementary gyristor equivalences.

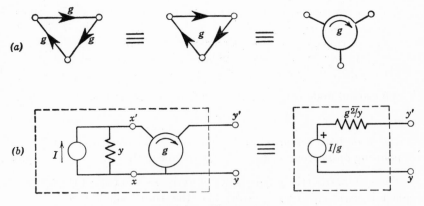

Fig. 3-18. The gyrator.

we can calculate the open-circuit voltage and short-circuit current of the box in Fig. 3-18(b) to obtain the Thévenin equivalent shown at the right. For g equal to unity in Fig. 3-18(b), the equivalent circuit yy' is the exact dual of the original circuit xx'. In other words, the gyrator is somewhat like an ideal transformer, except that it interchanges the

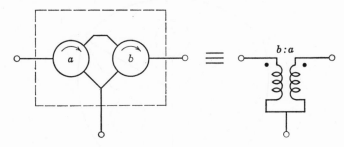

Fig. 3-19. The gyrator model of an ideal transformer.

roles of current and voltage at the output terminal pair yy'. An interchange in the roles of current and voltage does not affect power relationships, so that the gyrator is evidently a *passive lossless* element (Article 2.14). Since a double interchange of current and voltage brings us back to ideal-transformer-like behavior, two gyrators offer a way of making a topological model for the ideal transformer, as shown in Fig. 3-19. The ratio of gyrator admittances (right to left) is the turns ratio of the transformer (left to right).

The definitions of the gyristor and gyrator lead to the general circuit model and the admittance matrices shown in Fig. 3-20. For a network of $n + 1$ nodes, the general model will contain $n(n + 1)/2$ ordinary branches and $n(n - 1)/2$ gyrators. In terms of the short-circuit admittance parameters of the network (the elements of the short-circuit admittance matrix), the admittances of the ordinary branches in the model are given by

$$b_{jk} = -\tfrac{1}{2}(y_{jk} + y_{kj}), \quad \text{for } k \neq 0, j \tag{3.28}$$

$$b_{j0} = \sum_{k=1}^{n} \tfrac{1}{2}(y_{jk} + y_{kj}) \tag{3.29}$$

$$b_{jj} = 0 \tag{3.30}$$

with the understanding that b_{jk} and b_{kj} refer to the same branch. The gyrator admittances are given by

$$g_{jk} = \tfrac{1}{2}(y_{jk} - y_{kj}) \tag{3.31}$$

with the understanding that g_{jk} and $-g_{kj}$ are different names for the same gyrator. The gyrator subscript order indicates the reference direction of gyrator circulation and reversing the order of subscripts is equivalent to reversing the reference direction.

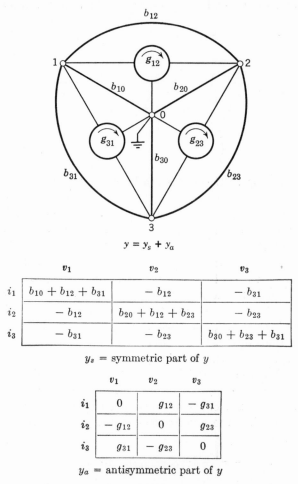

$$y = y_s + y_a$$

	v_1	v_2	v_3
i_1	$b_{10} + b_{12} + b_{31}$	$- b_{12}$	$- b_{31}$
i_2	$- b_{12}$	$b_{20} + b_{12} + b_{23}$	$- b_{23}$
i_3	$- b_{31}$	$- b_{23}$	$b_{30} + b_{23} + b_{31}$

y_s = symmetric part of y

	v_1	v_2	v_3
i_1	0	g_{12}	$- g_{31}$
i_2	$- g_{12}$	0	g_{23}
i_3	g_{31}	$- g_{23}$	0

y_a = antisymmetric part of y

Fig. 3-20. A general circuit model based upon gyrators g and ordinary branches b, together with the symmetric and antisymmetric parts of the associated short-circuit admittance matrix.

Were we to take node 1, instead of node 0, as the datum node in Fig. 3-20, the gyrator g_{23} would disappear and the model would contain, instead, a new gyrator across nodes 1, 2, and 3. Hence, in a general network model composed of ordinary branches and gyrators, the location of gyrators is somewhat open to choice. The ordinary branches can be thought of as strings connecting each pair of nodes. The gyrators can be visualized as triangular membranes, each of whose edges coincides with one of the strings. Just as the branches of a tree must not form any closed loops, the restriction on (independent) gyrator location is simply that the membranes must not form any closed spatial pockets. In a network of $n + 1$ nodes the aggregate gyrator membrane (a) has $n(n - 1)/2$ triangles, (b) connects all pairs of strings, and (c) forms no closed pockets. Any two of these three requirements are sufficient.

Now let us return to a branch network, in which a gyrator is imbedded, and examine the way in which the gyrator admittance influences the value of the network determinant. The gyrator consists of three gyristor branches. The set of all trees in the network can be divided into three classes: those containing none of the gyrator branches, those containing one, and those containing two. With the ground node designated, we can do a bit of general mental bookkeeping to find that the trees containing only one gyrator branch will occur in pairs whose values are equal but of opposite sign. Hence trees containing only one gyrator branch can be ignored when the determinant is evaluated. Moreover, the trees containing two gyrator branches will occur in triplets whose values are the same except for algebraic signs. For any fixed choice of a ground node, it can be seen that the square of the gyrator admittance enters two of the tree values with a positive sign, and enters the third with a negative sign. As a consequence, we can expand Δ in terms of the square of the gyrator admittance to obtain

$$\Delta = (\Delta \text{ with gyrator erased}) + g^2(\Delta \text{ with gyrator collapsed}) \quad (3.32)$$

In functional notation,

$$\Delta(g) = \Delta(0) + g^2\Delta_g \quad (3.33)$$

where Δ_g is the cofactor of the gyrator. If the network contains more than one gyrator, $\Delta(0)$ and Δ_g can each be expanded in terms of one of the other gyrators, and so on until all of the gyrator-admittance squares have been partially factored. (Two gyrators having the same three terminals in common are, of course, equivalent to a single gyrator, and are therefore not susceptible to separate expansion.)

The use of the topological transmission rules for gyristors and gyrators is illustrated in Fig. 3-21. Remembering the gyristor-gyrator equivalence, Fig. 3-18(a), we find two transmission paths through the gyrator. The first transmission path consists of the uppermost gyristor branch and the meter branch. Collapsing these two branches leaves branch b in parallel with two oppositely directed equal gyristors which negate each other. Hence the value of Δ_1' given in the figure. The second transmission path consists of the meter plus the two lower gyristors in the gyrator. Each gyristor enters the path value with a minus sign, because each points away from the meter in that path. Finally, the determinant is evaluated with the aid of (3.33).

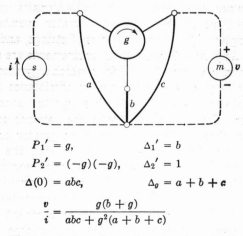

$$P_1' = g, \qquad \Delta_1' = b$$
$$P_2' = (-g)(-g), \qquad \Delta_2' = 1$$
$$\Delta(0) = abc, \qquad \Delta_g = a + b + c$$
$$\frac{v}{i} = \frac{g(b + g)}{abc + g^2(a + b + c)}$$

Fig. 3-21. The transfer impedance of a network containing a gyrator.

Having found the transmission expression in Fig. 3-21, we can easily obtain the expression for the transmission in the reverse direction through the network. With the source and meter interchanged, g changes sign in P_1' and P_2'. The denominator of the transfer impedance remains unaltered and the numerator becomes $-g(b - g)$. Hence, by choosing b equal to g we have a *unilateral* network whose reverse transfer impedance vanishes. This example emphasizes the fact that a *passive* network is not necessarily *reciprocal*.

3.11   Outline of a Proof of the Topological Transmission Laws

In Article 3.5 it was shown that an arbitrary linear network can be represented as a network of unistors. The admittance matrix of a unistor network takes the general form

$$\begin{bmatrix} \Sigma u_{1k} & -u_{21} & -u_{31} & \cdots & -u_{n1} \\ -u_{12} & \Sigma u_{2k} & -u_{32} & \cdots & -u_{n2} \\ -u_{13} & -u_{23} & \Sigma u_{3k} & \cdots & -u_{n3} \\ \vdots & \vdots & \vdots & & \vdots \\ -u_{1n} & -u_{2n} & -u_{3n} & \cdots & \Sigma u_{nk} \end{bmatrix} \qquad (3.34)$$

We assume here that the network has $n + 1$ nodes numbered from 0 to n, node 0 is ground, u_{jj} vanishes, and the summations indicated in (3.34) are carried out over $k = 0, 1, 2, \cdots, n$. Now let

$$\Delta_M = \text{determinant of the network admittance matrix} \quad (3.35)$$

$$\Delta_T = \text{sum of the proper trees in the network} \quad (3.36)$$

Our first task is to show that Δ_M and Δ_T are equal. The definition of the determinant of a matrix (2.35) tells us that the determinant is the sum of products of the matrix elements, taken n at a time, with no two elements in the product coming from the same row or the same column of the matrix. It is apparent, from (3.34), therefore, that Δ_M is a sum of terms, each of which is a product of unistor admittances, and that

$$u_{ik} \text{ and } u_{ij} \text{ cannot both appear in a term of } \Delta_M \quad (3.37)$$

In other words, no two of the unistors in a term of Δ_M can *radiate* from the same node in the network, but two or more may *terminate* upon the same node.

Consider the possible network locations for the n unistors appearing in a single term of Δ_M. Our network has $n + 1$ nodes so a tree must have n branches. Hence

$$\text{a term of } \Delta_M \text{ is either a tree or it contains a loop} \quad (3.38)$$

If the term contains a loop (that is, if two or more of the unistors associated with that term form a loop in the network), then all unistors in the loop must point in the same direction around the loop, for otherwise (3.37) is violated.

We shall now show that a loop is impossible. Suppose the loop consists of unistors u_{12}, u_{23}, u_{34}, and u_{41}. There is no loss of generality in choosing this subscript progression since the numbering of nodes is arbitrary (except for the ground node, which cannot appear in a loop because unistors u_{0j} are absent). In the admittance matrix, add the first row to the second row, then add the second row to the third row, and then add the third to the fourth. This leaves the value of Δ_M unaltered. It follows directly from the form of (3.34) that the four unistor admittances will thereupon appear in the matrix positions

u_{12}			$-u_{41}$	
	u_{23}		$-u_{41}$	
		u_{34}	$-u_{41}$	

$$(3.39)$$

and nowhere else in the matrix. Hence the product $u_{12}u_{23}u_{34}u_{41}$ cannot appear in a term of Δ_M, for these elements cannot be selected from four *separate* rows. The argument obviously generalizes to any number of unistors in the loop.

Having eliminated loops, we return to trees. Consider a *proper* tree in which all unistors point toward ground. If we reverse the directions of *some* of the unistors, we violate (3.37). Moreover, we cannot reverse *all* unistor directions because unistors u_{0j} are absent. Hence

all terms of Δ_M are *proper* unistor trees, in which all unistors
point toward ground   (3.40)

It remains to demonstrate that all such unistor trees in the network will appear as terms of Δ_M, and that they will all appear with unity coefficients. Each node in a proper tree (other than the ground node) has one and only one unistor radiating from that node. Choose any such tree $u_{1i}u_{2j}u_{3k} \cdots u_{nr}$. In the admittance matrix, add row 1 to row i, then add row 2 to row j, then add row 3 to row k, and so forth. After the first addition, unistor u_{1i} appears only on the main diagonal, in the first row and first column. *None of the later additions can alter this situation*, since u_{1i} exists in no other row. After the second addition, unistor u_{2j} is permanently fixed in the second row and second column, and nowhere else. The same applies to all succeeding unistors in the tree. One of the tree elements must, of course, be some unistor u_{p0} terminating upon the ground node. When we come to this one we shall not do any addition of rows, since u_{p0} already appears in the pth row and column and nowhere else. After completion of the process described above, the tree unistors are located only along the main diagonal of the matrix and each appears with a coefficient equal to $+1$. Hence

all proper unistor trees in the network appear as terms of Δ_M (3.41)

Finally, in view of (3.40) and (3.41),

$$\Delta_M = \Delta_T \tag{3.42}$$

With (3.42) established, a proof of the topological transmission law can now be constructed. Figure 3-22(a) shows a unistor network with an attached source and meter. One end of the meter is grounded. Let

Z = transfer impedance v/i of the network in Fig. 3-22(a)   (3.43)

Δ_M = determinant of network in Fig. 3-22(a)   (3.44)

Δ'_M = determinant of network in Fig. 3-22(b), including the
unistors u and $-u$ (3.45)

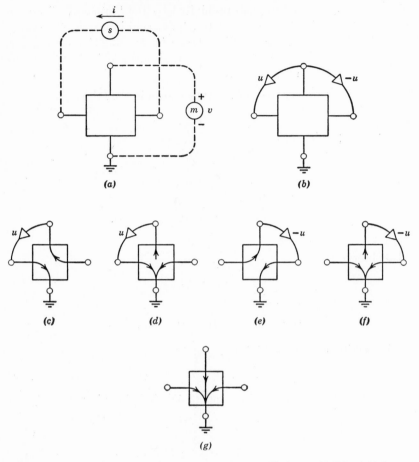

Fig. 3-22. (a) A transfer impedance measurement. (b) An equivalent experiment. (c), (d), (e), (f), (g) Possible types of proper unistor trees in network (b).

Also let

$$u = 1/Z \tag{3.46}$$

whence it follows that

$$\Delta_M' = 0 \tag{3.47}$$

for if u is the reciprocal of Z, then the unistors in network (b) supply just enough current at the lateral nodes to satisfy the equilibrium equations of the network. In the light of (3.42), Δ_M' may be evaluated as the sum of proper trees in network (b). No proper tree can contain both of the unistors u and $-u$, and certain tree configurations containing one

of these two unistors are also prohibited by the "properness" requirement that all unistors must point toward ground in a tree. The proper
trees fall into the five categories shown in Fig. 3-22(c) through (g).
Each type contains paths between external nodes as indicated by lines
within the box. Let

T_k = sum of proper trees of the type shown in the kth part of
Fig. 3-22   (3.48)

and, in particular, let

$$T_c = uC \qquad (3.49)$$

$$T_d = uD \qquad (3.50)$$

$$T_e = -uE \qquad (3.51)$$

$$T_f = -uF \qquad (3.52)$$

Also observe that

$$T_g = \Delta_T \qquad (3.53)$$

Now, from (3.49) through (3.53)

$$\Delta_M{}' = u(C + D - E - F) + \Delta_T \qquad (3.54)$$

By inspection of Fig. 3-22(d) and (f),

$$D = F \qquad (3.55)$$

and from (3.46), (3.47), (3.54), and (3.55), it follows immediately that

$$Z = \frac{E - C}{\Delta_T} \qquad (3.56)$$

If we "plug" the box pattern in Fig. 3-22(e) into the circuit (a), it is
apparent that trees of type (e) provide *positive transmission paths* between the meter and the source. Similarly, trees of type (c) are associated with negative transmission paths. Thus E is identifiable as that
part of the numerator of the topological transmission law (3.15) arising
from positive transmission paths and their cofactors, whereas C takes
care of the negative transmission paths and their cofactors.

This establishes the topological transmission law governing the
transfer impedance of a unistor network. The validity of the law for
voltage sources or current meters follows easily by means of elementary
source transformations and Ohm's law. Finally, since both gyristors
and ordinary branches can be defined in terms of unistors, the topological laws applicable to gyristors and ordinary branches can be deduced
directly from those for unistors.

3.12 Absorption of a Node

As a complement to the material in the preceding article, something should be said about node absorption. Suppose that in a unistor network N, having n nodes, only the first r nodes are accessible for electrical measurements. Consider also another unistor network N', having r nodes, all of which are accessible. By a proper choice of the unistor admittances u_{jk}' in N' we can make N and N' entirely equivalent, insofar as electrical measurements at the accessible nodes can detect.

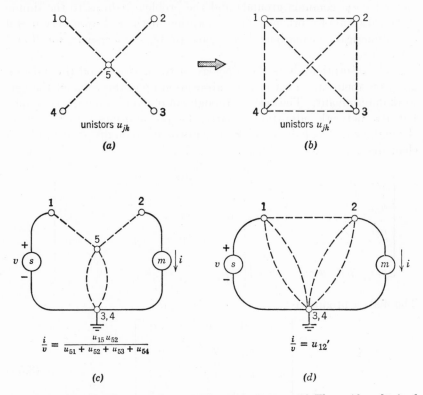

$$\frac{i}{v} = \frac{u_{15} u_{52}}{u_{51} + u_{52} + u_{53} + u_{54}}$$

$$\frac{i}{v} = u_{12}'$$

(c)　　　　　　　　　　(d)

Fig. 3-23. Absorption of a node. (a) The original star. (b) The residue obtained by absorbing node 5. (c), (d) Identical transfer admittances in the two networks.

In such a case, we say that N' is *equivalent* to N *with respect to* the *designated* set of *accessible nodes*. Alternatively, we can say that N' is a *residue* of N, obtained by *absorbing* the inaccessible nodes.

Figure 3-23 shows the absorption of a single node. To insure equivalence of the residue, it is sufficient to equate each short-circuit admittance of the residue to the corresponding transmission measured at the accessible nodes of the original network. It follows directly that the general rule for *absorption of node p* is

$$u_{jk}{}' = u_{jk} + \frac{u_{jp}u_{pk}}{\sum_i u_{pi}} \tag{3.57}$$

where, of course, $u_{jj} = u_{jj}{}' = 0$.

One way to calculate a network transmission T is to absorb one node after another until only the nodes at the source and meter remain. The residue then contains, at most, nine unistors (or four, if the source and meter have a common ground) and the problem reduces to the simple standard form of a bridge. The absorption method is often very useful for numerical calculations but tends to be cumbersome for literal solutions.

Node absorption alters the topology of the network and this raises a question about the effect of node absorption upon the value of the network determinant. The answer, though not obvious, is relatively simple. Let the network admittance matrix be postmultiplied by a certain elementary matrix having unity elements on its main diagonal and extra elements only in its first row,

$$\begin{bmatrix} y_{11} & y_{12} & y_{13} & \cdots & y_{1n} \\ y_{21} & y_{22} & y_{23} & \cdots & y_{2n} \\ y_{31} & y_{32} & y_{33} & \cdots & y_{3n} \\ \vdots & \vdots & \vdots & & \vdots \\ y_{n1} & y_{n2} & y_{n3} & \cdots & y_{nn} \end{bmatrix} \begin{bmatrix} 1 & -\dfrac{y_{12}}{y_{11}} & -\dfrac{y_{13}}{y_{11}} & \cdots & -\dfrac{y_{1n}}{y_{11}} \\ 0 & 1 & 0 & \cdots & 0 \\ 0 & 0 & 1 & \cdots & 0 \\ \vdots & \vdots & \vdots & & \vdots \\ 0 & 0 & 0 & \cdots & 1 \end{bmatrix} \tag{3.58}$$

The matrix product is

$$\begin{bmatrix} y_{11} & 0 & 0 & \cdots & 0 \\ y_{21} & y_{22}{}' & y_{23}{}' & \cdots & y_{2n}{}' \\ y_{31} & y_{32}{}' & y_{33}{}' & \cdots & y_{3n}{}' \\ \vdots & \vdots & \vdots & & \vdots \\ y_{n1} & y_{n2}{}' & y_{n3}{}' & \cdots & y_{nn}{}' \end{bmatrix} \tag{3.59}$$

wherein

$$y_{jk} = -u_{kj}, \quad j \neq k \tag{3.60}$$

$$y_{jj} = \sum_i u_{ji} \tag{3.61}$$

$$y_{jk}' = y_{jk} - \frac{y_{j1}y_{1k}}{y_{11}} \tag{3.62}$$

Now let

$$u_{jk}' = u_{jk} + \frac{u_{j1}u_{1k}}{\sum_i u_{1i}} \tag{3.63}$$

and it follows that

$$y_{jk}' = -u_{kj}', \quad j \neq k \tag{3.64}$$

$$y_{jj}' = \sum_{i=2}^{n} u'_{ji} \tag{3.65}$$

Thus the last $n - 1$ rows and columns of (3.59) are identifiable as the admittance matrix for the network residue obtained by absorbing node 1. Let

Δ = determinant of the original network $\tag{3.66}$

Δ' = determinant of the residue network after absorption of node 1 $\tag{3.67}$

Since postmultiplication of a matrix by an elementary matrix does not change the value of the determinant, we see from (3.58) and (3.59) that

$$\Delta = y_{11}\Delta' \tag{3.68}$$

or, for absorption of an arbitrary node p,

$$\Delta' = \frac{\Delta}{y_{pp}} = \frac{\Delta}{\sum_i u_{pi}} \tag{3.69}$$

Hence,

absorption of a node *divides* the network determinant by the short-circuit admittance of that node $\tag{3.70}$

PROBLEMS

3.1 Construct a necessary and sufficient set of definitions and rules which specify correct use of the laws

$$T = \sum P_k'\Delta_k'/\Delta, \qquad \Delta = \sum P_k\Delta_k$$

in reciprocal branch network analysis. Start by defining "network" and "transmission."

3.2 Find i_2/i_1 and i_3/i_1 in Fig. P3-1 (a), where the letters represent branch admittances. Find v_2/i_1 in Fig. P3-1 (b).

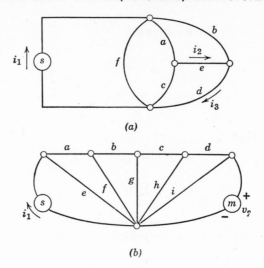

(a)

(b)

Fig. P3-1

3.3 Find the source-to-meter transmission for each of the networks in Fig. P3-2. Letters are branch admittances. The rules fail in Fig. P3-2(a). Explain.

3.4 Find the number of trees in a network whose branches are the edges of a cube.

3.5 Using the topological transmission laws, prove that $0 \leq (i_m/i_s) \leq 1$ for a network of positive resistors, where the source i_s and the meter i_m have a common ground.

3.6 Using the topological transmission laws, prove that $0 \leq |v_m/v_s| \leq 1$ for a network of positive resistors.

3.7 If Δ is defined as the sum of the trees in a network, prove the "path expansion," $\Delta = \sum P_k \Delta_k$, where P_k is the kth path between two chosen nodes and Δ_k is the cofactor of path P_k, that is, the Δ of the network remaining when P_k is collapsed.

3.8 Prove that the Δ of a network is the Δ-product of the separate parts. Define, carefully, a separate part.

3.9 Using the topological laws, prove that for a reciprocal branch network:

(a) The open-circuit transfer impedances in opposite directions are equal.

(b) The short-circuit transfer admittances in opposite directions are equal.

(c) The open-circuit transfer-voltage ratio in one direction is equal to the negative of the short-circuit transfer-current ratio in the opposite direction. Be careful about reference polarities. Statement (c) is convenient for the description of reciprocity in the ideal model of a magnetic transformer. Why?

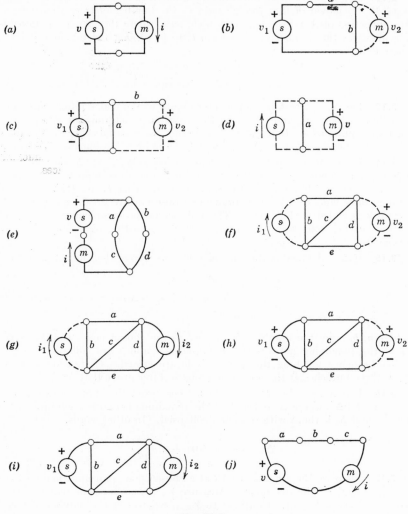

Fig. P3-2

3.10 Using the topological laws, prove that

$$Z \text{ faced by } A = \frac{\Delta \text{ with } A \text{ collapsed}}{\Delta \text{ with } A \text{ erased}}$$

where A is any branch in the network.

3.11 Show that in a network of 1-ohm resistors, Δ is equal to the number of different trees.

3.12   In a network of 1-ohm resistors, a particular branch A faces a resistance R. Removal of that branch reduces the number of trees from t to t_0. Reconnection of A across some new node pair, where the facing resistance is R', increases the number of trees from t_0 to t'. Using the topological laws, show that

$$\frac{t_0}{t} = \frac{1}{1+R}, \qquad \frac{t'}{t_0} = 1 + R'$$

3.13   Let Δ_y be the admittance determinant of the node-voltage equations of a branch network and let Δ_z be the impedance determinant of the loop-current equations of that network. Verify, in a number of significantly different examples, that Δ_y/Δ_z = product of the branch admittances.

3.14   In the topological transmission law $T = \sum P_k' \Delta_k'/\Delta$, multiply numerator and denominator by the product of the network branch impedances, and then attempt to recognize the rules for evaluating T directly in terms of branch impedances. (A set of branches whose erasure breaks all loops in a network is called a "link set." The link set is the complement or dual of a tree.) Test your new rules on a network consisting of a simple ring of branches.

3.15   If Δ is defined as the sum of the trees, prove the "node expansion"

$$\Delta = a\Delta_a + b\Delta_b + c\Delta_c$$
$$+ \, ab\Delta_{ab} + ac\Delta_{ac} + bc\Delta_{bc}$$
$$+ \, abc\Delta_{abc}$$

where a, b, c are the branches connected to the chosen node, and Δ_{ij} is the Δ of the remaining network when branches i and j are collapsed and all other branches touching the chosen node are erased. (Extension to more than three branches at the node is obvious.) First prove that $\Delta_a = \Delta_b = \Delta_c$.

3.16   If Δ is defined as the sum of the trees, prove the "branch expansion," $\Delta = \Delta_0 + a\Delta_a$, where Δ_0 is the Δ of the remaining network when branch a is erased and Δ_a is the Δ with branch a collapsed. In other words,

$$\Delta = f(a) = f(0) + a\frac{\partial f(a)}{\partial a}$$

3.17   Measure the admittance Y_1 at a chosen node pair and then coalesce (solder together) the two nodes. Measure Y_2 at another node pair and then coalesce that node pair. Continue to Y_{n-1}, where n is the number of nodes in the original network. Prove that $\Delta = Y_1 Y_2 Y_3 \cdots Y_{n-1}$.

3.18   Cut a branch and measure the admittance Y_1 at the cut. Cut another branch (leaving the first cut open) and measure the admittance Y_2 at the second cut. Continue until all loops in the network are interrupted by cuts. Prove that $(Y_1 Y_2 \cdots Y_m)(\Delta)$ = product of the branch admittances. Find m in terms of the number of branches b and the number of nodes n in the original network.

3.19   Let Y_k be the sum of the admittances of the branches connected to node k. Show that for a network of n nodes

$$\Delta = [Y_1 Y_2 Y_3 \cdots Y_{n-1}]^*$$

where the asterisk denotes that the multiplication is to be carried out with a special algebra in which

$$xy = \begin{cases} 0, & \text{if } x \text{ and } y \text{ are the same branch} \\ xy, & \text{if } x \text{ and } y \text{ are different branches} \end{cases}$$

$$x + y = \begin{cases} 0, & \text{if } x \text{ and } y \text{ are the same branch} \\ x + y, & \text{if } x \text{ and } y \text{ are different branches} \end{cases}$$

3.20 Construct a network of eight nodes and eight branches which has the maximum number of trees.

3.21 Repeat Problem 3.20 with nine branches.

3.22 Repeat Problem 3.20 with twelve branches.

3.23 Show that the number of trees in a "full" network (a branch between each pair of nodes) is n^{n-2}, where n is the number of nodes. *Hint:* Let all branch admittances be 1 mho and evaluate the admittance determinant.

3.24 Show that the resistance between two nodes in a full network of 1-ohm resistors is $2/n$. *Hint:* Make use of symmetry.

3.25 Using the topological transmission laws, find the voltage transfer ratio of a "twin-T" RC filter terminated in a resistance R_0.

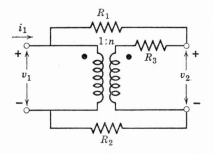

Fig. P3-3

3.26 Using the branch model of a transformer, find the input impedance v_1/i_1 and the voltage-transfer ratio v_2/v_1 of the circuit in Fig. P3-3. *Hint:* First draw an equivalent network in which v_2 and v_1 have a common ground.

3.27 Find v_2/v_1 and i_1/v_1 for the circuit in Fig. P3-4, assuming that conductance G is adjusted to minimize the frequency dependence of i_1/v_1. Let $G_0 = \sqrt{C/L}$.

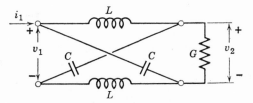

Fig. P3-4

3.28 Show that erasure of a node i and all its connecting branches (other than a source or meter node) does not affect the transmission through a network, provided each branch admittance y_{jk} (for a branch between nodes j and k) is replaced by a new admittance

$$y_{jk}' = y_{jk} + \frac{y_{ji}y_{ik}}{\sum_r y_{ir}}$$

This node elimination is called the star-to-mesh transformation.

3.29 Show that star-to-mesh elimination of node i yields a new network whose determinant Δ' is related to the original Δ by

$$\Delta = \Delta' \sum_r y_{ir}$$

3.30 Show that the transmission T of a network is a linear rational function of any single specified branch admittance y. In short,

$$T = \frac{A + By}{C + Dy}$$

where A, B, C, D are parameters dependent only upon the admittances of branches other than branch y.

3.31 Prove the topological transmission law for a linear reciprocal branch network.

3.32 Evaluate the Δ of the "tetrahedron" network in Fig. P3-5 by:
(*a*) Identification of all trees.
(*b*) Path expansions.
(*c*) Node expansions.
(*d*) Branch expansions.
(*e*) The special algebra of Problem 3.19.

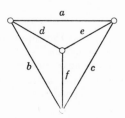

Fig. P3-5

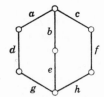

Fig. P3-6

3.33 Evaluate the Δ of the network in Fig. P3-6 by:
(*a*) First eliminating some nodes with the star-to-mesh transformation, then using the results of Problem 3.29.
(*b*) Multiplying the sum of the various cut-set impedance products by the branch-admittance product of the network.

3.34 Let Δ_{jk} denote the Δ of the network resulting when nodes j and k are joined. Illustrate by a simple special case the fact that $\Delta_{12} = \Delta_{23} + \Delta_{31}$

for the network shown in Fig. P3-7, and give an argument for its general validity.

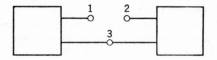

Fig. P3-7

3.35 A network has an even number of nodes which are numbered in succession from 1 to n, and a 1-ohm branch runs from each even-numbered node to each odd-numbered node. Find the resistance R measured (a) between two even-numbered nodes, (b) between an even-numbered node and an odd-numbered node. *Hint:* Exploit symmetry.

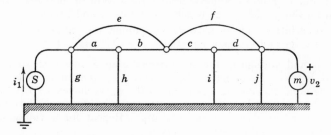

Fig. P3-8

3.36 Find the transfer impedance v_2/i_1 of the "tandem bridged-T" network shown in Fig. P3-8. You may, if you wish, make use of the identity given in Problem 3.34.

3.37 Figure P3-9 shows a network composed of two subnetworks, 1 and 2, having exactly two nodes in common. Let Δ_1 and Δ_1' be the determinants of subnetwork 1 with its two external terminals open-circuited and short-circuited, respectively, and similarly for subnetwork 2. Show that the identity in Problem 3.34 can be recast in the form $\Delta = \Delta_1\Delta_2' + \Delta_1'\Delta_2$, where Δ is the determinant of the complete network shown in Fig. P3-9. What is the physical interpretation of the quotient Δ/Δ', where $\Delta' = \Delta_1'\Delta_2'$?

3.38 The unistor and gyristor are defined in Fig. P3-10. State carefully the modifications of the topological transmission laws which are necessary in order to accommodate networks containing unistors and gyristors.

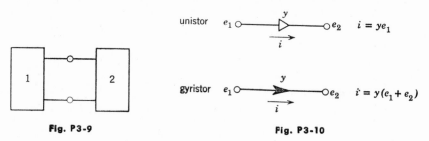

Fig. P3-9

Fig. P3-10

3.39 Using the topological transmission laws for networks containing unistors, calculate the voltage gain, input impedance, and output impedance of a simple two-stage grounded-emitter transistor amplifier. Ignore emitter impedance in the transistor model.

3.40 A gyrator is equivalent to three equal gyristors connected to form a triangle, with all gyristors pointing in the same direction around the triangle. If an impedance Z is connected across two terminals of a gyrator, find the impedance measured at some other terminal pair of the gyrator.

3.41 Show that for a network containing a gyrator, $\Delta = \Delta^{oc} + g^2\Delta^{sc}$, where Δ is the admittance determinant of the network, Δ^{oc} and Δ^{sc} are computed with the gyrator erased (open-circuited) and collapsed (short-circuited), respectively, and g is the gyrator admittance.

3.42 A gyrator has terminals 1, 2, 3 and a second gyrator has terminals 4, 5, 6. Terminals 1 and 4 are joined and an admittance y is connected between 2 and 5. Find the admittance determinant of the network. Interpret the result for the special case in which y is infinite (2 and 5 joined).

3.43 An arbitrary linear network containing no *independent* sources is described by its node-voltage equations, $i_j = \sum_k y_{jk}v_k$, where i_i and v_i are the current and voltage in the ith external source, one such source being connected between the reference node and each remaining node. Define the floating admittance matrix in terms of the y_{jk} coefficients. Let the reference node be numbered n. Give the rules for computing an arbitrary open-circuit transfer impedance of the network. Repeat for a voltage-transfer ratio. Repeat for a current-transfer ratio.

3.44 Describe the manner in which a simple admittance branch y appears in the floating matrix of a network.

3.45 Repeat Problem 3.44 for a gyrator g.

3.46 Repeat Problem 3.44 for a transconductance g_m.

3.47 Show that an arbitrary network (described by an arbitrary admittance matrix) can always be synthesized with (*a*) unistors alone, (*b*) gyristors plus reciprocal branches, (*c*) gyrators plus reciprocal branches.

3.48 Find the source-to-meter transmission for each of the circuits in Fig. P3-11. (Replace all circuit symbols for electronic devices by suitable low-frequency linear incremental models containing unistors.)

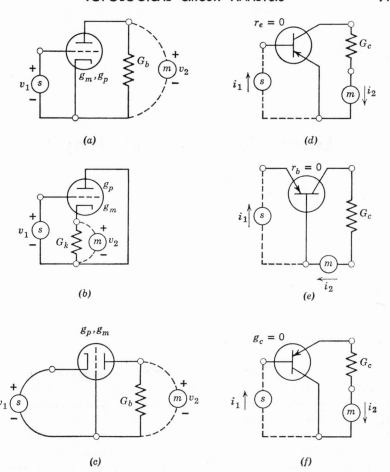

Fig. P3-11

C H A P T E R   F O U R

Linear Signal-Flow Graphs

4.1   Introduction

A signal-flow graph is a *diagram* of the *relationships* among a number of *variables*. When these relationships are linear, the graph represents a set of simultaneous linear algebraic equations. The advantage of such representation is that the solution of the equations has a simple interpretation in terms of the structure of the graph. Any problem involving simultaneous linear relationships among a number of variables can be formulated directly as a signal-flow graph and *solved directly by inspection* of the graph.

In this chapter we shall build up the necessary background of flow-graph theory and technique, so that the methods will be available for application to electronic circuit and system problems in the following chapters. You will not see any electronic circuits in this chapter, mainly because we wish to emphasize that a flow graph is an abstraction with a personality of its own, quite apart from any connection with a *specific* physical system. Moreover, were we to introduce these flow-graph techniques entirely in the context of electronic circuits, it might appear that they have no other application, whereas a knowledge of flow-graph methods is helpful in many other situations. Problems in automatic control, mechanics, multiple reflection of space waves, and conditional probability can be cited as examples.

4.2 The Linear Signal-Flow Graph

A signal-flow graph is a network of directed branches which connect at nodes. Branch jk originates at node j and terminates upon node k, the direction from j to k being indicated by an arrowhead on the branch.

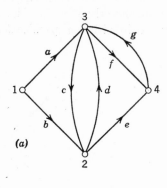

(a)

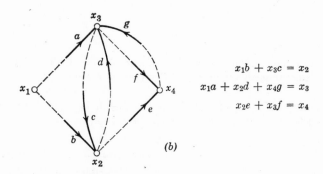

$$x_1 b + x_3 c = x_2$$
$$x_1 a + x_2 d + x_4 g = x_3$$
$$x_2 e + x_3 f = x_4$$

(b)

Fig. 4-1. A linear signal-flow graph.

Each branch jk has associated with it a quantity called the branch transmission t_{jk}, and each node j has an associated quantity called the node signal x_j. The various node signals are related by the equations

$$\sum_j x_j t_{jk} = x_k, \qquad k = 1, 2, 3, \cdots \tag{4.1}$$

A typical flow graph is shown in Fig. 4-1(a). In a specific example such as this, it is convenient to designate the various branch transmissions by different letters (a, b, c, $\cdots$) rather than by a single letter with double subscripts (t_{jk}).

A *dependent* node has one or more *incoming* branches. Notice that each dependent node is associated with an explicit algebraic equation. This association is emphasized in Fig. 4-1(b). Each equation gives the node signal as the algebraic sum of the signals entering via the incoming branches. Each entering signal is the product of the branch transmission and the signal at the node from which that branch originates. It is important to observe that there is no "Kirchhoff current law" here. The signal at a given node is the sum of the incoming signals, and the presence of *outgoing* branches does not directly affect the signal at that node. The outgoing branches have to do with the specification of *other* signals at *other* nodes.

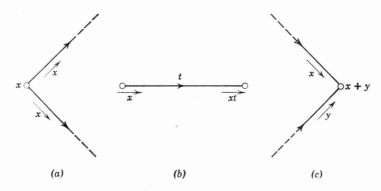

(a)   (b)   (c)

Fig. 4-2. An interpretation of signal flow in a graph. (a) Radiation from a node. (b) Transmission through a branch. (c) Reception at a node.

Specifically, the flow of signals in the graph is to be interpreted as shown in Fig. 4-2. This interpretation follows directly from the equations (4.1). Alternatively, Fig. 4-2 may be taken as the basic statement of flow-graph properties, whereupon the equations (4.1) follow from Fig. 4-2. A signal-flow graph, in which the signals are understood to obey the rules laid down in Fig. 4-2, contains exactly the same information as the associated set of algebraic equations. The difference is merely one of notation. Thus we can say that a linear signal-flow graph *is* a set of linear algebraic equations written in a special graphical language which utilizes branches, nodes, and arrowheads, rather than the "plus" and "equals" marks of ordinary algebraic notation.

The flow-graph equations are in "cause-and-effect" form. Each dependent node signal is expressed *once* as an explicit *effect* due to other node signals acting as *causes*. A given signal appears as an effect in only *one* equation. In the other equations, this signal plays the role of a cause. The formulation of equations in cause-and-effect form is very convenient for a large class of physical problems, including many electronic circuit problems. The advantage of cause-and-effect formulation and flow-graph representation is that the equations can be solved directly by inspection of the graph. The desired solution evaluates the signal at a given dependent node in terms of the signal at the source node. A *source node* is one having *only outgoing branches*. The source-node signal is an independent variable in the algebraic equations and all other variables can be expressed in terms of the independent variable. If more than one source node is present in a graph, we can consider the effect of each source separately, since the equations are linear and superposition applies.

4.3 Elementary Equivalences

Solution by inspection requires the knowledge of certain topological properties of flow graphs. Figure 4-3 presents a number of elementary equivalences which follow directly from Fig. 4-2. The transformation

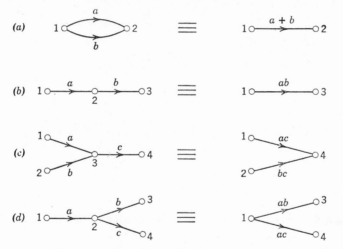

Fig. 4-3. Elementary equivalences. (*a*) Addition. (*b*) Multiplication. (*c*), (*d*) Distribution, or, in the opposite direction, factoring.

indicated in Fig. 4-4 is a more general form of distribution which includes (*b*), (*c*), and (*d*) of Fig. 4-3. The transformation is not, in general, reversible. Given four arbitrary values for the branch transmissions in Fig. 4-4(*b*), we should not expect to find an equivalent graph in the form of Fig. 4-4(*a*).

The elementary transformations in Figs. 4-3 and 4-4 reduce the number of branches or nodes in the graph, and one might at first expect that by the successive application of such transformations a graph could be reduced to a single branch connecting the source to some chosen dependent node. However, if the graph contains any closed chains of dependency, then one or more self-loops will eventually appear, as indicated in Fig. 4-5.

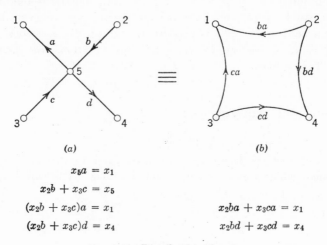

(a)   (b)

$$x_5 a = x_1$$

$$x_2 b + x_3 c = x_5$$

$$(x_2 b + x_3 c) a = x_1 \qquad\qquad x_2 b a + x_3 c a = x_1$$

$$(x_2 b + x_3 c) d = x_4 \qquad\qquad x_2 b d + x_3 c d = x_4$$

Fig. 4-4. Distribution of a star.

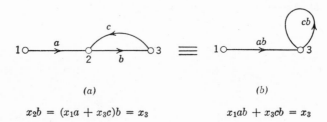

(a)   (b)

$$x_2 b = (x_1 a + x_3 c) b = x_3 \qquad\qquad x_1 a b + x_3 c b = x_3$$

Fig. 4-5. The appearance of a self-loop, following distribution of branch b.

4.4   The Effect of a Self-Loop

The effect of a self-loop at some node upon the transmission through that node is analyzed in Fig. 4-6(a). Let the node signal be x, whence the signal returning around the self-loop is xt. Now, since the node signal is the algebraic sum of the signals entering that node, the external signal arriving from the left must be equal to $x(1 - t)$. Hence the effect of the self-loop t is to divide an external signal by the factor $(1 - t)$ as that signal passes through the node. This holds for all t.

Another interpretation (valid for $|t| < 1$) is offered in Fig. 4-6(b). Consider the many different possible routes by which the signal can find its way from the source x_1 to the dependent node x_2. The most obvious route is that through the two branches whose transmissions are unity. The signal can also circulate once around the self-loop before

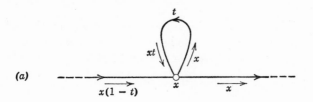

(a)

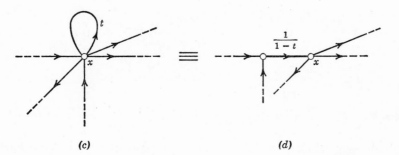

(b)

$$\frac{x_2}{x_1} = 1 + t + t^2 + t^3 + \cdots = \frac{1}{1-t}$$

(c)   (d)

Fig. 4-6. The effect of a self-loop.

proceeding onward to its destination. It might also circulate twice or three times, or more, around the self-loop. In effect, there are an infinite number of different routes from the input to the output and their transmissions are $1, t, t^2, t^3, \cdots$. Since these routes are effectively in parallel, we may expect the net transmission to be the sum of the route transmissions, as shown in Fig. 4-6(b). The infinite geometric series sums to the reciprocal of $(1 - t)$, which verifies our previous result.

When several branches enter and leave the node, as indicated in Fig. 4-6(c), it is easy to see that the proper replacement for the self-loop follows the scheme shown in Fig. 4-6(d).

4.5   Absorption of a Node

With the aid of the elementary transformations and the self-loop replacement, any node in a graph can be absorbed as shown in Fig. 4-7(a). Absorption of a given node s yields a new graph, from which node s and

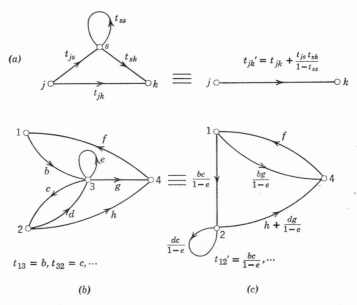

Fig. 4-7.   Absorption of node s, yielding a new graph with branch transmissions t_{jk}'.

all its connecting branches are missing. Although node s no longer shows in the new graph, its effect is included in the new branch-transmission values t_{jk}', where

$$t_{jk}' = t_{jk} + \frac{t_{js}t_{sk}}{1 - t_{ss}} \tag{4.2}$$

Node absorption corresponds to elimination of a variable by substitution in the associated algebraic equations.

It is convenient to speak of the node or nodes to be absorbed as *inaccessible* nodes. All other nodes in the original graph are said to be *accessible*. After absorption of the inaccessible nodes, the new graph is

called the *residue* of the original graph.   The point is that a graph and
its residue are indistinguishable on the basis of transmission measurements made at the accessible nodes.

Figure 4-7(c) shows the residue resulting after absorption of node 3 in
the graph of Fig. 4-7(b).   Observe that a new self-loop appears at node 2,
accounting for the original transmission from node 2 to node 3 and
thence back to node 2.   The residue includes the effects of all signal
transmissions *through* the node which has been absorbed.

4.6   The Transmission of a Flow Graph

The transmission T of a flow graph is equal to the signal appearing
at some designated dependent node per unit of signal originating at some
specified source node.   A *sink* is a node having only *incoming* branches.
If the graph contains one source and one sink, as illustrated in Fig.
4-8(a), then the symbol T stands for the source-to-sink transmission of
the graph.   When the graph contains several sinks, or no sinks, the

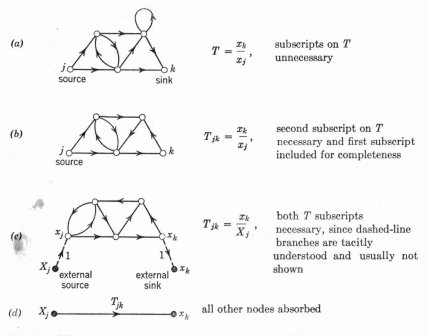

(a) $T = \dfrac{x_k}{x_j}$,   subscripts on T
unnecessary

(b) $T_{jk} = \dfrac{x_k}{x_j}$,   second subscript on T
necessary and first subscript
included for completeness

(c) $T_{jk} = \dfrac{x_k}{X_j}$,   both T subscripts
necessary, since dashed-line
branches are tacitly
understood and usually not
shown

(d) $X_j \xrightarrow{\; T_{jk} \;} x_k$ all other nodes absorbed

Fig. 4-8.   The meaning of graph transmission T_{jk} for a graph having (a) one source
and one sink, (b) one source and either no sink or several sinks, (c) an arbitrary
structure, perhaps with neither sources nor sinks.   (d) Reduction to a single branch
by absorption of all nodes other than sources and sinks.

symbol T becomes ambiguous and we shall agree to add subscripts indicating the two nodes between which the transmission is to be measured. Figure 4-8(b) offers an example. In the general case, for a graph of arbitrary structure, we shall define the *graph transmission* T_{jk} as *the signal appearing at node k per unit of external signal injected at node j*. In other words, T_{jk} is the transmission *from* an implied external source connected at node j *to* an implied external sink connected at node k, as indicated in Fig. 4-8(c).

With the external source and sink attached, all other nodes may be absorbed, thereby reducing the graph to the single branch shown in Fig. 4-8(d). The transmission of this branch is, of course, equal to the graph transmission T_{jk}.

4.7 The General Flow Graph

Figure 4-9(a) shows a full graph with all possible external sources and sinks. A two-node graph is illustrated here for simplicity, since the extension to a general graph of n nodes is straightforward. The solution of the formal problem is indicated in Fig. 4-9(b). The equations in Fig. 4-9(a) must be solved to give each x_k explicitly in terms of the external source signals X_j.

Matrix notation can be used for a more compact statement of the problem. Figure 4-9(c) shows a schematic flow graph in which each node signal is a row matrix and each branch transmission is a square matrix. Solution for matrix x in terms of matrix X yields the single matrix branch indicated in Fig. 4-9(d). Notice the similarity between Fig. 4-6(b) and Fig. 4-9(c) and (d). Solution of the general flow-graph transmission problem is equivalent to the replacement of a matrix self-loop by a matrix branch, which involves, at least formally, the inversion of a matrix having as many rows (and columns) as there are dependent nodes in the original flow graph.

4.8 Evaluation of a Graph Transmission
by Identification of Paths and Loops

Having set down the formal problem, we shall now study certain topological properties of flow graphs which will permit us to evaluate a particular graph transmission by inspection of the structure of the graph. The significant topological features of a flow graph are its paths and its loops. Let us define *path:* a continuous succession of branches, traversed in the indicated branch directions, along which no node is encountered more than once   (4.3)

path transmission (*P*): product of the branch transmissions along that path   (4.4)

loop (*sometimes called a feedback loop*): a simple closed path, along which no node is encountered more than once per cycle   (4.5)

loop transmission (*L*): product of the branch transmissions in that loop   (4.6)

For convenience of discussion the terms "path" and "path transmission" will be used somewhat interchangeably, as will the terms "loop" and

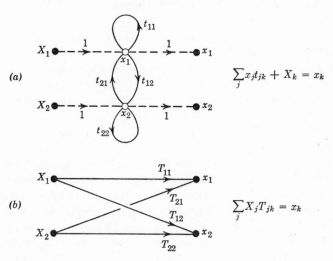

or, in matrix form,

$$X = (X_1 \quad X_2), \qquad x = (x_1 \quad x_2),$$

$$T = \begin{pmatrix} T_{11} & T_{12} \\ T_{21} & T_{22} \end{pmatrix}, \qquad t = \begin{pmatrix} t_{11} & t_{12} \\ t_{21} & t_{22} \end{pmatrix}, \qquad I = \begin{pmatrix} 1 & 0 \\ 0 & 1 \end{pmatrix}$$

Fig. 4-9. Formal algebraic solution of the flow-graph transmission problem.

"loop transmission." For example, we may speak of "the sum of paths P_1 and P_2" when what we really mean is "the sum of the transmissions P_1 and P_2 of paths 1 and 2." No confusion arises since the meaning is always clear from the context. We have already done this sort of thing in talking about branches and branch transmissions. For example, "branches a and b" really means "the branches whose transmissions are a and b."

To illustrate the definitions let us return momentarily to Fig. 4-1. In a finite graph there are always a finite number of loops and also a finite number of paths from one specified node to another. The graph of Fig. 4-1(a) has exactly four different paths from node 1 to node 4, namely af, ace, bdf, and be. Do not mistake ade for a path. If we call ade a path we violate the law by traversing "d" street (a one-way street) in the wrong direction. Self-intersecting paths such as $bdce$ are also prohibited by the definition.

Figure 4-1(a) has exactly three loops, cd, fg, and ceg. The succession dfe is not a loop since branch e points in the wrong direction. Also, $cdceg$ is not a proper loop because nodes 2 and 3 are encountered twice in each complete cycle of the succession. In short, the loops and paths as we wish to define them here are just what one might expect them to be on the basis of an uncomplicated first guess. Mathematically speaking, a loop is a "simple" closed oriented curve and a path is a segment of such a curve.

As we shall see, the transmission T_{jk} of the flow graph can be expressed entirely in terms of the various loops in the graph and the various paths from node j to node k. The graph of Fig. 4-10(a) contains four different loops and one (source-to-sink) path. Absorption of nodes 1 and 5 yields graph (b). Subsequent absorption of nodes 2 and 4 then gives us the simple form (c), from which the transmission can be evaluated by inspection, as indicated in Fig. 4-10(d). After clearing the numerator and the denominator of fractions and substituting the symbols for path and loop values, we arrive at the final form shown in Fig. 4-10(e). The most interesting property of this transmission expression is that the denominator contains *no* products of loops that touch in the graph. The first and second loops, for instance, touch each other in the graph and the product L_1L_2 is accordingly missing from the transmission expression.

We can now make a guess at the general rule. Each term of the denominator is the product of a set of nontouching loops. The algebraic sign of the term is plus (minus) for an even (odd) number of loops in the set. The graph of Fig. 4-10(a) has no sets of three or more nontouching loops. Taking the loops two at a time, we find only three permissible sets. When the loops are taken one at a time, the question of touching does not arise, so that each loop in the graph is itself an admissible "set." For completeness of form we may also consider the set of loops taken "none-at-a-time" and, by analogy with the zeroth power of a number, interpret the set product as the unity term in the denominator of Fig. 4-10(e).

(a)

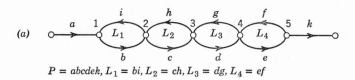

$$P = abcdek, L_1 = bi, L_2 = ch, L_3 = dg, L_4 = ef$$

(b)

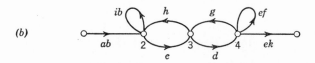

(c)

(d) $$T = \frac{\left(\dfrac{abc}{1 - ib}\right)\left(\dfrac{dek}{1 - ef}\right)}{1 - \left(\dfrac{hc}{1 - ib} + \dfrac{dg}{1 - ef}\right)}$$

(e) $$T = \frac{P}{1 - (L_1 + L_2 + L_3 + L_4) + (L_1 L_3 + L_1 L_4 + L_2 L_4)}$$

Fig. 4-10. The transmission of a multiloop graph.

Before attempting to postulate the general form of the numerator, let us consider another example. Figure 4-11(a) shows a somewhat different transmission problem in which the source-to-sink path does not touch all of the loops. Here we can absorb the last four nodes in the order 5, 4, 3, and 2 to obtain the transmission (b) in the form of a continued fraction. After reduction to a single proper fraction and substitution of the path and loop symbols, we arrive at the final expression given in Fig. 4-11(c). In this case, the numerator contains not only the path but

(a)

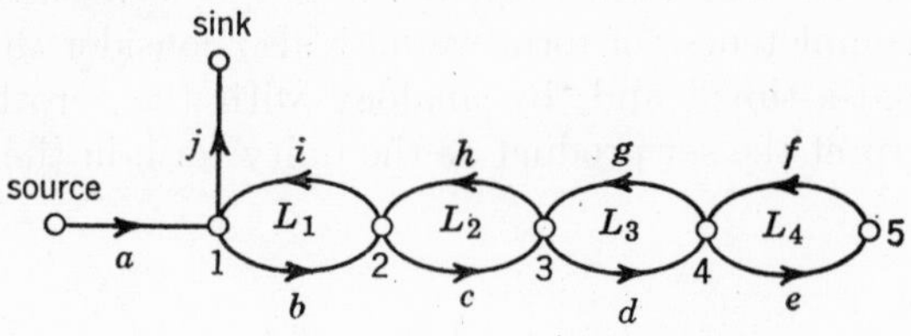

$$P = aj, \; L_1 = bi, \; L_2 = ch, \; L_3 = dg, \; L_4 = ef$$

(b) $T = \dfrac{aj}{1 - \dfrac{bi}{1 - \dfrac{ch}{1 - \dfrac{dg}{1 - ef}}}}$

(c) $T = \dfrac{P[1 - (L_2 + L_3 + L_4) + (L_2L_4)]}{1 - (L_1 + L_2 + L_3 + L_4) + (L_1L_3 + L_1L_4 + L_2L_4)}$

Fig. 4-11. The transmission of another multiloop graph.

(a)

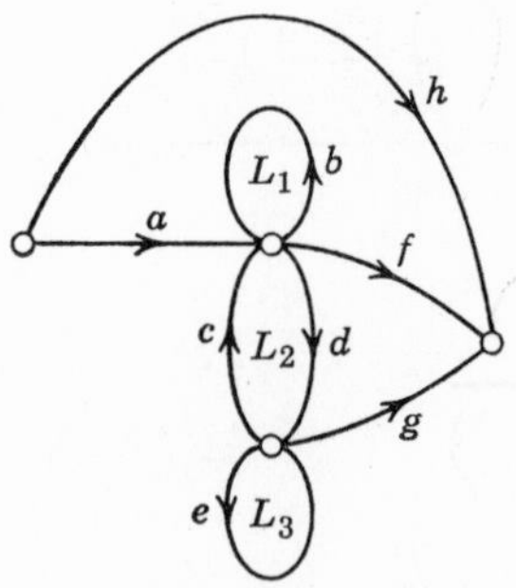

$$P_1 = h$$
$$P_2 = af$$
$$P_3 = adg$$

$$L_1 = b$$
$$L_2 = cd$$
$$L_3 = e$$

(b) $T = \dfrac{P_1[1 - (L_1 + L_2 + L_3) + L_1L_3] + P_2[1 - L_3] + P_3[1]}{[1 - (L_1 + L_2 + L_3) + L_1L_3]}$

For an arbitrary flow graph containing p
paths (from node j to node k) and m loops,

(c) $T_{jk} = \dfrac{[(P_1 + P_2 + \cdots + P_p)(1 - L_1)(1 - L_2) \cdots (1 - L_m)]^*}{[(1 - L_1)(1 - L_2) \cdots (1 - L_m)]^*}$

* Drop terms containing products of touching loops or paths.

Fig. 4-12. A general expression for flow-graph transmission in terms of paths and loops.

also some of the loops. Observe now that the bracketed factor in the numerator can be obtained from the denominator by striking out those terms involving loop L_1, the only loop that touches path P.

The picture is becoming clearer and one more example will help to bring it further into focus. The graph of Fig. 4-12(a) has three different (source-to-sink) paths and three different loops. Absorption of the two central nodes yields the transmission expression (b). The numerator is a weighted sum of the paths, in which each path is multiplied by a bracketed weighting factor. Observe that each of these factors is constructed in exactly the same way as the denominator, with the *additional* restriction that it contains only those loops that do *not* touch the associated path.

We can now hypothesize the general rule for evaluating any flow-graph transmission. Figure 4-12(c) gives the general expression in compact form. The asterisk here denotes that, in multiplying the factors within the brackets, we shall agree to nullify (set equal to zero) any term that includes a product of two loops, or a path and a loop, which touch in the graph. This hypothesis is, as a matter of fact, correct. A proof will arise from the properties of flow graphs developed in the next few articles.

4.9   Node Splitting

Splitting a node divides that node into a new source and a new sink. All branches entering that node remain attached to the new sink and all branches leaving that node remain attached to the new source, as shown in Fig. 4-13(a) and (b). When both of the nodes are split in the graph of Fig. 4-13(c), the result is as shown in (d). When a node is split, the original symbol for the node signal and the original node number will both be retained at the new source, whereas the node signal and node number at the new sink will be designated by primes. Our purpose in introducing the notion of node splitting is to facilitate the definition of loop transmission for a node or a branch in the next article. Node splitting is also useful, for example, in an alternative description of the process of node absorption (Article 4.5). To absorb a designated node, split all *other* nodes, evaluate all source-to-sink transmissions, represent each of these as a branch, and then rejoin the split nodes.

4.10   The Loop Transmission of a Node or a Branch

The loop transmission τ of a node is the signal returned to that node per unit of signal sent out by that node. More precisely,

τ_j = transmission between the new source-sink pair created by
splitting node j (4.7)

Figure 4-14(a) offers an example. Another way of explaining or interpreting the loop transmission of a node is the following. Select some
node j and absorb all other (nonsource, nonsink) nodes in the graph.
Then τ_j is just equal to the transmission of the self-loop appearing at

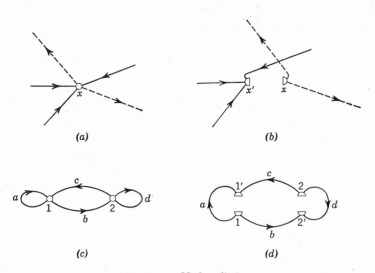

Fig. 4-13. Node splitting.

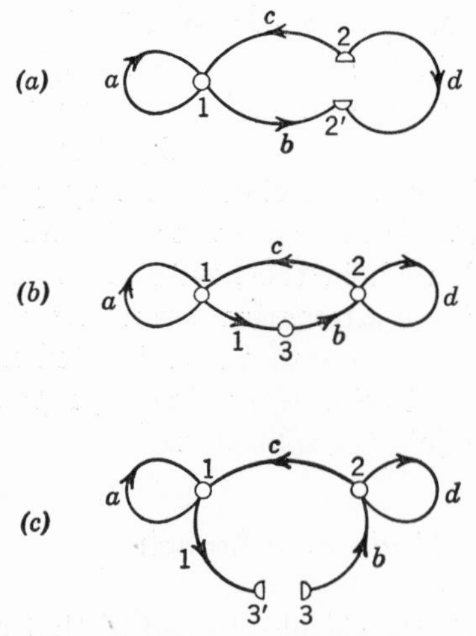

(a) $\tau_2 = \dfrac{x_2{}'}{x_2} = d + \dfrac{cb}{1-a}$

(b)   Branch b factored to
       show an interior node, 3

(c) $\tau_b = \tau_3 = \dfrac{x_3{}'}{x_3} = \dfrac{bc}{(1-d)(1-a)}$

Fig. 4-14. The loop transmission of a node or a branch.

node j in the residue. Evidently τ_j will be different from zero only if the original graph has at least one feedback loop containing node j.

The loop transmission of a branch can now be defined very easily if we first factor that branch into a cascade combination of two branches whose transmission product is the same as that of the original branch. Such factoring produces a new node called an *interior node* of that branch, as illustrated in Fig. 4-14(b). The loop transmission of a branch is, by definition, equal to the loop transmission of an interior node of that branch. Figure 4-14(c) is a specific example.

4.11 The Determinant of a Flow Graph

The determinant of a flow graph is the quantity which appears as the denominator in the graph transmission expression. We shall first define the graph determinant in a somewhat different fashion and then deduce its relationship to the graph transmission. By definition, the *determinant of a flow graph* is given by

$$\Delta = (1 - \tau_1')(1 - \tau_2') \cdots (1 - \tau_n') \qquad (4.8)$$

where

$$\tau_k' = \text{value of } \tau_k \text{ with nodes } k + 1, k + 2, \cdots, n \text{ split} \qquad (4.9)$$

Quantity τ_k' is called the *partial* loop transmission of node k, since τ_k' is to be computed or measured with only part of the graph (the first k nodes) present. The value of a particular τ_k' will be dependent upon the order in which we have chosen to number the nodes of the graph. The partial loop transmission of node k is just equal to the transmission of the self-loop appearing at node k when nodes $1, 2, 3, \cdots, k - 1$ are absorbed.

Figure 4-15 shows (a) particular choice of node numbers in a simple graph having three nodes, and (b), (c), (d) the portions of the graph (indicated by solid branches) which enter into the calculation of the partial loop transmission at each of the three nodes.

Now consider the effect of an interchange in the numbers of nodes k and $k + 1$. For convenience in studying this effect we can absorb the first $k - 1$ nodes and split (or erase) all nodes having numbers higher than $k + 1$. The resulting graph is indicated in Fig. 4-16(a). The split nodes and their attached branches need not be shown since such branches cannot enter the calculation of τ_k' or τ_{k+1}'. When the two node numbers are interchanged, as in Fig. 4-16(b), the partial loop transmissions τ_k' and τ_{k+1}' assume new values. However, by direct calculation, we find that the product $(1 - \tau_k')(1 - \tau_{k+1}')$ remains unaltered. Since τ_1',

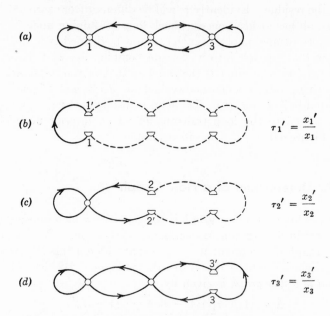

(a)

(b) $\tau_1' = \dfrac{x_1'}{x_1}$

(c) $\tau_2' = \dfrac{x_2'}{x_2}$

(d) $\tau_3' = \dfrac{x_3'}{x_3}$

τ_k' = loop transmission of node k as measured with all higher-numbered nodes split or erased

$$\Delta = (1 - \tau_1')(1 - \tau_2') \cdots (1 - \tau_n')$$

Fig. 4-15. Definition of the graph determinant Δ in terms of a set of "partial" loop transmissions τ_k'.

Nodes $1, 2, \cdots, k - 1$ all absorbed

Nodes $k + 2, k + 3, \cdots, n$ all split

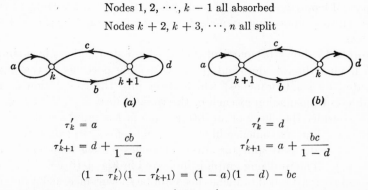

(a)

(b)

$$\tau_k' = a \qquad\qquad \tau_k' = d$$

$$\tau_{k+1}' = d + \frac{cb}{1 - a} \qquad\qquad \tau_{k+1}' = a + \frac{bc}{1 - d}$$

$$(1 - \tau_k')(1 - \tau_{k+1}') = (1 - a)(1 - d) - bc$$

Fig. 4-16. The invariance of $(1 - \tau_k')(1 - \tau_{k+1}')$ under an interchange of node numbers k and $k + 1$.

$\tau'_2, \cdots, \tau'_{k-1}$ and $\tau'_{k+2}, \tau'_{k+3}, \cdots, \tau'_n$ are obviously unaffected by an interchange in the numbers of nodes k and $k + 1$, we have the result that the value of the determinant Δ is not affected by an interchange in the numbers of two consecutively numbered nodes. Now, since any node-numbering order can be obtained from any other node-numbering order by a succession of adjacent interchanges (for example, the sequence 123 can be transformed into the sequence 321 by the successive adjacent interchanges 123, 213, 231, 321), we arrive at the general result that *the value of the graph determinant Δ is independent of the order in which the nodes are numbered.*

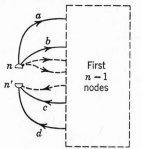

$\tau'_1, \tau'_2, \cdots, \tau'_{n-1}$ are independent of a, b, c, d
τ'_n is a linear function of $a, b, c,$ and $d,$
 and does *not* contain the
 products ab or cd

Fig. 4-17.   Dependence of τ'_k upon the transmissions of confluent branches.

We shall next consider the dependence of τ'_n upon the transmissions of branches connected to node n. Figure 4-17 shows node n split into a source n and sink n'. Two branches are said to be *confluent* if they both originate, or both terminate, at the same node. Thus, in Fig. 4-17 branches a and b are confluent, as are branches c and d. It follows from the node absorption process (or, in fact, from the very nature of signal flow in a graph) that τ'_n is a linear function of the transmission of each branch connected to node n and that τ'_n cannot involve the transmission *product* of two branches confluent at node n. Moreover, $\tau'_1, \tau'_2, \cdots, \tau'_{n-1}$ are evidently independent of the transmissions of branches connected to node n. Since Δ is independent of node numbering we can choose any node in the network and assign it the highest number n, whence it follows that the *graph determinant Δ is a linear function of each branch transmission in the graph, and is therefore equal to unity plus an algebraic sum of terms, each term having one or more different branch transmissions as factors.* Moreover, *the transmission product of two confluent branches cannot appear in the graph determinant Δ.*

4.12   Expansion of the Determinant in Loops

We can find out still more about Δ by considering subgraphs. A subgraph is what remains when certain branches in the original graph are erased. (For completeness we shall allow the possibility of erasing "no" branches. In other words, the set of all subgraphs includes the

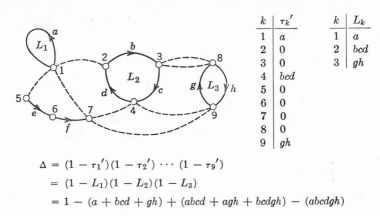

k	τ_k'
1	a
2	0
3	0
4	bcd
5	0
6	0
7	0
8	0
9	gh

k	L_k
1	a
2	bcd
3	gh

$$\Delta = (1 - \tau_1')(1 - \tau_2') \cdots (1 - \tau_9')$$
$$= (1 - L_1)(1 - L_2)(1 - L_3)$$
$$= 1 - (a + bcd + gh) + (abcd + agh + bcdgh) - (abcdgh)$$

Fig. 4-18.   A nonconfluent subgraph (solid lines) and its determinant Δ.

original graph.) Erasing a branch is equivalent to setting the transmission of that branch equal to zero. Hence the erasure of a branch causes some terms of Δ to vanish (those terms containing that branch as a factor), but leaves all other terms of Δ unchanged. It is apparent, therefore, that each of the terms appearing in a subgraph Δ will also appear as terms in the Δ of the complete graph. Conversely, any chosen term of the graph Δ is a term in the Δ of some subgraph, in particular, the subgraph containing only those branches which appear in the chosen term. Now, since no term of Δ can involve the product of confluent branches, we need consider only nonconfluent subgraphs. A *nonconfluent subgraph* is one having no pairs of confluent branches. Thus, *every term in the Δ of a nonconfluent subgraph is also a term in the graph Δ; and conversely, any chosen term in the graph Δ is a term in the Δ of some nonconfluent subgraph.*

Figure 4-18 shows a typical nonconfluent subgraph which, by its definition, may contain only loops (such as a, bcd, gh) and open paths (such as ef), none of them touching each other. The determinant of a nonconfluent subgraph can be evaluated rather easily, because some of the quantities τ_k' vanish and the others are equal to the loops L of the subgraph, as shown in Fig. 4-18. Notice that open paths such as ef

cannot enter the calculation of the determinant. Hence, each term of the subgraph Δ, and consequently each term in the Δ of the complete graph, is a simple *product of nontouching loops*. To find the determinant of the complete graph, therefore, we must include all possible sets of nontouching loops which are embedded in that graph.

This brings us to a principal result, the so-called loop expansion of the determinant. For a graph having m different loops, the *loop expansion* of the determinant may be written as

$$\Delta = [(1 - L_1)(1 - L_2) \cdots (1 - L_m)]* \qquad (4.10)$$

* with the understanding that we shall drop
terms containing products of touching loops.

An equivalent form is

$$\Delta = 1 - \sum_k L_k^{(1)} + \sum_k L_k^{(2)} - \sum_k L_k^{(3)} + \cdots \qquad (4.11)$$

where

$L_k^{(r)}$ = product of the kth possible combination of r nontouching loops   (4.12)

4.13 Factorable Determinants

A subsidiary result of some interest has to do with graphs whose feedback loops form nontouching subgraphs. To find the loop subgraph of any flow graph, simply remove all of those branches not lying in feedback loops, leaving all of the loops and nothing but the loops. In general, the loop subgraph may have a number of nontouching parts.

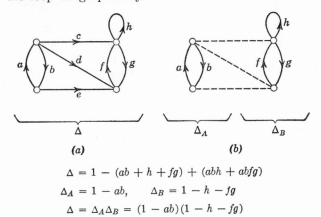

$$\Delta = 1 - (ab + h + fg) + (abh + abfg)$$
$$\Delta_A = 1 - ab, \qquad \Delta_B = 1 - h - fg$$
$$\Delta = \Delta_A \Delta_B = (1 - ab)(1 - h - fg)$$

Fig. 4-19. The determinant of a graph whose loop subgraph has two separate parts.

The useful fact is that the *determinant of a complete flow graph is equal to the product of the determinants of each of the nontouching parts in its loop subgraph.*

The proof follows directly from (4.10), and an illustrative example is given in Fig. 4-19.

4.14   Expansion on a Node or on a Branch

Figure 4-20 shows the effect of adding a new node $n + 1$ to a graph of n nodes. The addition of a new node and its associated branches will in general produce certain new loops L_k. Hence additional terms must

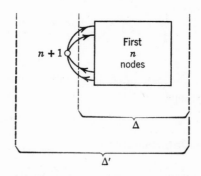

Δ' = the Δ of the complete graph of $n + 1$ nodes

Δ = the Δ of the graph with node $n + 1$ split or removed

L_k = transmission of the kth loop containing node $n + 1$

Δ_k = the Δ of that part of the graph not touching loop L_k

$$\Delta' = \Delta - \sum_k L_k \Delta_k$$

Fig. 4-20.   Expansion of the determinant at a node.

be added to the original determinant Δ to obtain the new determinant Δ' of the complete graph including the new node. Let Δ_k be the determinant of that part of the graph *not* touching the newly formed loop L_k. With this notation we have

$$\Delta' = \Delta - \sum_k L_k \Delta_k \tag{4.13}$$

Equation (4.13) accounts for all possible nontouching loop sets in Δ'. The addition of node $n + 1$ creates new loops L_k, but the only loop sets of Δ' not already present in Δ are the nontouching sets $L_k \Delta_k$. The negative sign in (4.13) suffices to preserve the sign rule, since the product of L_k and a positive term of Δ_k will contain an odd number of loops.

With the aid of relation (4.13) we can expand the determinant on any node of the graph. Similarly, we can "expand on a branch" by carrying the expansion out with respect to an interior node of that branch.

Figure 4-21 illustrates the manner in which a determinantal expression may be compacted by means of such an expansion. In this particular example, an interior node (shown as a solid circle) is first introduced in one of the central branches. With this interior node split, the loop

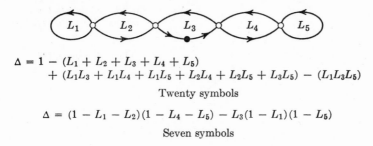

$$\Delta = 1 - (L_1 + L_2 + L_3 + L_4 + L_5)$$
$$+ (L_1L_3 + L_1L_4 + L_1L_5 + L_2L_4 + L_2L_5 + L_3L_5) - (L_1L_3L_5)$$

Twenty symbols

$$\Delta = (1 - L_1 - L_2)(1 - L_4 - L_5) - L_3(1 - L_1)(1 - L_5)$$

Seven symbols

Fig. 4-21. Expansion of Δ at a branch.

subgraph separates into two parts, with the result that its determinant is factorable. When the split node is reconnected, only one new loop is formed, namely L_3. The part of the graph not touching this new loop is once again composed of two separate parts, L_1 and L_5. In this example, mainly because the expansion accomplishes separation of the loop subgraph into nontouching parts, the number of symbols in the determinantal expression is considerably reduced (from twenty to seven). The compactness achieved by expansion will depend, of course, upon the structure of the graph and upon the choice of the expansion node or branch.

Figure 4-22(a) shows a slightly more complicated structure together with the associated determinantal expression. Branches d and h can be factored as indicated in Fig. 4-22(b) and the new node thereby introduced (a black node in the figure) is a convenient one for expansion, since the loop subgraph has two separate parts (b and $acei$) when this node is split. The first bracketed expression in Fig. 4-22(b) is the determinant of one of these parts ($acei$). This subdeterminant has been further factored on branch i (or e) to obtain the more compact expression shown within the brackets. When the split node is reconnected, four new loops are formed. Of these four loops, two contain branch d, namely dg and def. Loop dg fails to touch the self-loop c, and so must be multiplied by the determinant of that part $(1 - c)$. Similarly, branch h

appears in two of the newly formed loops, and one of these, hf, has the nontouching loop factor $(1 - a)$. By means of expansion and branch factoring, the number of symbols in the expression is reduced from thirty-three to fifteen.

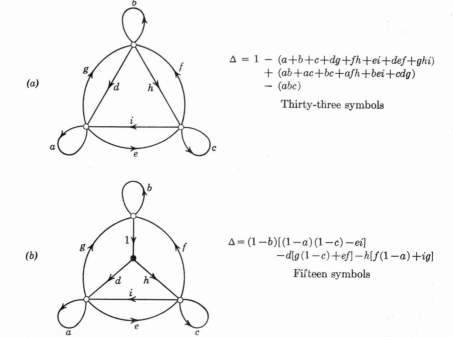

(a)

$$\Delta = 1 - (a+b+c+dg+fh+ei+def+ghi)$$
$$+ (ab+ac+bc+afh+bei+cdg)$$
$$- (abc)$$

Thirty-three symbols

(b)

$$\Delta = (1-b)[(1-a)(1-c)-ei]$$
$$-d[g(1-c)+ef]-h[f(1-a)+ig]$$

Fifteen symbols

Fig. 4-22. Expansion of Δ in a general three-node graph, after factoring branches d and h.

4.15   Outline of a Proof of the General Transmission Expression

With reference to Fig. 4-20, let τ be the loop transmission of node $n + 1$. Thus, τ is equal to τ'_{n+1}. With this notation, it follows from (4.8) that

$$\frac{\Delta'}{\Delta} = 1 - \tau \tag{4.14}$$

By substitution of (4.13) into (4.14) we find that

$$\tau = \frac{1}{\Delta} \sum_k L_k \Delta_k \tag{4.15}$$

Now, with node $n + 1$ permanently split, τ is just the source-to-sink transmission of the graph, and L_k is the kth source-to-sink path. This leads us to the general expression for the transmission of any flow graph.

$$T = \frac{1}{\Delta} \sum_k P_k \Delta_k \qquad (4.16)$$

where

T = source-to-sink graph transmission; the sink signal per
     unit of source signal $\qquad (4.17)$

P_k = transmission of the kth source-to-sink path $\qquad (4.18)$

Δ = graph determinant $\qquad (4.19)$

Δ_k = cofactor of the kth path (the determinant of that part of
     the graph not touching the kth path) $\qquad (4.20)$

Quantity Δ_k has been referred to here as the cofactor of path P_k. In general, we may speak of the *cofactor* of any specified portion of a graph, thereby denoting the determinant constructed from those loops not touching the specified portion. In Fig. 4-22(a), for example, the cofactor of loop hf arises from the single branch a and is equal to $(1 - a)$. Similarly, the cofactor of loop b is the expression within the first set of brackets in Fig. 4-22(b).

A cofactor Δ_k in expression (4.16) can be found by either striking out those terms of Δ which contain branches touching path P_k, or erasing path P_k and all touching branches, and then evaluating the determinant of the remaining subgraph. These two procedures are equivalent and it is often convenient to use one as a check against the other.

Figure 4-23 offers another interpretation of the flow-graph transmission expression. If the transmission from node j to node k is equal to T_{jk}, and if the system is then closed externally by the addition of a branch from k to j whose transmission is equal to the reciprocal of the graph transmission T_{jk}, then the loop transmission of this added branch is identically equal to unity and the determinant Δ' of the externally closed graph must vanish. Hence, T_{jk} can be found by formulating Δ', equating it to zero, and solving for T_{jk}. From the standpoint of this interpretation, the calculation of a flow-graph transmission is covered in the general problem of evaluating a flow-graph determinant.

4.16 Inversion of a Path or Loop

The algebraic equations associated with a linear flow graph are in cause-and-effect form. In each equation, one of the variables is ex-

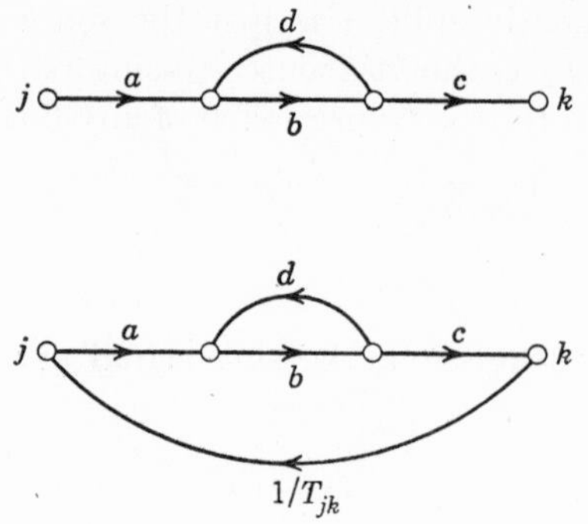

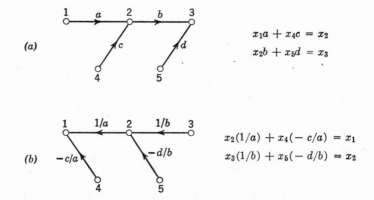

(a) $j \circ \xrightarrow{\ a\ } \quad \xrightarrow{\ b\ } \quad \xrightarrow{\ c\ } \circ k$ $T_{jk} = \dfrac{abc}{1 - bd}$

(b) $j \circ \xrightarrow{\ a\ } \quad \xrightarrow{\ b\ } \quad \xrightarrow{\ c\ } \circ k$ $\Delta' = 1 - \left(bd + \dfrac{abc}{T_{jk}} \right) = 0 \text{ yields}$

$1/T_{jk}$ $T_{jk} = \dfrac{abc}{1 - bd}$

To find T_{jk} in an arbitrary graph:

1. Attach a branch from k to j and call its transmission $1/T_{jk}$ (not $1/T_{kj}$).
2. Evaluate the determinant Δ' of the resulting graph.
3. Set $\Delta' = 0$, and solve for T_{jk}.

Fig. 4-23. Interpretation of T_{jk} as an inverse branch transmission in a closed graph.

pressed as an explicit effect due to the other variables acting as causes. A given variable must play the role of a dependent effect in only one of the equations, as illustrated in Fig. 4-24(a), for otherwise two nodes

(a)
$$x_1 a + x_4 c = x_2$$
$$x_2 b + x_5 d = x_3$$

(b)
$$x_2(1/a) + x_4(-c/a) = x_1$$
$$x_3(1/b) + x_5(-d/b) = x_2$$

Let t_{jk} be any branch in the path to be inverted and t_{ik} be any other branch, not in the path, whose nose k touches the path. To invert the path, replace t_{jk} by $t_{kj}' = 1/t_{jk}$ and replace t_{ik} by $t_{ij}' = -t_{ik}/t_{jk}$.

Fig. 4-24. Inversion of a path.

would be required for the same variable and the graph would be discon- nected. However, nothing prevents us from recasting the set of equa- tions in any one of a number of equally valid cause-and-effect forms,

Figure 4-24(b) gives one example. Here the first equation has been solved for x_1 in terms of x_2 and x_4, and the second equation has been solved for x_2 in terms of x_3 and x_5. This reverses the directions of branches a and b in the original graph and shifts the noses of branches c and d to new locations as shown in Fig. 4-24(b). It is a simple matter to identify the general flow-graph transformation rules which correspond to such manipulations of the equations. The general rule can be explained as follows. *To invert a branch b which runs from node j to node k, first move all branch noses at node k to the new position j and move the tail of branch b from j to k. Then replace transmission b by $1/b$ and multiply by $(-1/b)$ the transmissions of all other branches whose noses have been moved. To invert a path or loop, simply invert all branches in that path or loop.* Fortunately, the process is easier to visualize than it is to describe in words, as a moment's study of Fig. 4-24 will verify.

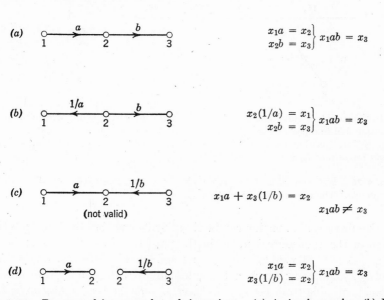

Fig. 4-25. Proper and improper branch inversions. (a) A simple graph. (b) Inversion of a path (consisting of the single branch a) which originates at a source. (c) Inversion of a path (branch b) not originating at a source, yielding an incorrect graph. (d) Inversion of branch b, yielding a correct but disconnected graph with two nodes needed for the same variable x_2.

If a connected cause-and-effect flow-graph structure is to be preserved, then *the only allowable inversions are* (1) *the inversion of a path which originates at a source node, or* (2) *the inversion of a loop.* Any path originating at a source is a proper candidate for inversion, as illustrated in Fig. 4-25(b). However, if we try to invert a path which does not start at a source, then trouble arises, as shown in Fig. 4-25(c). This trouble is circumvented in Fig. 4-25(d), but the result is a disconnected graph.

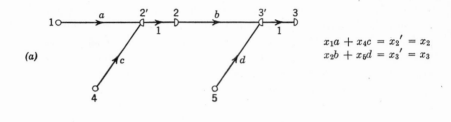

$$x_1 a + x_4 c = x_2{}' = x_2$$
$$x_2 b + x_5 d = x_3{}' = x_3$$

(a)

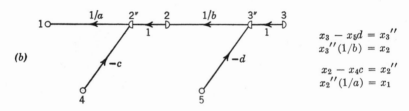

$$x_3 - x_5 d = x_3{}''$$
$$x_3{}''(1/b) = x_2$$

$$x_2 - x_4 c = x_2{}''$$
$$x_2{}''(1/a) = x_1$$

(b)

In the path to be inverted, split the nodes and connect the split halves with unity-transmission branches. Now, to invert the path, reverse the arrows and invert the transmissions in that path, and change the algebraic signs of other branches whose noses touch that path.

Fig. 4-26. Inversion of a path whose nodes have been stretched. (a) The original graph. (b) The inversion of path ab.

The process of inversion can be simplified somewhat by first stretching each of the (nonsource) nodes in the path to be inverted, as shown in Fig. 4-26(a). To *stretch* node j, first split node j into a source j and a sink j', and then reconnect the split halves with a unity-transmission branch running from j' to j. *To invert a path (or loop) whose nodes have been stretched, reverse the directions of branches in that path, invert their transmissions, and simply change the algebraic sign of the transmissions of any other branches whose noses touch that path (or loop).* Observe that the primed signals at the tail ends of the stretched nodes lose their identity during the process of inversion. Before inversion the node signal $x_j{}'$ is equal to x_j. After inversion $x_j{}'$ must be given a new name, say $x_j{}''$, since in general it is no longer equal to x_j.

Inversions of the type illustrated in Fig. 4-24 preserve the relationships existing among all of the node signals, but the graphical structure undergoes a metamorphosis.   Inversions of the type illustrated in Fig. 4-26 preserve the general shape of the graph, but the primed node signals undergo a metamorphosis.   The relationships among the un-primed node signals remain, of course, unchanged.   We shall refer to the first and second types of inversion as "node-preserving" and "branch-preserving" inversions.   A *node-preserving* inversion retains the identities of all node signals, whereas a *branch-preserving* inversion retains the locations of all branches (but reverses some of the branch directions). For some graphs it may not be necessary to stretch the nodes in order to prepare for a branch-preserving inversion.   In particular, if every node having more than one incoming branch is restricted to have at most one outgoing branch, then the graph is already in proper form for a branch-preserving inversion.   The block diagrams of automatic control systems are commonly constructed in just this form with "summing points," where a number of branches converge but only one branch radiates, and "branching points," where a single entering branch separates into two or more outgoing paths.   The signal associated with a "summing point" is not preserved by an inversion of the second type.

The two types of inversion are compared in Fig. 4-27.   Part (*a*) of the

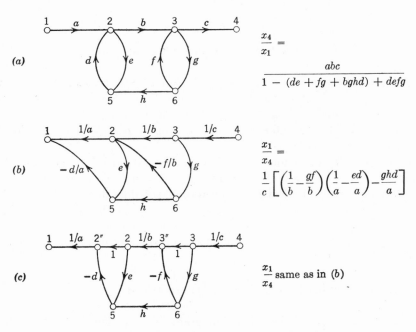

$$\frac{x_4}{x_1} = \frac{abc}{1 - (de + fg + bghd) + defg}$$

$$\frac{x_1}{x_4} = \frac{1}{c}\left[\left(\frac{1}{b} - \frac{gf}{b}\right)\left(\frac{1}{a} - \frac{ed}{a}\right) - \frac{ghd}{a}\right]$$

$\dfrac{x_1}{x_4}$ same as in (*b*)

Fig. 4-27. Inversion of a source-to-sink path.

figure shows the original graph in which path abc is to be inverted. A node-preserving inversion of this path yields a new graph (b) whose source-to-sink transmission is the inverse of the source-to-sink transmission in Fig. 4-27(a). The quotient of node signals x_1 and x_4 is, of course, the same in each graph. The transmission is inverted in graph (b) simply because the roles of the source and sink have been interchanged. Graph (c) shows the result of a branch-preserving inversion, following the stretching of nodes 2 and 3.

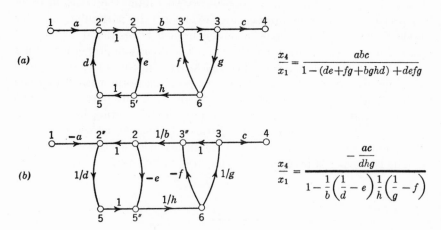

Fig. 4-28.   Inversion of a loop $(bghd)$.

Figure 4-28(a) shows the original graph with nodes 2, 3, and 5 stretched, preparatory to inversion of loop $bghd$. Node 6 has only one incoming branch and therefore need not be stretched. In Fig. 4-28(b) the loop is inverted and the source-to-sink transmission is evaluated for comparison with (a).

All possible inversions of a flow graph correspond to all possible arrangements of a set of algebraic equations in cause-and-effect form. Once a physical problem has been formulated directly as a flow graph with the aid of cause-and-effect reasoning, any and all other cause-and-effect formulations of the problem (involving the same set of variables) are directly obtainable by the topological process of inversion.

4.17   Normalization of Branch Transmissions

Since the transmission of a flow graph is dependent only upon the transmissions of paths and loops, it is evident that the branch trans-

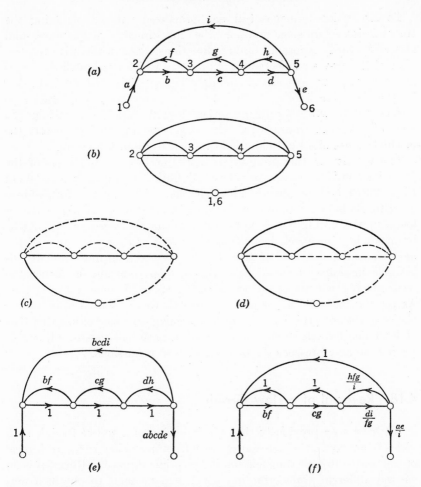

Fig. 4-29. Normalization or scaling. (*a*) A flow graph. (*b*) The same graph with branch directions ignored and with the sink joined to the source. (*c*), (*d*) Two possible trees. (*e*), (*f*) Normalization of the tree branches to the value unity.

missions may be scaled or normalized in any way we may desire so long as such scaling or normalization does not alter the values of the path and loop transmissions. Figure 4-29(*a*) shows a flow graph and (*e*) and (*f*) indicate two of the many possible ways in which certain branch transmissions can be normalized to unity without changing the source-to-sink transmission expression. Normalization permits us to characterize a transmission structure in terms of a minimum number of independent parameters without loss of generality.

To see which branches can be normalized without changing the transmission expression, first join the sink directly to the source and also temporarily ignore all branch directions, as shown in Fig. 4-29(b). Now pick a tree, a connected set of branches which touches all the nodes and does not form any closed circuits. Two possible trees are indicated by the solid lines in Fig. 4-29(c) and (d). The tree branches may be normalized to unity (or to any other desired values) after which the remaining branch transmissions can always be adjusted to restore the original values of all path and loop transmissions in the graph.

The validity of this procedure can be justified on the basis of the following considerations. Any closed circuit in the graph, such as $fghi$ in Fig. 4-29(a), is either already a feedback loop or can be transformed into a feedback loop by branch-preserving inversions of certain paths or loops in the graph. It is apparent that normalization of all of the branches in a feedback loop would irrevocably alter the value of the loop transmission. One of the branches in the loop must remain adjustable in order to recoup the original loop transmission, hence the requirement that the branches to be normalized must form a tree. As for the business of connecting the sink to the source prior to the choice of the tree, this is no more than a convenient way of insuring that at least one branch in each source-to-sink path will remain adjustable so that we may preserve the original path transmissions.

4.18   Reversal of a Flow Graph

We have seen previously that the inversion of a source-to-sink path yields a new graph whose source-to-sink transmission is the reciprocal of the source-to-sink transmission in the original graph. Reversal is an entirely different transformation which can be used to obtain a new graph having the same transmission as a given graph. *Reversal of a flow graph is accomplished by reversing the directions of all branches in the graph.* Specifically, reversal replaces each branch t_{jk} by a new branch $t_{kj}' = t_{jk}$. For a graph having one source and one sink *reversal yields a new graph whose source-to-sink transmission is exactly the same as that of the original graph.* The invariance of the source-to-sink transmission is obvious, since reversal gives a new graph having exactly the same set of paths, and the same sets of nontouching loops, as those in the original graph.

Figure 4-30 shows a flow graph (a) and the reversed graph (b). Observe that although the source-to-sink transmission is not changed by reversal the relationships among the signals at the intermediate nodes are in general completely different after reversal.

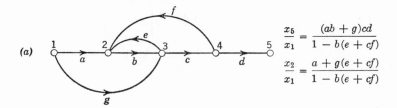

(a)

$$\frac{x_5}{x_1} = \frac{(ab + g)cd}{1 - b(e + cf)}$$

$$\frac{x_2}{x_1} = \frac{a + g(e + cf)}{1 - b(e + cf)}$$

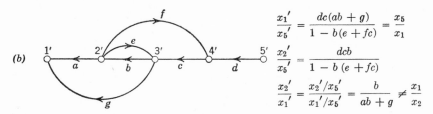

(b)

$$\frac{x_1'}{x_5'} = \frac{dc(ab + g)}{1 - b(e + fc)} = \frac{x_5}{x_1}$$

$$\frac{x_2'}{x_5'} = \frac{dcb}{1 - b(e + fc)}$$

$$\frac{x_2'}{x_1'} = \frac{x_2'/x_5'}{x_1'/x_5'} = \frac{b}{ab + g} \neq \frac{x_1}{x_2}$$

Fig. 4-30. Reversal of a flow graph.

The reversal of a graph is equivalent to transposition of the branch matrix of that graph ($t_{kj}' = t_{jk}$). Consequently, the graph transmission matrix is also transposed by reversal of the graph. In short, $T_{kj}' = T_{jk}$.

PROBLEMS

4.1 In each of the flow graphs in Fig. P4-1, absorb node n (or both m and n, if both are designated) to obtain a new graph, equivalent with respect to transmissions among the remaining nodes.

4.2 Evaluate, by inspection, the source-to-sink transmissions of each of the flow graphs in Fig. P4-2. Where convenient, use appropriate expansions to reduce the number of symbols in the transmission expression. In part (m), how many different paths are present? (Fig. P4-2 on pages 125 and 126.)

4.3 Calculate the loop transmission of (a) branch b, (b) branch d, (c) node n, for each of the flow graphs in Fig. P4-1.

4.4 Construct a proof for the signal-flow-graph transmission rules, paralleling as closely as possible the proof given in Chapter 3 for the unistor-network transmission rules. (Lots of luck, Charlie.)

4.5 Invert a source-to-sink path in each of the flow graphs of Fig. P4-2 and verify that the new source-to-sink transmission is the reciprocal of the old transmission. Use (a) node-preserving inversion, (b) branch-preserving inversion.

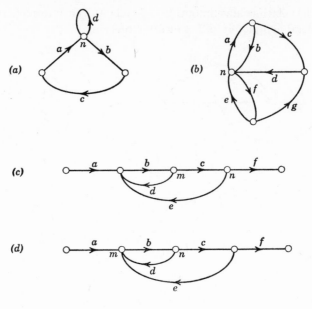

Fig. P4-1

4.6 Normalize the flow graphs in Fig. P4-2(c), (d), (e), and (k) so that a maximum number of branches have unity transmission, without changing the source-to-sink transmission.

4.7 Write the algebraic equations associated with the flow graphs in Fig. 4-2(e), (g), (h), (i), (j), and (k) and solve them to verify the transmission expression obtained by inspection.

4.8 Given the equations

$$ax_0 + ex_2 + hx_3 + jx_4 = x_1$$
$$bx_1 + fx_3 + ix_4 \quad\quad = x_2$$
$$cx_2 + gx_4 \quad\quad\quad = x_3$$
$$kx_0 + dx_3 \quad\quad\quad = x_4$$

draw a suitable flow graph and find the transmission x_4/x_0. Verify the answer by algebraic methods.

4.9 Given the equations

$$Ax_1 + Bx_2 + Cx_3 = x_0$$
$$Dx_1 + Ex_2 \quad\quad = 0$$
$$Fx_2 + Gx_3 = x_0$$

first recast the equations in a form suitable for interpretation as a flow graph, then draw the graph and find x_3/x_0. Verify the result by algebraic solution.

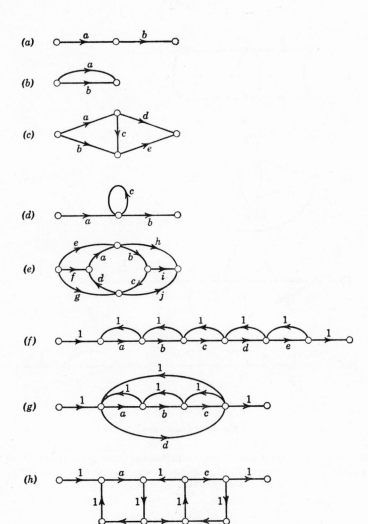

Fig. P4-2

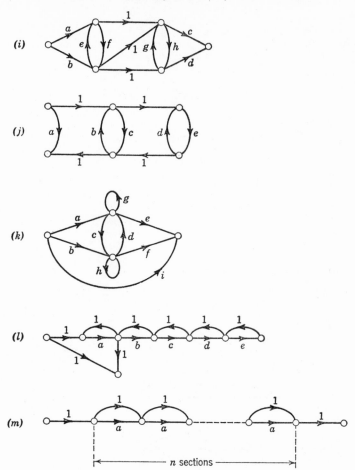

Fig. P4-2 (continued)

4.10 The following transmission expressions arise from different signal-flow graphs. Synthesize a flow graph for each source-to-sink transmission expression, such that each branch transmission in the graph is a different letter.

(a) $\dfrac{abcd}{1 - be - bcf}$

(b) $h + \dfrac{abcd}{1 - be - cf - bcg}$

(c) $\dfrac{(e + ag + adi)(f + bh + bcj) + ij(1 - abcd)}{1 - abcd}$

(d) $\dfrac{ah(1 - cf - dg)}{(1 - be)(1 - dg) - cf}$

Flow-Graph Circuit Analysis

5.1 Introduction

The equations associated with a linear flow graph are in cause-and-effect form, with each variable expressed explicitly in terms of others. Physical problems are often very conveniently formulated in just this form. To begin with an elementary example, consider the circuit shown in Fig. 5-1(a). Our problem is to choose a convenient set of circuit variables and then formulate a complete and independent set of cause-and-effect relationships among those variables. The resulting flow graph can then be solved to find the output voltage V in terms of the specified input E. A very simple formulation is indicated in Fig. 5-1(b). First visualize the current I as an explicit *effect* due to the *cause* E, as is specified by the first branch in the flow graph. The second branch states, in turn, that voltage V is an effect caused by current I, and this completes the flow graph. By inspection of the graph, $V/E = R_2/(R_1 + R_2)$.

Another formulation is given in Fig. 5-1(c). Here V is first expressed as an explicit effect produced by E and I acting as causes, as indicated by the two flow-graph branches directed into node V. Current I is, in turn, caused by voltage V according to the conductance law for resistance R_2. In this case the chain of cause-and-effect reasoning has closed upon itself to produce a loop in the flow graph. This set of equations is apparently complete because the independent variable E is the only source node in the flow graph and all pertinent information (including the values of all circuit parameters) has been utilized in formulating the problem. Moreover, the equations are independent; we have not written the same equation twice. Specifically, each new

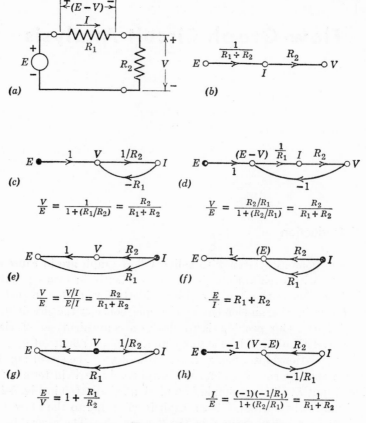

Fig. 5-1.   Flow graphs for a simple circuit.

cause-and-effect relationship brings some new information into the formulation, a new circuit parameter value or a new Kirchhoff current or voltage constraint.

The remaining parts of Fig. 5-1 show some of the other possible ways in which this particular circuit problem can be formulated as a flow graph. In the physical problem E is the primary cause, whereas I and V are resulting effects. We may, however, *choose* a value of I and then calculate the value of E *required* to produce that I. The resulting equations will, from the analysis viewpoint, treat I as a primary cause (source node) and E as a resulting effect (dependent node) *produced* by the chain of calculations, as in Fig. 5-1(e). This does not in any way alter the physical role of E. In particular, graph (e) does not necessarily imply that current I is an electrical source in the circuit diagram. The primary *physical* source does not *necessarily* appear as a source node in the flow graph, although such appearance is probably natural and convenient in most formulations.

The flow graph in Fig. 5-1 (e) is obtainable directly from graph (c) by a node-preserving inversion (Article 4.16) of the path from E to I. This illustrates the fact that once a flow graph has been constructed for a physical problem *all other possible cause-and-effect formulations involving the same variables are obtainable by flow-graph inversions.*

Graph (g) in Fig. 5-1 results from inversion of the unity branch in (c) or branch R_2 in (e). Here V is the source node but the functional relationship between E and V is, of course, the same as in (c) and (e). Graph (d) can be converted to graph (c) by first absorbing the second node ($E - V$) and then executing a node-preserving inversion of the loop. Graph (f) arises from graph (c) after a branch-preserving inversion of the path from E to I in (c). Similarly, branch-preserving inversion of the loop in (c) yields graph (h). Notice that node-preserving inversions give different flow-graph structures involving the same variables as in (c), (e), and (g), whereas branch-preserving inversions retain the original schematic shape of the graph but alter the identity of the signal at a node having more than one incoming branch, as in (c), (f), and (h).

Cause-and-effect formulation of a physical problem is an arbitrary process. Judgment is involved both in the choice of variables and in the plan of formulation. It is possible to choose the variables and carry out the formulation according to a rigid preassigned scheme which always works and which does not change from one problem to the next. However, formal methods often lead to cumbersome graphs. (In other words, one cannot have both freedom and security.) In this chapter we shall first develop certain formal procedures and then, with these serving as a background, we shall lead into more flexible flow-graph formulations which often yield a simpler graph more clearly related to the physical problem.

5.2 Two-Terminal-Pair Networks

Many electronic circuits and systems are conveniently representable as interconnections of three-terminal subnetworks. Figure 5-2(a)

shows a three-terminal building block, together with two pairs of terminal variables in terms of which its behavior can be completely specified. The network is assumed to be linear, so that some linear relationship of the general form

$$k_1E_1 + k_2E_2 + k_3I_1 + k_4I_2 = k_5 \tag{5.1}$$

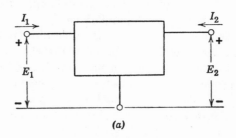

(a)

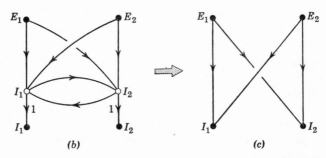

(b)   (c)

Fig. 5-2. A three-terminal network.   (a) Definition of the two-terminal-pair variables E_1, I_1 and E_2, I_2.   (b) A flow graph of two linear relationships among the four variables.   (c) The residue graph.

must exist among the four current and voltage variables.   Moreover, physical intuition tells us that two of the four variables are independently specifiable.   For example, if voltage sources are attached to the network at E_1 and E_2, the two sources are in general independently adjustable to any desired values.   Specification of the two voltages fixes the values of the currents I_1 and I_2.   Equation (5.1) allows independent specification of three of the variables.   If, however, only two of the variables are to be independently specifiable, then another linear relationship

$$k_6E_1 + k_7E_2 + k_8I_1 + k_9I_2 = k_{10} \tag{5.2}$$

must also exist.

The pair of equations (5.1) and (5.2) characterize the network completely. Let us assume that Fig. 5-2(a) is a linear incremental model, in which case the parameters k_5 and k_{10} vanish. With k_5 and k_{10} set equal to zero in (5.1) and (5.2), we can solve (5.1) for I_1 in terms of E_1, E_2, and I_2, and solve (5.2) for I_2 in terms of E_1, E_2, and I_1 to obtain a flow graph of the form shown in Fig. 5-2(b). The two unity-transmission branches may then be appended, as indicated in (b), and the intermediate nodes may be absorbed to give the residue in (c). Figure 5-2(c) shows that really only four flow-graph branches are required for a complete and general description of the two-terminal-pair network. To see the same thing another way, first drop the constant terms k_5 and k_{10} and rewrite (5.1) and (5.2) in the forms

$$k_1E_1 + k_2E_2 = -k_3I_1 - k_4I_2 \tag{5.3}$$

and

$$k_6E_1 + k_7E_2 = -k_8I_1 - k_9I_2 \tag{5.4}$$

which can be expressed as the matrix equation

$$\begin{pmatrix} k_1 & k_2 \\ k_6 & k_7 \end{pmatrix} \begin{pmatrix} E_1 \\ E_2 \end{pmatrix} = \begin{pmatrix} -k_3 & -k_4 \\ -k_8 & -k_9 \end{pmatrix} \begin{pmatrix} I_1 \\ I_2 \end{pmatrix} \tag{5.5}$$

Premultiplication of both sides by the inverse of the right-hand square matrix then yields

$$\left[\begin{pmatrix} -k_3 & -k_4 \\ -k_8 & -k_9 \end{pmatrix}^{-1} \begin{pmatrix} k_1 & k_2 \\ k_6 & k_7 \end{pmatrix} \right] \begin{pmatrix} E_1 \\ E_2 \end{pmatrix} = \begin{pmatrix} I_1 \\ I_2 \end{pmatrix} \tag{5.6}$$

and this reduces to the short-circuit admittance matrix equation

$$\begin{pmatrix} Y_{11} & Y_{12} \\ Y_{21} & Y_{22} \end{pmatrix} \begin{pmatrix} E_1 \\ E_2 \end{pmatrix} = \begin{pmatrix} I_1 \\ I_2 \end{pmatrix} \tag{5.7}$$

which contains exactly four independent parameters.

The six possible choices of independent variable pairs are covered in Fig. 5-3. These correspond to the six matrix transformations presented previously in Fig. 2-15.

In parts (e) and (f) of Fig. 5-3, the flow graph is not conveniently interpretable as a simple circuit model. The reason is as follows. In Fig. 5-3(a) through (d), each of the flow-graph branch transmissions can be measured by an experiment in which a single source and a single meter are attached to the network. In (e) and (f), however, two sources and two meters are required for the experimental evaluation of each branch transmission. For example, to evaluate parameter A in Fig. 5-3(e), we can attach external voltage sources on each side of the net-

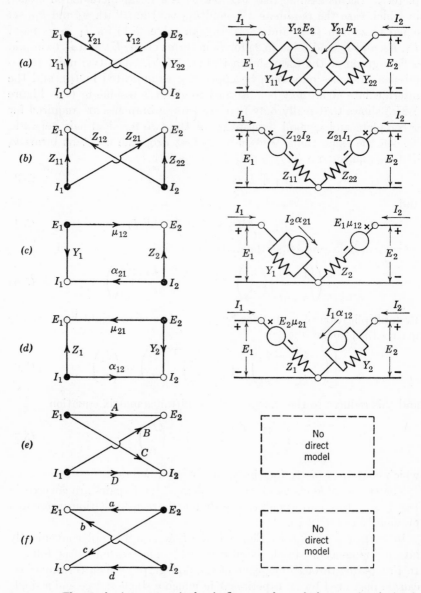

Fig. 5-3. The six basic two-terminal-pair flow graphs and the associated circuit models. (a) Short-circuit admittance. (b) Open-circuit impedance. (c) Forward-voltage transfer (reverse-current transfer). (d) Forward-current transfer (reverse-voltage transfer). (e) Forward transfer. (f) Reverse transfer.

work, set E_1 to the value unity, and then agree to adjust E_2 until the input current I_1 has the value specified in advance. The setting of E_2 is then numerically equal to A. Any of the circuit models in (a) through (d) may be utilized as network representations of the flow graphs (e) and (f) but the circuit parameters will not be as simply related to the flow-graph branch transmissions as is the case in (a) through (d).

Figure 5-4 shows flow graphs and circuit models for some reciprocal (reciprocity-obeying) networks. A two-terminal-pair reciprocal network can be completely characterized in terms of three, rather than four, complex parameters. Hence parts (a) and (b) of Fig. 5-4 are general models that can be used to represent an arbitrary three-terminal reciprocal linear network. The model (d) likewise has three independent parameters and is therefore general, provided we permit complex values of the transformer turns ratio n. Reciprocity is manifested in Fig. 5-4(c) through (f) by upper and lower branch transmissions that are equal in magnitude but of opposite algebraic sign. The flow graph in Fig. 5-4(a) is convenient in that it permits each of the three circuit parameters to appear as one and only one branch transmission. Absorption of the two intermediate junctions in Fig. 5-4(a) yields a residue graph having the form of Fig. 5-3(a), in which Y_{21} and Y_{12} are both equal to Y_m, the reciprocal mutual admittance.

Conversion from one of the six two-terminal-pair forms to another is illustrated in Fig. 5-5. Let us begin with the forward-voltage-transfer graph in Fig. 5-3(c). To prepare for a branch-preserving inversion, four unity-transmission isolation branches are first appended as shown in Fig. 5-5(a). Inversion of the path from I_2 to E_2 yields graph (b), whose terminal residue is recognizable as the short-circuit-admittance form. To obtain, instead, the reverse-voltage-transfer form (e), we can invert both the path from I_2 to E_2 and a path from E_1 to I_1, as shown in (d). The reverse-voltage-transfer parameters are then evaluated directly in terms of the forward-voltage-transfer parameters by inspection of graph (d).

The six basic models are in general completely equivalent and interchangeable and flow-graph inversion offers a simple and direct means of computing one set of parameters in terms of another set. Observe, however, that in certain special cases one of the six models may be especially convenient or appropriate while some of the others are intractable. In particular, the ideal transformer, Fig. 5-4(c), is nicely representable on either the forward-voltage-transfer basis or the forward-current-transfer basis, Fig. 5-3(c) or (d), whereas both the short-circuit-admittance parameters and the open-circuit-impedance parameters of the ideal transformer are infinite in value.

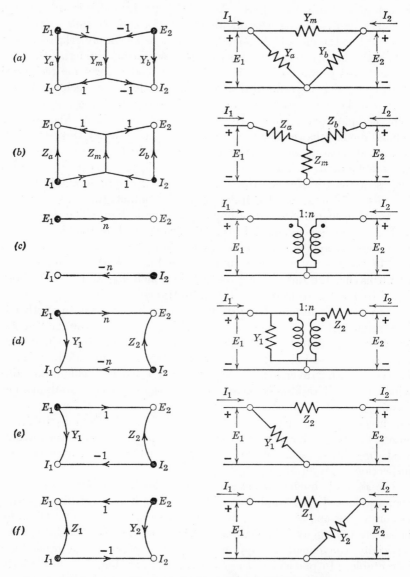

Fig. 5-4. Flow graphs for reciprocal circuit models.

In addition to the six basic models given in Fig. 5-3, many other special-purpose models can be constructed. Figure 5-6 shows one such model in which the reciprocal or mutual component of transfer impedance Z_m and the unilateral component of forward-transfer impedance Z_u are placed in evidence. This model has enjoyed much use as an

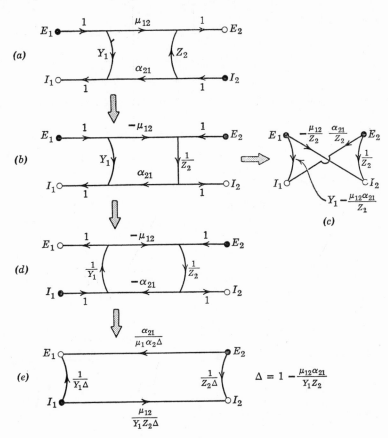

Fig. 5-5. Conversion of parameters by flow-graph path inversion.

incremental representation of the common-base and common-emitter transistor, since its four parameters are closely related to the physical properties of the transistor. The circuit in Fig. 5-6 is nevertheless quite general and can be used as a model for an arbitrary three-terminal network. It is different from, but equivalent to, any one of the six basic circuits and is closely related to the open-circuit-impedance form.

The models in Fig. 5-3 are all based upon the same choice of terminal-

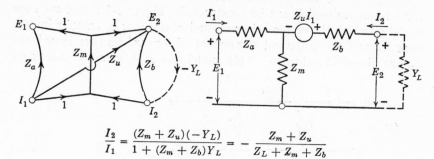

$$\frac{I_2}{I_1} = \frac{(Z_m + Z_u)(-Y_L)}{1 + (Z_m + Z_b)Y_L} = -\frac{Z_m + Z_u}{Z_L + Z_m + Z_b}$$

Fig. 5-6.   A general model based on mutual impedance Z_m and unilateral impedance Z_u.

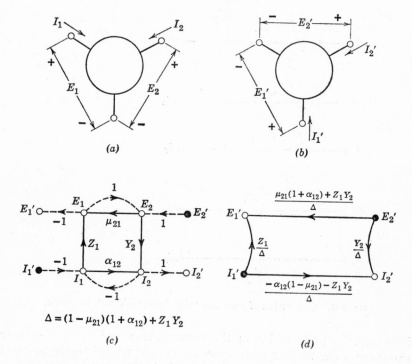

$$\Delta = (1 - \mu_{21})(1 + \alpha_{12}) + Z_1 Y_2$$

(c)   (d)

Fig. 5-7.   Conversion to a new choice of terminal-pair variables.

pair variables. There are, however, three fundamentally distinct choices of two-terminal-pair variables for a three-terminal network. Two of these are compared in Fig. 5-7. Part (c) of the figure shows the forward-current-transfer flow graph for the terminal variables defined in (a). The dashed-line branches specify relationships between the variables in Fig. 5-7(a) and (b). By inspection of graph (c), we can evaluate the corresponding parameters for the new terminal-pair basis (d). Six possible model forms and three possible terminal-pair choices means that there are eighteen fundamentally distinct but equivalent representations for a three-terminal network, not to mention other special-purpose models. The point to be made here is that memorization or even tabulation of these eighteen different parameter sets is hardly worthwhile. More important is the ability to convert from one form to another with facility and confidence.

5.3 Cascaded Two-Terminal-Pair Networks

When two or more two-terminal-pair networks are placed in cascade, as shown in Fig. 5-8(a), the flow graph for the complete system is readily formulated by juxtaposition of the corresponding two-terminal-pair flow graphs, as illustrated in (b). Two flow graphs can be cascaded only if they are compatible. Compatibility here means juxtaposition of source and nonsource nodes. In Fig. 5-8(b), for example, node e_3 is a source and e_2 is not. Similarly, node i_2 is a source and i_3 is not. Compatibility allows us to insert the dashed-line branches, indicated in Fig. 5-8(b), which state that e_3 is equal to e_2 and that i_2 is the negative of i_3.

Instead of inserting the dashed-line branches, we can simply move the two separate flow graphs together until node e_2 coalesces with node e_3 and node i_2 coalesces with node i_3, after first changing the algebraic signs of branches Z_2 and α_{21}. It is permissible to coalesce two nodes in a flow graph provided one or both of them are source nodes and provided the two node signals are known to be equal. *Coalescing two nonsource nodes destroys an equation and produces an incorrect graph.*

By inspection of the completed graph in Fig. 5-8(b) we obtain the forward-voltage-transfer parameters of the cascaded combination in terms of the forward-voltage-transfer parameters of the two individual parts. The result is shown in (c). Now suppose we wish to find the voltage transmission e_4/e_s of the complete system, with the source resistance Z_s and the load admittance Y_L attached as shown in Fig. 5-8(a). In this particular example, involving the cascade of only two component networks, the calculations are actually somewhat simpler if we work with graph (b) rather than with graph (c). Affixing three new branches to account for the source and the load, we have the form shown in Fig. 5-8(d), and the desired transmission expression follows from expansion of Δ at node i_2.

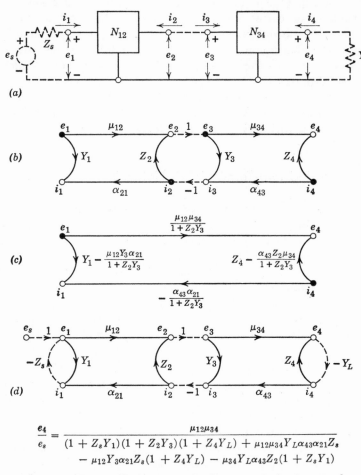

$$\frac{e_4}{e_s} = \frac{\mu_{12}\mu_{34}}{(1 + Z_sY_1)(1 + Z_2Y_3)(1 + Z_4Y_L) + \mu_{12}\mu_{34}Y_L\alpha_{43}\alpha_{21}Z_s}$$
$$- \mu_{12}Y_3\alpha_{21}Z_s(1 + Z_4Y_L) - \mu_{34}Y_L\alpha_{43}Z_2(1 + Z_sY_1)$$

Fig. 5-8. Flow graphs for a cascade of two-terminal-pair networks.

Observe that the insertion of series impedance or shunt admittance between the two cascaded networks does not alter the basic form of the complete flow graph. In particular, if the elementary network shown in Fig. 5-4(f) is connected in cascade between the two networks in Fig. 5-8(a), then the series impedance can be lumped with Z_2 and the

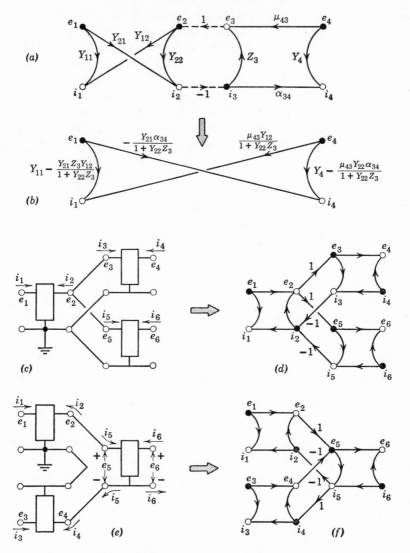

Fig. 5-9. Some other compatible interconnections of two-terminal-pair flow graphs.

shunt admittance with Y_3. On the other hand, insertion of the flow graph in Fig. 5-4(e) between the two flow-graph parts in Fig. 5-8(b) produces a complete graph in which two new loops are present and the structure is basically altered.

Figure 5-9 illustrates a few of the many other possible interconnections of two-terminal-pair flow graphs. A short-circuit-admittance graph is compatible in cascade with a forward-voltage-transfer graph, as indicated in (a). The over-all terminal residue (b) is another short-circuit-admittance graph. Parts (c) through (f) of Fig. 5-9 show that the forward-voltage-transfer flow-graph representation is compatible for both single-to-parallel cascading (c) and series-to-single cascading (e). In Fig. 5-9(d), for example, the interconnection branches state that e_3 and e_5 are both equal to e_2 and that i_2 is the negative sum of i_3 and i_5. Here again we could simply coalesce nodes e_2, e_3, e_5 and nodes i_2, i_3, i_5, after first modifying the graph to accomplish replacement of node signal i_2 by its negative.

5.4   The Primitive Flow Graph for a Branch Network

Interconnection of two-terminal-pair "building blocks" is a useful and systematic way of formulating flow graphs. A more general and still more systematic method will now be described. For the moment assume that the network to be analyzed is composed entirely of current sources, voltage sources, and ordinary reciprocal branches. The formulation method is based upon the topology of the network and begins with the choice of a tree,

> *tree:* a connected set of branches touching all nodes in the network but not forming any loops   (5.8)

We shall also speak of links,

> *link:* any branch not included in a specified tree   (5.9)

Collapsing all the branches in a tree reduces all voltage differences in the network to zero, whereas erasing all the branches in a link set interrupts all loops in the network and reduces all network currents to zero. The formulation proceeds as follows.

> Choose a tree containing all of the voltage sources in the network but none of the current sources. The associated link set therefore contains all of the current sources. Express the link voltages in terms of the tree-branch voltages. Express the tree-branch currents in terms of the link currents. Complete the flow graph with branches whose transmissions are the link admittances and tree-branch impedances   (5.10)

It is clearly possible to choose a tree containing all of the voltage sources and none of the current sources, for otherwise the voltage sources or the current sources would not be independently specifiable. Once a tree has been chosen the method outlined above leads unambiguously to a proper graph, which we shall call the primitive graph.

Figure 5-10 offers perhaps the simplest nontrivial example. There are two possible trees containing the voltage source and not containing the current source. To proceed, let us choose the tree consisting of branch z_T and the voltage source v_T', which leaves y_L and the current source i_L' as links. Since a tree provides one and only one path between any two given nodes, link voltages are easy to identify as algebraic sums of

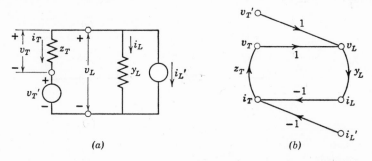

Fig. 5-10. Formulation in terms of tree impedance and link admittance.

branch voltages. In Fig. 5-10(a) link voltage v_L is the sum of v_T' and v_T, as indicated by the two uppermost branches in the flow graph (b). Also because a tree provides exactly one path between two network nodes, the current in any tree branch is easy to identify in terms of the link currents. Each link current flows around the loop formed by that link and the tree path joining the ends of that link. Hence the two lowermost branches in Fig. 5-10(b). Branches z_T and y_L then complete the flow graph as shown.

A more complicated example that better illustrates the general form is offered in Fig. 5-11. The network is shown in (a) and, as an aid to visualization of the tree, the network graph (b) is also shown. A suitable tree, containing the voltage source but not the current source, is indicated by the heavy-line branches in (b), and the links are shown as dashed-line branches. The choice of branch reference directions for current and voltage is arbitrary, but once these directions are assigned they must be kept throughout the formulation. We shall agree to use the Ohm's law voltage and current reference polarities shown in Fig. 5-11(c), both for ordinary branches and for sources. The voltage and current reference directions for any element are such that positive branch current and positive branch voltage mean positive power *absorbed* by that element. It is to be understood that the simplified arrow notation in (d) denotes current and voltage polarities as in (c), for any branch or source.

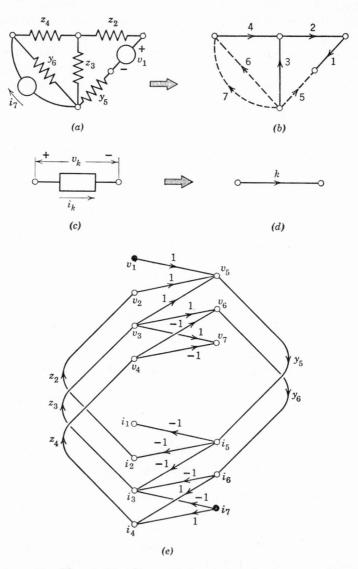

Fig. 5-11. The primitive flow graph, based upon the chosen tree 1234.

The formulation scheme already described leads to the primitive flow graph in Fig. 5-11(e). The general structure illustrated in Fig. 5-11 (e) can be represented more compactly as in Fig. 5-12 (a), which shows a matrix flow graph. The associated matrix equations are

$$(v_T' + v_T)\mu = v_L \tag{5.11}$$

$$v_L y_L = i_L \tag{5.12}$$

$$(i_L' + i_L)\alpha = i_T \tag{5.13}$$

$$i_T z_T = v_T \tag{5.14}$$

wherein v_T', v_T, i_L', and i_L are row vectors, μ and α are transformation matrices, and y_L and z_T are diagonal matrices. For the network example in Fig. 5-11, we have,

$$v_T' = (v_1 \quad 0 \quad 0 \quad 0) \tag{5.15}$$

$$v_T = (0 \quad v_2 \quad v_3 \quad v_4) \tag{5.16}$$

$$v_L = (v_5 \quad v_6 \quad v_7) \tag{5.17}$$

$$i_L' = (0 \quad 0 \quad i_7) \tag{5.18}$$

$$i_L = (i_5 \quad i_6 \quad 0) \tag{5.19}$$

$$i_T = (i_1 \quad i_2 \quad i_3 \quad i_4) \tag{5.20}$$

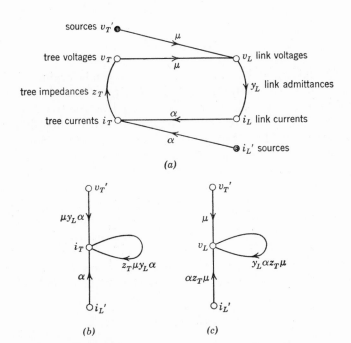

Fig. 5-12. Matrix flow graphs. (*a*) The primitive flow graph. (*b*) The tree-current graph. (*c*) The link-voltage graph.

$$\mu = \begin{pmatrix} 1 & 0 & 0 \\ 1 & 0 & 0 \\ 1 & 1 & 1 \\ 0 & -1 & -1 \end{pmatrix} \tag{5.21}$$

$$\alpha = \begin{pmatrix} -1 & -1 & -1 & 0 \\ 0 & 0 & -1 & 1 \\ 0 & 0 & -1 & 1 \end{pmatrix} \tag{5.22}$$

$$z_T = \begin{pmatrix} 0 & 0 & 0 & 0 \\ 0 & z_2 & 0 & 0 \\ 0 & 0 & z_3 & 0 \\ 0 & 0 & 0 & z_4 \end{pmatrix} \tag{5.23}$$

$$y_L = \begin{pmatrix} y_5 & 0 & 0 \\ 0 & y_6 & 0 \\ 0 & 0 & 0 \end{pmatrix} \tag{5.24}$$

The elements μ_{jk} and α_{jk} in matrices μ and α can be evaluated directly by inspection of the circuit graph, Fig. 5-11(b). The kth column of μ (or the kth row of α) selects that loop formed by the tree and the kth link. For example, the first column of μ shows that the first link voltage v_5 is the sum of the first three tree voltages v_1, v_2, and v_3. Similarly, the second column of μ states that the second link voltage v_6 is equal to the difference of two tree voltages $v_3 - v_4$. As for α, the first column states that i_1 is the negative of the first link current i_5. Similarly, the fourth column of α contains the information that the fourth tree-branch current i_4 is equal to the sum of two of the link currents i_6 and i_7, and independent of the other link current i_5. In short, each column of μ corresponds to the equation for a link voltage in terms of the tree-branch voltages, and each column of α is associated with an equation giving a tree current in terms of the link currents. The symmetry of the formulation shows that

$$\alpha_{jk} = -\mu_{kj} \tag{5.25}$$

In other words, the α matrix is the negative of the transposed μ matrix.

A primitive flow graph, such as that in Fig. 5-11(e), can be solved by application of the flow-graph transmission rules. More can be said about the general form of the solution, however, and the matrix flow graph in Fig. 5-12(a) is convenient for this purpose. Matrices behave like ordinary numbers except that multiplication is not commutative. Hence a matrix flow graph can be manipulated like an ordinary flow graph, provided we maintain the proper sequence of branch transmissions wherever they appear as products. With this fact in mind we can absorb nodes v_T, v_L, and i_L in Fig. 5-12(a) to obtain the residue shown in (b). The associated matrix equation is

$$i_T = (i_T z_T + v_T')\mu y_L \alpha + i_L' \alpha \tag{5.26}$$

Collecting the terms containing i_T, we have

$$i_T[I - z_T \mu y_L \alpha] = v_T' \mu y_L \alpha + i_L' \alpha \tag{5.27}$$

where I is the unit matrix. Multiplication of both sides by the inverse of the bracketed matrix gives the solution for the tree-branch currents i_T in terms of the network sources v_T' and i_L':

$$i_T = [v_T' \mu y_L \alpha + i_L' \alpha][I - z_T \mu y_L \alpha]^{-1} \tag{5.28}$$

Relation (5.28) shows that the effect of a self-loop in a matrix flow graph is to postmultiply the transmission path into that node by a factor equal to the inverse of the matrix return difference, the return difference being the unit matrix minus the self-loop transmission matrix. This is a generalization of the elementary self-loop equivalence for ordinary (nonmatrix) flow graphs. Were we to solve for v_L, rather than i_T, the residue graph would be as shown in Fig. 5-12(c), for which the solution is

$$v_L = [i_L' \alpha z_T \mu + v_T' \mu][I - y_L \alpha z_T \mu]^{-1} \tag{5.29}$$

5.5   Node-Voltage and Loop-Current Analysis

Figure 5-13 shows a network containing enough sources so that we can select a tree made up entirely of these sources. We can always begin the analysis of any network in this way by first attaching the necessary sources. Assuming for the moment that the sources are all independent voltage generators, we find that the primitive matrix flow graph reduces to the particularly simple form indicated in Fig. 5-13(c). The associated matrix equation is

$$i_T = v_T' \mu y_L \alpha \tag{5.30}$$

Equation (5.30) is recognizable as the form to which (5.28) reduces

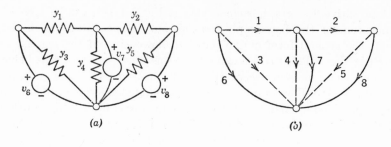

(a)   (b)

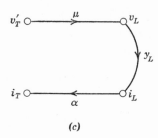

(c)

Fig. 5-13. (a) A network containing a tree of sources. (b) The network graph. (c) The primitive matrix flow graph.

when both z_T and i_L' vanish. For the network in Fig. 5-13(a), with branch reference polarities assigned as in (b), we have

$$i_T = (i_6 \quad i_7 \quad i_8) \tag{5.31}$$

$$v_T' = (v_6 \quad v_7 \quad v_8) \tag{5.32}$$

$$\mu y_L \alpha =$$

$$\begin{pmatrix} 1 & 0 & 1 & 0 & 0 \\ -1 & 1 & 0 & 1 & 0 \\ 0 & -1 & 0 & 0 & 1 \end{pmatrix} \begin{pmatrix} y_1 & 0 & 0 & 0 & 0 \\ 0 & y_2 & 0 & 0 & 0 \\ 0 & 0 & y_3 & 0 & 0 \\ 0 & 0 & 0 & y_4 & 0 \\ 0 & 0 & 0 & 0 & y_5 \end{pmatrix} \begin{pmatrix} -1 & 1 & 0 \\ 0 & -1 & 1 \\ -1 & 0 & 0 \\ 0 & -1 & 0 \\ 0 & 0 & -1 \end{pmatrix} \tag{5.33}$$

$$-\mu y_L \alpha = \begin{pmatrix} y_1 + y_3 & -y_1 & 0 \\ -y_1 & y_1 + y_2 + y_4 & -y_2 \\ 0 & -y_2 & y_2 + y_5 \end{pmatrix} \tag{5.34}$$

The negative of the matrix product $\mu y_L \alpha$ is immediately recognizable as the short-circuit-admittance matrix discussed in Chapter 2. The negative sign follows from the algebraic-sign convention for source voltage and source current, which differs from that in Chapter 2.

If we now specify that the sources in Fig. 5-13(a) are fixed currents, rather than fixed voltages, then voltages v_6, v_7, and v_8 can be found

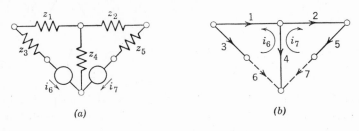

(a)   (b)

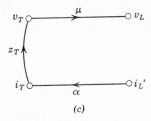

(c)

Fig. 5-14. (a) A network containing a link set of sources. (b) The network graph. (c) The primitive matrix flow graph.

in terms of i_6, i_7, and i_8 by inversion of relation (5.30) to obtain the open-circuit-impedance matrix equation

$$v_T' = i_T[\mu y_L \alpha]^{-1} \tag{5.35}$$

Figure 5-14 shows a second way in which the primitive graph can be made simple. Here we have *inserted* sources into the network in such a way that the sources form a complete link set. (A link set is a set of branches whose erasure is necessary and sufficient to open all loops in the network.) On this basis the primitive matrix flow graph reduces to the form in Fig. 5-14(c). The associated matrix equation is

$$v_L = i_L' \alpha z_T \mu \tag{5.36}$$

and, in this particular example, we have

$$v_L = (v_6 \quad v_7) \tag{5.37}$$

$$i_L' = (i_6 \quad i_7) \tag{5.38}$$

$$\alpha z_T \mu = \begin{pmatrix} -1 & 0 & 1 & -1 & 0 \\ 0 & 1 & 0 & -1 & 1 \end{pmatrix} \begin{pmatrix} z_1 & 0 & 0 & 0 & 0 \\ 0 & z_2 & 0 & 0 & 0 \\ 0 & 0 & z_3 & 0 & 0 \\ 0 & 0 & 0 & z_4 & 0 \\ 0 & 0 & 0 & 0 & z_5 \end{pmatrix} \begin{pmatrix} 1 & 0 \\ 0 & -1 \\ -1 & 0 \\ 1 & 1 \\ 0 & -1 \end{pmatrix}$$

(5.39)

$$-\alpha z_T \mu = \begin{pmatrix} z_1 + z_3 + z_4 & z_4 \\ z_4 & z_2 + z_4 + z_5 \end{pmatrix}$$

(5.40)

As mentioned previously, the chosen tree provides one and only one path between the two terminal nodes of a given link. Each link, together with its associated tree path, forms a loop in the network. Hence the kth link current may be thought of as a loop current i_k flowing in the kth loop so defined. The kth row of the μ matrix contains information about the presence of tree branches in the kth loop and about the orientation of their reference direction around that loop. In relation (5.39), for example, the first row of the μ matrix states that the first link current i_6 flows in a loop containing branches 1, 3, and 4, and that the reference directions of branches 3 and 4 are opposed to the reference direction of loop current. The loop-impedance matrix (5.40) shows the self-impedance of the first loop $z_1 + z_3 + z_4$, the self-impedance of the second loop $z_2 + z_4 + z_5$, and the mutual impedance z_4 common to both loops in Fig. 5-14(b). The mutual impedance is negative because current i_6 flowing in branch 4 tends to produce a voltage which opposes the flow of loop current i_7.

Relation (5.36) is the form to which (5.29) reduces when both v_T' and y_L vanish. Treating the link-set sources as specified voltages rather than specified currents, we can invert the matrix equation (5.36) to find the loop currents in terms of the specified source voltages

$$i_L' = v_L[\alpha z_T \mu]^{-1}$$

(5.41)

The formulation leading to relations (5.30) and (5.35) is called the *node-voltage basis of analysis*. When formulating a network problem on the node-voltage basis, we first attach a tree of current sources to the network as illustrated in Fig. 5-13(a). The sources are temporarily treated as independent voltages for the purpose of formulating the current-equilibrium equations (5.30). Once these equations are formulated, however, the currents flowing in the attached source branches are once again treated as given quantities and the problem is to solve for the node voltages *caused* by the current-source excitations of the network. The solution is obtainable by matrix inversion, as in (5.35), or by inversion of various source-to-sink transmission paths in the primitive flow graph, to give a new graph in which the source currents appear as source nodes and the node voltages appear as dependent nodes.

When the tree of sources has one node common to all of the sources, as in Fig. 5-13(a), the voltage equations are said to be on the *datum-node* or *ground-node* basis. Datum-node formulation is often convenient but certainly not necessary. Any tree set of voltages can be taken as the starting point. In Fig. 5-13(a), for example, the source v_8 might just as well be located across branch y_2 instead of branch y_5.

The formulation leading to equations (5.36) and (5.41) is called the *loop-current basis of analysis*. On the loop basis, we first insert a link set of voltage sources, which are temporarily treated as current sources, as in Fig. 5-14(a), for the purpose of formulating the voltage-equilibrium

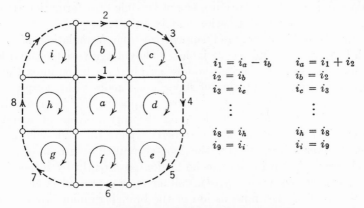

$$i_1 = i_a - i_b \qquad i_a = i_1 + i_2$$
$$i_2 = i_b \qquad i_b = i_2$$
$$i_3 = i_c \qquad i_c = i_3$$
$$\vdots \qquad\qquad \vdots$$
$$i_8 = i_h \qquad i_h = i_8$$
$$i_9 = i_i \qquad i_i = i_9$$

Fig. 5-15.   Mesh currents in a planar network.

equations (5.36) involving the loop-current variables. Once the equations are formulated, the sources return to their role as independent voltages exciting the network, and the analysis problem consists of solving for the loop currents produced by this excitation. As before, the answer may be found by matrix inversion (5.41) or by suitable path inversions in the primitive flow graph to obtain a new graph in which the voltage sources appear as source-node signals.

It is often convenient to work with a set of loop currents that do not correspond directly to any set of link currents. An example is offered in Fig. 5-15. A *planar* network is any network that can be mapped upon the surface of a sphere without overlapping or intersection of branches. For a planar network a very convenient loop-current set consists of the currents circulating in the individual meshes of the network, as indicated by the letters in Fig. 5-15. The number of meshes in a planar network is evidently equal to the number of links in a link set. However, in this particular example it is not possible to identify every mesh current with a single link current (the links are shown as dashed-line branches and are numbered from 1 to 9 in Fig. 5-15). Nevertheless, the link and mesh currents are related by simple linear equations that allow us to calculate the mesh currents from the link currents or the link currents from the mesh currents. In other words, the link-current row matrix i_L is related to the mesh-current row matrix i_M through an α-type reversible matrix transformation, $i_L = i_M \alpha_{ML}$. For mesh currents in a planar network, the inverse exists and $i_M = i_L \alpha_{ML}^{-1}$. For an arbitrary network, planar or otherwise, the necessary and sufficient condition for the independence of a chosen set of loop-current variables is that the α-type transformation from those loop currents to a set of link currents be a reversible transformation; that is, the inverse of the transformation matrix must exist.

Figure 5-16 illustrates and summarizes the formulation of a flow graph in terms of primitive variables, node-voltage variables, and loop-current variables. The primitive flow graph (b) is based upon the tree z_1, z_2, z_3, and v_7. Absorption of superfluous nodes yields graph (c), in which only tree voltages and link currents appear. Further reduction of the graph, by absorption of nodes (and absorption of the self-loops that appear when those nodes are absorbed), yields the node-voltage flow graph (d), or, alternatively, the loop-current flow graph (e). Any branch transmission in (d) can be evaluated directly by inspection of (c). For example, in graph (d), voltage v_2 is expressed in terms of v_1 and v_3. To find the transmission of the branch running from v_1 to v_2, therefore, we must return to graph (c), set v_3 equal to zero, and temporarily treat v_1 as a source node. Under these conditions the transmission from v_1 to v_2 in (c) is $y_4 z_2/(1 + y_4 z_2 + y_5 z_2)$. Multiplication of the numerator and the denominator of this fraction by y_2, the reciprocal of z_2, gives the branch transmission $y_4/(y_2 + y_4 + y_5)$ shown in (d).

Any branch transmission in Fig. 5-16(d) can also be evaluated directly by inspection of network (a). Graph (d) shows v_2 expressed in terms of v_1 and v_3. Hence to find the transmission of the branch running from v_1 to v_2, we return to network (a), set v_3 equal to zero (collapse branch z_3), temporarily treat v_1 as a source voltage, and evaluate by inspection the voltage ratio v_2/v_1. With v_3 grounded, branches z_2 and z_5 are in parallel and the quantity v_2/v_1 is identifiable as a simple potentiometer or voltage-divider ratio $y_4/(y_2 + y_4 + y_5)$.

To find the transmission of the branch running from i_4 to i_5 in (e), we return to network (a), set loop current i_6 equal to zero, temporarily treat loop current i_4 as a fixed source quantity, and then evaluate the ratio i_5/i_4. Current i_4 induces a voltage $i_4 z_2$ in loop 5 and this mutual

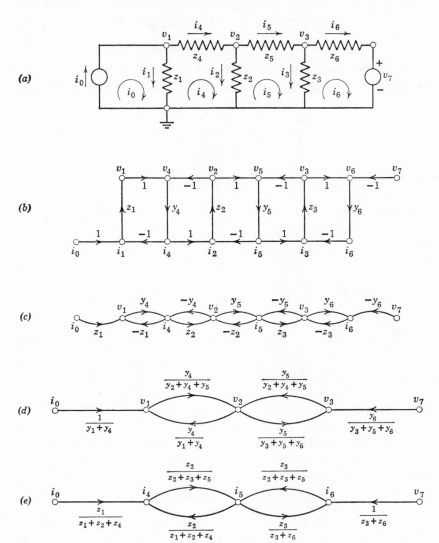

Fig. 5-16. Flow graphs for a ladder network.

induced voltage may then be divided by the self-impedance $(z_2 + z_3 + z_5)$ of loop 5 to find that component of i_5 due to i_4. The result is the branch transmission $z_2/(z_2 + z_3 + z_5)$ appearing in graph (e).

The classical node-voltage equations of the network are

$$v_1(y_1 + y_4) - v_2y_4 = i_0 \qquad (5.42)$$

$$-v_1y_4 + v_2(y_2 + y_4 + y_5) - v_3y_5 = 0 \qquad (5.43)$$

$$-v_2y_5 + v_3(y_3 + y_5 + y_6) = v_7y_6 \qquad (5.44)$$

For interpretation as the flow graph in Fig. 5-16(d), these equations can be put in cause-and-effect form by solving the first equation for v_1 in

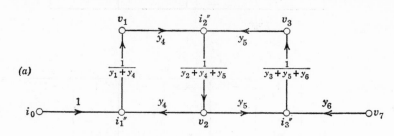

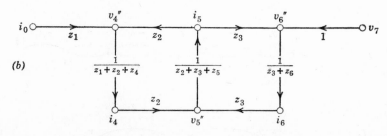

Fig. 5-17. The node-voltage and loop-current flow graphs for a ladder network.

terms of v_2 and i_0, the second equation for v_2 in terms of v_1 and v_3, and the third for v_3 in terms of v_2 and the source voltage v_7. A similar procedure identifies the classical loop-current equations

$$i_4(z_1 + z_2 + z_4) - i_5z_2 = i_0z_1 \qquad (5.45)$$

$$-i_4z_2 + i_5(z_2 + z_3 + z_5) - i_6z_3 = 0 \qquad (5.46)$$

$$-i_5z_3 + i_6(z_3 + z_6) = -v_7 \qquad (5.47)$$

with the flow graph (e). Figure 5-17 shows modified versions of the node-voltage and loop-current flow graphs in which the coefficients in the classical equations are very simply related to the branch transmissions in the graph. Current i_2'' in Fig. 5-17(a) is that current *entering* node 2 in the network *due* to node voltages other than v_2. Since current is conserved at any node, i_2'' may be visualized as flowing *out* of node 2 via the self-impedance of that node $1/(y_2 + y_4 + y_5)$, its product with that impedance being the node voltage v_2. Similarly, voltage v_5'' in Fig. 5-17(b) is the voltage induced in loop 5 by other loop currents, and loop current i_5 is given by the quotient of the induced voltage and the self-impedance of the loop. The flow graphs in Fig. 5-17 reduce to those in Fig. 5-16(d) and (e) upon absorption of the double-primed variables.

5.6   Unilateral Constraints

In Articles 5.4 and 5.5 flow graphs were formulated for reciprocal branch networks. The extension to nonreciprocal networks, such as the linear incremental models of vacuum-tube and transistor circuits, is straightforward. Figure 5-18(a) shows a circuit containing a unilateral transconductance g_m, represented here as a dependent current source $g_m e_g$ controlled by the voltage e_g'. The control voltage is designated by a prime in order to facilitate formulation of the flow graph (b). The prime distinguishes the network *voltage* e_g' from the *number* e_g appearing as a factor in the value of the source current $g_m e_g$. With e_g' thus distinguished from e_g we may imagine temporarily that $g_m e_g$ is an *independent* current source whose relationship to e_g' has not yet been specified. From this viewpoint the circuit in Fig. 5-18(a) is no different from the reciprocal branch networks treated in the previous articles. Choice of the tree $z_1 z_2$ leads to the solid-line portion of the flow graph in Fig. 5-18(b). The arrangement of nodes is the same as that employed in Fig. 5-11, tree variables on the left and link variables on the right. Were $g_m e_g$ actually an independent source current, the solid-line portion of the flow graph would tell the whole story. However since e_g' controls $g_m e_g$, in acccordance with the auxiliary constraint $e_g = e_g'$, we must add the dashed-line branch g_m, as shown. The graph is then complete and any of the variables can be found in terms of the single independent quantity i_0.

Other unilateral constraints, such as the μ of a vacuum triode or the α of a transistor, can be accommodated in exactly the same manner, as illustrated by the remaining parts of Fig. 5-18. The constraint is first removed to allow the dependent source to act as an independent source during the first part of the flow-graph formulation. The constraint can then be included by adding a final branch to the flow graph. In Fig. 5-18, graph (d) is based upon the tree μe_g, r_p, and z_1. Incidentally, graph (d) is not in true primitive form; voltage e_g' has been expressed

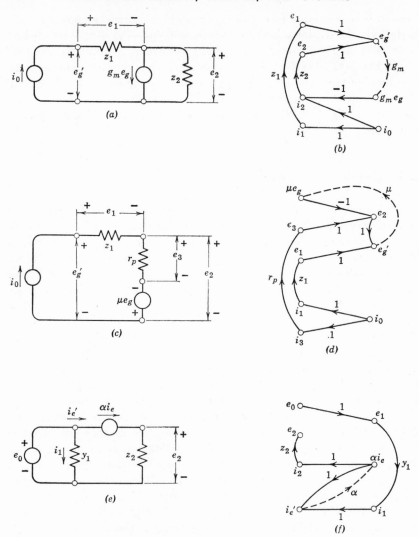

Fig. 5-18. Primitive flow graphs augmented by unilateral constraints.

in terms of e_1 and e_2 for simplicity, rather than in terms of e_1, e_3, and μe_g.

The formulations in Fig. 5-18 have been carried out on the primitive basis but this is not a necessity for circuits containing unilateral elements. Formulations involving smaller sets of variables, such as the loop or node variables, are equally valid and useful. The principle is the same; treat dependent sources as though they were independent and then append flow-graph branches representing the unilateral constraints.

5.7   The Node-Voltage Flow Graph for a Unistor Network

A nonreciprocal network can be treated as a reciprocal branch network in which dependent sources are embedded.   Alternatively, as discussed in Chapter 3, a nonreciprocal circuit can be represented as a

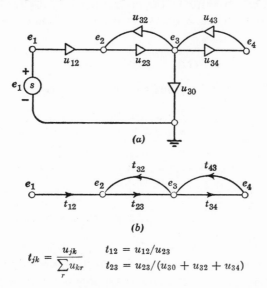

$$t_{jk} = \frac{u_{jk}}{\sum_r u_{kr}} \qquad \begin{aligned} t_{12} &= u_{12}/u_{23} \\ t_{23} &= u_{23}/(u_{30} + u_{32} + u_{34}) \end{aligned}$$

Fig. 5-19.   (a) A unistor network.   (b) The associated flow graph.

network of branchlike unistors, as illustrated in Fig. 5-19(a).   The node potentials of a unistor network must satisfy equations of the general form

$$e_k \sum_r u_{kr} = \sum e_j u_{jk} \tag{5.48}$$

The left-hand side of (5.48) represents current flowing away from node k through the outward-directed unistors.   The right-hand side is the current entering node k from the inward-directed unistors.   To place the general equation in cause-and-effect form, simply rewrite (5.48) to show e_k as an explicit function of the other node potentials e_j:

$$e_k = \sum_j e_j u_{jk} / \sum_r u_{kr} \tag{5.49}$$

This leads immediately to interpretation as a flow graph having branch transmissions t_{jk}, where

$$e_k = \sum e_j t_{jk} \tag{5.50}$$

and

$$t_{jk} = u_{jk}/\sum_r u_{kr} \tag{5.51}$$

Figure 5-19(b) illustrates the fact that the node-voltage flow graph for a unistor network has, after erasure of the unistors leading to ground, the same topological structure as the unistor network itself. By inspection of the flow graph in Fig. 5-19, the transmission from e_1 to e_4 is

$$\frac{e_4}{e_1} = \frac{t_{12}t_{23}t_{34}}{1 - t_{23}t_{32} - t_{34}t_{43}} \tag{5.52}$$

and after substitution according to (5.51), we have

$$\frac{e_4}{e_1} = \frac{\dfrac{u_{12}u_{23}u_{34}}{u_{23}(u_{30} + u_{32} + u_{34})u_{43}}}{1 - \dfrac{u_{23}u_{32}}{(u_{30} + u_{32} + u_{34})u_{23}} - \dfrac{u_{34}u_{43}}{u_{43}(u_{30} + u_{32} + u_{34})}} \tag{5.53}$$

which reduces to

$$\frac{e_4}{e_1} = \frac{u_{12}u_{23}u_{34}}{u_{30}u_{23}u_{43}} = \frac{u_{12}u_{34}}{u_{30}u_{43}} \tag{5.54}$$

With voltage source e_1 collapsed in Fig. 5-19(a), the only proper unistor tree is $u_{30}u_{23}u_{43}$. The flow-graph determinant involves loops whereas the unistor-network determinant is made up of trees. Consider an arbitrary flow-graph loop such as

$$t_{jk}t_{ki}t_{ij} = \frac{u_{jk}u_{ki}u_{ij}}{\left(\sum_r u_{kr}\right)\left(\sum_r u_{ir}\right)\left(\sum_r u_{jr}\right)} \tag{5.55}$$

The denominator in (5.55) contains the term $u_{jk}u_{ki}u_{ij}$. Hence, when the loop transmission $t_{jk}t_{ki}t_{ij}$ is subtracted from unity and the result collected over a single common denominator, the closed loop of unistors disappears from the resulting numerator. With unistor loops excluded, only unistor trees can remain. By such arguments the topological transmission rules for unistor networks can be deduced from the flow-graph transmission law. In short, the unistor rules and flow-graph rules are intimately related and (5.51) is the key relationship through which either one can be deduced from the other.

Figure 5-19 tells how to construct a flow graph for a unistor network. In Fig. 5-20 we turn the problem around and ask for a unistor network (b) corresponding to a given node-voltage flow graph (a). The syn-

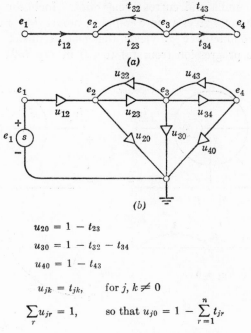

$$u_{20} = 1 - t_{23}$$

$$u_{30} = 1 - t_{32} - t_{34}$$

$$u_{40} = 1 - t_{43}$$

$$u_{jk} = t_{jk}, \qquad \text{for } j, k \neq 0$$

$$\sum_r u_{jr} = 1, \qquad \text{so that } u_{j0} = 1 - \sum_{r=1}^{n} t_{jr}$$

Fig. 5-20. (a) A flow graph. (b) An equivalent unistor network.

thesis problem has a very simple solution. Let

$$\sum_r u_{jr} = 1 \tag{5.56}$$

at every network node j other than ground and the driving point. Under this assumption it follows immediately from (5.51) that

$$t_{jk} = u_{jk} \tag{5.57}$$

for all unistors not connected to ground. The unistors u_{j0} that *are* directed into the ground node can then be adjusted in value to satisfy (5.56). This completes the synthesis as illustrated in Fig. 5-20(b).

5.8 Basic Transistor and Vacuum-Triode Models

The examples in this article are intended to draw together and further illustrate the principles of flow-graph formulation developed in the preceding articles. Figure 5-21(a) is a crude linear incremental model of the transistor. The flow graph (c) has two unity branches accounting for conservation of current at the central junction and an α branch representing a unilateral current constraint. Inclusion of the emitter and base resistances gives a more complete model (b). Finally, addition of collector conductance g_c yields the general model shown in Fig. 5-22(a). The progression from (c) to (d) in Fig. 5-21 and thence to

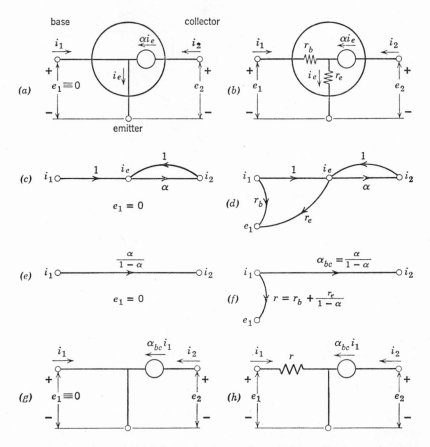

Fig. 5-21. The common-emitter transistor with negligible collector conductance. (a) An approximate circuit model. (c) The corresponding flow graph. (e) The terminal residue. (g) An equivalent circuit. (b), (d), (f), (h) The same sequence with emitter and base resistances included.

part (b) of Fig. 5-22 illustrates a general approach which might be called *flow-graph formulation by approximation and correction*. In a typical transistor under usual operating conditions, the base resistance, the emitter resistance, and the collector conductance are all small. By this we mean that the products $r_b g_c$ and $r_e g_c$ are less than unity by one or

more orders of magnitude.   Hence the circuit model and the flow graph
in Fig. 5-21(a) and (c) represent a reasonable first approximation to the
analysis of the network shown in Fig. 5-22(a).   The formulation is

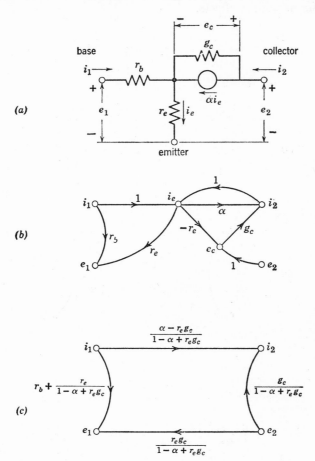

Fig. 5-22.   The common-emitter transistor model.

carried out with a view toward the forward-current-transfer-basis
terminal residue indicated in Fig. 5-22(c) which suggests that we treat
i_1 as a current source and e_2 as a voltage source.   Consequently, i_1
appears as a source node in Fig. 5-21(c).   Flow-graph branches may
then be added, as in Fig. 5-22(b), to *correct* the *approximate* values of
e_1 and i_2 indicated in Fig. 5-21(c).

Flow-graph formulation by approximation and correction is a non-
systematic process requiring judgment on the part of the user.   In

analyzing a circuit or network one should first attempt to recognize the major interactions (usually closely related to the function that circuit is designed to perform) and then correct the approximate flow graph to account for secondary effects.

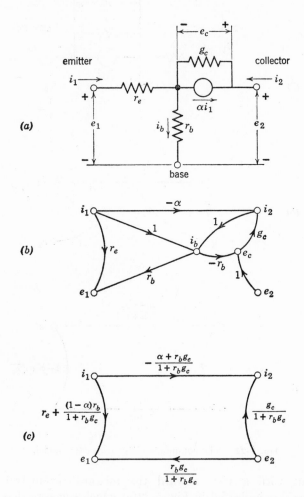

Fig. 5-23. The common-base transistor model.

Approximation-and-correction formulation is more an attitude than a definite process. If a circuit is too complicated to analyze by inspection, then simply *erase* or *collapse* some of the circuit elements until only the important skeleton remains. Make corrections *later, after* you have constructed an understandable and meaningful approximate flow graph.

A knowledge of some of the general properties of primitive flow graphs (Articles 5.4, 5.5, and 5.6) is sometimes a help and a guide in

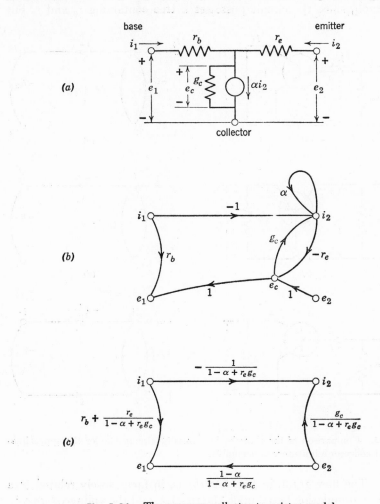

Fig. 5-24. The common-collector transistor model.

those problems where the primitive formulation is not followed in detail. In beginning the construction of a flow graph for the circuit in Fig. 5-22(a), for example, we might first decide that it would be desirable to have resistances r_b and r_e and conductance g_c (rather than conductances g_b and g_e and resistance r_c) appear as transmissions in the flow graph (the flow graph will be more meaningful and easier to interpret if minor effects in the circuit appear as small transmissions in the flow graph). A knowledge of primitive graphs enables us to recognize at the outset that r_b, r_e, and g_c *can* be made to appear as transmissions in the flow graph, since the circuit possesses a tree containing r_b and r_e but

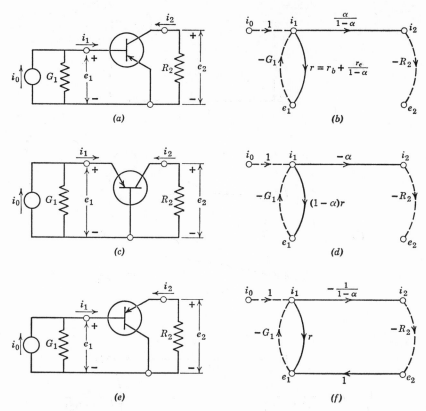

Fig. 5-25. Comparison of the three basic transistor circuits, under the approximation that collector admittance is negligible.

not g_c. The flow graph in Fig. 5-22(b) is, in fact, closely related to a primitive formulation based upon the tree $r_b r_e$ and the voltage source e_2.

Figures 5-23 through 5-33 continue with the flow-graph representations of various other basic transistor and vacuum-triode circuits. All the circuits discussed here are linear incremental models. Hence polarizing or biasing arrangements do not appear in Figs. 5-25 and 5-33. Some of the vacuum-triode formulas are presented on both the voltage-source (μ) basis and the current-source (g_m) basis. For comparison, observe that the voltage amplifications e_2/e_1 of the three basic triode circuits all become very simple formulas when expressed in terms of g_m, g_p, and the load g_2, as in Fig. 5-26(f), Fig. 5-29(b), and Fig. 5-31(b).

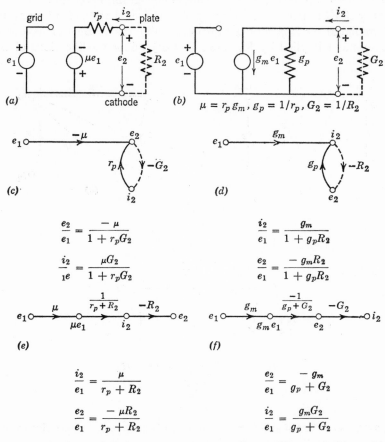

Fig. 5-26. Analysis of the common-cathode triode amplifier. (*a*) The voltage-source model. (*b*) The current-source model. (*c*), (*d*), (*e*), (*f*) Associated flow graphs.

Figure 5-27 shows the effect of grid-to-plate admittance, an effect that becomes significant at high frequencies because of interelectrode and stray grid-to-plate capacitance. Figures 5-26(*e*) and 5-29(*a*) offer an interesting comparison of the cathode follower and the common-cathode amplifier. Figure 5-30 reiterates a point made previously in connection with the first figure of this chapter. Although e_g is not the primary physical source in Fig. 5-28(*a*), we may begin the formulation by *assuming* a value of e_g and then construct a graph that gives the value of the physical source e_1 required to produce the assumed value of e_g. The resulting ratio of e_2 to e_1 is the same as that in Fig. 5-29(a), and the two graphs are related through a simple flow-graph inversion.

Figure 5-31 illustrates the very important fact that when a flow graph is formulated for a given experiment, such as the voltage transmission measurement implied by Fig. 5-31(a), only minor modifications of the

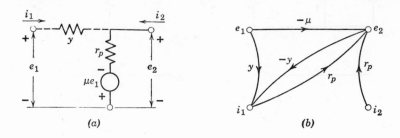

(a)   (b)

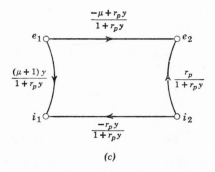

(c)

Fig. 5-27.   The effect of grid-to-plate admittance in a common-cathode triode model.

flow graph are required in order to accommodate it to a slightly different experiment, such as the output-impedance measurement depicted in Fig. 5-31(c). Replacement of the load resistance R_2 in (a) by the voltage source shown in (c) is equivalent to erasure of the conductance branch in (b) to obtain the output-impedance graph (d).

Figures 5-25 and 5-33 show that the three basic triode circuits are approximate duals of their respective transistor counterparts. The dual of a circuit is another circuit whose equilibrium equations look exactly like those of the original circuit when current and voltage are interchanged. [The *exact* dual of Fig. 5-25(b), the common-emitter tran-

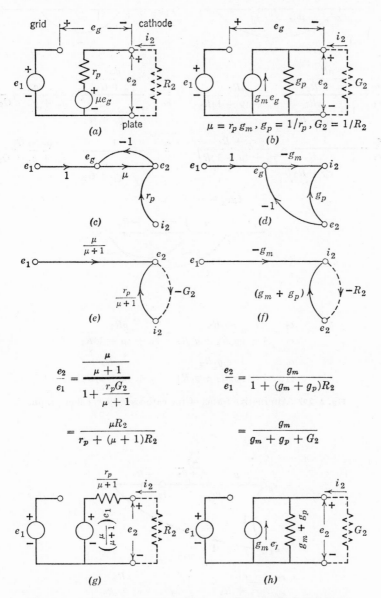

Fig. 5-28. The common-plate triode amplifier (cathode follower).

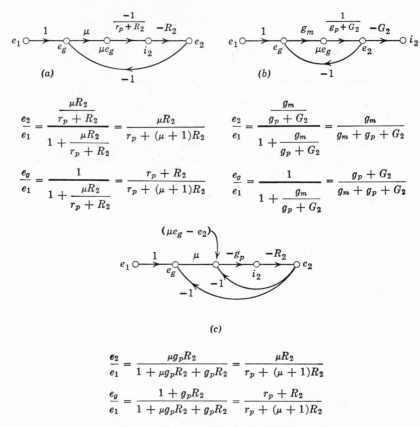

$$\frac{e_2}{e_1} = \frac{\dfrac{\mu R_2}{r_p + R_2}}{1 + \dfrac{\mu R_2}{r_p + R_2}} = \frac{\mu R_2}{r_p + (\mu + 1)R_2}$$

$$\frac{e_g}{e_1} = \frac{1}{1 + \dfrac{\mu R_2}{r_p + R_2}} = \frac{r_p + R_2}{r_p + (\mu + 1)R_2}$$

$$\frac{e_2}{e_1} = \frac{\dfrac{g_m}{g_p + G_2}}{1 + \dfrac{g_m}{g_p + G_2}} = \frac{g_m}{g_m + g_p + G_2}$$

$$\frac{e_g}{e_1} = \frac{1}{1 + \dfrac{g_m}{g_p + G_2}} = \frac{g_p + G_2}{g_m + g_p + G_2}$$

$$\frac{e_2}{e_1} = \frac{\mu g_p R_2}{1 + \mu g_p R_2 + g_p R_2} = \frac{\mu R_2}{r_p + (\mu + 1)R_2}$$

$$\frac{e_g}{e_1} = \frac{1 + g_p R_2}{1 + \mu g_p R_2 + g_p R_2} = \frac{r_p + R_2}{r_p + (\mu + 1)R_2}$$

Fig. 5-29. Alternative forms of the cathode-follower flow graph.

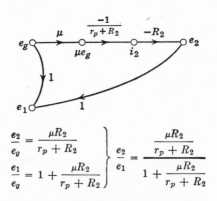

$$\left.\begin{aligned}\frac{e_2}{e_g} &= \frac{\mu R_2}{r_p + R_2} \\ \frac{e_1}{e_g} &= 1 + \frac{\mu R_2}{r_p + R_2}\end{aligned}\right\} \qquad \frac{e_2}{e_1} = \frac{\dfrac{\mu R_2}{r_p + R_2}}{1 + \dfrac{\mu R_2}{r_p + R_2}}$$

Fig. 5-30. Another formulation of the cathode-follower flow graph.

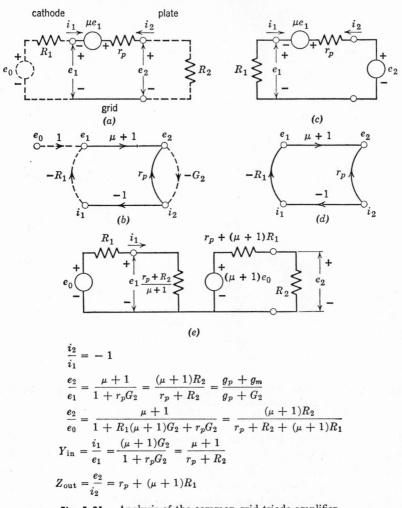

Fig. 5-31. Analysis of the common-grid triode amplifier.

$$\frac{i_2}{i_1} = -1$$

$$\frac{e_2}{e_1} = \frac{\mu + 1}{1 + r_p G_2} = \frac{(\mu + 1)R_2}{r_p + R_2} = \frac{g_p + g_m}{g_p + G_2}$$

$$\frac{e_2}{e_0} = \frac{\mu + 1}{1 + R_1(\mu + 1)G_2 + r_p G_2} = \frac{(\mu + 1)R_2}{r_p + R_2 + (\mu + 1)R_1}$$

$$Y_{\text{in}} = \frac{i_1}{e_1} = \frac{(\mu + 1)G_2}{1 + r_p G_2} = \frac{\mu + 1}{r_p + R_2}$$

$$Z_{\text{out}} = \frac{e_2}{i_2} = r_p + (\mu + 1)R_1$$

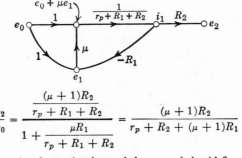

$$\frac{e_2}{e_0} = \frac{\dfrac{(\mu + 1)R_2}{r_p + R_1 + R_2}}{1 + \dfrac{\mu R_1}{r_p + R_1 + R_2}} = \frac{(\mu + 1)R_2}{r_p + R_2 + (\mu + 1)R_1}$$

Fig. 5-32. An alternative form of the grounded-grid flow graph.

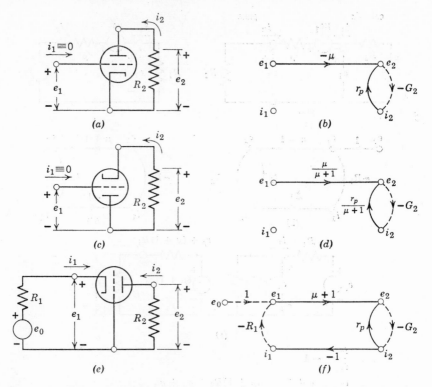

Fig. 5-33. Comparison of the three basic triode circuits, under the approximation that grid-to-plate and grid-to-cathode admittances are negligible.

sistor, would be a triode with zero plate resistance but nonzero grid-to-cathode conductance.] The forward current-transfer representation is convenient for the basic transistor circuits because each of these circuits has a significant short-circuit forward-current-transmission ratio, small short-circuit input resistance, and small open-circuit output conductance. The dual of this statement holds for the three basic triode circuits, so that the forward-voltage-transfer representation is more convenient. The duality between Figs. 5-25 and 5-33 stands out even more strongly when we evaluate the short-circuit forward-current-transmission ratios of the transistor in terms of the base-to-collector current-amplification factor α_{bc}.

$$\frac{\alpha}{1 - \alpha} = \alpha_{bc} \tag{5.58}$$

$$\alpha = \frac{\alpha_{bc}}{\alpha_{bc} + 1} \tag{5.59}$$

$$\frac{1}{1-\alpha} = \alpha_{bc} + 1 \qquad (5.69)$$

Figures 5-25, 5-33, and relations (5.58) through (5.60) show that the base-to-collector current-amplification factor of the transistor is analogous to the dual of the grid-to-plate voltage-amplification factor of the triode.

5.9   The Cathode-Coupled Amplifier

In this article and the two following articles, the analysis of three different vacuum-tube amplifiers provides further illustration of flow-graph formulation. Analysis of the cathode-coupled amplifier in Fig. 5-34(a) starts from the linear incremental circuit model (b). One way

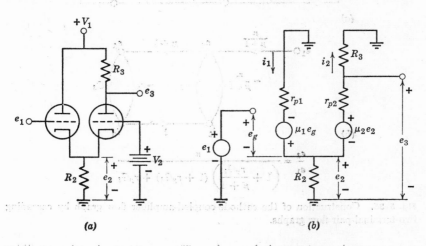

(a)   (b)

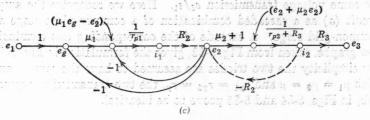

(c)

$$\frac{e_3}{e_1} = \frac{\dfrac{\mu_1 R_2}{r_{p1}}\left[\dfrac{(\mu_2+1)R_3}{r_{p2}+R_3}\right]}{1 + \dfrac{(\mu_1+1)R_2}{r_{p1}} + \dfrac{(\mu_2+1)R_2}{r_{p2}+R_3}}$$

Fig. 5-34. The cathode-coupled amplifier; a cathode follower driving a grounded-grid stage.

to approach the analysis of this circuit is to imagine that resistance R_2 has been temporarily replaced by a voltage source e_2. Currents i_1 and i_2 can then be formulated in terms of e_1 and e_2 as indicated by the solid-line branches in Fig. 5-34(c). Upon replacement of the voltage source e_2 by the resistance R_2, we can complete the graph with the two dashed-line branches which state that e_2 is produced by the difference of i_1 and i_2 flowing in resistance R_2. Figure 5-35 shows another way of calculating

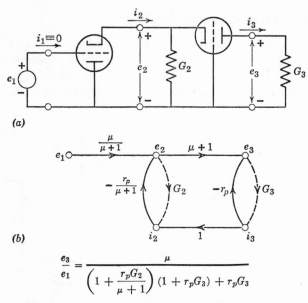

$$\frac{e_3}{e_1} = \frac{\mu}{\left(1 + \dfrac{r_p G_2}{\mu + 1}\right)(1 + r_p G_3) + r_p G_3}$$

Fig. 5-35. Construction of the cathode-coupled-amplifier flow graph by cascading two-terminal-pair flow graphs.

the same voltage transmission e_3/e_1. Here we recognize the amplifier circuit (a) as a cascaded combination of a common-plate stage and a common-grid stage. A cascade of the corresponding two-terminal-pair flow graphs, taken from Fig. 5-33, gives the formulation in Fig. 5-35(b). For simplicity the two triodes are assumed to have the same μ and r_p. With $\mu_1 = \mu_2 = \mu$ and $r_{p1} = r_{p2} = r_p$, the two transmission expressions e_3/e_1 in Figs. 5-34 and 5-35 prove to be identical.

5.10 The Cascode Amplifier

Figure 5-36 shows (a) the cascode amplifier and (b) the linear incremental circuit model applicable in some middle range of frequencies.

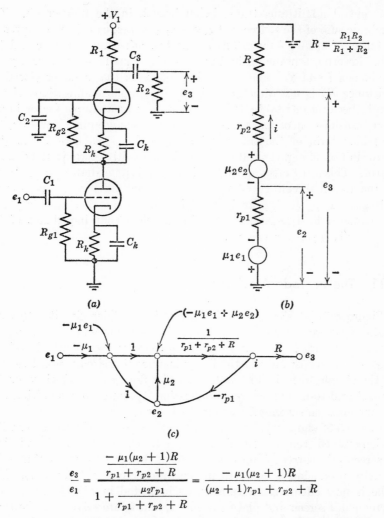

Fig. 5-36. The "cascode" circuit; a grounded-cathode stage driving a grounded-grid stage. (*a*) The *RC*-coupled circuit. (*b*) The incremental model for middle frequencies. (*c*) A flow graph.

This amplifier, like the cathode-coupled amplifier, can be analyzed as a cascade of two basic triode configurations. For variety of illustration, let us begin instead with a process of cause-and-effect reasoning which leads to the flow graph shown in (*c*). One possible line of reasoning runs as follows. The current i is caused by the two source voltages $\mu_1 e_1$ and $\mu_2 e_2$ acting upon the series resistance $r_{p1} + r_{p2} + R$. This gives us the central admittance-transmission branch in the flow graph. The algebraic sum of the source voltages $-\mu_1 e_1 + \mu_2 e_2$ can then be expressed in terms of e_1 and i by means of the two left-hand branches and the three lowermost branches in Fig. 5-36(c). Finally e_3 is given by the product of i and R. The output impedance of the amplifier (faced by resistance R) is not directly available by simple modifications of this graph, because resistance R does not appear as a simple factor in the loop transmission of any node or branch in the graph. However, the simplified form of the transmission expression e_3/e_1 contains R as a factor in the numerator and also as a single additive term in the denominator. This form, after multiplication by e_1, is immediately recognizable as the terminal voltage of a non-ideal source having an open-circuit voltage $-\mu_1(\mu_2 + 1)e_1$, an internal impedance $(\mu_2 + 1)r_{p1} + r_{p2}$, and an attached load resistance R. Hence the output impedance of the amplifier is $(\mu_2 + 1)r_{p1} + r_{p2}$.

5.11   The Pentode Amplifier

Figure 5-37(a) shows a typical pentode amplifier circuit. In some medium range of frequencies, where the coupling and bypass capacitances C_1, C_k, C_s, and C_2 have negligible reactance, the screen-grid voltage is essentially constant and the linear incremental circuit model reduces to the simple form in Fig. 5-37(b). The flow graph (c) gives us the control-grid-to-plate voltage amplification A_{gp} under the condition that the incremental screen-grid voltage e_2 is zero.

Figure 5-38 shows what happens when the screen-grid bypass capacitor C_s is removed from the circuit in Fig. 5-37(a). Incremental variations in screen-grid current i_s must now flow in the screen load resistance R_2, thereby producing a non-zero incremental screen-grid signal e_s. The tube is now effectively a tetrode, as indicated in Fig. 5-38(a). The incremental screen and plate currents i_s and i_p are related to the three terminal voltages through the six conductance parameters shown in Fig. 5-38(b). This flow graph may in fact be taken as a definition of the conductance parameters. Addition of the screen and plate load resistances, as in (c), leads to the complete flow graph (d) from which we can find the voltage transmission e_p/e_g.

A somewhat simpler formulation can be obtained by working in terms of the special voltage-transmission ratios A_{jk}, instead of the conductance parameters and load resistances. Quantity A_{jk} is defined as the voltage-transmission ratio from terminal j to terminal k under the special condition that terminal voltages other than j or k are set equal to zero. The flow graph in Fig. 5-38 serves as a definition of the parameters A_{jk}. The plate voltage e_p can be visualized as a superposition of two effects, one due to e_g and the other due to e_s. Similarly, e_s is a superposition of effects due to e_g and e_p. To interpret one of the

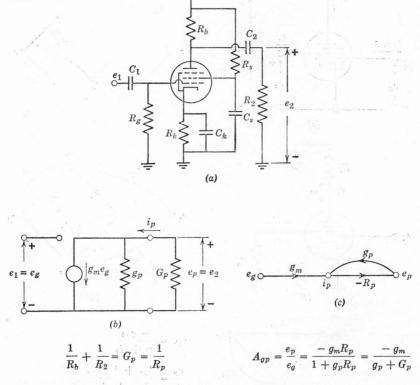

$$\frac{1}{R_b} + \frac{1}{R_2} = G_p = \frac{1}{R_p}$$

$$A_{gp} = \frac{e_p}{e_g} = \frac{-g_m R_p}{1 + g_p R_p} = \frac{-g_m}{g_p + G_p}$$

Fig. 5-37. A pentode amplifier. (a) The RC-coupled circuit. (b) The middle-frequency incremental circuit model. (c) The flow graph.

A-parameters, say a_{gp}, as a physical measurement, we observe from the flow graph that A_{gp} is just equal to the ratio e_p/e_g provided e_s is held at the value zero. The corresponding physical measurement involves setting R_s equal to zero in Fig. 5-38(c) and then measuring the transmission from e_g to e_p, with R_p in place. The flow graph (e) is, of course, obtainable from the flow graph (d) by absorption of nodes i_p and i_s and elimination of the resulting self-loops at nodes e_s and e_p.

The plate-to-screen transconductance g_{ps} of a pentode is actually a negative number (increasing the plate voltage modifies the electric field in the neighborhood of the screen-grid wires and thereby decreases the fraction of cathode current captured by the screen. This effect predominates over the exceedingly small increase in cathode current produced by an increase in the plate voltage). The other conductance

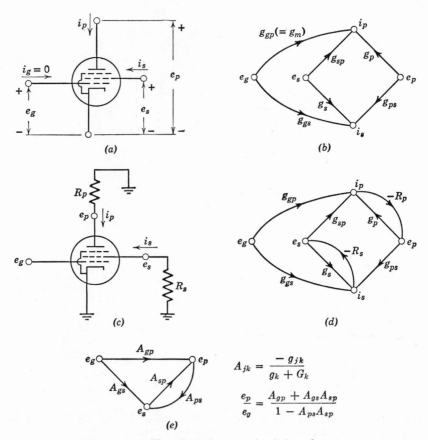

Fig. 5-38. The effect of screen-circuit impedance.

parameters of the pentode are all positive. It follows that A_{pg} is positive and that all of the other A-parameters are negative. The transmission expression e_p/e_g in Fig. 5-38(e) tells us, therefore, that the presence of series resistance R_s in the screen-grid circuit of a pentode amplifier tends to reduce the grid-to-plate voltage amplification of the circuit.

Flow-graph representations of circuit and systems problems in Chapters 7 and 9 provide further examples of the process of flow-graph formulation.

PROBLEMS

5.1 The circuit model in Fig. 5-6 is to be used as a representation of the common-emitter transistor connection. Evaluate the parameters of the model in terms of the transistor parameters r_e, r_b, r_c, and a.

5.2 Repeat Problem 5.1 for the common-base connection.

5.3 Repeat Problem 5.1 for the common-collector connection.

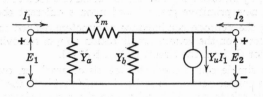

Fig. P5-1

5.4 The dual of the circuit model in Fig. 5-6 is shown in Fig. P5-1. Evaluate the parameters in the model in terms of the vacuum-triode parameters μ and r_p, for use of the model as a representation of the common-cathode triode connection.

5.5 Repeat Problem 5.4 for the common-plate (cathode-follower) connection.

5.6 Repeat Problem 5.4 for the common-grid connection.

5.7 How would you modify the models in Problems 5.4 through 5.6 to include the effects of interelectrode capacitance?

5.8 Using the forward-current-transfer ("h-parameter") flow-graph representation, Fig. 5-3(d), for each transistor, find the equivalent forward-current-transfer parameters of an amplifier consisting of two common-emitter transistors in cascade. Substitute suitable numerical values taken from published data on a chosen transistor type operating at low frequency.

5.9 Repeat Problem 5.8 for a common-emitter transistor driving a common-collector transistor in cascade.

5.10 Repeat Problem 5.8 for two common-collector transistors in cascade.

5.11 Using the forward-voltage-transfer representation, Fig. 5-3(c), for each triode, discuss the important properties of each of the nine different amplifiers comprising all possible two-triode cascade combinations of the three basic triode connections.

5.12 A full bridge circuit (including detector-arm and source-arm impedances) has the configuration of a tetrahedron, with each branch corresponding to an edge of the tetrahedron.

(a) Choose a tree and construct a primitive flow graph.

(b) Find, from the graph, the source-to-detector transmission of the bridge.

(c) Reduce the flow graph to obtain a new graph corresponding to a set of node-pair voltage equations.

(d) Reduce the primitive graph to a new graph corresponding to a set of loop-current equations.

5.13   Two identical common-collector transistors are connected in a cascade consisting of a current source (having a shunt resistance in parallel), an ideal transformer, the first transistor, an ideal transformer, the second transistor, another ideal transformer, and the load resistance.   Discuss the possibility of maximizing the over-all current amplification of the system by adjustment of the turns ratios of the three transformers.   Consider two cases:

(a)   The transistor has $r_e = r_b = 0$ and r_c is neither zero nor infinite.

(b)   The transistor has infinite r_c but nonzero r_e and r_b.

In each case, formulate the problem on the forward-current-transfer basis.

5.14   Show, by an example, that the inversion of a loop in a primitive flow graph gives a new primitive graph based upon a different choice of a tree.

5.15   Using the pentode conductance parameters defined in Fig. 5-38(b), discuss the effect upon the voltage amplification e_2/e_1 of removing the cathode bypass capacitor C_k from the circuit in Fig. 5-37(a).

5.16   For a simple common-emitter transistor amplifier, construct a flow graph from the unistor-network model and verify that both the flow-graph and the unistor-network transmission rules give the same voltage amplification.

5.17   A gyrator is an ideal two-terminal-pair element characterized by a short-circuit admittance matrix in which $Y_{11} = Y_{22} = 0$ and $Y_{12} = -Y_{21} = G$, where G is a real conductance.

(a)   Draw a suitable flow graph and from it find the input impedance of the gyrator when a load impedance Z_L is attached across the output terminals.

(b)   Modify the flow graph to include an additional conductance G_0 attached as indicated in Fig. P5-2(a).   Show that the resulting two-terminal-

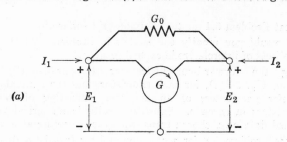

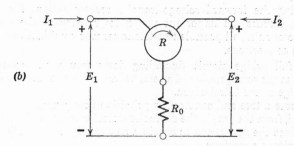

Fig. P5-2

pair circuit can be made unilateral by proper choice of G_0, and find the forward-voltage-transfer parameters of the "unilateralized" circuit.

(c)   Repeat for the dual case indicated in Fig. P5-2(b.) Here it is more convenient to work with open-circuit impedances.

5.18   A *negative impedance converter* is an ideal two-terminal-pair element characterized by the relation $E_1I_1 \equiv E_2I_2$, where polarities are defined as in Fig. 5-2(a) of the text.   The simplest special case is $E_1 = E_2$.

(a)   Draw a forward-voltage-transfer flow graph and show that a load impedance Z_L at the output terminals reflects at the input terminals as an apparent input impedance $-Z_L$.

(b)   In what ways is a negative impedance converter similar to and different from an ideal transformer?

(c)   Change to the new choice of terminal pairs indicated in Fig. 5-7(b) and describe the converter in terms of forward-voltage-transfer parameters based upon the new variables.   Synthesize the associated circuit model, as shown in Fig. 5-3(c).   Compare this model with that obtained from Fig. 5-3(c) *without* first changing to new terminal pairs.

(d)   Repeat the entire problem for the *dual* case $I_2 = -I_1$.   Remember to "dualize" (interchange the words "voltage" and "current") in the statement of the problem.

5.19   On the basis of Fig. 5-4(e) and (f), construct a suitable flow graph for a ladder network having three series branches and four shunt branches. From the flow graph, calculate the open-circuit transfer impedance of the ladder.   Let all branch impedances have the value z for simplicity.

5.20   Discuss the statement, "In a voltage amplifier consisting of cascaded stages, the input admittance may possibly be influenced appreciably by changes in the load impedance, even though the per-stage reverse current amplification is very small in comparison to unity."

C H A P T E R   S I X

Signal Analysis

6.1 Introduction

A signal is the physical embodiment of a message. Music, news, and orders are examples of messages sent by people. Nature also transmits messages; the frequency of radiation from a radio star tells the astronomer something about that star; the terminal voltage produced by the random motion of electrons within a resistor contains information about the temperature of that resistor. Natural messages are classified by man as either desirable or undesirable depending entirely upon whether they help or interfere with what he is trying to do.

The word "signal" may designate a physical variable, the time variation of the variable, or some characteristic of that time variation. In electronic circuits and systems the signals of interest are usually either voltage or current, although other quantities such as the charge on a capacitor, the magnetic flux in an inductor, or the deflection of a spot on the face of a cathode-ray tube may also be of interest as signals. Electronic systems are designed to perform linear or nonlinear operations upon an input signal to produce an output signal, which may differ from the original input in some desirable manner and which also always differs unavoidably from the original in some undesirable fashion. Figure 6-1 (b) shows a signal containing a message pulse (a) plus unwanted contamination tending to interfere with our recognition of the message.

In order to evaluate or design an electronic circuit or system, we must first know something about how to characterize the communication and control signals upon which it will feed and operate. Any signal can be recorded as a curve of signal value versus time, as in Fig. 6-1. For some signals the time-function plot tells us all we want to know about the signal. In general, however, the signal may be more conveniently described in terms of certain other characteristics derived from the time function. In particular, a signal can be resolved into elemental periodic components having different frequencies, such that the total signal is

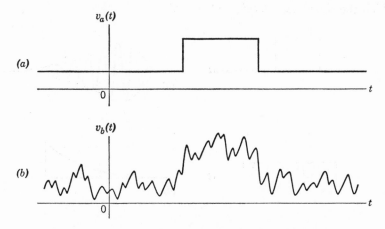

Fig. 6-1. Plots of two signals. (a) A transmitted signal. (b) A received signal.

the sum of these components. The resolution of a signal into *additive* components is especially suitable for the study of systems that perform *linear* operations on the signal, since a linear system operates independently upon each component, just as though other components were not present, and the total output signal of the system is therefore easy to calculate (at least in principle) by simple addition. A very large class of important operations, including amplification, filtration, and many types of frequency conversion, are inherently linear. Moreover, the frequency-component description of the signal is also convenient for the study of many basic nonlinear operations. Consider, for example, a system whose output signal at any time is the square of the value of the input signal at that time. Frequency resolution of the signal permits us to state that the output signal "contains frequencies" that are the sums and differences of the frequencies contained in the input signal.

This chapter begins with a general discussion of additive signal components that serves as a background for the following development of Fourier analysis. The last part of the chapter is devoted to illustrative applications of the theory.

6.2   Pulse Signals

Qualitatively, a pulse signal is one whose value is negligibly small except in some finite region of the time scale, as illustrated by the examples in Fig. 6-2. A pulse signal is "epochal" in character; there exists an epoch or locality somewhere along the infinite time scale at which the signal can be said to "occur."

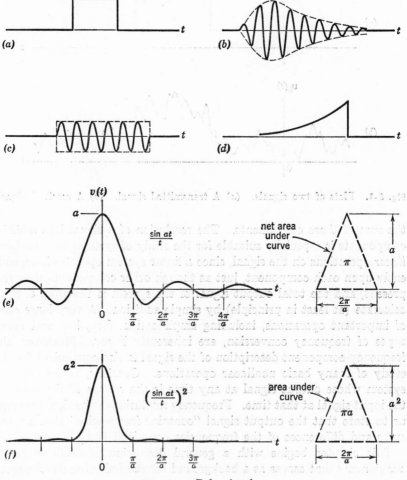

Fig. 6-2. Pulse signals.

If a voltage pulse is applied across a unit inductance, the integral of that signal is a measure of the resulting change in the inductor current. On the other hand, a current signal applied to a unit capacitance delivers an amount of charge equal to the signal integral. Hence the integral

$$\int_{-\infty}^{\infty} v(t) \, dt \equiv \int v \, dt \tag{6.1}$$

is an important parameter of a pulse signal. For simplicity of notation we shall sometimes omit the limits of integration; it is understood that the limits are infinite unless otherwise specified.

Another important parameter of a pulse signal is the *integral square* of its magnitude, which we shall call the *energy* of the signal

$$\text{energy} = \int |v|^2 \, dt \tag{6.2}$$

For a voltage or current signal the integral square is a measure of the amount of energy delivered to a unit resistance by that signal. We shall in fact define a *pulse signal* or *energy signal* as any signal whose energy is *nonzero* and *finite*

$$0 < \int |v|^2 \, dt < \infty \tag{6.3}$$

The signal recorded in Fig. 6-2(e) and its square (f) are pulse forms which play a central role in some of the analysis later in the chapter. For *both* of these pulse forms it happens that the net area under the curve is just equal to the area of a triangle whose three vertices lie at the maximum of the function and at the first zeros of the function on either side of the maximum. Hence signal (e) in Fig. 6-2 has an integral π and an energy πa.

The "Gaussian" pulse in Fig. 6-3(a) is another basic signal for which we shall have much further use. Observe that the shape of the pulse is approximated with remarkable accuracy by a triangle of the same maximum height and the same area. The *unit impulse* $u_0(t)$ is defined as the limiting form of the Gaussian pulse:

$$u_0(t) = \lim_{t_0 \to 0} \left[\frac{1}{t_0} e^{-\pi \left(\frac{t}{t_0} \right)^2} \right] \tag{6.4}$$

The unit impulse is infinitely high, infinitesimally narrow, and is characterized by its unit area

$$\int u_0 \, dt = 1 \tag{6.5}$$

The unit impulse will be depicted as a narrow heavy vertical bar as in Fig. 6-3(b). Since the energy in a pulse of given shape is proportional to the width and to the square of the height, it follows that the energy of a unit impulse is infinite

$$\int u_0{}^2 \, dt = \infty \tag{6.6}$$

However, we tend to think in terms of the limiting process rather than the limit itself,* and from this viewpoint an approximation to the unit

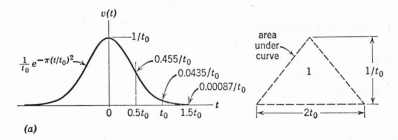

(a)

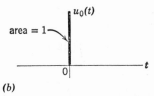

(b)

Fig. 6-3. The Gaussian pulse (a) and the unit impulse (b).

impulse has arbitrarily large, but finite, energy and therefore remains in the category of pulse signals.

6.3   Periodic Signals

A periodic signal is one that exhibits cyclic repetition at regular intervals as time progresses, as exemplified by the waves in Fig. 6-4. A periodic signal can be defined as any signal for which

$$v(t) = v(t + T), \quad \text{for all } t \tag{6.7}$$

The smallest constant T which satisfies (6.7) is called the *period* of the signal. By iteration of relationship (6.7) we have

$$v(t) = v(t + nT), \quad n = 0, \pm 1, \pm 2, \cdots \tag{6.8}$$

---

* As a student once said, "The unit impulse is a thing that is so small you can't see it, except at one place, where it is so big you can't see it. In other words, you can't see it at all; at least I can't."

Once we know the behavior of a periodic signal over a time interval T, its entire past is known and its future behavior is predictable. Hence a periodic signal is an inefficient message vehicle; once we have heard a full period of the signal we might as well stop listening. Nevertheless, periodic signals are of great importance in system analysis because a

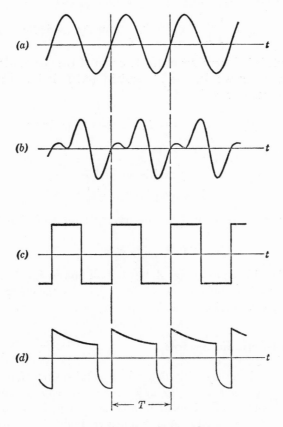

Fig. 6-4. Periodic signals.

knowledge of the response of a system to a periodic signal enables us to deduce much about the response of that system to other classes of signals.

The integral of a periodic signal is either indeterminate or infinite. The *time mean* or *time average* exists, however, and is defined as

$$\langle v \rangle = \lim_{a \to \infty} \frac{1}{2a} \int_{-a}^{a} v(t) \, dt \tag{6.9}$$

Time averaging is a general operation which may be applied to any signal, periodic or not. Henceforth, piecewise-linear bracketing around any quantity v indicates that v is a function of time and that $\langle v \rangle$ is computed according to the definition (6.9).

For periodic signals the average over all time is the same as the average over one period T

$$\langle v \rangle = \frac{1}{T} \int_{t_1}^{t_1+T} v(t) \, dt, \qquad \text{for } v(t) \text{ periodic} \qquad (6.10)$$

and the result is independent of the location of that period-long interval of time. In other words, the integral in (6.10) is independent of t_1. Hence (6.10) may be replaced by

$$\langle v \rangle = \frac{1}{T} \int_{-T/2}^{T/2} v(t) \, dt, \qquad \text{for } v(t) \text{ periodic} \qquad (6.11)$$

without loss of generality.

The *average power* of any signal is defined as

$$\text{average power} = \langle |v|^2 \rangle \qquad (6.12)$$

and a *power signal* is defined as one having nonzero but finite average power

$$0 < \langle |v|^2 \rangle < \infty \qquad (6.13)$$

A periodic signal is a power signal, but not all power signals are periodic. For a periodic signal the average power is given by the energy per period multiplied by the number of periods per second.

6.4   Almost-Periodic Signals

An almost-periodic signal is defined as a finite sum of periodic components (or, more generally, as any signal that can be approximated arbitrarily closely for all time by a finite sum of periodic components). Thus every periodic signal is also "almost periodic" but the converse is not necessarily true. For example, consider

$$\cos t + \cos \sqrt{2}\, t \qquad (6.14)$$

It is impossible to find a value T for which the periodicity test (6.7) is satisfied. Hence (6.14) is not periodic, but is obviously almost periodic.

The almost-periodic signal (6.14) can be visualized as the result of a limiting process in which the period of a periodic signal becomes infinite. In particular, if the signal

$$\cos \omega_1 t + \cos \omega_2 t \qquad (6.15)$$

is periodic with a basic period T, then it must be possible to find two whole numbers m and n such that

$$\omega_1 T = 2\pi m \tag{6.16}$$

$$\omega_2 T = 2\pi n \tag{6.17}$$

We may assume that m and n do not have a whole-number common factor, for the existence of such a common factor would allow us to identify a new period T, smaller by that factor. The quotient of (6.16) and (6.17) is

$$\frac{\omega_2}{\omega_1} = \frac{n}{m} \tag{6.18}$$

For the signal

$$\cos t + \cos 1.41t \tag{6.19}$$

we have $m = 100$, $n = 141$, and $T = 200\pi$. Thus signal (6.19) has a period much larger than the periods of either of its two additive components. As we increase the number of decimal places in (6.19) for a better approximation to the value $\sqrt{2}$, skipping those approximations that have either 5 or an even number in the last decimal place, the period of the signal becomes arbitrarily large and (6.14) is therefore the limit of a sequence of periodic signals having ever-larger periods.

Almost-periodic signals provide a link or steppingstone between periodic signals and the random signals to be discussed shortly. Some random signals, like almost-periodic signals, have average power but are nonperiodic.

6.5 Random Signals

Random means unpredictable; hence a random signal is one whose value we cannot be sure of in advance. Such signals originate from a machine, device, or system about which we have incomplete knowledge. More complete knowledge may be either difficult (or impossible) to obtain or, if obtainable, not usable because of its complexity. A random signal is said to be *generated* by a *random process* and is often called a *sample function* of the process. (A specific signal is only one sample of the ensemble of different possible signals associated with the process.) The point is that the randomness of the process is a consequence of our inability or unwillingness to describe that process in full detail.

Figure 6-5(a) shows a pulse signal whose location and width are known but whose height is not predictable in advance. Let us assume, however, that the characteristics of the signal generator are such that only three pulse heights v_1, v_2, and v_3 are possible and that these three levels have probabilities of occurrence p_1, p_2, and p_3. The probabilities p_k are defined as follows. First construct a large number N of signal generators, alike except for those "random" differences allowed by our

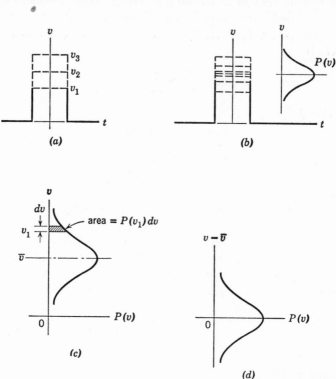

Fig. 6-5. Probability density $P(v)$ of signal amplitude.

incomplete knowledge of the device. Let n_k be the number of signal generators producing the pulse height v_k. Then probability p_k is defined as the limit approached by the quotient n_k/N as N is made arbitrarily large. [For example, if the pulse height in Fig. 6-5(a) is equal to the total number of heads appearing in two independent tosses of an ideal coin, then v_1, v_2, and v_3 have the values 0, 1, and 2, respectively. In a large number of idealized double-coin-toss experiments, symmetry tells us to expect, on the average, in a group of four such experiments, no heads once, one head twice, and two heads once. Hence, p_1, p_2, and p_3 have the values 0.25, 0.50, and 0.25, respectively.] Such a definition of probability requires, of course, the tacit assumption that the limit exists.

The sum of the probabilities of all possible mutually exclusive possibilities is always equal to unity

$$1 = \sum_k p_k \qquad (6.20)$$

a fact that follows from the definition of p_k. The *mean* or *ensemble-average* value of v is defined as the weighted sum of the various values, each weighted according to its probability

$$\bar{v} = \sum_k p_k v_k \qquad (6.21)$$

Quantity $\bar{v}$ is just the average of the values of v produced by the *ensemble* of similar but randomly different signal generators. In exactly the same way we can compute the mean-square pulse height.

$$\overline{v^2} = \sum_k p_k v_k{}^2 \qquad (6.22)$$

The time integral of $\overline{v^2}(t)$ would be the ensemble-average energy output from our ensemble of signal generators.

When the possible signal levels v_k form a continuum rather than a discrete set, the probability of a single specified signal value becomes vanishingly small. There remains, however, a definite probability p that the signal will fall within some specified interval Δv of the v scale, and the quotient $p/\Delta v$ approaches a meaningful limit as Δv becomes arbitrarily small. Hence we can define a *probability-density* function $P(v)$ such that $P(v_1)\,dv$ is the probability of v occurring in an infinitesimal interval dv located at the point v_1

$$P(v_1)\,dv = p(v_1 < v < v_1 + dv) \qquad (6.23)$$

We say that the signal in Fig. 6-5(b) has a *continuous* amplitude distribution whereas that in (a) has a *discrete* amplitude distribution. It is sometimes convenient to shift the v scale by an amount $\bar{v}$, as shown in Fig. 6-5(c) and (d), so that the function $P(v)$ has its "center of gravity" located at the origin. The area contained by the curve $P(v)$ between any two values v_1 and v_2 is equal to the probability that v lies between v_1 and v_2. Hence the discrete distribution in Fig. 6-5(a) has a probability-density function consisting of three *impulses*, located at positions v_1, v_2, and v_3 and having areas p_1, p_2, and p_3, respectively.

As a natural extension of (6.20), (6.21), and (6.22) in the continuous case, we have

$$1 = \int_{-\infty}^{\infty} P(v) \, dv \qquad (6.24)$$

$$\bar{v} = \int_{-\infty}^{\infty} P(v) v \, dv \qquad (6.25)$$

$$\overline{v^2} = \int_{-\infty}^{\infty} P(v) v^2 \, dv \qquad (6.26)$$

The ensemble average of any function of v can be found in the same way as a weighted integral of that function over the entire range of v

$$\overline{f(v)} = \int_{-\infty}^{\infty} P(v) f(v) \, dv \qquad (6.27)$$

The simple rectangular pulse in parts (a) and (b) of Fig. 6-5 is only one example of a signal having random properties. Another example, one which points the way toward the general statistical description of any random signal, is the following. Consider a signal consisting of two successive nonoverlapping rectangular pulses, each of unit duration. Let v_a and v_b be the heights of the first and second pulses and assume that both heights are randomly distributed. In this case, the statistics of the signal are described by the *joint*-probability-density function $P(v_a, v_b)$. The average energy in this signal is the double integral of $P(v_a, v_b)(v_a{}^2 + v_b{}^2)$, integrated over both v_a and v_b. Only if the two pulses are generated by independent random processes can we express $P(v_a, v_b)$ as a product of the two simpler functions $P_a(v_a) P_b(v_b)$.

A sequence of n adjacent rectangular pulses having heights $v_a, v_b, v_c, \cdots, v_n$ may be employed as a stepwise approximation to a wide variety of signals in the time interval covered by the pulses. Thus we see that the general description of a random signal involves a joint-probability-density function of an unlimited number of random variables $P(v_a, v_b, v_c, \cdots)$. In practice, the complete statistics are usually too difficult to estimate, too inconvenient to measure, or too cumbersome to work with, and we are usually content with the second-order distribution functions $P(v_j, v_k)$, for various j and k (that is, $j = a, b, c, \cdots$ and $k = a, b, c, \cdots$).

6.6 Stationary Random Processes

A stationary random process is one whose statistical properties do not change with time. Signals (sample functions) generated by such processes have the property that a "long enough" segment of any signal from the process, recorded at some time in the past, has essentially the same statistics as another segment of the signal observed at some future time; a signal (sample function) from a stationary process cannot be used to "tell what time it is." Specifically, the second-order probability-density function $P[v(t_1), v(t_1 + a)]$ is the same for any choice of the time t_1, and likewise for all higher-order functions. (If such an invariance does not hold for the higher-order functions but does hold

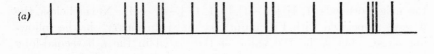

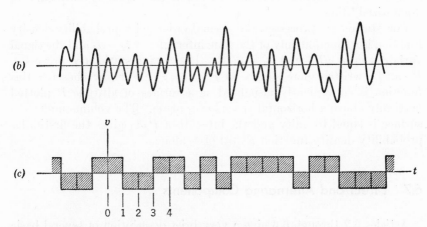

Fig. 6-6. Signals (sample functions) generated by stationary random processes.

for first-order and second-order functions, then we say that the process is "stationary with respect to second-order statistics.") In short, stationarity means that probabilities do not vary with time.

Figure 6-6 shows samples of three different random signals. Sample (a) is a random train of impulses, each having the same area. In any time interval of specified length the probability of occurrence of n pulses is the same as that in any other time interval of the same length. The process is stationary. Figure 6-6(b) shows a sample of a continuous stationary random process, such as the noise voltage appearing at the terminals of a resistor held at constant temperature in thermal equilibrium with its environment. The time average of the squared voltage computed over a large time interval of specified length is just as good an estimate of the average power as that taken from any other time interval of the same length. The sample signal illustrated in Fig. 6-6(c) is generated by successive tosses of an ideal coin. The coin is tossed once per second to determine the value of the signal during the following 1-second time interval; $+1$ for heads and -1 for tails. The process is obviously not stationary in the strict sense since $P[v(t), v(t + a)]$ is not independent of t. For example, the function $P[v(0.25), v(0.75)]$ is concentrated in the neighborhoods $[1, 1]$ and $[-1, -1]$, whereas $P[v(0.75), v(1.25)]$ shows concentrations of probability density in all four of the neighborhoods $[1, 1], [1, -1], [-1, 1], [-1, -1]$. Nevertheless, the process associated with Fig. 6-6(c) is "quasi-stationary" in the following sense. Let v_k be the value of the signal in the kth second-long interval of the time scale, whence it follows that $P(v_k, v_{k+m})$ is independent of k for any chosen integer m. In short, the signal is stationary in "quantized" time.

For stationary processes the second-order joint-probability-density function is a function only of the time interval $\tau = t_2 - t_1$ and the signal variables $v_1 = v(t_1)$ and $v_2 = v(t_2)$. Hence, for stationary processes, P can be written more simply as $P(v_1, v_2; \tau)$. For any chosen τ this function is conveniently visualized as a surface of altitude P plotted vertically above a horizontal v_1 versus v_2 plane. The volume under the surface is equal to unity and the integral of $P\, dv_1$ gives the first-order probability-density function $P_2(v_2)$ of v_2 alone.

6.7   Direct and Alternating Components

Articles 6.2 through 6.6 give a very brief description of several basic signal classes. These classes are by no means exhaustive, but they provide useful models for many of the signals encountered in practice. We turn now to the subject of *signal components*. Three fundamental signal-component pairs are discussed in this article and the two articles that follow.

Any power signal, including periodic, almost-periodic, and random signals, can be resolved into direct and alternating components. The *direct component* of a signal is defined as

$$v_{\mathrm{dc}} = \langle v \rangle \tag{6.28}$$

and the *alternating component* is what remains of the signal after removal of the direct component

$$v_{\mathrm{ac}} = v - v_{\mathrm{dc}} \tag{6.29}$$

It follows from the definition of the time average (6.9) that the alternating component has zero time-average value;

$$\langle v_{ac} \rangle = \langle v - \langle v \rangle \rangle = \langle v \rangle - \langle v \rangle = 0 \tag{6.30}$$

The total signal is, of course, just the sum of its alternating and direct components

$$v = v_{dc} + v_{ac} \tag{6.31}$$

The average power can now be calculated in terms of the direct and alternating components. For a real signal the average power is

$$\langle v^2 \rangle = \langle v_{dc}^2 + 2v_{dc}v_{ac} + v_{ac}^2 \rangle \tag{6.32}$$

Since the averaging process is a linear operation, the average of a sum may be replaced by the sum of the individual averages

$$\langle v^2 \rangle = \langle v_{dc}^2 \rangle + \langle 2v_{dc}v_{ac} \rangle + \langle v_{ac}^2 \rangle \tag{6.33}$$

Quantity v_{dc} is a constant and therefore may be relocated as a factor external to the averaging process

$$\langle v^2 \rangle = v_{dc}^2 + 2v_{dc}\langle v_{ac} \rangle + \langle v_{ac}^2 \rangle \tag{6.34}$$

In view of (6.30), this leads to the final result

$$\langle v^2 \rangle = v_{dc}^2 + \langle v_{ac}^2 \rangle \tag{6.35}$$

which states that *the average power in any signal is the sum of the average powers of the direct and alternating components.*

Now consider a signal $v(t)$ which has a probability density $P(v)$ at some designated time t. The *mean component* is $\bar{v}$, as defined by (6.25), and the *deviation component* v_d is defined as the difference

$$v_d = v - \bar{v} \tag{6.36}$$

Hence v is the sum of its mean and deviation components

$$v = \bar{v} + v_d \tag{6.37}$$

From (6.24), (6.25), and (6.36) it follows directly that the deviation component has zero mean value

$$\bar{v}_d = \int P(v)(v - \bar{v}) \, dv = \left[\int P(v)v \, dv - \bar{v} \int P(v) \, dv \right] = 0 \tag{6.38}$$

The mean-square value is given by

$$\overline{v^2} = \int P(v)(\bar{v} + v_d)^2 \, dv \tag{6.39}$$

and this is equivalent to the sum of three integrals

$$\overline{v^2} = (\bar{v})^2 \int P(v) \, dv + 2\bar{v} \int P(v)v_d \, dv + \int P(v)v_d^2 \, dv \tag{6.40}$$

In the light of (6.38) we have the final result

$$\overline{v^2} = (\bar{v})^2 + \overline{v_d^2} \tag{6.41}$$

The mean-square signal value is the square of the mean plus the mean-square deviation.

For many random signals of interest, $P(v)$ is independent of time and $\bar{v}$ and $\overline{v_d^2}$ are identifiable as v_{dc} and $\langle v_{ac}^2 \rangle$, respectively. As an important special case, let us compute the average power for a stationary random process having a Gaussian amplitude distribution

$$P_a(v) = \frac{1}{a\sqrt{2\pi}} e^{-\frac{1}{2}\left(\frac{v}{a}\right)^2} \tag{6.42}$$

Such a process is a good model for the thermal noise voltage appearing at the terminals of a resistor in thermal equilibrium with its environment. When written in the form (6.42), the Gaussian function contains the parameter a, called the *standard deviation* of the distribution. The coefficient before the exponential has been chosen to make

$$\int P_a(v)\,dv = 1 \tag{6.43}$$

Centering the distribution at the value zero, as in (6.42), involves no loss of generality, since a shift to any nonzero $\bar{v}$, as in Fig. 6-5(d), merely increases the mean-square value by an amount $(\bar{v})^2$, as indicated by (6.41). Differentiation of (6.42) gives

$$\frac{dP_a}{dv} = -\left(\frac{v}{a^2}\right)P_a \tag{6.44}$$

and again

$$\frac{d^2 P_a}{dv^2} = \left[\left(\frac{v}{a}\right)^2 - 1\right]\frac{P_a}{a^2} \tag{6.45}$$

Meanwhile, observe that

$$\int_{-\infty}^{\infty} \frac{d^2 P_a}{dv^2}\,dv = \frac{dP_a(\infty)}{dv} - \frac{dP_a(-\infty)}{dv} = 0 \tag{6.46}$$

Hence, integration of (6.45) yields the relationship

$$\int P_a(v)v^2\,dv = a^2 \int P_a(v)\,dv \tag{6.47}$$

which is identifiable as

$$\overline{v^2} = a^2 = \text{variance} \tag{6.48}$$

Thus in a stationary random process having a Gaussian amplitude distribution the a-c power (the mean-square a-c voltage) is equal to the square of the standard deviation, a quantity usually referred to as the *variance* of the Gaussian distribution.

6.8   Even and Odd Components

The *even* and *odd components* of any signal are defined as

$$v_e(t) = \tfrac{1}{2}[v(t) + v(-t)] = v_e(-t) \qquad (6.49)$$

and

$$v_o(t) = \tfrac{1}{2}[v(t) - v(-t)] = -v_o(-t) \qquad (6.50)$$

so that

$$v = v_e + v_o \qquad (6.51)$$

Figure 6-7 (*a*) through (*c*) shows the even and odd components of a pulse signal. Parts (*d*) through (*f*) of Fig. 6-7 illustrate the fact that these components will, in general, change when the location of the time origin is altered.

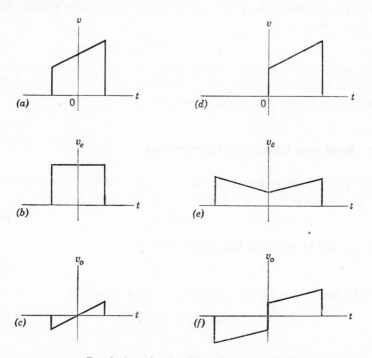

Fig. 6-7.   Resolution of a signal into its even and odd parts.

The net area under the odd component of any pulse signal is identically equal to zero

$$\int v_o \, dt = 0 \qquad (6.52)$$

Similarly, the time-average value of the odd component of any *power signal* must vanish

$$\langle v_o \rangle = 0 \qquad (6.53)$$

Thus the even part of the signal has the same time average as the signal itself

$$\langle v \rangle = \langle v_e \rangle \qquad (6.54)$$

Squaring (6.51) and averaging, we have the average power

$$\langle v^2 \rangle = \langle v_e{}^2 + 2v_e v_o + v_o{}^2 \rangle \qquad (6.55)$$

Since the product of an even function and an odd function is a new odd function, it follows that

$$\langle v_e v_o \rangle = 0 \qquad (6.56)$$

Hence the middle term on the right of (6.55) contributes nothing to the average and

$$\langle v^2 \rangle = \langle v_e{}^2 \rangle + \langle v_o{}^2 \rangle \qquad (6.57)$$

Thus *the average power in a signal is the sum of the average powers contained in its even and odd parts.* The same applies to a pulse signal, provided we speak of its energy instead of its power.

6.9   Real and Imaginary Components

For a signal whose instantaneous value is a complex number, the *real* and *imaginary* parts form a fundamental component pair

$$v = v_r + jv_i \qquad (6.58)$$

The *complex conjugate* of the signal value is

$$v^* = v_r - jv_i \qquad (6.59)$$

and the real and imaginary parts are therefore given by

$$v_r = \tfrac{1}{2}(v + v^*) \qquad (6.60)$$

and

$$jv_i = \tfrac{1}{2}(v - v^*) \qquad (6.61)$$

The squared magnitude is equal to the product of the signal and its complex conjugate, and since $j^2 = -1$ in the algebra of complex numbers, we have the familiar result

$$|v|^2 = vv^* = |v_r|^2 + |jv_i|^2 = v_r{}^2 + v_i{}^2 \qquad (6.62)$$

As before, *the square of the signal magnitude is the sum of the squares of the magnitudes of its two components.* Here, however, the identity holds for every instantaneous complex value of the signal and no ensemble averaging or time averaging is involved.

In the mathematics of signal analysis and circuit analysis, complex signals usually appear as complex exponential functions of the form

$$e^{jt} = \cos t + j \sin t \qquad (6.63)$$

Relation (6.63) can be demonstrated by power-series expansion of each of the three terms. For the complex exponential signal we have, therefore,

$$|e^{jt}|^2 = \cos^2 t + \sin^2 t = 1 \qquad (6.64)$$

6.10 Comparison of Vectors

We have seen that for properly chosen components the energy or power in a signal is the sum of the energies or powers in the signal components. This suggests a geometric analogy in which, for properly chosen components, the squared length of a vector is the sum of the squares of the lengths of its components. As we shall see, the word "analogy" is really not strong enough, because the two problems are *identical.* The vector problem is reviewed here and the intimate relationship with signal analysis is established in the following article.

Figure 6-8(a) shows two space vectors v_1 and v_2. Let us ask the question, "How much of vector v_1 lies in the direction v_2?" Most people who have had anything to do with vector calculations will immediately reply, "Why, of course, an amount equal to the *projection* of vector v_1 upon the direction v_2." Such an answer involves the tacit assumption that vector v_1 is resolved into *orthogonal* components, one of them lying in direction v_2. *Orthogonal* components of a vector are aligned at right angles to each other so that the sum of the squares of their lengths is equal to the square of the length of the vector. We really should have asked, "To what new length $v_2{}'$ should vector v_2 be adjusted so that the length of the difference vector $v_1 - v_2{}'$ is a minimum?" The question is now precise and the answer follows directly. Let vector v_2 be multiplied by a real scale factor c_{12}, so that $c_{12}v_2$ is a vector having the same direction as v_2. The length of $c_{12}v_2$ can then be adjusted by changing the scale factor c_{12}.   (For negative c_{12}, the vector $c_{12}v_2$ points in a direction opposite to that of v_2.)   By definition, the "amount of v_1 in direction v_2" is $c_{12}v_2$, where c_{12} is assumed to be chosen for minimum length of the difference vector $v_1 - c_{12}v_2$, as indicated in Fig. 6-8(b). Similarly, the amount of v_2 in direction v_1 is $c_{21}v_1$, as shown in Fig. 6-8(c).   Observe that c_{12} and c_{21} are, in general, unequal.

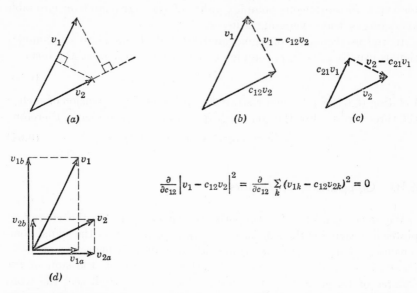

Fig. 6-8.   Extraction of a vector component $c_{12}v_2$ from a vector v_1 by minimization of the squared length of the remaining vector.   (Vertical bars $|v|$ here denote the length of any vector v.)

The geometry problem is simple, involving only the construction of a perpendicular upon a straight line.   The analytical problem is also simple, requiring only the minimization of a function by variation of a parameter c_{12}.   For the analytical formulation the vectors v_1 and v_2 are expressed in terms of their orthogonal components in the co-ordinate space, as in Fig. 6-8(d).   The squared length $|v_1 - c_{12}v_2|^2$ of the difference vector is just the sum of the squares of the lengths of its orthogonal components $(v_{1a} - c_{12}v_{2a})^2 + (v_{1b} - c_{12}v_{2b})^2$.   For minimum length of the difference vector, the condition is

$$\frac{\partial}{\partial c_{12}} |v_1 - c_{12}v_2|^2 = \frac{\partial}{\partial c_{12}} \sum_k (v_{1k} - c_{12}v_{2k})^2 = 0 \qquad (6.65)$$

After the differentiation has been carried out, solution for c_{12} yields

$$c_{12} = \frac{\sum_k v_{1k} v_{2k}}{\sum_k v_{2k}^2} = \frac{v_1 \cdot v_2}{v_2 \cdot v_2} \qquad (6.66)$$

The summation appearing in the numerator of c_{12} is called the "dot product" or "inner product" of the two vectors v_1 and v_2 and is usually denoted by a heavy dot indicating a special brand of multiplication applicable to vector quantities. The dot product of two vectors is the product of their lengths multiplied by the cosine of the angle between the two vector directions. (For the particular example in Fig. 6-8 we have $v_1 \cdot v_2 = v_{1a} v_{2a} + v_{1b} v_{2b}$.) The denominator, $v_2 \cdot v_2$, is just the square of the length of v_2.

To summarize, the formula (6.66) allows us to calculate the *projection* $c_{12} v_2$ of vector v_1 upon direction v_2. In other words, $c_{12} v_2$ is the *amount* of v_2 *contained* or *imbedded* in v_1.

6.11   Comparison of Signals

Figure 6-9(a) shows a signal $v_1(t)$ consisting of two adjacent rectangular pulses, a and b, each of unit width. The energy (integral square) of this signal is $v_{1a}^2 + v_{1b}^2$, a quantity identical in form to the squared length of vector v_1 in Fig. 6-8(d). Another signal of the same type but different shape is shown in Fig. 6-9(b). Observe, at this point, that Fig. 6-8(d) and Fig. 6-9(a) and (b) are merely two different ways of presenting exactly the same information, namely, the four numbers v_{1a}, v_{1b}, v_{2a}, and v_{2b}.

Let us now multiply $v_2(t)$ by a real scale factor c_{12} which changes its height but not its shape (just as a scalar multiplier changes the length of a vector but not its direction), subtract this from $v_1(t)$, and then ask for the value of c_{12} which minimizes the energy of the difference signal $v_1(t) - c_{12} v_2(t)$. The energy of the difference signal is just the summation appearing in (6.65) and the desired value of c_{12} is therefore given by (6.66). Given a signal of waveform $v_2(t)$, we can say that $v_1(t)$ *contains* an *amount* $c_{12} v_2(t)$ of that particular waveform $v_2(t)$.

The analysis generalizes immediately to pulse signals of arbitrary shape. An arbitrary signal may be sliced vertically into narrow adjacent pulses. The signal is then identifiable as a vector in multi-dimensional space, its components along the orthogonal co-ordinates of that space being the heights of the pulses. In the limit of very narrow pulses, the summation in (6.65) becomes an integral

$$\frac{\partial}{\partial c_{12}}\int (v_1 - c_{12}v_2)^2 \, dt = 0 \tag{6.67}$$

Differentiation and solution for c_{12} gives

$$c_{12} = \frac{\int v_1 v_2 \, dt}{\int v_2{}^2 \, dt} \tag{6.68}$$

Parameter c_{12} is called the *correlation coefficient* of the two signals v_1 and v_2. (This coefficient, convenient for identification with the Fourier

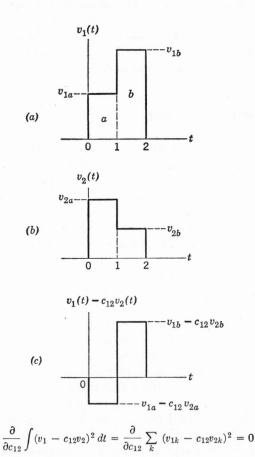

$$\frac{\partial}{\partial c_{12}}\int (v_1 - c_{12}v_2)^2 \, dt = \frac{\partial}{\partial c_{12}}\sum_k (v_{1k} - c_{12}v_{2k})^2 = 0$$

Fig. 6-9. Extraction of a signal component $c_{12}v_2(t)$ from a signal $v_1(t)$ by minimization of the energy in the remaining signal.

series, differs slightly from the normalized coefficient defined in much of the mathematical literature.) The correlation of two entities means, in general terms, the extent to which those two entities are alike or similar. The correlation coefficient tells us how much of one signal shape we must extract from another so as to leave a minimum of energy in the remaining signal. If c_{12} *vanishes*, then the two signals are said to be *orthogonal*, since the energy of their sum is the sum of their energies.

The derivations above have been carried out for real vector components and real signals. Since complex signals are also of interest the result (6.68) must be generalized. For complex signals the energy is defined as the integral of the squared magnitude of the signal, as in (6.2). Hence we must work with the quantity

$$\left|v_1 - c_{12}v_2\right|^2 = (v_1 - c_{12}v_2)(v_1{}^* - c_{12}{}^*v_2{}^*) \tag{6.69}$$

in which c_{12} is now complex. Carrying out the indicated multiplications and integrating, we find

$$\int \left|v_1 - c_{12}v_2\right|^2 dt = \int \left|v_1\right|^2 dt - 2\,\text{Re}\,[c_{12}{}^*\int v_1 v_2{}^*\,dt] + \left|c_{12}\right|^2 \int \left|v_2\right|^2 dt \tag{6.70}$$

in which Re means "the real part of" and the asterisk denotes complex conjugation. The middle integral on the right is a complex number and may be expressed in polar form

$$\int v_1 v_2{}^*\,dt = Ae^{j\theta} \tag{6.71}$$

We must now adjust both the magnitude and the polar angle of the complex parameter c_{12} to minimize the energy integral (6.70). The optimum angle for c_{12} is the θ in (6.71), for then the bracketed quantity in (6.70) has a maximum real part. Therefore, we *choose*

$$c_{12} = \left|c_{12}\right|e^{j\theta} \tag{6.72}$$

Substitution of (6.71) and (6.72) into (6.70) gives

$$\int \left|v_1 - c_{12}v_2\right|^2 dt = \int \left|v_1\right|^2 dt - 2\left|c_{12}\right|A + \left|c_{12}\right|^2 \int \left|v_2\right|^2 dt \tag{6.73}$$

It remains to minimize the energy further by adjustment of the *magnitude* of the parameter c_{12}. To proceed,

$$\frac{\partial}{\partial\left|c_{12}\right|}\int \left|v_1 - c_{12}v_2\right|^2 dt = -2A + 2\left|c_{12}\right|\int \left|v_2\right|^2 dt = 0 \tag{6.74}$$

from which we obtain

$$\left|c_{12}\right| = \frac{A}{\int \left|v_2\right|^2 dt} \tag{6.75}$$

and multiplication of both sides of the equation by $e^{j\theta}$ gives the final result

$$c_{12} = \frac{\int v_1 v_2^* \, dt}{\int |v_2|^2 \, dt} \tag{6.76}$$

Similarly,

$$c_{21} = \frac{\int v_2 v_1^* \, dt}{\int |v_1|^2 \, dt} \tag{6.77}$$

To reiterate, the choice (6.76) results in the minimum remaining energy when the component $c_{12}v_2$ is extracted from signal v_1. Hence the extracted component $c_{12}v_2$ and the remaining signal $v_1 - c_{12}v_2$ must be orthogonal. Thus,

$$\int |v_1|^2 \, dt = \int |c_{12}v_2|^2 \, dt + \int |v_1 - c_{12}v_2|^2 \, dt \tag{6.78}$$

The energy quotient of signals $c_{12}v_2$ and v_1 is a convenient measure of the similarity of waveforms v_1 and v_2. Let the *correlation efficiency* be defined as

$$C_{12} = \frac{\int |c_{12}v_2|^2 \, dt}{\int |v_1|^2 \, dt} \tag{6.79}$$

The correlation efficiency is obviously real and nonnegative. In the vector interpretation, C_{12} is identifiable as $\cos^2 \theta$, where θ is the angle between the two vectors v_1 and v_2. Substitution of (6.76) into (6.79) yields, after a little manipulation,

$$C_{12} = \frac{\left| \int v_1 v_2^* \, dt \right|^2}{\int |v_1|^2 \, dt \int |v_2|^2 \, dt} = C_{21} \tag{6.80}$$

It follows that

$$C_{12} = c_{12}c_{21} \tag{6.81}$$

$$0 \le C_{12} \le 1 \tag{6.82}$$

$$C_{11} = C_{22} = 1 \tag{6.83}$$

The quantity $(1 - C_{12})$ is the *minimum possible fractional amount of remaining energy* after a component having the wave form $v_2(t)$ has been extracted from a given signal $v_1(t)$. We say that a portion C_{12} of the energy in v_1 is carried by or contained in a component of the form v_2.

For power signals, which have infinite energy but finite average power, the integrals may be replaced by averages to obtain

$$c_{12} = \frac{\langle v_1 v_2{}^* \rangle}{\langle |v_2|^2 \rangle} \tag{6.84}$$

$$c_{21} = \frac{\langle v_2 v_1{}^* \rangle}{\langle |v_1|^2 \rangle} \tag{6.85}$$

$$C_{12} = \frac{|\langle v_1 v_2{}^* \rangle|^2}{\langle |v_1|^2 \rangle \langle |v_2|^2 \rangle} = c_{12} c_{21} \tag{6.86}$$

When v_1 is a power signal but v_2 is an energy signal, the correlation coefficient c_{12}, as given in (6.76), is still meaningful but (6.77) and (6.80) both vanish and (6.86) is indeterminate in form. However, the quotient

$$T_{12} = \frac{\left| \int v_1 v_2{}^* \, dt \right|^2}{\langle |v_1|^2 \rangle \int |v_2|^2 \, dt} \tag{6.87}$$

exists, has the dimensions of time, and may be called the *effective correlation time* of the energy signal with the power signal. The extraction of a pulse component from a power signal takes a "bite" out of that power signal and the effective "length" of the bite is the effective correlation time. The average power of $v_1(t)$ multiplied by T_{12} is the amount of energy removed from $v_1(t)$ by extraction of the pulse component $c_{12} v_2(t)$.

In Figure 6-10 two pulse signals are compared on the basis of the foregoing correlation concepts. If v_2 were a rectangular pulse of unit length, instead of the sinusoidal pulse shown in Fig. 6-10(b), the correlation efficiency C_{12} would have the value 1/3. The value of C_{12} in Fig. 6-10 is only slightly less than 1/3. From the correlation viewpoint, a half-period sinusoidal pulse and a rectangular pulse of the same length are close relatives. Figure 6-11 offers a specific interpretation of the effective correlation time T_{12}. Extraction of the pulse component $c_{12} v_2$ from the steady signal v_1 leaves the gap shown in Fig. 6-11(c). The decrease in energy associated with this gap or bite is the same as that in (d), where *all* of the signal is removed over an interval equal to T_{12}. In Fig. 6-12, two periodic signals are compared. Although the two waveforms are somewhat different, nevertheless three-quarters of the power in v_1 can be removed by extraction of a component of the type v_2. If v_2 in Fig. 6-12 were shifted one-quarter period to the right or to the left, however, the correlation efficiency would fall to zero. Thus, for two periodic signals having the same period, the correlation efficiency is itself a periodic function of the relative shift or displacement along the time axis of one signal with respect to the other.

Figure 6-13 shows samples of two "noise" signals n_1 and n_2, random signals generated by successive independent tosses of an ideal coin.

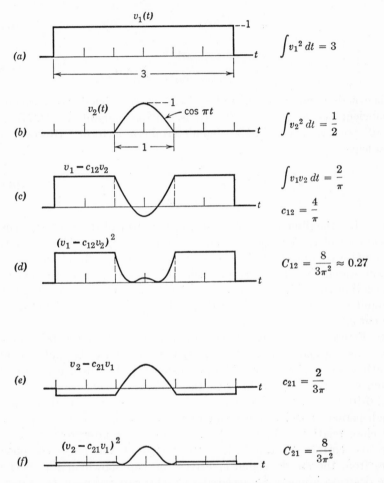

Fig. 6-10. Correlation coefficients for a sinusoidal pulse and a rectangular pulse.

Signal s is a periodic square wave. In terms of these three signals we can construct a crude model of a hypothetical signal transmission problem. Suppose that a radio transmitter is installed on the top of a high mountain, a transmitter so designed that it sends a signal n_2 when the cosmic-ray intensity at the mountaintop lies below a certain level but sends the signal s when the intensity of cosmic rays exceeds that level. Suppose also that, along the transmission path between the sending station and a distant receiving station, a noise or interference n_1 is unavoidably added to the signal, perhaps by atmospheric effects or perhaps by radar or other man-made machinery unavoidably located

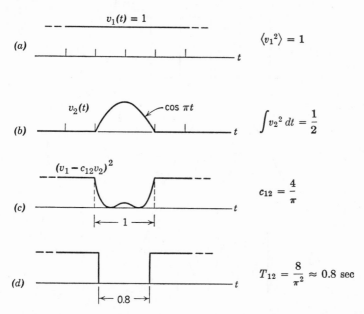

Fig. 6-11. The effective correlation time T_{12} of a power signal v_1 and a pulse signal v_2.

in the vicinity of the receiver. Our received signal, therefore, will look something like either the sample $n_1 + n_2$ or $n_1 + s$ in Fig. 6-13. Our problem is to extract from the received signal the information about cosmic-ray activity upon the mountaintop. A computer can be built to perform the operation of correlation, that is, integration or averaging of the product of two signals. Let us generate a square wave s at the receiver and correlate this locally generated signal with the received signal. The table in Fig. 6-13 shows the correlation efficiencies and coefficients obtained by correlating signal s with each of the signals in the figure, including s itself. The fourth and fifth columns of the table are of immediate interest here. Signal s correlates weakly with $n_1 + n_2$ but relatively strongly with $n_1 + s$ and this marked difference in correlation allows us to make a very good guess as to which of the two possible messages is being transmitted from the remote outpost.

The table in Fig. 6-13 is based upon the finite sample lengths shown.

For longer and longer sample lengths we would expect the numbers in the upper row of the table to approach 0, 0, 1, 0, 0.5, 0.5, and 0, with those in the lower row approaching 0, 0, 1, 0, 1, 1, and 0. The product of s with $n_1 + n_2$ is likely to be positive as often as negative so that for a very long sample the average value over the sample may be expected to

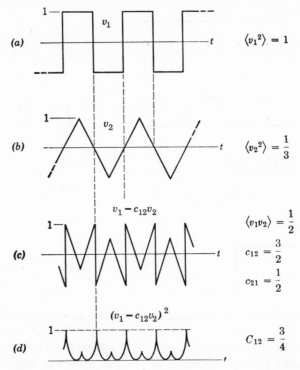

Fig. 6-12. Correlation coefficients for a pair of periodic signals.

become arbitrarily small. The correlation efficiency between s and $n_1 + s$ has a theoretical value of 0.5, reflecting the fact that half of the power in $n_1 + s$ is carried in a component of the form s. The operation implied by the symbol c_{vs} involves straight integration and is therefore linear (as contrasted with C_{vs} which involves a square of an integral). The linearity of operation c_{vs} is evidenced in the table of Fig. 6-13. For example, the correlation coefficient between s and $n_1 + n_2$ minus that between s and $n_1 - n_2$ is just equal to twice the correlation between s and n_2; for $(n_1 + n_2) - (n_1 - n_2)$ is just twice n_2.

The point is that the presence of a periodic signal, buried in additive random noise, can be detected by correlation with another signal having the same period. If the average power of the periodic signal is considerably less than that of the additive random noise, then, of course, a very long sample must be used in order to reduce the uncertainty of detection

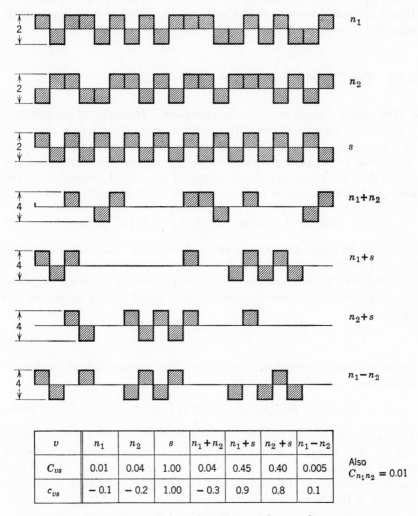

v	n_1	n_2	s	$n_1 + n_2$	$n_1 + s$	$n_2 + s$	$n_1 - n_2$
C_{vs}	0.01	0.04	1.00	0.04	0.45	0.40	0.005
c_{vs}	-0.1	-0.2	1.00	-0.3	0.9	0.8	0.1

Also
$C_{n_1 n_2} = 0.01$

Fig. 6-13. Correlation coefficients for noise samples n and a square wave s.

In the limit of an arbitrarily long sample, it is theoretically possible to detect the presence of a periodic signal having arbitrarily small average power relative to the power in the additive random interference. All of this follows from the statistical characteristics of the basic coin-tossing experiment, which are discussed in detail in Article 7.40. For the present, it is sufficient to state that in the ensemble of all possible sequences generated by N independent tosses of an ideal coin, the ensemble average of the square of the difference (heads minus tails) is proportional to N. Hence the signal-to-noise power ratio *after* correlation detection may be expected to increase in proportion to the length of the sample.

6.12   The Correlation Function

Any signal correlates perfectly with itself. However, if we correlate a signal not with itself but with a replica of itself shifted or displaced by an amount τ along the time axis, then we may expect the amount of correlation to be somewhat less. The dependence of correlation upon this shift is an important characteristic of any signal. Specifically, the *autocorrelation function* of any pulse signal $v(t)$ is defined here as

$$\psi(\tau) = \int v(t)v^*(t - \tau) \, dt = \int v(t + \tau)v^*(t) \, dt \qquad (6.88)$$

As usual, the integral is to be carried out over all t. Later in the chapter we shall see that $\psi(\tau)$ contains information about the relative amounts of energy in the different frequency components of v. For τ equal to zero the correlation function has a value equal to the energy in the signal

$$\psi(0) = \int |v|^2 \, dt \qquad (6.89)$$

As an obvious generalization of (6.88), the *crosscorrelation function* is defined as

$$\psi_{12}(\tau) = \int v_1(t)v_2^*(t - \tau) \, dt = \int v_1(t + \tau)v_2^*(t) \, dt \qquad (6.90)$$

This definition applies provided at least one of the two signals is a pulse signal. The autocorrelation function ψ_{11} is recognizable as a special case of ψ_{12} occurring when signals v_1 and v_2 are the same. For zero τ the crosscorrelation function is just the integral appearing in the numerator of the correlation coefficient (6.76)

$$\psi_{12}(0) = \int v_1 v_2^* \, dt \qquad (6.91)$$

The correlation-function integral may be written in either of the two equivalent forms indicated in (6.90). The integral is evidently the same whether we shift the second signal to the right along the time axis by an amount τ or shift the first signal to the left by the same amount.

Writing ψ_{21} in the second of the two equivalent forms

$$\psi_{21}(\tau) = \int v_2(t + \tau)v_1{}^*(t) \, dt \tag{6.92}$$

permits immediate identification of the fundamental relationship

$$\psi_{12}(\tau) = \psi_{21}{}^*(-\tau) \tag{6.93}$$

Hence, also

$$\psi_{11}(\tau) = \psi_{11}{}^*(-\tau) \tag{6.94}$$

Thus, the autocorrelation function exhibits *conjugate symmetry*; the real part is an even function of τ and the imaginary part is odd.

Figure 6-14 shows the crosscorrelation function of a pair of pulse signals. One of the signals is a rectangular pulse so that, in this particular example, the area under the plot of the product v_1v_2 is proportional to the shaded area shown in the figure. For zero τ, the area is small, as shown in Fig. 6-14(a). As τ is increased from zero the pulse v_2 shifts to the right as in (b), (c), and (d), and $\psi_{12}(\tau)$ varies with the size of the shaded area. Remember that the correlation function is a function of the relative shift τ between the two signals and not a function of the "physical time" upon which v_1 and v_2 are explicitly dependent. In the correlation integral the physical time t plays the role of a dummy variable and disappears in the integration.

The correlation coefficients defined previously are simply related to the correlation functions

$$c_{12}(\tau) = \frac{\psi_{12}(\tau)}{\psi_{22}(0)} \tag{6.95}$$

$$c_{21}(\tau) = \frac{\psi_{21}(\tau)}{\psi_{11}(0)} \tag{6.96}$$

where $c_{12}(\tau)$ is the coefficient for v_1 and v_2 under the condition that v_2 is shifted to the right by an amount τ. Similarly, the correlation efficiency (with v_2 shifted) is given by

$$C_{12}(\tau) = \frac{\psi_{12}(\tau)\psi_{21}(-\tau)}{\psi_{11}(0)\psi_{22}(0)} = \frac{|\psi_{12}(\tau)|^2}{\psi_{11}(0)\psi_{22}(0)} \tag{6.97}$$

Since $C_{11}(0)$ is equal to unity, and since no C can be greater than unity, we have the fundamental restriction

$$|\psi_{11}(\tau)| \leq \psi_{11}(0), \qquad \text{for all } \tau \tag{6.98}$$

In other words, the maximum value of any *autocorrelation* function occurs at the origin.

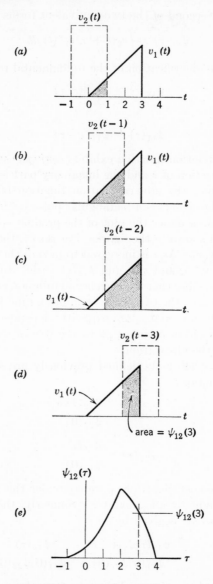

Fig. 6-14. Construction of a correlation function.

The area under a correlation function is closely related to the areas of the two signals being correlated. The area under the correlation curve is given by

$$\int \psi_{12}(\tau) \, d\tau = \int \int v_1(t) v_2{}^*(t - \tau) \, dt \, d\tau \qquad (6.99)$$

Now, in view of the identity

$$\int_{-\infty}^{\infty} f(x)\,dx \equiv \int_{-\infty}^{\infty} f(x_0 \pm x)\,dx \tag{6.100}$$

we can carry out the τ integration to obtain

$$\int \psi_{12}\,d\tau = \left[\int v_1\,dt\right]\left[\int v_2\,dt\right]^* \tag{6.101}$$

In short, the area under a correlation function is the product of the areas of the two correlated signals. When v_1 is a power signal and v_2 is an

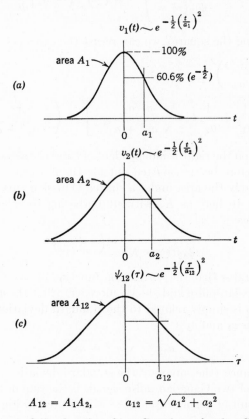

$$A_{12} = A_1 A_2, \qquad a_{12} = \sqrt{a_1{}^2 + a_2{}^2}$$

Fig. 6-15. The correlation function of two Gaussian pulses is a Gaussian pulse.

energy signal, the τ integration may be replaced by an averaging process to obtain

$$\langle\psi_{12}\rangle = \langle v_1\rangle \left[\int v_2\,dt\right]^* \tag{6.102}$$

Figure 6-15 gives a result of special interest. *The correlation function of any two Gaussian pulses is itself a Gaussian pulse.* To demonstrate this, let

$$v_1 = e^{-\frac{1}{2}\left(\frac{t}{a_1}\right)^2} \tag{6.103}$$

and

$$v_2 = e^{-\frac{1}{2}\left(\frac{t}{a_2}\right)} \tag{6.104}$$

whence

$$\psi_{12}(\tau) = \int e^{-\frac{1}{2}\left[\left(\frac{t}{a_1}\right)^2+\left(\frac{t-\tau}{a_2}\right)\right]} dt \tag{6.105}$$

By "completing the square" we can recast the exponent in the form

$$\left(\frac{t}{a_1}\right)^2 + \left(\frac{t-\tau}{a_2}\right)^2$$
$$= \left[\sqrt{\frac{1}{a_1^2} + \frac{1}{a_2^2}}\, t - \frac{a_1/a_2}{\sqrt{a_1^2 + a_2^2}}\, \tau\right]^2 + \left(\frac{\tau}{\sqrt{a_1^2 + a_2^2}}\right)^2 \tag{6.106}$$

The last term on the right is independent of t and the associated exponential may therefore be transported outside the integral. The remaining integral is merely the area under a shifted Gaussian curve, an area that we shall refer to here as K, without bothering to calculate its value exactly. Hence,

$$\psi_{12}(\tau) = Ke^{-\frac{1}{2}\left(\frac{\tau}{\sqrt{a_1^2+a_2^2}}\right)} \tag{6.107}$$

This demonstrates that the correlation function of two Gaussian pulses is itself a Gaussian pulse and shows, moreover, that the standard deviation a_{12} of ψ_{12} is simply related to the standard deviations a_1 and a_2 of the two signals v_1 and v_2

$$a_{12} = \sqrt{a_1^2 + a_2^2} \tag{6.108}$$

Thus the variance (the square of the standard deviation) of the correlation function of two Gaussian pulse signals is the sum of their variances.

Another result of general usefulness is indicated in Fig. 6-16. Let

$$v_1 = f(t) \tag{6.109}$$

$$v_2 = u_0(t - t_0) \tag{6.110}$$

so that

$$\psi_{12}(\tau) = \int f(t)u_0(t - \tau - t_0)\, dt \tag{6.111}$$

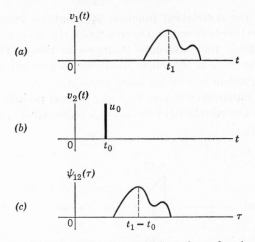

Fig. 6-16. The correlation function of a pulse and an impulse.

The impulse function $u_0(t - \tau - t_0)$ has appreciable amplitude only in the neighborhood of t near $\tau + t_0$. Hence the integrand in (6.111) is equivalent to an impulse of area $f(\tau + t_0)$. Therefore,

$$\psi_{12}(\tau) = f(\tau + t_0) \tag{6.112}$$

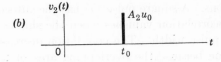

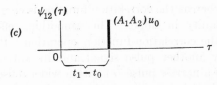

Fig. 6-17. The correlation function of two impulses.

For an impulse v_2 located at t_0 the correlation function ψ_{12} looks just like v_1 shifted to the left by an amount t_0. When v_1 is also an impulse, we have the special case shown in Fig. 6-17. It is apparent in this example that the correlation function ψ_{12} contains information as to the time separation between two narrow pulse signals v_1 and v_2 but lacks information about their absolute locations in time. The correlation function in Fig. 6-17 is obviously unaltered if we shift both pulses v_1 and v_2 to the right or left by the same amount.

Figure 6-18 illustrates the fact that any desired periodic signal can be constructed as the correlation function of a pulse signal v_1 and a periodic impulse train v_2.

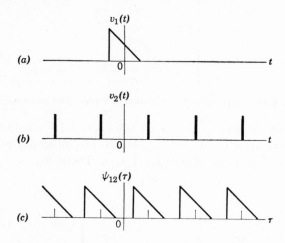

Fig. 6-18. The correlation function of a pulse and a periodic impulse train.

Figure 6-19 gives further examples of pulse signals and the associated correlation functions. A square pulse (a) has the autocorrelation shown in (b). The autocorrelation vanishes when the shift τ, in either direction, exceeds the pulse width. The correlation decreases linearly from its maximum value because the overlapping area of the pulse and its delayed replica is a linear function of the shift. Notice that the signal is discontinuous whereas the correlation function is continuous, although it has a discontinuity in slope. This smoothing effect is a general characteristic of the correlation-function operation. Parts (c) and (d) of Fig. 6-19 show another pulse signal and its autocorrelation. The crosscorrelation of a narrow pulse (e) with a wider pulse (f) is indicated in (g). Observe that the crosscorrelation closely resembles the shape of the wider pulse, except for the fact that the discontinuities have been smeared or spread out into regions of rapid but continuous variation, regions whose width is the same as that of the narrow pulse. Further evidence of the smoothing effect of correlation appears in the last three parts of the figure. Signal v_2 consists of a sharp rise followed by rapid wiggles. Correlation of this signal with a pulse v_1, whose width is several times the width of the individual wiggles appearing in v_2, gives a correlation function ψ_{21} in which the sharp rise is ameliorated and the wiggles are greatly reduced.

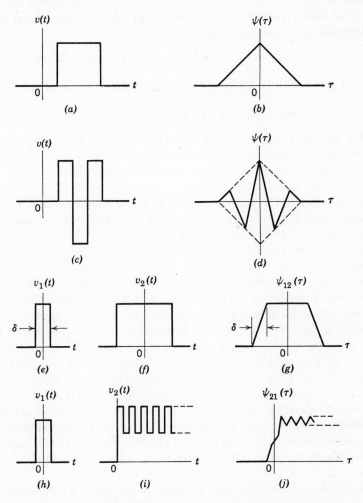

Fig. 6-19. Correlation functions of various signals and signal pairs.

We shall now derive a property of correlation functions that is extremely useful for practical calculation of ψ_{12} from v_1 and v_2. For convenience of notation let

$$\psi_{12}^{(k)}(\tau) = \frac{d^k}{d\tau^k}\psi_{12}(\tau) \qquad (6.113)$$

and

$$\psi_{12}^{(k)}(\tau) = \int_{-\infty}^{\tau} \psi_{12}^{(k+1)}(\tau) \, d\tau \qquad [\text{provided } \psi_{12}^{(k)}(-\infty) = 0] \qquad (6.114)$$

Because of the equivalence of the two integral forms in (6.90), differentiation or integration of ψ_{12} with respect to τ can be carried out under the integral sign on either v_1 or v_2

$$\psi_{12}^{(k)}(\tau) = (-1)^k \int v_1(t)[v_2^{(k)}(t-\tau)]^* \, dt = \int v_1^{(k)}(t+\tau)[v_2(t)]^* \, dt \qquad (6.115)$$

Hence ψ_{12} can be differentiated j times on v_1 and k times on v_2 to obtain

$$\psi_{12}^{(j+k)}(\tau) = (-1)^k \int v_1^{(j)}(t)[v_2^{(k)}(t-\tau)]^* \, dt \qquad (6.116)$$

With k set equal to the negative of j, relation (6.116) tells us that the crosscorrelation function is unchanged (apart from a possible negative sign) if v_1 is differentiated j times and v_2 is integrated (from $-\infty$ to t) j times, before calculation of ψ_{12}.

An example of the use of (6.116) is given in Fig. 6-20. For this example j and k have the values 0 and 1. In Fig. 6-20 the derivative of v_2 consists of three impulses, as shown in (c). The discontinuous jumps in v_2 are to be visualized as regions of rapid but continuous change, in which case the derivative consists of arbitrarily narrow pulses whose areas correspond to the heights of the jumps in v_2. The crosscorrelation function of each impulse with the triangular pulse v_1 is another triangular pulse, as indicated in (d), and their sum is (e), the negative of the derivative of ψ_{12}. Integration from $-\infty$ to τ then gives (the negative of) the desired crosscorrelation function. A process such as that in Fig. 6-20 is most convenient when at least one of the two signals reduces to a number of impulses after a few differentiations. We can, of course, force such a situation by first making a piecewise-linear approximation of one signal, in which case its second derivative is impulsive. The direct calculation of a correlation function may be much more tedious than the indirect process illustrated here, especially if the integration separates into various ranges whose limits change with τ.

In signal analysis it is often possible to recognize a somewhat complicated signal v_3 as the correlation function of two simpler signals v_1 and v_2. We can then establish a convenient relationship between the autocorrelation functions of v_1, v_2, and v_3. The route to the answer can be simplified considerably by the introduction of the following notation. Let f and f' denote any function and its conjugate-symmetric image

$$f = f(t) \qquad (6.117)$$

$$f' = f^*(-t) \qquad (6.118)$$

Also let the special multiplication symbol $\otimes$ denote the integral operation

$$v_1 \otimes v_2 = \int_{-\infty}^{\infty} v_1(\xi)v_2(t - \xi)\, d\xi = \int_{-\infty}^{\infty} v_2(\xi)v_1(t - \xi)\, d\xi \quad (6.119)$$

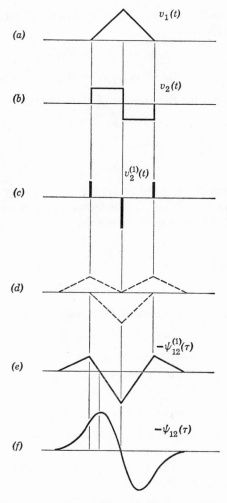

Fig. 6-20. Correlation preceded by differentiation and followed by integration.

which generates a new function of t from the two given functions $v_1(t)$ and $v_2(t)$. The equivalence of the two integral forms in (6.119) can be proved by an elementary change of variable and is analogous to the equivalence in (6.90). The time function $v_1 \otimes v_2$ is called the *convolution* of v_1 with v_2. We shall see much more of convolution in the next chapter where it arises more naturally in the study of linear transmission systems. For our immediate purposes convolution is no more than a notational convenience. The convenience lies in the fact that

$$v_1 \otimes v_2 \equiv v_2 \otimes v_1 \qquad (6.120)$$

From (6.117) through (6.119), and from the definition of a correlation function, we can identify

$$\psi_{11} = v_1 \otimes v_1' = \psi_{11}' \qquad (6.121)$$

$$\psi_{12} = v_1 \otimes v_2' = \psi_{21}' \qquad (6.122)$$

Now let $\psi_{12,12}$ stand for the autocorrelation function of ψ_{12}

$$\psi_{12,12} = \psi_{12} \otimes \psi_{12}' \qquad (6.123)$$

From (6.122) and (6.123) we find

$$\psi_{12,12} = (v_1 \otimes v_2') \otimes (v_1' \otimes v_2) \qquad (6.124)$$

The integral operations implied by $\otimes$ presumably may be performed in any order. Hence the $\otimes$ operation is associative and we may reassociate the signals in (6.124) differently to obtain

$$\psi_{12,12} = (v_1 \otimes v_1') \otimes (v_2 \otimes v_2') \qquad (6.125)$$

This is recognizable as

$$\psi_{12,12} = \psi_{11} \otimes \psi_{22}' \qquad (6.126)$$

a result which may be expressed in the compact form

$$\psi_{12,12} = \psi_{11,22} \qquad (6.127)$$

This gives us the desired relationship. If $v_3(t) = \psi_{12}(t)$, then $\psi_{33}(\tau)$ is equal to the crosscorrelation function of $\psi_{11}(t)$ and $\psi_{22}(t)$.

For power signals the *integral* ψ is replaced by the *average* ϕ, defined as

$$\phi(\tau) = \langle v(t)v^*(t - \tau) \rangle = \langle v(t + \tau)v^*(t) \rangle \qquad (6.128)$$

The entities ψ and ϕ are both called correlation functions, the only difference being that ψ is an integral, ϕ is an average, and each has its realm of applicability. The principal relationships involving ψ can be recast in the form of averages as follows

$$\phi(0) = \langle |v|^2 \rangle \qquad (6.129)$$

$$\begin{aligned} \phi_{12}(\tau) &= \langle v_1(t)v_2^*(t - \tau) \rangle \\ &= \langle v_1(t + \tau)v_2^*(t) \rangle \end{aligned} \qquad (6.130)$$

$$\phi_{12}(0) = \langle v_1 v_2^* \rangle \qquad (6.131)$$

$$\phi_{12}(\tau) = \phi_{21}^*(-\tau) \qquad (6.132)$$

$$\phi_{11}(\tau) = \phi_{11}{}^*(-\tau) \tag{6.133}$$

$$c_{12}(\tau) = \frac{\phi_{12}(\tau)}{\phi_{22}(0)} \tag{6.134}$$

$$c_{21}(\tau) = \frac{\phi_{21}(\tau)}{\phi_{11}(0)} \tag{6.135}$$

$$C_{12}(\tau) = \frac{|\phi_{12}(\tau)|^2}{\phi_{11}(0)\phi_{22}(0)} \tag{6.136}$$

$$|\phi_{11}(\tau)| \le \phi_{11}(0) \tag{6.137}$$

By analogy with (6.101) and (6.102), we have

$$\langle\phi_{12}\rangle = \langle v_1\rangle\langle v_2\rangle^* \tag{6.138}$$

a somewhat trivial result in view of the mutual orthogonality of a-c and d-c signals. The notation in (6.127) can be changed to the functional form

$$\psi(\psi_{12}, \psi_{12}) = \psi(\psi_{11}, \psi_{22}) \tag{6.139}$$

to place in evidence the character of each of the functions involved. Now, a ψ on one side of the equation may be replaced by ϕ provided we follow suit on the other side of the equation. An average is merely an integral divided by a large number representing the time interval over which that integral is carried out. Dividing both sides of an equation by that large number does not destroy the equality. The only point to be made here is that we can generate from (6.139) other relationships such as

$$\phi(\psi_{12}, \psi_{12}) = \psi(\phi_{11}, \psi_{22}) \tag{6.140}$$

for a power signal v_1 and a pulse signal v_2, or

$$\phi(\phi_{12}, \phi_{12}) = \phi(\phi_{11}, \phi_{22}) \tag{6.141}$$

for v_1 and v_2 both periodic. If v_1 and v_2 are both *random* power signals, however, the equality $\psi(\phi_{12}, \phi_{12}) = \psi(\phi_{11}, \phi_{22})$ does not hold; witness the counterexample $\phi_{12} \equiv 0$, ϕ_{11} and $\phi_{22} \not\equiv 0$, which can happen when v_1 and v_2 are generated by independent stationary random processes.

Figure 6-21 shows the autocorrelation function $\phi(\tau)$ of a simple periodic signal. For a periodic signal the averaging process need involve only one period. The autocorrelation function of a periodic signal is itself a periodic function with the same period, as is the crosscorrelation function of two different periodic signals having the same period, or the crosscorrelation function of a periodic signal and a pulse signal. For any sinusoid, the autocorrelation function is a cosine wave and hence contains no information about the absolute phase of the original sinusoidal signal.

The autocorrelation function of a random power signal can be constructed theoretically from the known statistical properties of the generating process, or it can be calculated approximately by shifting and multiplying a signal (sample function) from that process and

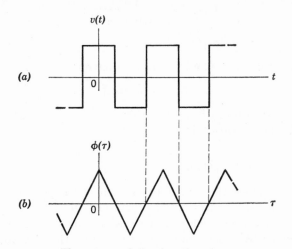

Fig. 6-21. The autocorrelation function of a square wave.

averaging over a finite time interval. For a stationary process the approximation may be expected to improve as the length of the time interval is increased.

We have chosen to define the correlation function of any power signal (whether periodic, almost-periodic, or random) as a time average of $v(t)v(t - \tau)$. For a random signal this calculation, based as it is on a single sample function $v(t)$, may not be representative of the process. Suitable modifications of the definition to meet various conditions can be explained in terms of the following pertinent examples.

Figure 6-22(a) shows three typical sample signals generated by a coin-tossing process. An ideal coin is tossed at 1-second intervals to determine the signal values, $+1$ for heads and -1 for tails. Although successive tosses occur 1 second apart, the absolute time is completely random. The first sample in (a) indicates tosses at the times $\cdots -2$, -1, 0, 1, 2, 3 $\cdots$, the second sample at the times $\cdots -1.67$, -0.67, 0.33, 1.33, 2.33 $\cdots$, and the third at times $\cdots -1.28$, -0.28, 0.72, 1.72, 2.72 $\cdots$. In general, the tosses occur at times

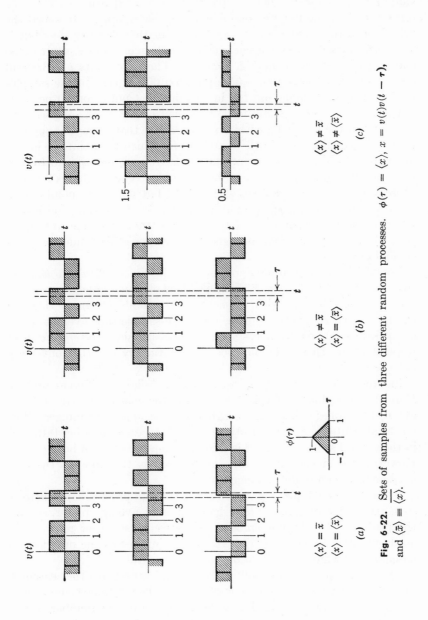

Fig. 6-22. Sets of samples from three different random processes. $\phi(\tau) = \langle x \rangle$, $x = v(t)v(t - \tau)$, and $\langle \bar{x} \rangle \equiv \overline{\langle x \rangle}$.

$r \pm n$, where n is an integer and r is a number between 0 and 1. The value r is fixed for any one sample but is evenly distributed over the range 0 to 1 in the infinite ensemble of possible samples. In short, the "clock" controlling the coin tosses "runs" neither fast nor slow but is "set" arbitrarily. Now consider definite values of t and τ, say $t = 3.9$ and $\tau = 0.4$, as shown in Fig. 6-22(a). The two points $t = 3.9$ and $t - \tau = 3.5$ fall within one square pulse on 60 per cent of the samples in the infinite ensemble and fall in two different pulses on 40 per cent of the samples. Let x stand for the product $v(t)v(t - \tau)$. We see that $x = 1$ when the points lie within one pulse and that x has the opposite values ± 1 equally often in those samples for which the points lie in two different pulses. (Two different pulse polarities are determined by two *independent* coin tosses.) Hence the ensemble-average value is $\bar{x} = 0.6$. Moreover, in any one sample, with τ fixed but not t, the points t and $t - 0.4$ fall within one square pulse 60 per cent of the time and in two different pulses 40 per cent of the time, so that the time average is $\langle x \rangle = 0.6$. The same reasoning goes through for other values of τ and we find $\phi(\tau) = \bar{x} = \langle x \rangle$.

For the particular process represented in Fig. 6-22(a), it *happens* that the ensemble average $\bar{x}$ is independent of time. Such a process is said to be *stationary* (with respect to x). It also *happens* that the ensemble average $\bar{x}$ is the same as the single-sample time average $\langle x \rangle$ for an arbitrarily chosen sample. Such a process is said to be *ergodic* (with respect to x). Every ergodic process is stationary but the converse is not necessarily true.

Figure 6-22(b) shows three samples from a slightly different process. Here the ensemble of "clocks" controlling the coin tosses are all "set" exactly the same; in each sample, the tosses occur only at integer values on the absolute time scale. In this case the process cannot be stationary in the general sense, because $\bar{x}$ is evidently dependent upon both t and τ. However, the single-sample time average $\langle x \rangle$ is the same as the time average of the ensemble average $\langle \bar{x} \rangle$.

In the third example, Fig. 6-22(c), the random process happens to be such that different samples may have different average power, so that the process is clearly not ergodic. Here we must either redefine the autocorrelation function as $\langle \bar{x} \rangle$ or restrict attention to some subset of the ensemble for which the definition $\langle x \rangle$ is meaningful.

The main point is simply this: consideration of the ensemble picture shows whether or not a single-sample time average is meaningful and, if that average is meaningful, leads to a suitable ensemble-average interpretation.

Figure 6-23(a) shows a segment of a slightly more complicated random signal generated from a sequence of independent tosses of the ubiquitous ideal coin. The time scale is divided into unit intervals, one coin toss being associated with each interval. The value of the signal in a given interval is equal to the number of heads minus the number of tails in the group of three coin tosses associated with that interval and the two adjacent intervals. Hence the only possible signal values are ± 1 and ± 3.

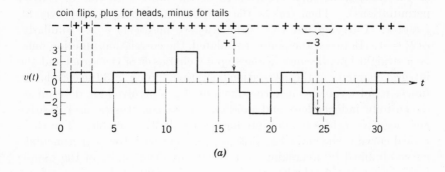

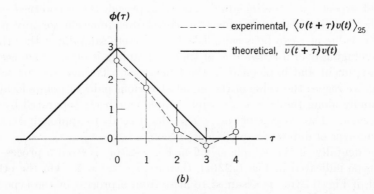

Fig. 6-23. (*a*) A segment of a sample generated from a sequence of coin tosses. $v(t)$ = number of heads minus number of tails in the three adjacent intervals $t - 1, t, t + 1$. (*b*) The autocorrelation function.

Let us first find the value of the correlation function for zero shift, $\phi(0) = \langle v^2 \rangle$. The expected frequency of occurrence of each of the different possible values of v is determined by the statistics of the coin-tossing process. There are two equally probable ways in which an ideal coin can fall and therefore eight distinct and equally probable ways in which three successive independent coin tosses can occur. Of these eight, two yield $v^2 = 9$, whereas the other six yield $v^2 = 1$. Hence, on the average, we should expect $\langle v^2 \rangle = (0.25)(9) + (0.75)(1) = 3$.

For $\tau = 1$, we have $\phi(1) = \langle zy \rangle$, where $z = v(t)$ and $y = v(t-1)$. The product zy is determined by four successive coin tosses. There are sixteen permutations of four successive tosses and each permutation gives a certain value of z and a certain value of y. Let z_j and y_k be the various possible values of z and y. Also let $p(z_j, y_k)$ be the probability of occurrence of the particular pair of values z_j and y_k (one-sixteenth of the number of such occurrences in the finite ensemble of sixteen permutations). Then $\langle zy \rangle$ is the summation of $p(z_j, y_k)z_jy_k$ over all j and k. Carrying out the arithmetic, we find $\phi(1) = 2$. Similarly, $\phi(2) = 1$. Between the points calculated, the correlation function must be a straight line, because of the steplike character of the signal and the integral character of the correlation operation. For $\tau \geq 3$ the correlation function must vanish, since the signal products involved are determined by entirely independent and random sets of coin tosses, and positive and negative values of such products are equally probable. The theoretical curve is shown in Fig. 6-23(b), together with the "experimental" curve obtained by averaging over twenty-five time units of the sample in Fig. 6-22(a). As the length of the averaging interval is increased, we would expect the experimental curve to approach the theoretical one.

The experimental evaluation of a correlation function for any particular value of τ can be accomplished by discrete sampling rather than by averaging over a *continuum* of time. Sampling is often much easier to instrument and implement in the laboratory. To find $\phi(\tau)$ by sampling, we record the value of the signal at various pairs of points located randomly along the time scale, each sample pair being separated by an interval τ. The average of the pair products tends to approach $\phi(\tau)$ as the number of different sample pairs becomes large.

Incidentally, if the sample signal in Fig. 6-23(a) is from a process of the type indicated in Fig. 6-22(a), then $\phi(\tau) = \langle x \rangle = \bar{x}$. On the other hand, if Fig. 6-23(a) is assumed to arise from a process of the type indicated in Fig. 6-22(b) (synchronism of tosses in the different samples), then $\phi(\tau) = \langle x \rangle = \bar{x}$ for *integer* values of τ, but $\phi(\tau) = \langle x \rangle = \langle \bar{x} \rangle \neq \bar{x}$ for arbitrary values of τ.

6.13   The Trigonometric Fourier Series for a Periodic Signal

We come now to the business of Fourier analysis: the representation of a signal as a sum of sinusoidal components having different frequencies. For a periodic signal of period T we might expect the component frequencies to be $f_k = k/T$, where $k = 0, 1, 2, 3 \cdots$ since sinusoids having these frequencies are the only sinusoids periodic in a time interval T.

Such components are said to be *harmonically* related and the sinusoid of frequency f_k is called the kth *harmonic* of the signal. The first harmonic is often referred to as the *fundamental* component, because it has the same period as the signal itself. The *zeroth* harmonic is, of course, just the time average or d-c part of the signal.

Two sinusoids having unequal frequencies are *orthogonal*:

$$\langle \cos \omega_1 t \cos \omega_2 t \rangle = \langle \sin \omega_1 t \sin \omega_2 t \rangle = \begin{cases} \frac{1}{2}, & \text{for } \omega_1 = \omega_2 \neq 0 \\ 0, & \text{for } \omega_1 \neq \omega_2 \end{cases} \tag{6.142}$$

$$\langle \cos \omega_1 t \sin \omega_2 t \rangle = 0, \qquad \text{for any } \omega_1 \text{ and } \omega_2 \tag{6.143}$$

Orthogonality of the Fourier components means that the extraction of one such component from a signal leaves a remaining signal in which all other harmonics are unaltered in value. Thus the Fourier components are independent in the same sense that the orthogonal components of a space vector are independent. The advantage of working with orthogonal components is simply analytical convenience.

A periodic signal v of period T is, in fact, orthogonal to all sinusoids except those having the harmonic frequencies ω_k. Specifically,

$$\langle v(t) \cos \omega t \rangle = \langle v(t) \sin \omega t \rangle = 0, \qquad \text{for } \omega \neq \omega_k \tag{6.144}$$

where

$$\omega_k = 2\pi k/T \tag{6.145}$$

Quantity ω is the "radian frequency" or "angular frequency," differing from the actual frequency f by a factor 2π. However, we usually refer to ω as simply the "frequency." The harmonic content of a signal is described by the correlation coefficients

$$A_k = 2\langle v(t) \cos \omega_k t \rangle \tag{6.146}$$

$$B_k = 2\langle v(t) \sin \omega_k t \rangle \tag{6.147}$$

The notation is slightly different here but $v(t)$, $\cos \omega_k t$, and A_k have the same places as v_1, v_2, and c_{12} in (6.76), and similarly for $v(t)$, $\sin \omega_k t$, and B_k. The factor 2 in (6.146) and (6.147) arises from the denominator of the correlation-coefficient formula.

Just as $c_{12}v_2$ was a component of v_1 in the earlier discussion of correlation coefficients, so $A_k \cos \omega_k t$ and $B_k \sin \omega_k t$ are the harmonic components of $v(t)$; and $v(t)$ is, of course, the sum (on k) of these components. In general, an infinite number of such components is required for an accurate representation of the signal. The sum of a finite number of harmonic components is an *approximation* to the actual signal

$$v(t) = \langle v \rangle + \sum_{k=1}^{n} (A_k \cos \omega_k t + B_k \sin \omega_k t) + \epsilon_n(t) \qquad (6.148)$$

and $\epsilon_n(t)$ is the difference or *error* between $v(t)$ and its approximation. Since the error is what remains after extraction of the components, we know that the harmonics are orthogonal, not only to each other, but also to the error. Hence

$$\langle v^2 \rangle = \langle v \rangle^2 + \frac{1}{2} \sum_{k=1}^{n} (A_k{}^2 + B_k{}^2) + \langle \epsilon_n{}^2 \rangle \qquad (6.149)$$

This finite-number-of-harmonics approximation, called a *finite Fourier series*, is, for a given n, the best possible approximation in the *mean-square sense*. Any change from these values of A_k or B_k can only increase the mean-square error $\langle \epsilon_n{}^2 \rangle$. This is inherent in the orthogonality of harmonic components and the definitions of the Fourier coefficients A_k and B_k.

We have as yet no reason to believe that the infinite Fourier series is a *complete* representation of the signal. Completeness of an infinite set of components means that the mean-square error approaches zero as the number of terms in the approximation becomes arbitrarily large. Completeness will be discussed later in the chapter. However, we can state here that the Fourier series is complete for all periodic signals of ordinary experience, signals having finite average power and a finite amount of accumulated positive or negative "variation" within one period. If one period of the signal can be drawn upon a piece of paper with a pencil, then we may expect the Fourier representation to be complete. Infinite average power or infinite total variation would use up the pencil (and all other pencils in the world) before completion of the sketch.

Figure 6-24(a) shows one period of an odd square wave and one half-period of its fundamental component (the dashed curve). Since this square wave is an odd function, only the odd-function harmonics $B_k \sin \omega_k t$ need be considered. After extraction of the fundamental component the remaining signal has the form shown in (b). A square wave contains no even-numbered harmonics, a property shared by any signal that is *odd* for a properly chosen time origin and *even* for some other properly chosen time origin. Hence the next component to be extracted is $B_3 \sin \omega_3 t$, as indicated by the dashed curve in Fig. 6-24(b); and so on down to (d), and beyond. The correlation efficiency between the square wave and its fundamental component is approximately 80 per cent.

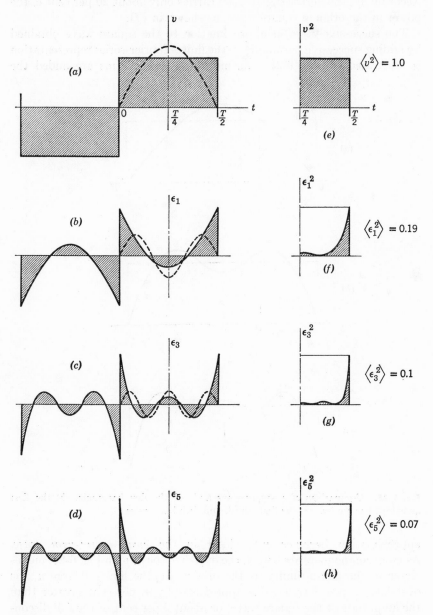

Fig. 6-24. Error ϵ_n remaining after removal of first, third, and fifth harmonics from a square wave.

Accordingly, the "error signal" $\epsilon_1(t)$ carries only about 20 per cent of the power in the original square wave, as shown in (f).

The successively better approximation to the square wave obtained by adding successive harmonics to the finite-Fourier-series representation is illustrated in Fig. 6-25. As more and more terms are added the

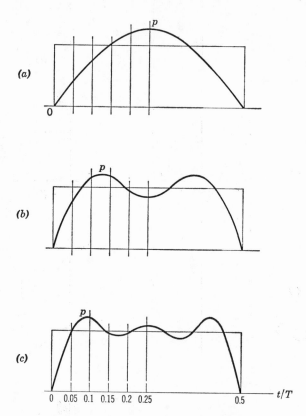

Fig. 6-25. Comparison of a square wave and (a) the first harmonic, (b) the first and third harmonics, (c) the first, third, and fifth harmonics.

approximation becomes ever closer in the *mean-square-error sense*. As more components are added, the overshoot peak p, in Fig. 6-25, moves closer to the discontinuity at the origin. In the limit of large n, the overshoot approaches a value approximately 18 per cent greater than the amplitude of the square wave, or about 9 per cent of the full discontinuous jump in the square wave occurring at the origin. The overshoot, called the Gibbs phenomenon, is followed by very rapid oscillations which die out within a vanishingly small distance from the discontinuity. Except in the immediate neighborhood of a discontinuity, the Fourier series converges exactly to the waveform of the signal. For periodic signals that are everywhere continuous and of bounded variation [defined in (6.212)] the Fourier series converges to an exact representation of the signal.

6.14 The Exponential Fourier Series

With the aid of the complex exponential function

$$\exp\,(j\omega t) = e^{j\omega t} = \cos\omega t + j\sin\omega t \tag{6.150}$$

the Fourier series can be placed in a much more compact form. The average value of the exponential function vanishes unless the frequency is zero

$$\langle e^{j\omega t}\rangle = \begin{cases} 1, & \text{for } \omega = 0 \\ 0, & \text{for } \omega \neq 0 \end{cases} \tag{6.151}$$

Hence two complex exponential functions do not correlate (are orthogonal) unless their frequencies are equal

$$\langle (e^{j\omega_a t})(e^{j\omega_b t})^* \rangle = \langle e^{j(\omega_a - \omega_b)t}\rangle = \begin{cases} 1, & \text{for } \omega_a = \omega_b \\ 0, & \text{for } \omega_a \neq \omega_b \end{cases} \tag{6.152}$$

For a periodic signal of period T, we might expect to find exponential harmonics not only at the frequencies ω_k, where

$$\omega_1 = 2\pi/T \tag{6.153}$$

and

$$\omega_k = k\omega_1 \tag{6.154}$$

but also at the negatives of these frequencies. Two complex exponentials having the frequencies $+\omega$ and $-\omega$ are orthogonal, but the trigonometric function $\sin\omega t$ (or $\cos\omega t$) is not orthogonal to the function produced by changing the sign of ω. If we ignore the negative frequencies in an exponential Fourier series, we ignore half of the independent functions in the set and the series is therefore incomplete.

The correlation coefficient for an exponential component at frequency ω_k is

$$V_k = \langle v(t)e^{-j\omega_k t}\rangle \tag{6.155}$$

and the Fourier series therefore takes the form

$$v(t) = \sum_{k=-n}^{n} V_k e^{j\omega_k t} + \epsilon_n(t) \tag{6.156}$$

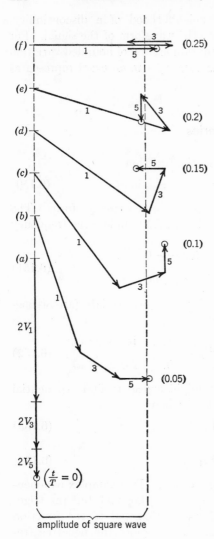

The coefficients V_k are in general complex numbers. As a consequence of orthogonality we have, as before,

$$\langle |v|^2 \rangle = \sum_{k=-n}^{n} |V_k|^2 + \langle |\epsilon_n|^2 \rangle \tag{6.157}$$

Finally, under the assumption that the series is complete,

$$v(t) = \sum_{k=-\infty}^{\infty} V_k e^{j\omega k t} \tag{6.158}$$

The summation (6.158) can be depicted in the complex plane as the "vector" addition of a succession of complex numbers, as illustrated in Fig. 6-26. It is apparent from (6.155) that $V_{-k} = V_k{}^*$ for a real signal. The "conjugate symmetry" of V_k permits us to sum the series over only the positive values of k, and twice the real part of this sum gives (apart from V_0) the value of the signal at any specified time t. When the signal is odd, all of the coefficients V_k are purely imaginary. Figure 6-26(a) shows the summation of the first three terms in the series for an odd square-wave signal. The time t increases from zero, in part (a) of the figure, to one-quarter period in part (f). The various vector diagrams have been plotted from different origins in the complex plane in

Fig. 6-26. Complex addition of first, third, and fifth harmonics in the exponential series of an odd square wave.

order to avoid overlapping. As time increases, each of the complex "vectors" in the string, representing a term in the complex Fourier series, rotates at a different speed so that the string curls in upon itself as depicted in Fig. 6-26. The real parts (horizontal components of the resultants) of the successive complex vector sums in Fig. 6-26 give the values of the signal at the corresponding times marked in Fig. 6-25(c).

Figure 6-26 is a graphic illustration of the way in which a string of little vectors (really complex numbers), spinning at different speeds, can curl up in such a manner that the projection of their sum upon the horizontal axis of the vector diagram approximates the desired signal. As more and more terms are added to the series, the number of vectors in the string becomes arbitrarily large and the tip of the string moves very quickly to the right during the first few positive moments of time. Rapid turning of the small vectors near the tip causes the string to curl into a spiral, and the spiral moves upward, curling tighter and tighter, with its extremity hovering closely about the abscissa representing the amplitude of the square wave.

The autocorrelation function of the signal is

$$\phi(\tau) = \left\langle \sum_i V_i e^{j\omega_i t} \sum_k V_k^* e^{-j\omega_k(t-\tau)} \right\rangle_t \qquad (6.159)$$

where the external subscript t emphasizes that the average is to be taken over t, not τ. Here again the convenience of orthogonal components becomes apparent, for the averaging process eliminates most of the product terms in (6.159), leaving the simple result

$$\phi(\tau) = \sum_k |V_k|^2 e^{j\omega_k \tau} \qquad (6.160)$$

Hence, as mentioned previously, the autocorrelation function of a periodic signal is itself periodic and can be expanded in a Fourier series. The coefficients are

$$\Phi_k = \langle \phi(\tau) e^{-j\omega_k \tau} \rangle_\tau \qquad (6.161)$$

The corresponding series is

$$\phi(\tau) = \sum_{k=-\infty}^{\infty} \Phi_k e^{j\omega_k \tau} \qquad (6.162)$$

and from (6.160) and (6.162) we recognize immediately that

$$\Phi_k = |V_k|^2 \qquad (6.163)$$

Thus the correlation function contains information about the frequency distribution of signal power. In particular, Φ_k is just equal to the average power carried by or associated with the kth exponential harmonic of the signal. For zero τ, (6.162) reduces to a sum of the Φ_k. Since $\phi(0)$ is the average power in the signal, relation (6.162) can be interpreted as a statement that signal power is conserved (invariant) under the transformation from the signal to its Fourier representation.

For real signals, relation (6.155) tells us that corresponding positive-frequency and negative-frequency coefficients are complex conjugates

$$V_k = V_{-k}^*, \qquad \text{for real } v(t) \qquad (6.164)$$

To see the relationship with the trigonometric series, let

$$V_k = \tfrac{1}{2}(A_k - jB_k) \tag{6.165}$$

and

$$V_{-k} = \tfrac{1}{2}(A_k + jB_k) \tag{6.166}$$

Trigonometric expansion of each exponential in (6.158) and pairing of terms gives

$$v(t) = V_0 + \sum_{k=1}^{\infty} \left[(V_k + V_{-k}) \cos \omega_k t + (V_k - V_{-k})j \sin \omega_k t \right] \tag{6.167}$$

and with the aid of (6.165) and (6.166) this is recognizable as the trigonometric series

$$v(t) = V_0 + \sum_{k=1}^{\infty} (A_k \cos \omega_k t + B_k \sin \omega_k t) \tag{6.168}$$

The transformation from a signal to its Fourier representation can be described with simplicity and beauty in terms of the vector-space interpretation of a signal. To reiterate, the signal (one period of a periodic signal) may be sliced into infinitesimally narrow pulses, each occupying a different position in time. These pulses are one possible set of orthogonal signal components; their sum is the signal and the sum of their energies is the signal energy (per period). Now imagine a multidimensional space containing a system of orthogonal co-ordinates. The signal may be thought of as a vector in that space, with the amplitude of each of the narrow pulses representing a component of that vector along one of the co-ordinate axes. The Fourier series also represents the signal as a sum of orthogonal component signals. Hence the vector space contains another system of orthogonal co-ordinates, rotated somehow with respect to the first, in which the components of the signal vector are its Fourier coefficients. Thus the transformation from a signal to its Fourier representation can be interpreted as a *rotation of the co-ordinate system in a vector space*. The signal-power equality (6.157) is a simple consequence of the fact that the length of a vector is independent of the choice of a co-ordinate system, or, to say it another way, the length of a vector is invariant under a rotation of the spacial co-ordinate frame. Although a vector space of more than three dimensions cannot be visualized, the concept is valuable. Many properties of three-dimensional space obviously extend to spaces of higher dimensionality so that geometric intuition becomes an aid to the understanding of signals. See Prob. 6.82 on p. 309.

6.15 Some Fundamental Properties of the Fourier Series

Certain basic operations performed upon a signal produce simple corresponding effects upon the Fourier-series coefficients. A knowledge of such properties is extremely useful for practical calculations and also helps to paint a more complete picture of the Fourier representation itself. Some of the most important relationships will now be listed. All of them follow in a straightforward manner from (6.155) and (6.158), with the usual tacit assumptions about convergence, differentiability, and integrability. We shall find use for nearly all of these special properties in the illustrative examples presented in Article 6.23.

Let the reversible transformation from the signal $v(t)$ to its Fourier-series coefficients V_k be denoted by a double-headed arrow

$$v(t) \leftrightarrow V_k \tag{6.169}$$

and similarly for any other periodic signal $w(t)$ with the same period and the corresponding coefficients W_k. Then,

superposition: $av(t) + bw(t) \leftrightarrow aV_k + bW_k$ (6.170)

reversal: $v(-t) \leftrightarrow V_{-k}$ (6.171)

delay: $v(t - t_0) \leftrightarrow V_k e^{-j\omega_k t_0}$ (6.172)

modulation: $v(t)e^{jm\omega_1 t} \leftrightarrow V_{k-m}$ (6.173)

differentiation: $\dfrac{d^n v(t)}{dt^n} \leftrightarrow (j\omega_k)^n V_k$ (6.174)

integration: $\displaystyle\int_{t_0}^{t} [v(t) - \langle v \rangle]\, dt \leftrightarrow \dfrac{V_k}{j\omega_k},$ for $k \neq 0$

(and d-c term of new series depends upon t_0)   (6.175)

correlation: $\langle v(t)w^*(t - \tau)\rangle \leftrightarrow V_k W_k{}^*$ (6.176)

convolution: $\langle v(t)w(\tau - t)\rangle \leftrightarrow V_k W_k$ (6.177)

conjugate multiplication: $v(t)w^*(t) \leftrightarrow \displaystyle\sum_i V_i W^*_{i-k}$ (6.178)

multiplication: $v(t)w(t) \leftrightarrow \displaystyle\sum_i V_i W_{k-i}$ (6.179)

Notice the duality of form between delay and modulation. Duality of form also stands out when we compare correlation with conjugate multiplication or convolution with multiplication. This should not be too surprising in the light of a vector-space interpretation. The transformation indicated by the double-headed arrow is merely a "rotation of co-ordinates" so that the transformation in one direction should have much the same properties as that in the opposite direction.

6.16 Transition to the Fourier Integral of a Pulse Signal

The complex exponential form of the Fourier series is highly compatible with the impedance concepts of circuit analysis, for which voltages and currents are represented in complex exponential form. Moreover, this form of the series leads smoothly into the Fourier integral now to be discussed. For a periodic function, the correlation coefficient can be obtained by averaging over one period

$$V_k = \frac{1}{T} \int_{-T/2}^{T/2} v(t)e^{-j\omega k t}\, dt \qquad (6.180)$$

Suppose that we wish to analyze a periodic signal consisting of repeated non-overlapping pulses such as those shown in Fig. 6-27(a). If the pulse width δ is not greater than the period T, we can define a function $V_T(\omega)$ characteristic of the pulse shape alone and independent of the value of T

$$V_T(\omega) = \int_{-T/2}^{T/2} v(t)e^{-j\omega t}\, dt \qquad (6.181)$$

For pulses of a given shape the function (6.181) remains unaltered as the period T is increased, whereas the Fourier coefficients V_k become vanishingly small. From (6.180) and (6.181) we see that

$$V_k = \frac{1}{T} V_T(\omega_k) = \frac{\omega_1}{2\pi} V_T(\omega_k) \qquad (6.182)$$

Hence, in terms of $V_T(\omega)$, the Fourier series takes the form

$$v(t) = \sum_{k=-\infty}^{\infty} V_T(\omega_k)e^{j\omega k t}\, \frac{\omega_1}{2\pi} \qquad (6.183)$$

Relations (6.181) and (6.183) are entirely equivalent to (6.155) and (6.158). However, (6.181) and (6.183) differ from (6.155) and (6.158) in two respects. First, the integral (6.181) is a generalization of the integral (6.180), in the sense that the frequency ω is allowed to have any value in (6.181) whereas only discrete frequencies are considered in (6.180). This is merely a matter of notation, since the function $V_T(\omega)$ is to be evaluated only at the discrete harmonic frequencies in (6.183). Second, the averaging factor $1/T$ appearing in (6.180) has been shifted

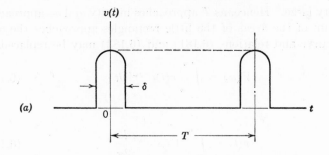

(a)

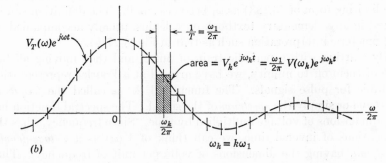

(b)

Fig. 6-27. An interpretation of the Fourier-series coefficients V_k for a periodic train of pulses.

to the Fourier series (6.183) where it appears as $\omega_1/2\pi$. Dimensionally, V_k is an average (volts) whereas $V_T(\omega)$ is an integral (volt-seconds).

The series (6.183) can be interpreted graphically as shown in Fig. 6-27(b). The function $V_T(\omega) \exp(j\omega t)$ is, in general, complex and requires two real curves (of its real and imaginary parts) for its complete description. However, the picture in Fig. 6-27(b) will suffice for an indication of the line of reasoning. The periodic signal has harmonic components only at the discrete frequencies $\omega_k/2\pi$, marked by vertical dashes in the figure. The value of the harmonic component $V_k \exp(j\omega_k t)$ is recognizable as the area of the shaded rectangle in Fig. 6-27(b), and (6.183) shows that the value of $v(t)$, for any specified t, is the sum of the areas of all such rectangles. Now, if we keep the same pulse shape in Fig. 6-27(a) but increase the spacing T between pulses, the function $V_T(\omega) \exp(j\omega t)$ remains the same but the little rectangles in Fig. 6-27(b) become narrower and crowd closer together. In the limit, as T becomes very large, the Fourier coefficients V_k all approach zero and the number of different harmonics in any preassigned frequency interval becomes very large. Hence, as T approaches infinity and ω_1 approaches zero, the sum of the areas of the little rectangles approaches the area under the curve and relations (6.181) and (6.183) may be replaced by

$$V(\omega) = \int_{-\infty}^{\infty} v(t)e^{-j\omega t}\,dt \tag{6.184}$$

and

$$v(t) = \int_{-\infty}^{\infty} V(\omega)e^{j\omega t}\frac{d\omega}{2\pi} \tag{6.185}$$

No trickery is required here. The integral (6.185) is, in fact, *defined* as the limiting form of (6.183) as ω_1 becomes small. The definition can be found in any elementary textbook on calculus, usually accompanied by a geometeric interpretation such as that in Fig. 6-27(b).

By starting with a periodic train of pulses and then moving all but one of them off to infinity, we have arrived at a Fourier representation suitable for pulse signals. The function $V(\omega)$ is called the *frequency spectrum* or simply the *spectrum* of the signal. The spectral function has the dimensions of voltage multiplied by time. Since frequency ω has the dimensions of inverse time, we can think of $V(\omega)$ as a *voltage-density spectrum*, having the dimensions of volts per unit of frequency. Thus the area under the $V(\omega)$ curve has the dimensions of voltage. A pulse signal has a continuous distribution of frequency components, each component being infinitesimally small. In this sense, the component "at" some specified frequency ω_a has an amplitude $V(\omega_a)\,d\omega/2\pi$ associated with the area under the curve between the frequencies ω_a and $\omega_a + d\omega$.

The integrals (6.184) and (6.185) are usually referred to as *Fourier transforms*; (6.184) is the *direct* transformation from time to frequency and (6.185) is the *inverse* transformation from the frequency domain back to the time domain. The spectrum $V(\omega)$ is often called the *transform* of the signal $v(t)$ and the signal is therefore the *inverse transform* of the spectrum.

For infinite n and zero mean-square error in (6.157), we have, by analogy,

$$\int_{-\infty}^{\infty} |v|^2\,dt = \int_{-\infty}^{\infty} |V(\omega)|^2\frac{d\omega}{2\pi} \tag{6.186}$$

which states that the energy in the signal is the same as the energy in the spectrum. To continue the analogy between the Fourier series and the Fourier integral, relations (6.161), (6.162), and (6.163) now convert to the forms

$$\Psi(\omega) = \int_{-\infty}^{\infty} \psi(\tau) e^{-j\omega\tau} \, d\tau \tag{6.187}$$

$$\psi(\tau) = \int_{-\infty}^{\infty} \Psi(\omega) e^{j\omega\tau} \frac{d\omega}{2\pi} \tag{6.188}$$

$$\Psi(\omega) = |V(\omega)|^2 \tag{6.189}$$

where $\Psi(\omega)$ is the *energy-density spectrum* of the signal. The area under the energy-density spectrum, between any two given frequencies ω_a and ω_b, represents that part of the total signal energy carried by frequency components in that range. If $\Psi(\omega)$ is plotted against ω, rather than $\omega/2\pi$, then an area under the curve must be divided by 2π in order to obtain the associated signal energy. Henceforth we shall assume, unless otherwise specified or indicated, that $\Psi(\omega)$ is to be plotted against the true frequency $\omega/2\pi$ in preference to the radian frequency ω.

If the signal $v(t)$ and the exponential function in (6.184) are both separated into their even and odd parts, the transformation can be expanded in the form

$$V(\omega) = 2\int_0^{\infty} v_e(t) \cos \omega t \, dt - j2 \int_0^{\infty} v_0(t) \sin \omega t \, dt \tag{6.190}$$

For real signals this replaces the complex integral (6.184) by the two real integrals in (6.190). From either (6.184) or (6.190) we can recognize the conjugate symmetry of the spectrum of a real signal

$$V(\omega) = V^*(-\omega), \quad \text{for real } v(t) \tag{6.191}$$

Hence, for a real signal, the even and odd parts of the spectrum are real and imaginary, respectively

$$V_e(\omega) = \text{Re}\,[V(\omega)], \quad \text{for real } v(t) \tag{6.192}$$

$$V_0(\omega) = \text{Im}\,[V(\omega)], \quad \text{for real } v(t) \tag{6.193}$$

Relation (6.190) shows that the spectrum of a real even signal is likewise real and even.

6.17 Some Fundamental Properties of Fourier Transforms

Several important properties of Fourier transformations will now be listed for subsequent use. Relations (6.195) through (6.203) are straightforward. The last four are less obvious but, in view of the analogy with (6.176) through (6.179), they should appear to be reasonable, or at least not unreasonable.

$$v(t) \leftrightarrow V(\omega) \tag{6.194}$$

superposition: $a_1v_1(t) + a_2v_2(t) \leftrightarrow a_1V_1(\omega) + a_2V_2(\omega)$
$$\tag{6.195}$$

reversal: $$v(-t) \leftrightarrow V(-\omega), \tag{6.196}$$

scaling: $$v\left(\frac{t}{a}\right) \leftrightarrow aV(a\omega),$$
for real positive a (6.197)

delay: $$v(t - t_0) \leftrightarrow V(\omega)e^{-j\omega t_0} \tag{6.198}$$

modulation: $$v(t)e^{j\omega_0 t} \leftrightarrow V(\omega - \omega_0) \tag{6.199}$$

spectral differentiation: $$t^n v(t) \leftrightarrow (j)^n \frac{d^n V(\omega)}{d\omega} \tag{6.200}$$

signal differentiation: $$\frac{d^n v(t)}{dt^n} \leftrightarrow (j\omega)^n V(\omega) \tag{6.201}$$

integration: $$\int_0^t v_e(t) \, dt + \int_{-\infty}^t v_0(t) \, dt \leftrightarrow \frac{V(\omega)}{j\omega} \tag{6.202}$$

integration: $$\int_{-\infty}^t v(t) \, dt - \frac{1}{2} \int_{-\infty}^\infty v(t) \, dt \leftrightarrow \frac{V(\omega)}{j\omega} \tag{6.203}$$

correlation:

$$\psi_{12}(\tau) = \int_{-\infty}^\infty v_1(t)v_2{}^*(t - \tau) \, dt \leftrightarrow V_1(\omega)V_2{}^*(\omega) = \Psi_{12}(\omega) \quad (6.204)$$

convolution:

$$v_1 \otimes v_2 = \int_{-\infty}^\infty v_1(t)v_2(\tau - t) \, dt \leftrightarrow V_1(\omega)V_2(\omega) \tag{6.205}$$

conjugate multiplication:

$$v(t) = v_1(t)v_2{}^*(t) \leftrightarrow \int_{-\infty}^\infty V_1(\omega)V_2{}^*(\omega - \xi) \frac{d\omega}{2\pi} = V(\xi) \quad (6.206)$$

multiplication:

$$v(t) = v_1(t)v_2(t) \leftrightarrow \int_{-\infty}^\infty V_1(\omega)V_2(\xi - \omega) \frac{d\omega}{2\pi} = V(\xi) \tag{6.207}$$

For a demonstration of relationship (6.204) we can substitute the integral formula for $\psi_{12}(\tau)$ into relation (6.187) to obtain

$$\Psi_{12}(\omega) = \int_{-\infty}^{\infty} \int_{-\infty}^{\infty} v_1(t)v_2{}^*(t-\tau)e^{-j\omega\tau}\, dt\, d\tau \qquad (6.208)$$

Replacement of the variable $t - \tau$ by a new dummy variable t' leads to the form

$$\Psi_{12}(\omega) = \int_{-\infty}^{\infty} \int_{-\infty}^{\infty} v_1(t)v_2{}^*(t')e^{-j\omega(t-t')}\, dt\, dt' \qquad (6.209)$$

which is recognizable as the product of two integrals

$$\Psi_{12}(\omega) = \left[\int_{-\infty}^{\infty} v_1(t)e^{-j\omega t}\, dt\right]\left[\int_{-\infty}^{\infty} v_2(t')e^{-j\omega t'}\, dt'\right]^* \qquad (6.210)$$

The right-hand side of (6.210) is immediately identifiable as the spectral product in (6.204). Item (6.205) is merely a slightly different form of (6.204). Relationships (6.206) and (6.207) then follow directly as a consequence of the duality or symmetry of the direct and inverse Fourier transforms.

6.18 Bounds on the Spectrum

The content, variation, and wiggliness of a pulse signal are defined here as follows:

$$\text{content} = \int_{-\infty}^{\infty} |v|\, dt \qquad (6.211)$$

$$\text{variation} = \int_{-\infty}^{\infty} \left|\frac{dv}{dt}\right|\, dt \qquad (6.212)$$

$$\text{wiggliness} = \int_{-\infty}^{\infty} \left|\frac{d^2v}{dt^2}\right|\, dt \qquad (6.213)$$

The *content* is the absolute integral of the signal and may be visualized as the total area enclosed between the signal curve and the time axis, areas above the axis and below the axis both being counted as positive. For example, the absolute area under the signal in Fig. 6-28(a) is the shaded area indicated in (b).

The *variation* is the absolute integral of the slope and therefore measures the total upward or downward excursion of the signal, both upward and downward movements being counted as positive. Since the ordinary derivative of a function is not defined at a point of discontinuity, there may appear to be difficulty with definition (6.212). Such difficulty can be overcome by the tacit assumptions that the discontinuous signal is only an idealization of the actual signal, and that the actual signal changes very rapidly but nevertheless continuously in the neighborhood of the idealized discontinuity. The difficulty can be avoided altogether by adopting a definition of variation which does not involve the derivative at all. The signal can first be represented as the sum of a nondecreasing function $v_{nd}(t)$ and a nonincreasing function $v_{ni}(t)$, as shown in Fig. 6-28(c). The variation of $v(t)$ in the time interval lying between any two times t_1 and t_2 is then given by $v_{nd}(t_2) - v_{nd}(t_1) - v_{ni}(t_2) + v_{ni}(t_1)$. However we may care to define the variation, it may be visualized as the total accumulated upward and downward motion of a point as that point traces a plot of the signal.

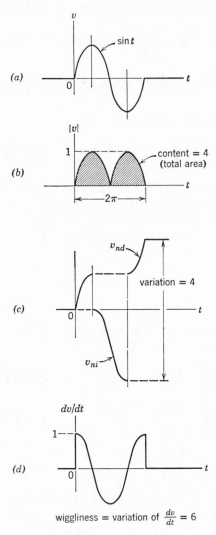

The third quantity, *wiggliness*, is the total variation of the slope of the signal. Any change in slope in either direction, whether instantaneous or gradual, represents a positive contribution to the wiggliness of the signal. In the definition of wiggliness, just as in the definition of variation, questions of discontinuity arise which can be dispatched in much the same manner. The wiggliness of the signal in Fig. 6-28(a) can be evaluated as follows. At the origin the slope changes suddenly from zero to $+1$, thereby contributing one unit of wiggliness. Thereafter the slope drops from $+1$ to -1, depositing two more units of wiggliness. Finally the slope changes from -1 back to $+1$ and thence suddenly to

Fig. 6-28. The form constants of a sinusoidal doublet.

zero, so that the total wiggliness is six. Wiggliness can also be visualized as the total variation of the derivative of the signal, as illustrated in Fig. 6-28(d). Figure 6-29 offers further examples. In the last three of these the original triangular pulse is shown as a dashed line for comparison.

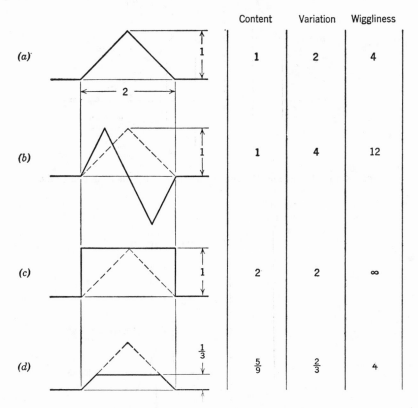

Fig. 6-29. Form constants for various pulses.

For any fixed ω the value of the Fourier integral (6.184) can be visualized as the resultant or sum of a very large number of infinitesimal complex vectors having various orientations in the complex plane. The total path length along this vector string is given by the absolute integral of v. Since the shortest distance between two points in the complex plane is a straight line, the path length along the string of vectors cannot be less than the length of their resultant. Hence

$$|V(\omega)| = \left| \int_{-\infty}^{\infty} v e^{-j\omega t}\, dt \right| \leq \int_{-\infty}^{\infty} |v|\, dt \qquad (6.214)$$

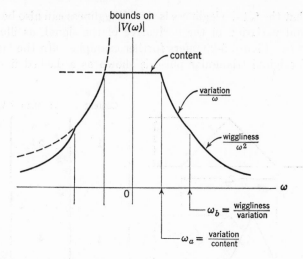

Fig. 6-30. Bounds on the spectrum imposed by the form constants.

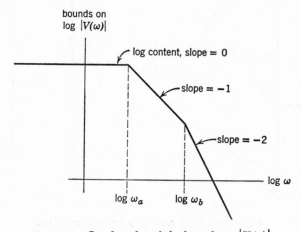

Fig. 6-31. Log-log plot of the bounds on $|V(\omega)|$.

With the aid of (6.201) similar inequalities involving the first and second derivatives of the signal can be obtained

$$\left| j\omega V(\omega) \right| \leq \int_{-\infty}^{\infty} \left| \frac{dv}{dt} \right| dt \tag{6.215}$$

$$\left| (j\omega)^2 V(\omega) \right| \leq \int_{-\infty}^{\infty} \left| \frac{d^2v}{dt^2} \right| dt \tag{6.216}$$

Hence the content, variation, and wiggliness of the signal impose bounds upon the signal spectrum

$$|V(\omega)| \le \begin{cases} \text{content} \\ \text{variation}/|\omega| \\ \text{wiggliness}/\omega^2 \end{cases} \qquad (6.217)$$

Figures 6-30 and 6-31 depict these bounds. In Fig. 6-32 the bounds are plotted to scale for comparison with the actual spectrum of a trapezoidal pulse.

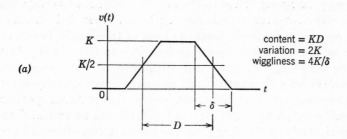

(a)

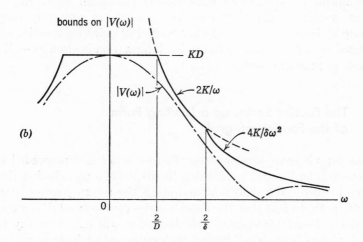

(b)

Fig. 6-32. Bounds on the spectrum of a trapezoidal pulse.

For a periodic signal, the content per period, variation per period, and wiggliness per period place bounds upon the magnitudes of the Fourier-series coefficients V_k. In particular,

$$\text{content} = \langle |v| \rangle \qquad (6.218)$$

$$\text{variation} = \left\langle \left| \frac{dv}{dt} \right| \right\rangle \qquad (6.219)$$

$$\text{wiggliness} = \left\langle \left| \frac{d^2v}{dt^2} \right| \right\rangle \tag{6.220}$$

$$|V_k| \le \begin{cases} \text{content} \\ \text{variation}/|\omega_k| \\ \text{wiggliness}/\omega_k{}^2 \end{cases} \tag{6.221}$$

Bounds on the energy-density spectrum $\Psi(\omega)$ can be found by squaring the bounds on $V(\omega)$. Depending upon the shape of the signal, the bounds may be strong (close to the actual spectrum at various points) or weak (far above the actual spectrum). However, it is usually possible to reason qualitatively from the form of the Fourier integral as to whether or not the actual spectrum lies close to the bound. In some cases the content, variation, and wiggliness of the autocorrelation function $\psi(\tau)$ offer stronger bounds upon the energy-density spectrum than those obtained by squaring the bounds on the signal spectrum.

Inequalities such as (6.214) through (6.216) can be extended to still higher derivatives of the signal but the resulting bounds would become more difficult to estimate by inspection of the signal waveform. The content, variation, and wiggliness of a signal are relatively easy to estimate by inspection and this offers rough but quick information about the signal spectrum. Rough but quick information is often exceedingly valuable in practical work.

6.19 The Fourier Series as a Limiting Form of the Fourier Integral

Thus far we have developed the Fourier series and proceeded from it to the Fourier integral by allowing the period of a periodic function to become infinite. We shall now undertake the return journey along a different path, to find that the Fourier series can be treated as a special case of the Fourier integral. This discussion will pave the way for a unified treatment of signals having both pulse and periodic components.

Given a periodic signal $v(t)$, we can define a truncated signal that includes exactly n periods of the wave. The truncated signal vanishes outside an interval of length nT and therefore has the character of a pulse signal. The corresponding spectrum is

$$V_{(n)}(\omega) = \int_{-nT/2}^{nT/2} v(t)e^{-j\omega t}\, dt \tag{6.222}$$

For n equal to unity the truncated signal is a pulse consisting of one period of the wave and the integral (6.222) is the same as that involved in the calculation of the correlation coefficient V_k. Let V_ω designate the correlation coefficient for an arbitrary frequency ω. Hence

$$V_{(1)}(\omega) = TV_\omega \qquad (6.223)$$

With n larger than unity the integral (6.222) is recognizable as the sum of the Fourier transforms of n different pulse signals, each of length T and each shifted one period with respect to its identical neighbors. The shifting formula (6.198) allows us to treat each of these pulses just

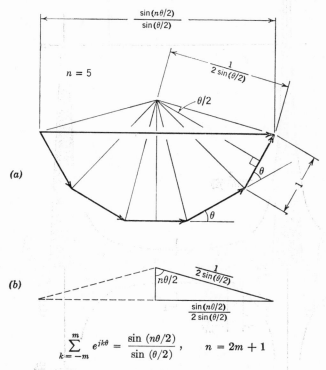

$$\sum_{k=-m}^{m} e^{jk\theta} = \frac{\sin (n\theta/2)}{\sin (\theta/2)}, \qquad n = 2m + 1$$

Fig. 6-33. Summation of a finite complex exponential series.

as though it were centered at the origin, provided we thereafter multiply each transform by the appropriate exponential phase factor. To be specific, the integral (6.222), taken over n periods, is equal to the integral over one period multiplied by the sum of complex exponentials shown in Fig. 6-33(a)

$$V_{(n)}(\omega) = TV_\omega \sum_{k=-m}^{m} e^{-jk\omega T}, \qquad n = 2m + 1 \qquad (6.224)$$

In the figure ωT has been replaced by θ for simplicity. The radius of curvature of the complex vector string is easily obtained from the geometry of the vector diagram and the half-length of the resultant may then be evaluated as shown in (b). Replacing the finite series in (6.224) by its sum gives

$$V_{(n)}(\omega) = TV_\omega \left[\frac{\sin (n\omega T/2)}{\sin (\omega T/2)} \right] \tag{6.225}$$

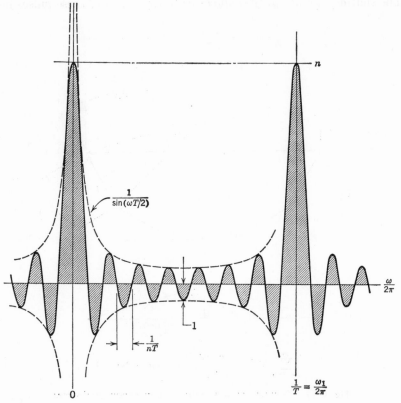

Fig. 6-34. A plot of $\dfrac{\sin (n\omega T/2)}{\sin (\omega T/2)}$ for $n = 15$.

The bracketed factor in (6.225) has the character illustrated in Fig. 6-34. At zero frequency the exponentials are all complex numbers of unit length pointing in the same direction, so that their sum is a maximum. As the frequency increases, the string shown in Fig. 6-33 curls in upon itself. The resultant or sum reaches zero when the string forms a complete circle. Immediately thereafter the resultant reverses direction and then oscillates with decreasing amplitude as the string curls still tighter, overlapping itself many times like a snake swallowing its tail. Eventually, of course, the string of vectors must uncurl again and lie flat, whereupon the whole process repeats as shown in Fig. 6-34.

As n becomes larger the spectral function in Fig. 6-34 tends to concentrate near the frequencies $k\omega_1/2\pi$. For very large n the neighborhood of each frequency $k\omega_1/2\pi$ looks very much like the curve in Fig. 6-2(e) but more compressed horizontally and stretched vertically. The net area under the curve in each such neighborhood therefore approaches the value $1/T$. In the limit of large n the spectrum in Fig. 6-34 behaves like a train of impulses, each of area $1/T$. Specifically,

$$V_{(n)}(\omega) \to V(\omega), \quad \text{for large } n \tag{6.226}$$

and

$$\frac{\sin (n\omega T/2)}{\sin (\omega T/2)} \to \frac{1}{T} \sum_k u_0 \left(\frac{\omega}{2\pi} - \frac{k\omega_1}{2\pi} \right) \tag{6.227}$$

so that

$$V(\omega) = \sum_k V_k u_0 \left(\frac{\omega}{2\pi} - \frac{k\omega_1}{2\pi} \right) \tag{6.228}$$

where V_k is the Fourier-series coefficient, the value of V_ω at the particular frequency $\omega_k = k\omega_1$. Relation (6.228) states that the voltage-density spectrum or Fourier transform of a *periodic signal* consists of *impulses* located at the harmonic frequencies of the signal and that the *area* of each impulse is the *same* as the value of the corresponding *coefficient* in the *Fourier series* of the periodic signal. If the spectrum is plotted against ω instead of $\omega/2\pi$, the spectrum spreads out and the areas of the impulses increase by the factor 2π

$$V(\omega) = 2\pi \sum_k V_k u_0(\omega - k\omega_1) \tag{6.229}$$

Figure 6-35 illustrates the transition from the continuous or distributed spectrum of a single pulse to the discrete spectrum of a periodic signal as more and more pulses are added. In the plots shown the interval between pulses is five times the pulse width but the picture would be qualitatively the same for any other pulse width or pulse shape.

Inverse transformation of (6.228) yields

$$v(t) = \int_{-\infty}^{\infty} V(\omega)e^{j\omega t} \frac{d\omega}{2\pi} = \sum_{k=-\infty}^{\infty} V_k e^{j\omega_k t} \tag{6.230}$$

The integral in (6.230) is simply the weighted sum of the impulse areas, the weighting factor being the exponential function evaluated at the frequency location of each impulse. Hence the inverse transform gives the Fourier series.

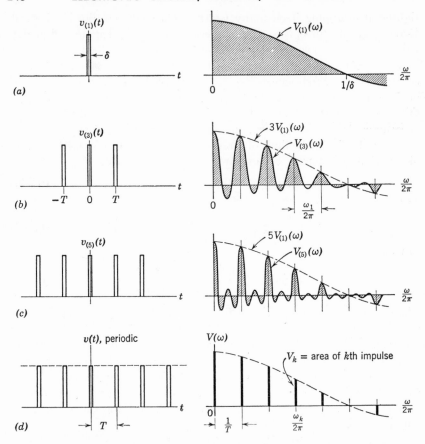

Fig. 6-35. The impulse spectrum of a periodic signal as a limiting form of the spectrum of a finite pulse train.

The squared magnitude of $V(\omega)$ is the energy-density spectrum of the signal. A squared impulse has infinite area, so that the energy-density spectrum is meaningless for a periodic signal. However, each harmonic of a periodic signal carries finite average power (and therefore infinite energy). Hence we may expect the *power-density spectrum* of a periodic signal to be made up of impulses having finite areas. By analogy with (6.229)

$$\Phi(\omega) = 2\pi \sum_k \Phi_k u_0(\omega - k\omega_1) \qquad (6.231)$$

The power-density spectrum $\Phi(\omega)$ is the Fourier transform of the autocorrelation function $\phi(\tau)$, and Φ_k are the coefficients in the Fourier series of $\phi(\tau)$.

In general, an almost-periodic signal cannot be expressed as a Fourier series, but it *can* be represented arbitrarily closely as the sum of two or more different Fourier series. Hence the voltage-density and power-density spectra of an almost-periodic signal do exist and are given by a superposition of the spectra of the different periodic components of the signal. If we build an almost-periodic signal out of an arbitrarily large number of very small periodic components whose periods are irrationally related, then the associated power-density spectrum is an arbitrarily dense distribution of infinitesimal impulses. In other words, the power-density spectrum contains some power in every small frequency interval and therefore may be visualized as a continuous spectrum. In this way, almost-periodic signals provide a link between periodic signals and random signals. A random signal from a stationary process, like a periodic signal, is characterized by a power-density spectrum but the spectrum is continuous rather than discrete.

6.20 Comparison of Spectra

Figure 6-36 summarizes the various transformation processes. The double-headed arrows stand for reversible processes such as the transformation from a signal to its density spectrum or to its Fourier series. The single-headed arrows stand for irreversible processes, in particular, calculation of a correlation function or calculation of the squared magnitude of a complex spectrum. In Fig. 6-36(a) there are two distinct routes from the pulse signal $v(t)$ to its energy-density spectrum $\Psi(\omega)$, one through the signal spectrum to its squared magnitude and the other through the autocorrelation function to its transform. Figure 6-36(b) shows a similar diagram for periodic signals. Here again there are two routes from the signal $v(t)$ to its power-density spectrum $\Phi(\omega)$, one through the Fourier series V_k to the Fourier series Φ_k and thence to the impulsive spectrum $\Phi(\omega)$, and the other through the autocorrelation function $\phi(\tau)$ to its transform $\Phi(\omega)$. Observe that the power-density *spectrum* $\Phi(\omega)$ is *not* the squared magnitude of the voltage-density *spectrum* $V(\omega)$. However, the *area* of each *impulse* in $\Phi(\omega)$ is the squared magnitude of the area of the corresponding *impulse* in $V(\omega)$.

For random signals resulting from stationary processes, there is only one convenient path from the signal $v(t)$ to its power-density spectrum $\Phi(\omega)$, as indicated in Fig. 6-36(c). The reason is that the Fourier integral diverges when applied to a signal from a stationary random process. To be sure, the Fourier integral of a periodic signal also diverges at each harmonic frequency but a convenient limiting process allows us to visualize the spectrum as impulses at those frequencies.

The functions $\Psi(\omega)$ and $\Phi(\omega)$ have been defined as Fourier transforms of the autocorrelation function $\psi(\tau)$ or $\phi(\tau)$. For pulse signals and periodic signals a connection has been established between these functions and the voltage-density spectrum of the signal, thereby directly identifying Ψ or Φ as the energy-density or power-density spectrum of

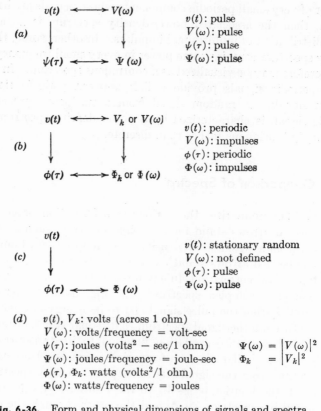

Fig. 6-36. Form and physical dimensions of signals and spectra.

the signal. In the case of stationary random processes such direct identification poses mathematical difficulties. We can ignore these difficulties and agree to accept Φ as a power-density spectrum on the basis of the strong analogy among the diagrams in Fig. 6-36. On the other hand, it might be worthwhile at this point to go quickly through a few mathematical manipulations that shed a little more light upon the character of Φ.

Let us first take a finite segment $v_a(t)$ of the sample function $v(t)$. The segment extends from $t = -a$ to $t = a$ and therefore has a definite and tractable transform $V_a(\omega)$. Looking toward large a we can write

$$\phi_a(\tau) = \frac{1}{2a} \int_{-\infty}^{\infty} v_a(t)v_a{}^*(t - \tau) \, dt \qquad (6.232)$$

$$\Phi_a(\omega) = \int_{-\infty}^{\infty} \phi_a(\tau)e^{-j\omega\tau} \, d\tau \qquad (6.233)$$

whence

$$\Phi_a(\omega) = \frac{1}{2a} \iint v_a(t)v_a{}^*(t - \tau)e^{-j\omega\tau} \, dt \, d\tau \qquad (6.234)$$

The variable change $\tau = t - t'$ then gives a double integral identifiable as

$$\Phi_a(\omega) = \left| \frac{1}{\sqrt{2a}} \int_{-\infty}^{\infty} v_a{}'(t)e^{-j\omega t} \, dt \right|^2 \qquad (6.235)$$

and since

$$V_a(\omega) = \int_{-\infty}^{\infty} v_a(t)e^{-j\omega t} \, dt = \int_{-a}^{a} v(t)e^{-j\omega t} \, dt \qquad (6.236)$$

we have

$$\Phi_a(\omega) = \left| \frac{V_a(\omega)}{\sqrt{2a}} \right|^2 \qquad (6.237)$$

For a stationary random process, $\phi_a(\tau)$ approaches a definite limit $\phi(\tau)$ as a becomes infinite, but $\Phi_a(\omega)$ in general does not. For example, the coin-toss square wave in Fig. 6–22(a) has a $\phi_a(\tau)$ containing not only the triangular pulse $\phi(\tau)$ but also, in the region $-2a < \tau < 2a$, a random component $r_a(\tau) = \phi_a(\tau) - \phi(\tau)$, for which $\overline{r_a} = 0$ and $\overline{r_a{}^2} = (2a - \tau)/(2a)^2$. At a particular ω, the transform $R_a(\omega)$ of $r_a(\tau)$ is essentially the sum of $4a$ independent samples of $r_a(\tau)$, so that $\overline{|R_a(\omega)|^2}$ does not vanish in the limit of large a. However, for large a, the $R_a(\omega)$ at a slightly different ω is effectively the sum of a different set of samples. Hence, if we do a bit of "frequency smoothing" by introducing

$$\Phi_{a\delta}(\omega) = \frac{1}{2\delta} \int_{\omega-\delta}^{\omega+\delta} \Phi_a(\xi) \, d\xi \qquad (6.238)$$

and then let $\delta \to 0$ *after* $a \to \infty$, we may expect to find that $R_{a\delta}(\omega)$ disappears and $\Phi_{a\delta}(\omega)$ approaches a definite limit $\Phi(\omega)$, which is the transform of the limit $\phi(\tau)$.

6.21 Completeness of the Fourier Representation

The question of completeness can be discussed in terms of the Fourier integral, whereupon the results will apply to the Fourier series as a special case. One possible procedure is the following. Given a pulse signal $v(t)$ and *assuming the existence* of its transform $V(\omega)$ defined by (6.184), we can then *define* an error

$$\epsilon_a(t) = v(t) - \int_{-a}^{a} V(\omega)e^{j\omega t}\frac{d\omega}{2\pi} \tag{6.239}$$

The finite limit integral in (6.239) will be called the *approximant* of the signal. As yet the approximant has no relationship with the signal $v(t)$, for that relationship is what we are setting out to find. At this stage in the development the approximant is merely something appearing in the arbitrary definition of the error.

By the very nature of the Fourier transformation, the error is uncorrelated with the approximant and the different frequencies in the approximant are uncorrelated with each other. Hence, just as in (6.157), orthogonality assures

$$\int_{-\infty}^{\infty} |\epsilon_a|^2\, dt = \int_{-\infty}^{\infty} |v|^2\, dt - \int_{-a}^{a} |V(\omega)|^2\frac{d\omega}{2\pi} \tag{6.240}$$

Meanwhile, back at the ranch,

$$|V(\omega)|^2 = \Psi(\omega) = \int_{-\infty}^{\infty} \psi(\tau)e^{-j\omega\tau}\, d\tau \tag{6.241}$$

where $\psi(\tau)$ is defined by (6.88). [Relationship (6.241) was demonstrated in equations (6.208) through (6.210).] Integration of (6.241) over a finite frequency range yields

$$\int_{-a}^{a} |V(\omega)|^2\frac{d\omega}{2\pi} = \int_{-\infty}^{\infty} \int_{-a}^{a} \psi(\tau)e^{-j\omega\tau}\frac{d\omega}{2\pi}\, d\tau \tag{6.242}$$

$$= \int_{-\infty}^{\infty} \psi(\tau)\left[\frac{\sin a\tau}{\pi\tau}\right]d\tau \tag{6.243}$$

The curve of $(\sin a\tau)/\pi\tau$, plotted as a function of τ, has a net positive area equal to unity for all positive values of parameter a. Moreover, for large a the area under the curve is concentrated near the origin cn the τ scale. Hence, provided the integral (6.243) converges for all a, and provided $\psi(\tau)$ is continuous at the origin, the function $(\sin a\tau)/\pi\tau$ may be treated, in the limit of large a, as a unit impulse. Thus

$$\lim_{a \to \infty} \int_{-\infty}^{\infty} \psi(\tau)\left[\frac{\sin a\tau}{\pi\tau}\right]d\tau = \psi(0) \tag{6.244}$$

provided

$$\left|\int_{-\infty}^{\infty} \psi(\tau)\left[\frac{\sin a\tau}{\pi\tau}\right]d\tau\right| < \infty, \qquad \text{for all } a \tag{6.245}$$

From (6.240), (6.243), (6.244), and the definition of $\psi(\tau)$, therefore,

$$\int_{-\infty}^{\infty} |V(\omega)|^2 \frac{d\omega}{2\pi} = \psi(0) = \int_{-\infty}^{\infty} |v|^2 \, dt \qquad (6.246)$$

Now, in view of (6.240), we arrive (tired but happy) at the final result that

$$\lim_{a \to \infty} \int_{-\infty}^{\infty} |\epsilon_a|^2 \, dt = 0 \qquad (6.247)$$

Thus the Fourier integral representation (6.185) of a pulse signal approximates that signal with negligible error energy, provided the autocorrelation function of that signal is such as to satisfy (6.245). In short, Fourier representation is not only orthogonal but also complete.

Finiteness of the energy, content, and variation of the signal are *sufficient* to insure the existence of its transform and the satisfaction of (6.245).

6.22 Some Pulse Signals and Their Spectra

This article and most of the remaining articles of the chapter are devoted to specific examples intended to illustrate the application of Fourier theory in signal analysis.

The first example is the Gaussian pulse shown in Fig. 6-37. As we have already seen in Fig. 6-15, the autocorrelation function is likewise a Gaussian pulse. Now we find that the transform or spectrum of a Gaussian pulse signal is *also* a Gaussian curve. Invariance of the Gaussian form under Fourier transformation is such a remarkable, beautiful, important, and useful phenomenon that it deserves closer investigation. Straightforward transformation of the signal would tell us the fact but not the reason. The interesting question is, "What function is its own transform?" To find the answer we must look for symmetry in the properties of the Fourier transform. Differentiation is the key, for

$$\frac{dv}{dt} \leftrightarrow j\omega V(\omega) \qquad (6.248)$$

and

$$tv(t) \leftrightarrow j\frac{dV}{d\omega} \qquad (6.249)$$

Hence if

$$\frac{dv}{dt} = \pm tv(t) \qquad (6.250)$$

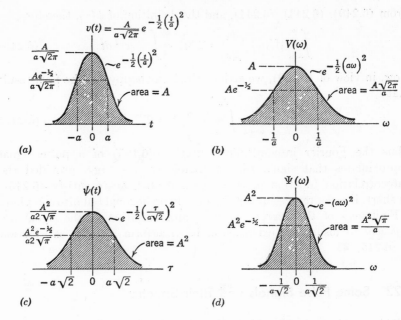

Fig. 6-37. The Gaussian pulse signal and its spectra.

then symmetry assures

$$\frac{dV}{d\omega} = \pm\omega V(\omega) \tag{6.251}$$

which means that the signal and its transform are the same function. In other words,

$$V(x) = Kv(x) \tag{6.252}$$

where K is a constant. Equation (6.250) separates into the form

$$\frac{dv}{v} = \pm t\, dt \tag{6.253}$$

which may be integrated to obtain

$$\log v = \pm\tfrac{1}{2}t^2 \tag{6.254}$$

The additive constant of integration is trivial here and has been ignored in (6.254). Discarding the plus sign (which would give a nontransformable signal), we have

$$v(t) = e^{-\frac{1}{2}t^2} \tag{6.255}$$

and

$$V(\omega) = Ke^{-\frac{1}{2}\omega^2} \tag{6.256}$$

Hence the Gaussian pulse can be *derived* from the assumption that the signal and its spectrum are the same function. [There are many other functions which transform into themselves. Any function $V(x) + v(x)\sqrt{2\pi}$, formed from a real even signal $v(x)$ and its spectrum $V(x)$, is a suitable example. Nevertheless, the Gaussian signal is the basic function arising from an analytic derivation.] To evaluate the constant K it is only necessary to equate the energies in the signal and its spectrum

$$\int_{-\infty}^{\infty} v^2 \, dt = \int_{-\infty}^{\infty} V^2 \frac{d\omega}{2\pi} \tag{6.257}$$

whereupon substitution of (6.255) and (6.256) gives

$$\int_{-\infty}^{\infty} e^{-t^2} \, dt = \frac{K^2}{2\pi} \int_{-\infty}^{\infty} e^{-\omega^2} \, d\omega \tag{6.258}$$

Since the two integrals in (6.258) are identical, it follows immediately that

$$K = \sqrt{2\pi} \tag{6.259}$$

and

$$e^{-\frac{1}{2}t^2} \leftrightarrow \sqrt{2\pi} \, e^{-\frac{1}{2}\omega^2} \tag{6.260}$$

A scaling operation (6.197) then leads directly to the transform pair shown in Fig. 6-37(a) and (b).

The functional position of the scale parameter a in Fig. 6-37 shows that *a narrow pulse has a wide spectrum* and *a wide pulse has a narrow spectrum*, a general property that goes far beyond this particular example. The first four parts of Fig. 6-38 show the limiting form of Fig. 6-37 as parameter a is made small. We see that an impulse signal has a flat spectrum extending over all frequencies. The infinite area under the energy-density curve $\Psi(\omega)$ reflects the fact that an impulse signal has infinite energy. The remaining parts of Fig. 6-38 show the limit approached as A and a both become large with the quotient A/a held fixed at the value $B\sqrt{2\pi}$, where B is a constant. Here we must switch from $\psi(\tau)$ to $\phi(\tau)$ for a meaningful autocorrelation function. A constant signal has an impulse spectrum. All of the power in the signal is concentrated in a single zero-frequency component. Parts (h) and (i) of Fig. 6-38 reiterate the fact that the area of an impulse changes by a factor 2π when the spectrum is plotted against $\omega/2\pi$ rather than ω. Observe that the area of the power-density-spectrum impulse is the square of the area of the voltage-density-spectrum impulse *only* if both spectra are plotted against the true frequency $\omega/2\pi$.

The next example is the square (or rectangular, if you wish) pulse shown in Fig. 6-39(a). The content and variation of the signal establish the spectral bounds indicated by the dashed line in (b). The square

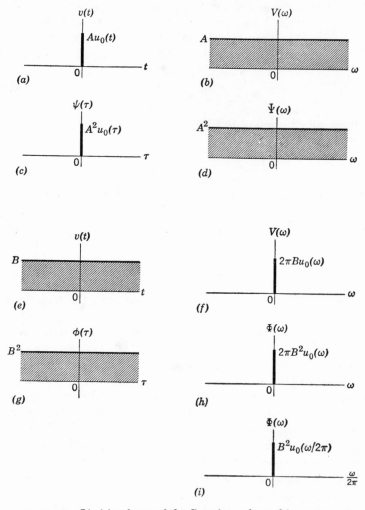

Fig. 6-38. Limiting forms of the Gaussian pulse and its spectra.

pulse is a special case of the trapezoidal pulse in Fig. 6-40(a). Two successive differentiations of the trapezoid reduce it to the four impulses indicated in Fig. 6-40(c) and the corresponding spectrum must be just the original spectrum $V(\omega)$ multiplied by $(j\omega)^2$. Now, with the aid of Fig. 6-38(a) and (b) and the time-delay relationship (6.198) we can evaluate *by inspection* the transform of the second derivative

$$\frac{A}{b-a}\left[(e^{jb\omega} + e^{-jb\omega}) - (e^{ja\omega} + e^{-ja\omega})\right] = (j\omega)^2 V(\omega) \quad (6.261)$$

whereupon division by $(j\omega)^2$ gives the spectrum of the original signal

$$V(\omega) = \frac{2A}{b-a}\left(\frac{\cos a\omega - \cos b\omega}{\omega^2}\right) \quad (6.262)$$

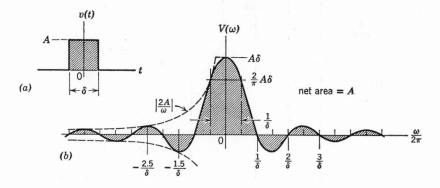

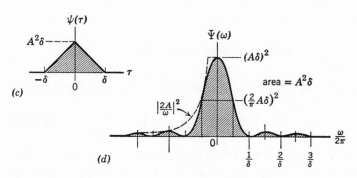

Fig. 6-39. The square-pulse signal and its spectra.

This can be put in the alternative form

$$V(\omega) = (b+a) A \left(\frac{\sin\left[\left(\dfrac{b+a}{2}\right)\omega\right]}{\left(\dfrac{b+a}{2}\right)\omega}\right)\left(\frac{\sin\left[\left(\dfrac{b-a}{2}\right)\omega\right]}{\left(\dfrac{b-a}{2}\right)\omega}\right)$$

$$(6.263)$$

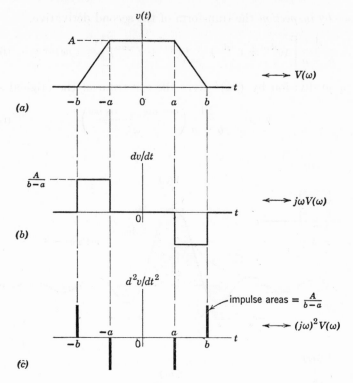

Fig. 6-40. The trapezoidal pulse.

The spectrum in Fig. 6-39(b) is, of course, a special case of (6.263)

$$V(\omega) = A\delta\left[\frac{\sin\,(\delta\omega/2)}{\delta\omega/2}\right] \qquad (6.264)$$

obtained by allowing the trapezoid to approach a rectangle ($a = b = \delta/2$). Similarly, by setting a equal to zero and b equal to δ we obtain the spectrum of a triangular pulse which is plotted in Fig. 6-39(c) and (d). The energy-density spectrum $\Psi(\omega)$ is just the square of $V(\omega)$ in this example, because $v(t)$ is real and even.

The analysis of the trapezoidal pulse illustrates the way in which tedious transform integration often can be avoided by differentiating the signal before carrying out the Fourier transformation. The compensating signal integration (division by $j\omega$) is much easier in the frequency domain. The method enjoys great generality because of the fact that any signal may be approximated as a piecewise-linear (or piecewise-parabolic) curve, in which case the signal reduces to impulses after two (or three) differentiations. Alternatively, a simple but crude stair-step approximation gives impulses after only one differentiation.

Even when such approximations are not convenient, the method may still be adaptable. Figure 6-41 offers an illustration. After a single differentiation the sawtooth pulse (a) takes the form (b). Now suppose

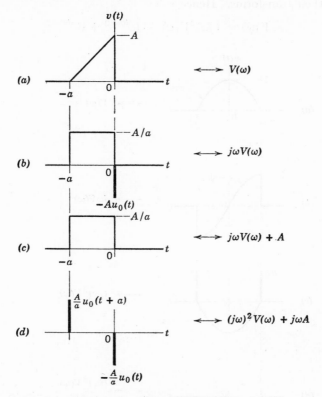

Fig. 6-41. The sawtooth pulse.

that we add an equal and opposite impulse to the signal in Fig. 6-41(b) to cancel the one shown. The result is the rectangular pulse remaining in (c), whose transform is augmented by the flat spectrum A of the added impulse. We are now free to perform a second differentiation which gives the two impulses in (d). Hence

$$\frac{A}{a}\left(e^{j\omega a} - 1\right) = (j\omega)^2 V(\omega) + j\omega A \qquad (6.265)$$

and solution for the original spectrum gives

$$V(\omega) = A\left(\frac{1 + j\omega a - e^{j\omega a}}{a\omega^2}\right) \qquad (6.266)$$

The cosinusoidal pulse in Fig. 6-42 illustrates a different adaptation of the method.   Two differentiations give the function shown in (c) and the impulses may be transferred to the frequency domain as in (d). Signals (a) and (d) are equal but of opposite sign and the same must be true of their transforms.   Hence

$$- V(\omega) = (j\omega)^2 V(\omega) - (e^{j\pi\omega/2} + e^{-j\pi\omega/2}) \qquad (6.267)$$

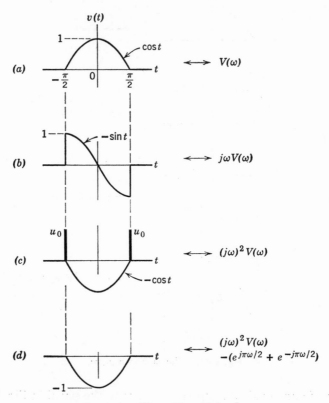

Fig. 6-42.   The cosinusoidal pulse.

which may be solved to obtain

$$V(\omega) = \frac{2 \cos (\pi\omega/2)}{1 - \omega^2} \qquad (6.268)$$

This spectrum, which we shall not bother to plot, looks somewhat like that of a square pulse, the main difference being the greater rapidity with which the spectrum decays as ω increases.   This is to be expected in view of the finite wiggliness of the cosinusoidal pulse.   The denominator of the function (6.268) vanishes for ω equal to unity. However, the numerator also vanishes at that point and the function has a definite limit, as can be computed from the derivatives of the numerator and the denominator

$$V(1) = \lim_{\omega \to 1} \frac{\pi \sin (\pi\omega/2)}{2\omega} = \frac{\pi}{2} \tag{6.269}$$

Like that of the cosinusoidal pulse, the transform of the exponential pulse shown in Fig. 6-43 can be evaluated easily by differentiation. The

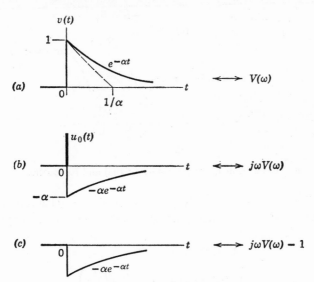

Fig. 6-43. The exponential pulse.

two pulse forms (a) and (c) in Fig. 6-43, and therefore their transforms, differ only by the factor $-\alpha$. Thus

$$-\alpha V(\omega) = j\omega V(\omega) - 1 \tag{6.270}$$

from which we find

$$V(\omega) = \frac{1}{\alpha + j\omega} = V_r + jV_i \tag{6.271}$$

Rationalization of (6.271) separates the real and imaginary parts

$$V_r(\omega) = \frac{\alpha}{\alpha^2 + \omega^2} \tag{6.272}$$

$$V_i(\omega) = \frac{-\omega}{\alpha^2 + \omega^2} \tag{6.273}$$

The spectra of the signal and the voltage-density spectra of its even and odd parts are plotted in Figs. 6-44 and 6-45.

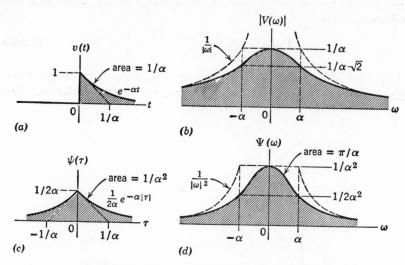

Fig. 6-44. The exponential-pulse signal and its spectra.

In the limit of small α the even part of the signal approaches the constant value $\frac{1}{2}$ and the odd part approaches the unit odd-symmetric step

$$v_e(t) \rightarrow \tfrac{1}{2} \tag{6.274}$$

$$V_r(\omega) \rightarrow \pi u_0(\omega) = \tfrac{1}{2} u_0 \left(\frac{\omega}{2\pi}\right) \tag{6.275}$$

$$v_o(t) \rightarrow \frac{t}{2|t|} \tag{6.276}$$

$$V_i(\omega) \rightarrow -\frac{1}{\omega} \tag{6.277}$$

In the limit of small α, therefore, we have the transform pairs

$$\tfrac{1}{2} \leftrightarrow \pi u_0(\omega) = \tfrac{1}{2} u_0 \left(\frac{\omega}{2\pi}\right) \tag{6.278}$$

$$\frac{t}{2|t|} \leftrightarrow \frac{1}{j\omega} \tag{6.279}$$

As α approaches zero the exponential pulse in Fig. 6-44(a) approaches the *unit step function*

$$u_{-1}(t) = \begin{cases} 1, & \text{for } t > 0 \\ 0, & \text{for } t \leq 0 \end{cases} \tag{6.280}$$

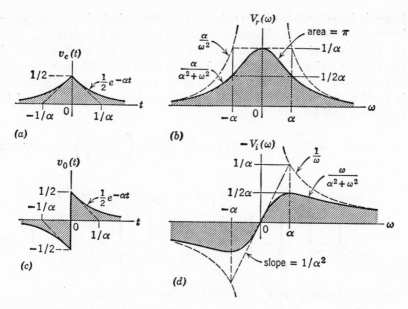

Fig. 6-45. Even and odd parts of the exponential-pulse signal and the associated real and imaginary parts of the signal spectrum.

and its transform is the sum of the transforms of the even and odd parts

$$u_{-1}(t) \leftrightarrow \pi u_0(\omega) + \frac{1}{j\omega} \tag{6.281}$$

Formally, the transform of a unit step signal does not exist, since the signal energy is infinite. However, as we have seen, the unit step signal is the limit approached by a sequence of transformable signals and the spectrum in (6.281) is the limit approached by the corresponding sequence of transforms.

The unit step signal can be visualized as the integral from $-\infty$ to t of the unit impulse $u_0(t)$. The general transform relationship (6.203) is consistent with this interpretation. The constant term on the left of (6.203) can be transferred from the time domain to the frequency domain, appearing there as an impulse $\pi u_0(\omega)$.

6.23 Some Periodic Signals and Their Spectra

Figure 6-46 shows a periodic impulse train in which each impulse has an area a. The impulses are indicated, as usual, by heavy vertical bars. Although the peak value of each impulse is actually arbitrarily large, it is nevertheless convenient to let the *height* of the bar symbol indicate the *area* of the impulse, as has been done in Fig. 6-46(a). Since the transform of a single pulse is the constant a, the coefficients V_k in the Fourier series of the periodic impulse train must all have the value a/T, where T is the period. Hence the discrete spectrum in Fig. 6-46(b) is itself a periodic function. The mathematical representation of the transform pair is

$$a \sum_{k=-\infty}^{\infty} u_0(t - kT) \leftrightarrow \frac{a}{T} \sum_{k=-\infty}^{\infty} u_0\left(\frac{\omega}{2\pi} - \frac{k}{T}\right) \qquad (6.282)$$

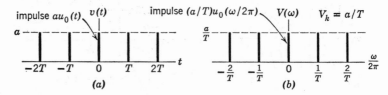

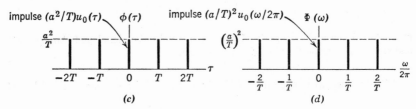

Fig. 6-46. The periodic impulse train and its spectra.

Thus a periodic impulse train (having unity period) is, like a single Gaussian pulse, its own transform. Moreover, the autocorrelation function, also like that of a Gaussian pulse, has the same functional form as the signal. The correlation function of one impulse with another is itself an impulse having an area equal to the product of the areas of the two pulses. Since $\phi(\tau)$ is an average rather than an integral, the area of the impulses in Fig. 6-46(c) is the "correlated area per period" a^2/T. For true impulses the average power of the periodic signal is theoretically infinite.

The next example is the square wave shown in Fig. 6-47(a). Differentiation yields an impulsive function (b) that is recognizable as the difference of two periodic impulse trains, one shifted to the left and the other to the right along the time scale. Shifting a periodic function merely multiplies each of its Fourier coefficients by an exponential factor, as specified in (6.172). Hence, knowing the Fourier series for a periodic impulse train, we can immediately identify the values of the Fourier-

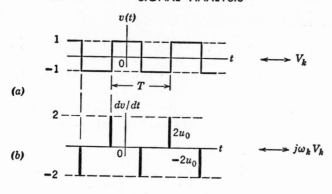

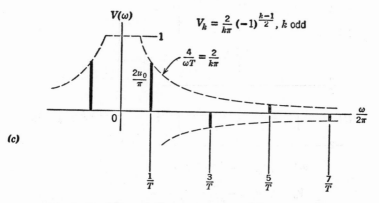

Fig. 6-47. The periodic square wave and its spectrum.

series coefficients for the combined wave in Fig. 6-47 (b). By inspection,

$$\frac{2}{T}\left(e^{j\omega_k T/4} - e^{-j\omega_k T/4}\right) = j\omega_k V_k \qquad (6.283)$$

which gives

$$V_k = \frac{2}{k\pi}\sin\left(\frac{k\pi}{2}\right), \qquad k \neq 0 \qquad (6.284)$$

The derivative of the signal contains no information about its d-c value so that the formula (6.284) can be used only for nonzero k. However, the direct component V_0 obviously vanishes, and the complete story of the Fourier coefficients can be written as

$$V_k = \begin{cases} \dfrac{2}{k\pi}(-1)^{\frac{k-1}{2}}, & k = \pm 1, \pm 3, \cdots \\ 0, & k = \pm 2, \pm 4, \cdots \end{cases} \qquad (6.285)$$

The form constants of the square wave are

$$\text{content} = \langle |v(t)| \rangle = 1 \tag{6.286}$$

$$\text{variation} = \left\langle \left| \frac{dv}{dt} \right| \right\rangle = \frac{4}{T} \tag{6.287}$$

and the corresponding bounds upon the Fourier-series coefficients are indicated by the dashed curve in Fig. 6-47(c). The square wave has

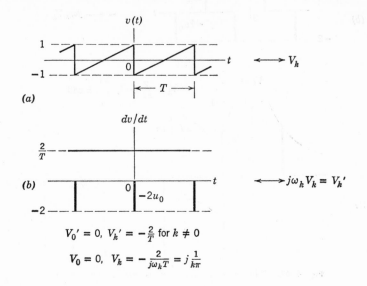

$$V_0' = 0, \quad V_k' = -\frac{2}{T} \text{ for } k \neq 0$$

$$V_0 = 0, \quad V_k = -\frac{2}{j\omega_k T} = j\frac{1}{k\pi}$$

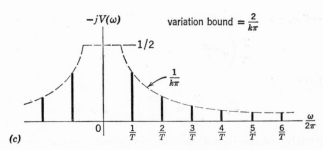

Fig. 6-48. The periodic sawtooth wave and its spectrum.

only odd-numbered harmonics which alternate in sign and decrease in magnitude in inverse proportion to the frequency.

Our next example is the sawtooth wave shown in Fig. 6-48(a). Let V_k' stand for the Fourier-series coefficients of its derivative (b). The derivative necessarily has zero average value so that V_0' vanishes.

Hence the spectrum V_k' is just like that of a periodic impulse train except for the absence of an impulse at zero frequency. Division by $j\omega_k$ gives the coefficients V_k of the sawtooth wave. The voltage-density spectrum is plotted in Fig. 6-48(c). In this case the variation bound is weak.

Next let us consider the periodic train of rectangular pulses shown in Fig. 6-49(a). The transform of a single rectangular pulse has already been discussed. In view of (6.181) and (6.182), the envelope of the

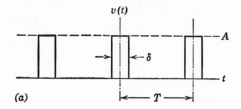

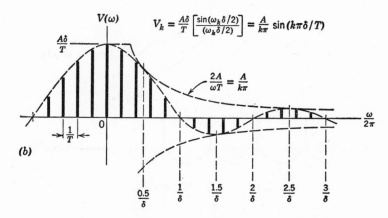

$$V_k = \frac{A\delta}{T}\left[\frac{\sin(\omega_k\delta/2)}{(\omega_k\delta/2)}\right] = \frac{A}{k\pi}\sin(k\pi\delta/T)$$

Fig. 6-49. The periodic rectangular wave and its spectrum.

discrete bar spectrum is just the single-pulse spectrum divided by the averaging factor T. The per-period content and variation give the bounds $A\delta/T$ and $2A/\omega T$, as indicated in Fig. 6-49(b). In the limit of small δ and large A (with the product $A\delta$ held fixed) the pulses approach impulses and the bar envelope broadens to approach the form in Fig. 6-46(b).

Figure 6-50 brings us to the next example, the full-rectified sinusoid. For subsequent convenience of comparison with the half-rectified sinusoid, the analysis will be carried out in terms of the "period" T indicated in Fig. 6-50(a). This is the period of the pure sinusoid whose rectification gives the signal $v(t)$. Double differentiation yields a form (c) consisting of the original signal (multiplied by a negative constant) plus a periodic impulse train. Hence we can write

$$-\omega_1{}^2 V_k + \frac{2A\omega_1}{T}\left(e^{j\omega_k T/4} + e^{-j\omega_k T/4}\right) = (j\omega_k)^2 V_k \qquad (6.288)$$

from which V_k is found to be

$$V_k = \frac{(4A\omega_1/T)\cos(\omega_k T/4)}{\omega_1{}^2 - \omega_k{}^2} = \frac{(2A/\pi)\cos(k\pi/2)}{1 - k^2}, \qquad k \neq \pm 1 \tag{6.289}$$

$$V_1 = V_{-1} = 0 \tag{6.290}$$

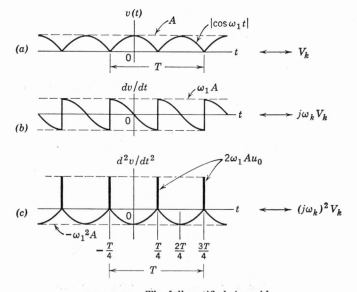

Fig. 6-50. The full-rectified sinusoid.

The "fundamental" harmonic V_1, and every other odd-numbered harmonic, obviously vanishes since the signal in Fig. 6-50(a) is actually periodic in a distance equal to half of the chosen "period" T.

The half-rectified and full-rectified sinusoids are compared in Fig. 6-51. For the amplitudes shown they *differ only by a pure sinusoid.* Hence, having found the Fourier series for the full-rectified wave:

$$v_f(t) = \frac{2A}{\pi} + \frac{4A}{3\pi}\cos 2\omega_1 t - \frac{4A}{15\pi}\cos 4\omega_1 t + \frac{4A}{35\pi}\cos 6\omega_1 t - \cdots \tag{6.291}$$

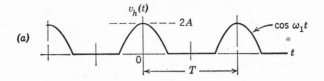

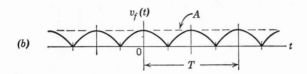

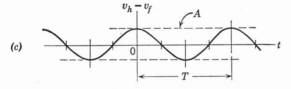

Fig. 6-51. The half-rectified and full-rectified sinusoids and their difference.

We need only add a single sinusoidal term to obtain the series for its half-rectified cousin:

$$v_h(t) = v_f(t) + A \cos \omega_1 t \qquad (6.292)$$

In Fig. 6-49 we saw how the spectrum of a single pulse (when divided by the period T) forms the envelope of the discrete bar spectrum of a periodic train of those pulses. This is a manifestation of a more general transform property that will be explained now in terms of Fig. 6-52. The periodically repeated exponential (e) is recognizable as the cross-correlation function of a single exponential (a) with a periodic impulse train (c). The previously derived relationship (6.204) tells us immediately that the spectrum (f) is the *product* of spectra (b) and (d). In general, *any periodic signal formed by superposition of identical shifted pulse signals has a spectrum equal to the product of the pulse-signal spectrum and the impulsive spectrum of a periodic unit-impulse train.* Moreover, the product relationship holds *even when the individual pulse signals overlap.* It is the overlapping of the exponential tails in Fig. 6-52(e) that is responsible for the amplitude value $1/[1 - \exp(-\alpha T)]$ of the periodic wave.

The "exponential sawtooth" in Fig. 6-53(a) is a relatively simple waveform but determination of its Fourier coefficients by direct time-domain integration is very tedious. Here again, much labor can be

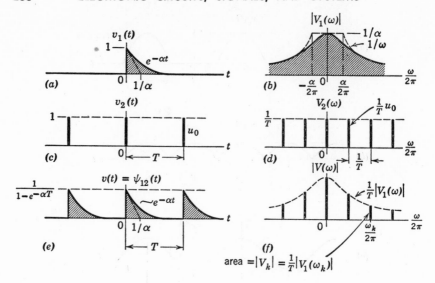

Fig. 6-52. The periodically repeated exponential and its spectrum.

circumvented by differentiating the signal before evaluating the Fourier-series coefficients. As indicated in (a), the exponential within each half-period is heading for a final value A (or $-A$). By inspection of the figure,

$$(A + 1)e^{-\alpha T/2} = A - 1 \qquad (6.293)$$

so that

$$e^{\alpha T/2} = \frac{A + 1}{A - 1} \qquad (6.294)$$

Although the three quantities α, T, and A are not independent, we shall find it convenient to employ all of them in the formulation of the problem. Now, by inspection of Fig. 6-53(b) and (c) we see that the second derivative is made up of the first derivative (multiplied by $-\alpha$) plus extra impulses forming two periodic impulse trains. Thus

$$2\alpha A\left(e^{j\omega_k T/2} - 1\right) - \alpha j\omega_k V_k = (j\omega_k)^2 V_k \qquad (6.295)$$

and since

$$e^{j\omega_k T/2} = e^{jk\pi} = (-1)^k \qquad (6.296)$$

we find

$$V_k = \frac{4\alpha A}{\omega_k{}^2 - j\alpha\omega_k}, \qquad k = \pm 1, \pm 3, \pm 5, \cdots \qquad (6.297)$$

For large A and small α the signal approaches a triangular wave and the

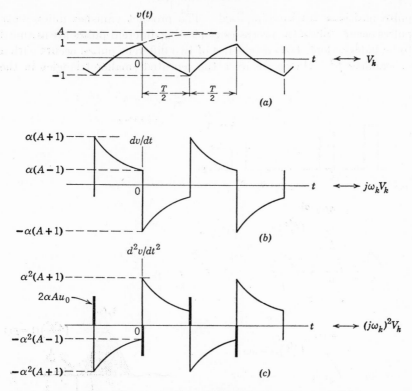

Fig. 6-53. The symmetric periodically repeated exponential.

harmonic amplitudes decrease inversely with the square of the frequency. For large α the signal approaches an odd square wave and the first power of ω becomes the dominant term in the denominator of (6.297).

6.24 Some Random Power Signals and Their Spectra

The random-erasure rectangular wave in Fig. 6-54(a) is a periodic train of rectangular pulses from which pulses are removed independently and randomly with a probability of erasure $1 - p$. In other words, each pulse has a probability p of occurrence or appearance. The auto-correlation function is plotted in Fig. 6-54(b). The value $\phi(0)$ is the average value of the squared signal. On the average we may expect p pulses per period and, since each has an energy $A^2\delta$, the average power of the signal is $A^2\delta p/T$. As τ changes from zero the autocorrelation function decreases linearly until there is no overlap between the signal and its shifted replica. For a shift of exactly one period, two different pulse positions are superimposed. The product vanishes unless both pulses occur. Since the processes generating different pulses are assumed to be independent, the coincidence of two different pulses occurs with a probability p^2. Hence we have the repeated smaller triangles in the

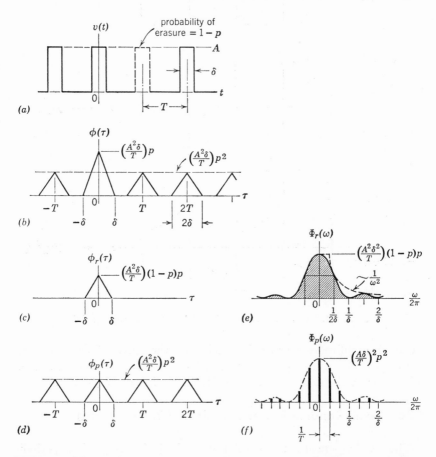

Fig. 6-54. The random-erasure rectangular wave and its random and periodic components.

correlation function. For convenience of discussion the autocorrelation function may be separated into two parts, as shown in Fig. 6-54(c) and (d), one ϕ_r associated with a purely random behavior and the other ϕ_p associated with periodic behavior. The corresponding power-density spectra are plotted in (e) and (f). The "periodic average power" in the signal is $\phi_p(0)$ and the fraction of the total average power $\phi(0)$

carried by the periodic component is just equal to p. As p approaches unity the random component disappears. On the other hand, the signal approaches purely random character for small values of p.

An exceedingly important special case arises when we make the pulses in Fig. 6-54(a) very narrow and bring them close together. First let

$$A\delta = a \tag{6.298}$$

$$\frac{p}{T} = \gamma \tag{6.299}$$

$$\delta = T \tag{6.300}$$

In terms of the new parameters a and γ the d-c power is

$$\left(\frac{A\delta}{T}\right)^2 p^2 = (a\gamma)^2 \tag{6.301}$$

Now, keeping a and γ fixed, let the period T become small, whence

$$T \to 0 \tag{6.302}$$

$$\delta \to 0 \tag{6.303}$$

$$p \to 0 \tag{6.304}$$

and the power-density spectrum of the random component becomes flat and approaches the value

$$\left[\left(\frac{A^2\delta^2}{T}\right)(1 - p)p\right] \to a^2\gamma \tag{6.305}$$

In the limit, the signal assumes the character indicated in Fig. 6-55(a). The impulses are distributed independently and randomly throughout the time continuum and the only signal parameters are the impulse area a and the average density of impulses γ. Such a signal is called a *Poisson distribution* of impulses. The signal in Fig. 6-55(a) is also sometimes referred to as "shot noise," by analogy with the microscopic or electronic model of current flow in a conduction process.

The crosscorrelation function of a Poisson impulse distribution with a pulse signal, such as that in Fig. 6-55(c), constitutes a stationary process and gives a random wave (e) whose power-density spectrum (f) is the product of those in (b) and (d). The permissibility of computing (f) as the simple product of (b) and (d) follows directly from the relationships (6.140) and (6.204) derived previously. Relation (6.140) allows us to compute the autocorrelation function of $v(t)$ in Fig. 6-55(e) by crosscorrelating ϕ_{11} and ψ_{22}. The transform identity (6.204) then identifies Φ as the product of Φ_{11} and Ψ_{22}.

As the parameter α in Fig. 6-55(c) is made smaller, the wide fluctuations of the signal (e) are ameliorated. The power-density spectrum (f) tells us that the ratio of a-c power to d-c power is $\alpha/2\gamma$, but gives us no information about the amplitude distribution of the signal. For simplicity of discussion, imagine that the exponential pulse in Fig. 6-55(c) is replaced by a square pulse. The instantaneous value of the signal $v(t)$ in (e) is determined by the number of impulses (a) falling within

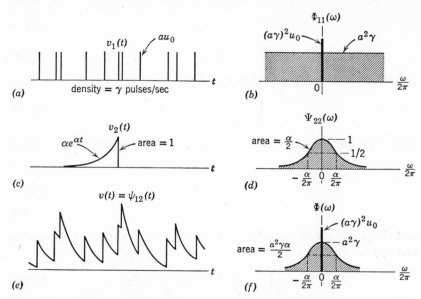

Fig. 6-55. Representation of a random overlapping pulse train (e) as the cross-correlation of a random impulse train (a) and a single pulse (c).

an interval equal to the width of the pulse signal (c). For a nonsquare pulse shape this statement becomes less definite but the effect is the same. Thus, to tell more about the amplitude distribution of the signal we shall need to know the relative probabilities of different numbers of Poisson-distributed impulses in a specified time interval. This brings us to the following digression.

For a Poisson (independent and random) distribution of points along the time scale, let

$$p_n(t) = \text{probability of exactly } n \text{ points in an interval } t \qquad (6.306)$$

$$\gamma = \text{average density of points} \qquad (6.307)$$

It is highly probable that no points will occur in a given infinitesimal interval dt and the probability of one point is very small. The probabilities of two or more points are infinitesimals of higher order. Thus, to the first order,

$$p_1(dt) = \gamma\, dt \tag{6.308}$$

$$p_0(dt) = 1 - \gamma\, dt \tag{6.309}$$

In an interval $t + dt$, therefore, only two possibilities need be considered. Either there are n points in t and no points in dt or $n - 1$ points in t and one point in dt

$$p_n(t + dt) = p_n(t)p_0(dt) + p_{n-1}(t)p_1(dt) \tag{6.310}$$

Substitution of (6.308) and (6.309) into (6.310) yields, after division of both sides by dt and cancellation of identical terms,

$$\frac{p_n(t + dt) - p_n(t)}{dt} = \gamma[p_{n-1}(t) - p_n(t)] \tag{6.311}$$

The left side is the definition of a derivative

$$\frac{dp_n(t)}{dt} = \gamma[p_{n-1}(t) - p_n(t)] \tag{6.312}$$

For n equal to zero we have

$$\frac{dp_0(t)}{dt} = -\gamma p_0(t) \tag{6.313}$$

(The term involving p_{-1} disappears because the probability of a negative number of points is zero.) Equation (6.313) separates

$$\frac{dp_0(t)}{p_0(t)} = -\gamma\, dt \tag{6.314}$$

integrates

$$\log p_0(t) = -\gamma t \tag{6.315}$$

and shows p_0 to be of exponential form

$$p_0(t) = e^{-\gamma t} \tag{6.316}$$

For nonzero n the solution is

$$p_n(t) = \frac{(\gamma t)^n e^{-\gamma t}}{n!} \tag{6.317}$$

as can be verified by substitution into (6.312). The normalized Poisson probabilities are plotted in Fig. 6-56 for visual appreciation of their character. Observe that the average number of points in an interval is also the most probable number, which should not be too surprising. Figure 6-57 shows the probabilities as a function of n for a fixed interval. If, in a given interval, the average or expected number of points is large,

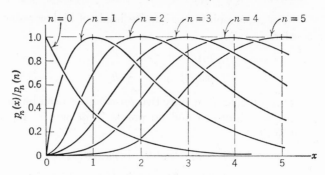

Fig. 6-56. The Poisson probabilities $p_n(x) = \dfrac{x^n e^{-x}}{n!}$.

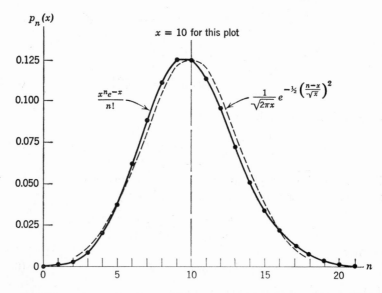

Fig. 6-57. The Poisson distribution, $P_n(x)$ versus n, and the Gaussian form approached for large x.

then the probability distribution approaches Gaussian form

$$p_n(t) \approx \frac{1}{\sqrt{2\pi\gamma t}}\, e^{-\frac{1}{2}\left(\frac{n-\gamma t}{\sqrt{\gamma t}}\right)^2}, \qquad \text{for large } \gamma t \qquad (6.318)$$

and, in the limit, becomes a Gaussian probability-density function.

We can now return to Fig. 6-55. For a pulse (c) whose effective width covers, on the average, a large number of the impulses in (a), we may expect the signal $v(t)$ in (e) to have a Gaussian amplitude distribution centered about some nonzero mean value. The probability-density function is

$$P(v) = \frac{1}{\sqrt{2\pi \, \overline{v_{ac}}^2}} \, e^{\frac{-(v-\bar{v})^2}{2\overline{v_{ac}}^2}} \qquad (6.319)$$

The multiplying factor in front of the exponential is, of course, chosen to give a unit area under the probability-density curve $P(v)$ but the values of $\bar{v}$ and $\overline{v_{ac}}^2$ are as yet undetermined. The power-density spectrum $\Phi(\omega)$ allows us to find these values. By inspection of Fig. 6-55(f)

$$(\bar{v})^2 = \text{d-c power} = (a\gamma)^2 \qquad (6.320)$$

$$\overline{v_{ac}}^2 = \text{a-c power} = \frac{a^2\gamma\alpha}{2} \qquad (6.321)$$

and

$$\frac{\overline{v_{ac}}^2}{(\bar{v})^2} = \frac{\alpha}{2\gamma} \qquad (6.322)$$

We conclude this article with a comparison of the three signals shown in Fig. 6-58, a comparison that brings out some of the similarities and differences between periodic and stationary random processes. The random-reversal square wave (a) has a Poisson distribution of zero crossings. Our first job is to calculate its autocorrelation function (b)

$$\phi_{11}(\tau) = \langle v_1(t)v_1(t-\tau)\rangle = \overline{v_1(t)v_1(t-\tau)} \qquad (6.323)$$

The values $v_1(t)$ and $v_1(t-\tau)$ will be of like sign if the interval τ contains an even number of zero crossings and of opposite sign for an odd number of zero crossings in that interval. Hence

$$\overline{v_1(t)v_1(t-\tau)} = \sum_{n \text{ even}} p_n(\tau) - \sum_{n \text{ odd}} p_n(\tau) = \sum_n (-1)^n p_n(\tau) \qquad (6.324)$$

where $p_n(\tau)$ are the Poisson probabilities

$$p_n(\tau) = \frac{(\gamma\tau)^n e^{-\gamma\tau}}{n!} \qquad (6.325)$$

The power series is recognizable as that of an exponential function

$$\sum_n (-1)^n p_n(\tau) = e^{-\gamma\tau} \sum_{n=0}^{\infty} \frac{(-\gamma\tau)^n}{n!} = e^{-2\gamma\tau} \qquad (6.326)$$

with the immediate result that

$$\phi_1(\tau) = e^{-2\gamma|\tau|} \qquad (6.327)$$

The magnitude of τ, rather than τ itself, appears in (6.327) because a positive τ is assumed in (6.325) and we know the autocorrelation function to be even.

The wave in Fig. 6-58(c) also reverses randomly but reversals are allowed only at unit intervals of t. We might call it a "coin-toss square

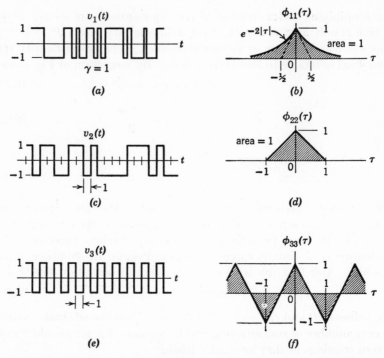

Fig. 6-58. Comparison of three rectangular waves. (a) Random reversal; density of zero crossings = 1. (c) Random reversal at integer values of t with probability 1/2; density of zero crossings = 1/2; (e) Periodic with period = 2; density of zero crossings = 1. (b), (d), (f) Autocorrelation functions.

wave." The random-erasure rectangular wave in Fig. 6-54(a) reduces to the coin-toss square wave when we set

$$\delta = T = 1 \tag{6.328}$$

$$A = 2 \tag{6.329}$$

and

$$p = \tfrac{1}{2} \tag{6.330}$$

and then subtract the unity average value. The corresponding auto-correlation function is shown in Fig. 6-58(d). Finally, the periodic square wave (e) has the periodic triangular autocorrelation function indicated in (f).

The three power-density spectra are plotted in Fig. 6-59. A square-root vertical scale is employed to magnify the skirts of the spectra, which otherwise would be too small for convenient comparison. Now consider the similarities and differences. The periodic square wave has a discrete spectrum; the power is concentrated at definite frequencies. The coin-toss square wave is less definite about its oscillatory behavior

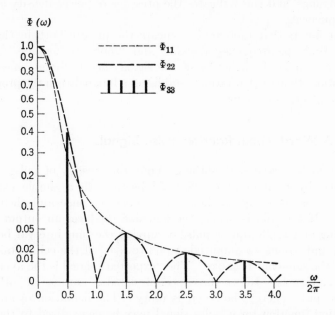

Fig. 6-59. Power spectra for the three rectangular waves.

but still has much in common with the periodic square wave. Its spectrum is distributed rather than discrete but the power still tends to concentrate somewhat in the vicinity of the square-wave harmonics. The random-reversal wave is even less inhibited than the coin-toss wave. Its possible reversal positions are distributed rather than quantized. This "additional randomness" smears or diffuses the spectrum still further, to such an extent that Φ_{11} has no ripples indicative of any basic periodicity.

All three of the spectra fall off inversely as the square of ω at high frequencies because all three of the signals are discontinuous. The power in a given high-frequency interval (say, the interval between 3 and 4 in Fig. 6-59) is related to the average density of zero crossings.

The random-reversal wave and the periodic wave have very nearly the same amount of power in such a frequency interval, whereas the coin-toss wave, with half as many reversals per second as the other two waves, has only about half as much power in the same interval. Neither of the two random waves contains a direct component (which would appear as an impulse at the origin in the power spectrum) but both exhibit high power *density* at frequencies near zero. The statistics of the process predict the relatively frequent occurrence of long intervals between zero crossings, and this indicates the presence of power density at very low frequencies.

The point is that randomness smears the picture both in the time domain and the frequency domain, and "more randomness" (fewer restrictions upon the behavior of the signal) begets "more smearing." This notion, though qualitative, establishes a link between the properties of different types of signals.

6.25   A Word About Random Pulse Signals

Thus far we have said nothing about the spectra of pulse signals generated by random processes. To begin with a simple example, consider a coin-tossing machine which operates once and then stops forever. If the coin is heads, the machine produces an output signal consisting of a single square pulse occupying the time interval between 0 and 1 and having an amplitude equal to $+1$. If the coin is tails, the pulse is the same but negative. The "expected" signal is the average of these two signals. Hence the expected signal is nothing at all! The expected pulse energy, however, is unity. The definition of an autocorrelation function for a pulse signal may be generalized to the form

$$\psi(\tau) = \int \overline{v(t)v(t-\tau)} \, dt \equiv \overline{\int v(t)v(t-\tau) \, dt} \qquad (6.331)$$

where the bar indicates, as usual, the probability-weighted average taken over the ensemble of different possible signals. In short, if we work with the average correlation function, then the corresponding spectrum $\Psi(\omega)$ represents the ensemble-average frequency distribution of signal energy.

On the other hand, we may wish to have a description of the ensemble energy spectrum that retains some information about the location of the signal along the absolute time scale (as would be the case for a radar echo signal whose epoch measures target range). One possibility is to define a truncated signal $v_0(t)$, such that $v_0(t) = v(t)$ for $t < t_0$, and $v_0(t) = 0$ for $t > t_0$. Then the autocorrelation function $\psi_0(\tau, t_0)$ and the energy-density spectrum $\Psi_0(\omega, t_0)$ exhibit a "build-up" as parameter t_0 increases through the epoch of time where the signal is localized. An energy-density spectrum that varies with time is sometimes a useful concept, but care must be taken to give the associated physical experiment a proper interpretation.

6.26   Crosscorrelation of Spectra

In previous examples some use has been made of the fact that the crosscorrelation function of two signals has a spectrum equal to the product of their spectra. The dual relationship is also useful. If a signal can be recognized as the product of two simpler signals, then its spectrum is obtainable as the crosscorrelation function of the two simpler spectra. The principle is illustrated in Fig. 6-60. The finite-duration sinusoid (d) is the product of a pure sinusoid (a) and a square pulse (c). Accordingly, the spectrum (i) may be obtained by locating a replica of the pulse spectrum (h) at each of the frequencies contained in the sinusoid spectrum (f). Similarly, the spectrum (j) is the correlation or convolution of (g) and (h). In this example it does not matter whether we speak of correlation or convolution, since the signals are real and even.

In Fig. 6-60(i) and (j) the dashed curves show the spectral bounds imposed by the content and variation of the signal. The bound in (i) is rather weak at large frequencies, being nine times higher than the small oscillations in the spectrum. It is interesting to compare this weakness of the bound with the fact that only one-ninth of the total signal variation occurs at the discontinuous edges of the signal (d). In spectrum (j), however, the bound could not be much closer to the spectrum without actually touching it. The bound in spectrum (j) appears to be unnecessarily high at the origin. However, the sum of signal (e) and signal (c) has the same content as (e) and only a slightly larger variation. The sum of spectra (h) and (j) would, in fact, touch the bound at zero frequency.

As the length of the sinusoidal segment (d) is increased, the width of each of its two main spectral lobes decreases. The longer the signal, the narrower the band of frequencies covered by each of its spectral lobes. For a signal of any finite length, however long, the significant spectral energy is distributed over a nonzero band of frequencies. This indicates the fundamental limitation upon the "resolving power" of a spectrum analyzer. It also shows that the frequency of a periodic phenomenon can be resolved with great precision if we are willing to exercise patience.

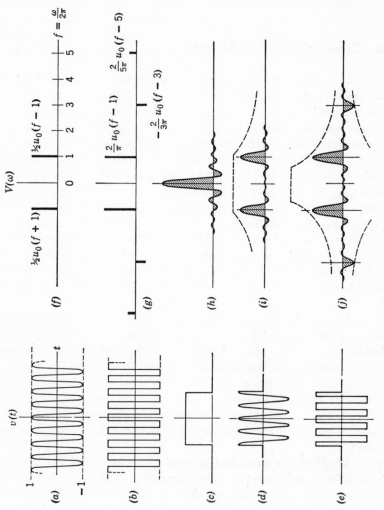

Fig. 6-60. Correlation of spectra.

6.27 The Sampling Theorem

The equivalence of signal multiplication and spectral convolution leads to an important special result called the sampling theorem. Assume that the signal in Fig. 6-61(a) has a spectrum (b) containing negligible energy outside some low-frequency region f_0. Most signals in the real world are of this type, although the location of f_0 for a given

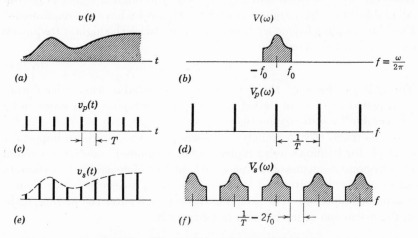

Fig. 6-61. The spectrum of a sampled signal.

signal depends upon what we mean by "negligible energy." Now suppose that the signal is multiplied by a periodic impulse train (c). The product v_s, shown in part (e), is called a *sampled signal* and is said to be obtained from v by *sampling* that signal. The period T is usually referred to as the *sampling interval* and

$$f_s = \frac{1}{T} \tag{6.332}$$

is the so-called *sampling frequency*. By inspection of the spectrum (f) we see that the margin or free space between shifted replicas of the original signal spectrum is given by

$$\text{margin} = f_s - 2f_0 \tag{6.333}$$

If such a margin exists, that is, if the individual spectral pulses do not overlap, then spectrum (f) contains no less information about the original signal than does the original spectrum (b). In other words, the original signal (a) is *recoverable* from the sampled signal (e), perhaps by passing the sampled signal through a frequency filter that tends to reject frequencies above f_0 but passes those frequency components below f_0 without distortion of the low-frequency spectrum. When the margin is negative, the spectral pulses in (f) overlap and the middle pulse is said to be *contaminated* by its overlapping neighbors. In general, the contamination represents some loss of information about the original signal, although in special cases it is sometimes possible to separate the contamination from the original signal spectrum by special processes. However, at least with ordinary filtering, the original signal is not recoverable when the margin is negative. Hence we have the requirement that the sampling frequency must be at least twice the highest frequency contained in the signal

$$f_s \geq 2f_0 \qquad (6.334)$$

To say it another way, the signal must be sampled at least twice during each period or cycle of its highest frequency component in order to be recoverable by ordinary means.

In the realm of signal analysis the sampling theorem is an important concept, for it allows us to replace a "band-limited" continuous signal by a discrete sequence of samples, without loss of generality. A discrete set of numbers is often much more convenient to contemplate than a continuous function. The sampling theorem will enter the picture again in the discussion of modulation in Chapter 8.

6.28   More About Combinations of Signals

When two signals are added, the spectrum of their sum is the sum of their spectra, because the transformation from a signal to its spectrum is a linear operation. Moreover, if the two signals are "completely uncorrelated," that is, orthogonal for any amount of time shift of one signal relative to the other, then the autocorrelation function of their sum is the sum of their autocorrelation functions. To see this, let

$$v_c(t) = v_a(t) + v_b(t) \qquad (6.335)$$

and it follows immediately from the definition of the autocorrelation function that

$$\phi_{cc} = \phi_{aa} + \phi_{ab} + \phi_{ba} + \phi_{bb} \qquad (6.336)$$

Under the assumption that v_a and v_b are completely uncorrelated, the crosscorrelation functions ϕ_{ab} and ϕ_{ba} must vanish, so that

$$\phi_{cc} = \phi_{aa} + \phi_{bb} \qquad (6.337)$$

Since the transform of the autocorrelation function is the power-density spectrum, we see that *the power spectrum of the sum of two uncorrelated signals is the sum of their power spectra.*

The amplitude distribution of a signal is described, at a specified time t, by a probability-density function $P(v)$. If signals v_a and v_b are independent (with respect to first-order statistics), that is, if $P_b(v)$ is not dependent upon the value of v_a, and vice versa, then the probability-density function of the sum of two signals is the convolution of their probability-density functions. For an explanation of this result let us assume first that v_a is a rectangular wave which therefore occupies one of the two discrete values x_1 and x_2, with probabilities of occurrence $p_a(x_1)$ and $p_a(x_2)$. Thus v_c can take the value v only if $v_a = x_1$ and $v_b = v - x_1$ or $v_a = x_2$ and $v_b = v - x_2$. In other words,

$$P_c(v) = p_a(x_1)P_b(v - x_1) + p_a(x_2)P_b(v - x_2) \qquad (6.338)$$

If v_a has more than two possible discrete values, relation (6.338) generalizes to the form

$$P_c(v) = \sum_k p_a(x_k)P_b(v - x_k) \qquad (6.339)$$

It is but a short step from the summation (6.339) to the integral

$$P_c(v) = \int_{-\infty}^{\infty} P_a(x)P_b(v - x) \, dx \qquad (6.340)$$

which applies when both v_a and v_b have continuous rather than discrete amplitude distributions. Thus P_c is recognizable as the convolution of P_a and P_b

$$P_c = P_a \otimes P_b \qquad (6.341)$$

Earlier in the chapter, the correlation function (which, for real even functions, is the same as convolution) of two Gaussian pulses was found to be another Gaussian pulse. In view of (6.341) this gives the important result that *the sum of two independent Gaussian-amplitude signals is itself a Gaussian-amplitude signal.*

Relation (6.341) suggests that the Fourier transform of $P(v)$ would be a convenient alternative description of the amplitude distribution, for the transform of the convolution of two functions is simply the product of the transforms. The transform of a probability-density function is called the *characteristic function* of the signal

$$Q(w) = \int_{-\infty}^{\infty} P(v)e^{-jwv} \, dv \qquad (6.342)$$

Thus

$$P(v) \leftrightarrow Q(w) \qquad (6.343)$$

and

$$Q_c = Q_a Q_b \qquad (6.344)$$

Since the integral of $P(v)$ is unity, we have

$$Q(0) = 1 \qquad (6.345)$$

and since $P(v)$ is never negative, it follows from (6.342) that

$$|Q(w)| \leq Q(0) \qquad (6.346)$$

Now consider the sum of n independent signals, each having the same characteristic function $Q(w)$. The characteristic function of their sum is

$$Q_n(w) = [Q(w)]^n \qquad (6.347)$$

For simplicity, assume that $Q(w)$ is real and even. The logarithm of Q may be expanded in a power series

$$\log Q(w) = a_0 + a_2 w^2 + a_4 w^4 + \cdots \qquad (6.348)$$

The constant term a_0 vanishes because of (6.345) and the odd powers are missing because $Q(w)$ is assumed to be even. We may expect the next coefficient a_2 to be negative, since

$$2a_2 = \left[\frac{d^2 \log Q}{dw^2} \right]_{w=0} = \left[\frac{d^2 Q}{dw^2} \right]_{w=0} = -\int_{-\infty}^{\infty} v^2 P(v) \, dv \quad (6.349)$$

For w less than some value w_1, the higher-order terms are small and we are left with

$$\log Q(w) \approx -\frac{1}{2} \left(\frac{w}{\sigma} \right)^2, \qquad \text{for } |w| < w_1 \qquad (6.350)$$

wherein a_2 has been replaced by $-1/2\sigma^2$. To continue,

$$\log Q_n(w) = n \log Q(w) \approx -\frac{1}{2} \left(\frac{w}{\sigma_n} \right)^2, \qquad \text{for } |w| < w_1 \quad (6.351)$$

where

$$\sigma_n = \sigma / \sqrt{n} \qquad (6.352)$$

Hence

$$Q_n(w) \approx e^{-\frac{1}{2} \left(\frac{w}{\sigma_n} \right)^2}, \qquad \text{for } |w| < w_1 \qquad (6.353)$$

A specific example is given in Fig. 6-62. Any curve that is parabolic (and convex upward) in the neighborhood of its maximum becomes Gaussian when raised to a sufficiently high power. If Q_n is Gaussian, then its transform P_n is likewise Gaussian.

The line of the above argument carries through just as well when the n independent signals do not have identical characteristic functions, so long as each factor Q has a broad maximum in comparison to the Gaussian curve approximating the product, as in Fig. 6-62. This brings us to the remarkable result (a paraphrasing of the "central limit" theorem of probability theory) that *the sum of a large number of independent signals is a Gaussian amplitude signal, provided each of the component signals is "small" in comparison to their sum,* that is, provided the characteristic function of each component signal has a broad maximum in comparison to the characteristic function of their sum.

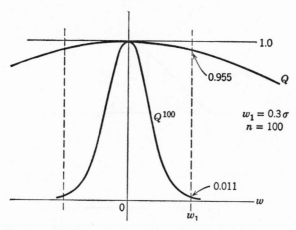

Fig. 6-62. The Gaussian form obtained by raising a curve $Q(w)$ to a high power. The curve $Q(w)$ is assumed to have a continuous negative second derivative near the origin.

The foregoing result offers an explanation of the Gaussian amplitude distribution possessed by many signals originating in nature. For example, the independent random motions of the electrons in a resistor produce a terminal voltage that can be visualized as the sum of a large number of very small independent voltage signals. This matches the experimental fact that the "thermal noise" voltage at the terminals of a resistor exhibits a Gaussian amplitude distribution.

The form of (6.340) reflects the fact that, if v_c has the value v and if v_a has the value x, then v_b must take the value $v - x$. Suppose, instead, that v_c is the product of v_a and v_b:

$$v_c(t) = v_a(t)v_b(t) \tag{6.354}$$

Now, if v_c has the value v and v_a has the value x, then v_b must take the value v/x. It can be shown that relation (6.340) must be replaced, in this case, by

$$P_c(v) = \int_{-\infty}^{\infty} P_a(x) P_b \left(\frac{v}{x}\right) \frac{dx}{|x|} \tag{6.355}$$

The signals v_a and v_b are, of course, assumed to be independent.

So much for the sums and products of signals. Let us turn now to the problem of a signal v_b whose instantaneous value is a nonlinear function of the corresponding instantaneous value of some other signal v_a,

$$v_b = f(v_a) \tag{6.356}$$

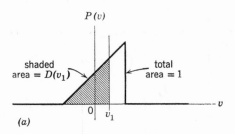

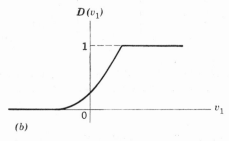

Fig. 6-63. (a) A probability-density function. (b) The associated distribution function.

The problem is to find the amplitude distribution of v_b given that of v_a. The probability-density function $P(v)$ is sometimes loosely referred to as the "distribution" of the signal. However, the name should be reserved for another animal

$$D(v_1) = \int_{-\infty}^{v_1} P(v) \, dv = p(v < v_1) \tag{6.357}$$

which is defined as the *distribution function* of the signal. The distribution function $D(v_1)$ is just equal to the probability that the signal v lies below the given value v_1. The geometrical interpretation is indicated in Fig. 6-63. Now suppose that the single-valued nonlinear function (6.356) has the curve in Fig. 6-64(a). The probability that v_b is less than v_1 is just equal to the total shaded area in Fig. 6-64(b), the integral of $P_a(v)$ taken only over those regions of v for which v_1 exceeds $f(v)$,

$$D_b(v_1) = \int_{f(v) < v_1} P_a(v)\, dv \qquad (6.358)$$

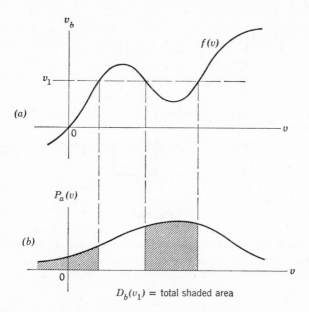

Fig. 6-64. The distribution of $f(v)$.

When $f(v)$ is monotonic (either a nondecreasing or a nonincreasing function of v), relation (6.358) reduces to the simple form

$$D_b[f(v)] = \begin{cases} D_a(v), & \text{for } f(v) \text{ nondecreasing} \\ 1 - D_a(v), & \text{for } f(v) \text{ nonincreasing} \end{cases} \qquad (6.359)$$

or

$$P_b[f(v)]\frac{df(v)}{dv} = \begin{cases} P_a(v), & \text{for } f(v) \text{ nondecreasing} \\ -P_a(v), & \text{for } f(v) \text{ nonincreasing} \end{cases} \qquad (6.360)$$

PROBLEMS

6.1 The signal $v_1(t) = \cos \omega_1 t + \cos \omega_2 t$ "contains" the frequencies ω_1 and ω_2. What frequencies are contained in the signal $v_2(t) = [v_1(t)]^2$?

6.2 (*a*) Show that the net area under the signal in Fig. 6-2(*e*) is π.

(*b*) Repeat for the signal in Fig. 6-2(*f*), where the area is πa.

6.3 Calculate the integral and the integral of the square for each of the following signals:

(*a*) $v(t) = u_0(t)$.

(*b*) $v(t) = \begin{cases} 0, \text{ for } t < 0. \\ e^{-at}, \text{ for } t > 0. \end{cases}$

(*c*) $v(t)$ as shown in Fig. P6-1.

(*d*) $v(t) = \dfrac{1}{1 + t}$.

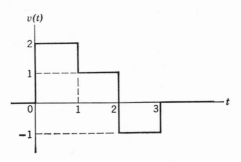

Fig. P6-1

6.4 What is the period of the signal $v(t) = \cos(\omega_0 t/4) + \sin(\omega_0 t/5)$?

6.5 Find the average of and the rms (square root of the mean square) of the signal shown in Fig. P6-2.

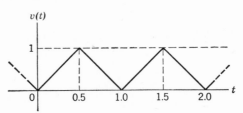

Fig. P6-2

6.6 Find the average power in the signal $v(t) = A \cos(100)t + B \sin(100 + \pi)t$. Also find the minimum and maximum *instantaneous* power. Sketch the waveform of the instantaneous power $[v(t)]^2$. Is $v(t)$ periodic?

6.7 (*a*) List, in a table of 64 rows and 6 columns, the ensemble of all possible sequences of heads and tails that could occur in an experiment consisting of six successive independent tosses of an ideal coin. Designate heads as 1 and tails as 0.

(*b*) Is each sequence equally probable? Why?

(*c*) Let x be the number of heads in a sequence. List the values of x in a seventh column.

(*d*) What is the ensemble average or mean value $\bar{x}$?

(*e*) Plot, versus x, the probability $p(x)$ of x (the relative frequency of occurrence in the ensemble of the value x).

(*f*) List the values of $(x - \bar{x})^2$ in an eighth column and find the mean-square deviation $\overline{(x - \bar{x})^2}$ and the rms deviation $[\overline{(x - \bar{x})^2}]^{\frac{1}{2}}$.

(*g*) Show that the mean-square deviation σ^2 is given by

$$\sigma^2 = \sum_{x=0}^{6} (x - \bar{x})^2 p(x)$$

(*h*) Compare the rms deviation σ obtained in part (*f*) with the theoretical formula $\sigma = \sqrt{n}/2$. In this problem, $n = 6$. Also verify the formula for $n = 4, 3, 2,$ and 1.

6.8 A random signal $v(t)$ is generated by throwing two dice, one red and one white, every millisecond. The value of $v(t)$ in volts at any time t is given by the number of red spots minus the number of white spots facing up.

(*a*) What is the probability-density function of the random variable v? Does it depend on time t?

(*b*) What is the ensemble mean $\bar{v}$ and the ensemble mean-square $\overline{v^2}$? Does either of these values check your intuition?

(*c*) Is the random process stationary? In what sense?

6.9 Give an example (preferably different from any in the text) of:

(*a*) A pulse signal.

(*b*) A periodic signal.

(*c*) An almost-periodic signal.

(*d*) A random signal.

(*e*) A signal generated by a stationary (or quasi-stationary) random process.

(*f*) A signal not in any of the above categories.

6.10 (*a*) Find the mean, the mean square, and the square of the mean for the current waveform shown in Fig. P6-3.

(*b*) The current $i(t)$ is applied to a resistance R. Calculate the total average power, the d-c power, and the a-c power dissipated in the resistance.

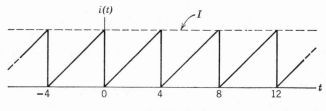

Fig. P6-3

6.11 Find and plot the even and odd parts of the signal in Fig. P6-4. Also show that the integral (over all time) of the signal is the same as the integral of the even part. Verify by direct calculation that the energy of the signal is the sum of the energies of the even and odd parts.

6.12 Show that the energy in any pulse signal is the sum of the energies contained in its even and odd parts.

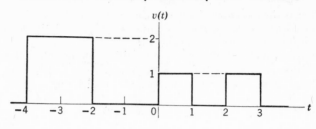

Fig. P6-4

6.13 Find the even and odd parts of $v(t) = \cos(\omega t + \theta)$ and verify their orthogonality.

6.14 Let

$$V = V_r + jV_i$$

$$I^* = I_r - jI_i$$

$$v(t) = V_r \cos \omega t - V_i \sin \omega t$$

$$i(t) = I_r \cos \omega t - I_i \sin \omega t$$

$$VI^* = P + jQ$$

$$p(t) = v(t)i(t)$$

where all major symbols are real numbers, except for $j = \sqrt{-1}$. Make a representative plot of the instantaneous power $p(t)$ and indicate on this plot the four significant dimensions P, $\sqrt{P^2 + Q^2}$, π/ω, and $(1/\omega) \tan^{-1}(V_i/V_r)$.

6.15 The output of a certain signal generator is known to be a rectangular pulse of duration T, starting at zero time. The amplitude of the pulse is not known in advance, but the characteristics of the signal generator suggest that the amplitude may have any value between $-V$ and $+V$, with no more preference for one part of this range than for another.

(a) Sketch and dimension the probability-density function $P(v, t)$ associated with this random signal. Treat t as a parameter.

(b) Calculate the mean (ensemble-average) signal $\overline{v(t)}$.

(c) Calculate the mean (ensemble-average) power $\overline{[v(t)]^2}$ and show that, at any specified t, it is the sum of the power of the mean $[\overline{v(t)}]^2$ and the "deviation" power $\overline{[v(t) - \overline{v(t)}]^2}$.

(d) Calculate the mean (ensemble-average) energy.

6.16 An ideal coin is tossed upon a drumhead, where it falls heads or tails with equal probability. The drum is then struck with a hammer; the coin flies high into the air and once again falls upon the drumhead.

(a) Find the probability-density function for the random variable t, where t is the number of tails appearing in three independent tosses (the initial toss plus two drumbeats) of the ideal coin.

(b) Repeat for the case in which the drum is struck only lightly, so that the probability of tails being followed by tails (or heads by heads) is $> \frac{1}{2}$.

6.17 An ideal coin lies upon a drumhead. The drum is struck periodically at 1-second intervals. The probability of the coin reversing its face in response to a drumbeat is $p = \frac{1}{3}$. Let $x(t)$ be a random variable that takes the value 1 when the coin shows heads and 0 when the coin shows tails.

(a) Find the probability p_k that the same face of the coin shows at two inspection times separated by a time interval k seconds, where k is an integer. *Hint:* If the general solution eludes you, restrict attention to the four values $k = 0, 1, 2, \infty$, which will indicate the character of the function p_k.

(b) From the results of part (a), describe the second-order probability-density function $P[x(t), x(t + k)]$, where k is an integer. Since P is independent of t (for integer values of k), this can be rewritten as $P(x, y; k)$, where x and y stand for $x(t)$ and $x(t + k)$. In particular, visualize the function as a surface of altitude P plotted above the x, y plane. Describe the surface for each of the cases $k = 0$, $k = 1$, and $k = 2$.

6.18 A yard is surrounded by two concentric fences, each containing a gate. The gates open and close independently and at random, with probabilities p and q of being open. Find the probability of escaping, at any given time, from the yard. (An escape consists of an instantaneous mad dash through *both* gates.)

6.19 A fence contains two gates which open and close independently and at random. Their probabilities of being open are p and q. Find the probability of being able, at a given time, to enter the yard enclosed by the fence.

6.20 Vectors u, v, and w all lie in the xy plane and no two of them have the same orientation. Suppose we desire to approximate v by a (vector) sum of components having the directions of u and w. Let

$$v = c_u u + c_w w + \epsilon$$

where the scalars c_u and c_w are chosen to minimize the magnitude $|\epsilon|$ of the error vector ϵ. Do *not* assume that u and w are orthogonal.

(a) First let c_w be zero and adjust c_u for minimum $|\epsilon|$. Using this value of c_u, readjust c_w for a new (smaller) minimum $|\epsilon|$. Indicate, by a suitable sketch in the xy plane, the succession of approximations to v resulting from the successive alternate adjustments of c_u and c_w.

(b) Repeat for the special case in which u and w are orthogonal, that is, $u \cdot w = 0$. What is the advantage of orthogonal components?

6.21 Let v_1 and v_2 be two vectors. Consider the three equations

$$\frac{\partial}{\partial c} |v_1 - cv_2|^2 = 0$$

$$c = \frac{v_1 \cdot v_2}{|v_2|^2}$$

$$|v_1|^2 = |cv_2|^2 + |v_1 - cv_2|^2$$

where $|x|^2$ means $x \cdot x$. Show that *each one* of the equations implies the *other two*.

6.22 A real pulse signal $v(t)$ is given. Let $x(t)$ and $y(t)$ be two orthogonal real pulse signals; $\int x(t)y(t)\, dt = 0$.

(a) Minimize $\int [v(t) - a_1 x(t)]^2\, dt$ by choice of a_1. Solve for a_1.

(b) Minimize $\int [v(t) - a_2 x(t) - b_2 y(t)]^2\, dt$ by choice of a_2 and b_2. Solve for a_2. Does $a_1 = a_2$?

(c) Let $u(t)$ and $w(t)$ be two real pulse signals that are not orthogonal. Minimize $\int [v(t) - c_1 u(t)]^2\, dt$ by choice of c_1. Solve for c_1.

(d) Minimize $\int [v(t) - c_2 u(t) - d_2 w(t)]^2\, dt$ by choice of c_2 and d_2. Solve for c_2. Does $c_1 = c_2$?

(e) What is the virtue of *orthogonal* component signals for the representation of a given signal?

(f) Show that when the minimization in part (b) is carried out the minimum value is

$$\int v^2(t)\, dt - \frac{\left[\int v(t)x(t)\, dt\right]^2}{\int x^2(t)\, dt} - \frac{\left[\int v(t)y(t)\, dt\right]^2}{\int y^2(t)\, dt}$$

and that each additional orthogonal function $z(t)$ added to the set of functions $x, y, \cdots$ therefore reduces the per-unit integral-square error of the representation by an amount

$$\frac{\left[\int v(t)z(t)\, dt\right]^2}{\left[\int v^2(t)\, dt\right]\left[\int z^2(t)\, dt\right]}$$

6.23 If two signals $v_1(t)$ and $v_2(t)$ are complex, show that the value of c_{12} which minimizes the time-average square of $|v_1(t) - c_{12}v_2(t)|$ is given by

$$c_{12} = \frac{\langle v_1 v_2{}^* \rangle}{\langle |v_2|^2 \rangle}$$

Show that the signals $[v_1(t) - c_{12}v_2(t)]$ and $c_{12}v_2(t)$ are then orthogonal.

6.24 Let $v_1(t) = \sin t + \cos 2t$ and $v_2(t) = e^{j\omega t}$. Find the correlation coefficient c_{12} as a function of the parameter ω. Also find the correlation coefficient c_{21} and the correlation efficiency C_{12}.

6.25 Find the value of the turns ratio n of the ideal transformer in Fig. P6-5 that results in minimum average power delivered to the resistance. Signals $v(t)$ and $f(t)$ are real and of such character that the time averages $\langle vf \rangle$ and $\langle f^2 \rangle$ are meaningful.

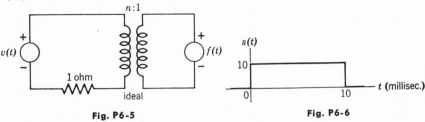

Fig. P6-5   Fig. P6-6

6.26 A radar system determines the range of a target by measuring the time delay suffered by a signal $s(t)$ during its round trip to the target. The signal used for transmission is shown in Fig. P6-6.

During transmission, however, noise $v(t)$ is unavoidably added to the signal $s(t)$. For a simple model of the noise, assume that $v(t)$ is the number of red spots minus the number of white spots facing up on two dice, one white

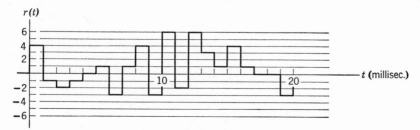

Fig. P6-7

and one red, which are quickly tossed every millisecond. The received echo $r(t)$ at the radar site is known to be of the form $\frac{1}{10}s(t) + v(t)$, and the recorded sample is shown in Fig. P6-7. The delay is known to lie between the bounds 0 and 10 milliseconds.

(a) Can you tell by looking at the received waveform $r(t)$ what delay occurred in transmission? Was the delay equal to an integer number of milliseconds?

(b) One way of estimating the delay is to compute the crosscorrelation function

$$\psi_{rs}(\tau) = \int r(t)[\tfrac{1}{10}s(t - \tau)]\, dt$$

for all relevant τ, and call the delay that value of τ at which $\psi_{rs}(\tau)$ is a maximum. Compute $\psi_{rs}(\tau)$ for the relevant values of τ and estimate the delay.

(c) Would a larger segment of $r(t)$ help in estimating the delay?

(d) Would a different estimate for τ result if s were used for crosscorrelation instead of $\frac{1}{10}s$? Is there any importance in the amplitude of the "reference" signal s used for crosscorrelation?

6.27 Suppose that $f(t)$ and $g(t)$ are two real pulse signals and λ is a real variable. The function $Q(\lambda)$ constructed from the integral

$$Q(\lambda) = \int [f(t) + \lambda g(t)]^2\, dt$$

is a quadratic in λ which is obviously nonnegative for all λ, since the integrand is positive for all t.

(a) What relation does this impose among the quantities $\int f^2(t)\, dt$, $\int g^2(t)\, dt$, and $\int f(t)g(t)\, dt$? (This is known as Schwartz's inequality.)

(b) Use the result to demonstrate that the autocorrelation function $\psi(\tau)$ of a pulse signal $v(t)$ satisfies the relation $|\psi(\tau)| \leq \psi(0)$, for any τ.

(c) Under what condition can equality hold in Schwartz's inequality?

(d) Using the result of part (c), state whether it is possible for equality to hold, in the relation given in part (b), for any nonzero τ? (Remember, these are *pulse* signals.)

6.28   Find the autocorrelation function of the signal $v(t) = a_1 \cos \omega_0 t + b_1 \sin 2\omega_0 t$.

6.29   Plot and dimension the autocorrelation function $\psi_{11}(\tau)$ for a pulse waveform consisting of two rectangular pulses, the first of height A and occupying the time interval between 0 and 1, the second of height B and occupying the time interval between 3 and 4.

6.30   For a random signal $v(t)$ generated by a random process, $\langle v \rangle$ indicates time averaging over one sample of the process and $\bar{v}$ denotes an ensemble average, at a specified time, over the ensemble of equally probable samples that *could* arise from the process.   The following conditions may or may not be met by the process:

(1) $\langle v(t)v(t - \tau) \rangle = \overline{v(t)v(t - \tau)}$

(2) $\langle v(t)v(t - \tau) \rangle = \overline{\langle v(t)v(t - \tau) \rangle}$

(3) $\langle v(t)v(t - \tau) \rangle = \langle \overline{v(t)v(t - \tau)} \rangle$

Give a simple but nontrivial example of a random process which:

(a)   Meets condition (1) for all τ and t.

(b)   Meets conditions (2) and (3) for all τ and t.

(c)   Does not meet condition (1) for all t, except for certain special values of τ.

(d)   Fails to meet conditions (2) and (3).

(e)   Can you think of a process that meets (2) but not (3), or (3) but not (2)?   Why?

6.31   Find the autocorrelation function of the signal $x(t)$ described in Problem 6.17.   In this case the properties of the process are such that the time average

$$\phi(k) = \langle x(t)x(t - k) \rangle$$

and the ensemble average

$$\phi(k) = \overline{x(t)x(t - k)}$$

are equivalent for integer values of k.   For noninteger values of k, we have

$$\phi(\tau) = \langle x(t)x(t - \tau) \rangle$$
$$= \overline{\langle x(t)x(t - \tau) \rangle}$$

Hint: If the general solution eludes you, restrict attention to the six points $\tau = -2, -1, 0, +1, +2, \infty$, which will indicate the character of the auto-correlation function.

6.32   Plot the autocorrelation function of a signal $v(t)$ consisting of a finite train of five square pulses, each of unit height, unit width, and with unit spacing between pulses.

6.33   Find the coefficients of the Fourier series for the signal $v(t) = 10 \sin 30t + 20 \sin 20t$.

6.34   It is desired to construct a series representation for a time function $v(t)$ in the form

$$v(\omega t) = \sum_{k=1}^{3} a_k g_k(\omega t) + \epsilon(t)$$

(a)   With the only specifications on the functions $g_k(t)$ being that they are periodic $[g_k(\omega t + 2\pi) = g_k(\omega t)]$ and orthogonal

$$\frac{1}{2\pi} \int_0^{2\pi} g_k(\omega t)g_p(\omega t)d(\omega t) = \begin{cases} 0, & \text{for } k \neq p \\ 1, & \text{for } k = p \end{cases}$$

find an expression for the mean-square error, $\langle |\epsilon(t)|^2 \rangle$, of the series representation of a function $v(\omega t)$ whose period is $2\pi/\omega$.

(b) Find an expression for the coefficients, a_k, by minimizing the mean-square error. Given that $g_k(\omega t)$ is an odd square wave of period $2\pi/k\omega$, find the coefficients when $v(\omega t)$ is a periodic odd triangular wave of period $2\pi/\omega$. What if $v(\omega t)$ is a periodic even triangular wave? Draw and dimension the error $\epsilon(t)$ for each case.

6.35 Given two periodic waves with arbitrary waveshapes except that the period of $v_1(t)$ is T and the period of $v_2(t)$ is $2T$, express $\phi_{12}(0)$ in terms of the Fourier coefficients of the two periodic waves. Can you write the answer by inspection?

6.36 A finite Fourier series containing only the coefficients V_{-n}, V_{-n+1}, $\cdots$, V_{n-1}, V_n is used as an approximation for a periodic time function $v(t)$. What is the mean-square error of this approximation in terms of $v(t)$ and the Fourier coefficients? Show that the error is orthogonal to each of the terms of the finite Fourier series.

6.37 Let $V(t) = [1 + \cos \omega_1 t] \cos (\omega_2 t + \phi)$.

(a) Find the a-c and d-c parts of $v(t)$ and show that these are orthogonal.
(b) Find the even and odd parts of $v(t)$ and show that these are orthogonal.
(c) Express $v(t)$ as a Fourier series.

6.38 Show that if a periodic function has the property that $f(t + \frac{1}{2}T) = -f(t)$, where T is the period, then the function has only odd harmonics in its Fourier series representation. Also show the converse of this statement.

6.39 An ideal voltage source $E \cos \omega_1 t$ is connected in series with an ideal rectifier and a resistance. The periodic voltage across the resistance is $v(t)$.

(a) Draw and dimension the waveform $v(t)$.
(b) Find the coefficients V_k in the exponential Fourier series for the voltage in part (a). Plot V_k versus k.
(c) Express the result of part (b) as a trigonometric series.
(d) Repeat parts (b) and (c) with the rectifier direction reversed.
(e) What effect does the time shift of a signal [that is, the replacement of t by $t \pm t_0$, resulting in $v(t \pm t_0)$ instead of $v(t)$] have upon the Fourier coefficients V_k?
(f) Use the result of part (e) to find (d) directly from (b).

6.40 The relationship

$$\int_{-\infty}^{\infty} |v(t)|^2 \, dt = \int_{-\infty}^{\infty} V(\omega) V^*(\omega) \frac{d\omega}{2\pi}$$

is an expression of energy conservation. If we attempt to demonstrate that the relationship is correct by using the Fourier integral transform

$$V(\omega) = \int_{-\infty}^{\infty} v(t)e^{-j\omega t} \, dt$$

the value of an integral of the limiting form

$$f(t) = \int_{-\infty}^{\infty} e^{j\omega t} \frac{d\omega}{2\pi}$$

is required.

(a) By investigating the transform properties of a rectangular pulse waveform with duration a and amplitude $1/a$ as a approaches zero, show that the transform pairs

$$u_0(t) = \int_{-\infty}^{\infty} e^{j\omega t} \frac{d\omega}{2\pi}$$

$$1 = \int_{-\infty}^{\infty} u_0(t) e^{-j\omega t} dt$$

hold for the unit impulse $u_0(t)$.

(b) Prove the energy relationship stated at the beginning of this problem.

6.41 Working directly from the two integral expressions representing the direct and inverse Fourier transformations:

(a) Find the Fourier transforms of

(1) $f(t - t_0)$

(2) $\dfrac{df(t)}{dt}$

(3) $\dfrac{d^n f(t)}{dt^n}$

(4) $\int f(\tau) f(t - \tau) \, d\tau$

in terms of the transform $F(\omega)$ of $f(t)$.

(b) Show that the odd part of $F(\omega)$ comes from the odd part of $f(t)$ and the even part of $F(\omega)$ comes from the even part of $f(t)$.

(c) Is $1/j\omega$ an odd function of $j\omega$? What function $f(t)$ will give this as a transform? [Consider the transform $-j\omega/(a^2 + \omega^2)$ and allow a to become small through positive values.]

6.42 Voltages $v_1(t)$, $v_2(t)$, and $v_3(t)$ are real pulse signals, having the Fourier transforms $V_1(\omega)$, $V_2(\omega)$, and $V_3(\omega)$, respectively.

(a) If $v_1(\tau) = \int v_2(t) v_3(\tau - t) \, dt$, show that $V_1(\omega) = V_2(\omega) V_3(\omega)$.

(b) If $v_1(t) = v_2(t) v_3(t)$, show that $V_1(\omega) = \int V_2(\eta) V_3(\omega - \eta) (d\eta/2\pi)$,

where η is the dummy variable of integration.

(c) Comment on the analogy between parts (a) and (b).

6.43 Given the voltage spectral density $V(\omega)$ of a voltage pulse $v(t)$, how is $V(\omega)$ modified if $v(t)$ is replaced by the integral of $v(t)$ between the limits $-\infty$ and t? Assume that the signal defined by the integral has the properties of an energy signal. What restrictions does this place on $v(t)$?

6.44 Calculate the content, variation, and wiggliness of the function

$$f(t) = 1 - t^2, \quad \text{for } |t| < 1$$

$$(t) = 0, \qquad \text{for } |t| \geq 1$$

What is $F(\omega)$? Sketch the bounding curves determined by the content, variation, and wiggliness of $f(t)$. Sketch $F(\omega)$ on the same plot.

6.45 The function $f(t)$ is given by

$$f(t) = 0, \quad \text{for } t \le 0$$
$$f(t) = e^{-t}, \quad \text{for } t > 0$$

Calculate the transform $F(\omega)$ and sketch $|F(\omega)|^2$. Determine the bounds placed on $|F(\omega)|^2$ by the content, variation, and wiggliness of $f(t)$. Calculate the autocorrelation function $\psi(\tau)$. Determine the bounds placed on $|F(\omega)|^2$ by the content, variation, and wiggliness of $\psi(\tau)$. Which set of bounds is stronger?

6.46 Calculate the transform $F(\omega)$ of the pulse

$$f(t) = 1, \quad \text{for } |t| \le 1$$
$$f(t) = 0, \quad \text{for } |t| > 1$$

Compare the magnitude $|F(\omega)|$ with the bound imposed by the variation of $f(t)$. Is $|F(\omega)|$ ever equal to the bound? Under what circumstances is the transform magnitude $|F(\omega)|$ of an even function $f(t)$ equal to the bound imposed by the variation of $f(t)$? *Hint:* Because

$$\omega F(\omega) = -\int_{-\infty}^{\infty} (\sin \omega t) f'(t)\, dt$$

for an even function $f(t)$, the question could have been phrased as follows: Under what conditions does the equality

$$\left| \int_{-\infty}^{\infty} (\sin \omega t) f'(t)\, dt \right| = \int_{-\infty}^{\infty} |f'(t)|\, dt$$

hold? The prime denotes the time derivative.

6.47 For a periodic signal $v(t)$ of period $T = 2\pi/\omega_1$, the Fourier series coefficients V_k obey the inequalities

$$|V_k| \le \frac{1}{T(k\omega_1)^n} \int_0^T \left| \frac{d^n v(t)}{dt^n} \right| dt$$

where k and n are integers and n is nonnegative.

(a) Demonstrate the validity of these inequalities.

(b) Plot $|V_k|$ versus k for the signal $v(t) = \cos t$. For this signal, what region of the $|V_k|$-versus-k plane is allowed by the inequalities above?

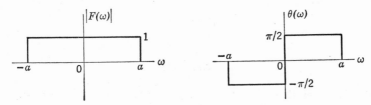

Fig. P6-8

6.48 (a) A signal $f_1(t)$ has the Fourier transform $F(\omega) = |F(\omega)| e^{j\theta(\omega)}$. The curves $|F(\omega)|$ and $\theta(\omega)$ are shown in Fig. P6-8. Find $f_1(t)$.

(b)   The signal $f_1(t)$ is shifted by $0, \pm 3\,\dfrac{\pi}{a}, \pm 6\,\dfrac{\pi}{a}, \cdots, \pm k3\,\dfrac{\pi}{a}$ seconds. A waveform, $f_2(t)$, is formed by summing all of these shifted functions; in particular, $f_2(t) = \displaystyle\sum_{k=-\infty}^{\infty} f_1\left(t - \frac{k3\pi}{a}\right)$. Find $f_2(t)$ in closed form.

(c)   Write the Fourier series for $f_2(t)$.

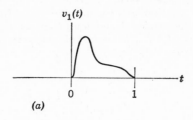

(a)

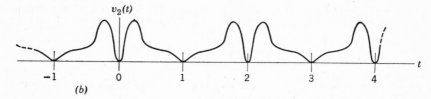

(b)

Fig. P6-9

6.49   Given $V_1(\omega)$, the complex voltage-density spectrum (Fourier transform) of $v_1(t)$, find the Fourier series for $v_2(t)$, where $v_1(t)$ and $v_2(t)$ are related as indicated in Fig. P6-9. Also find the voltage-density spectrum and the power-density spectrum of $v_2(t)$.

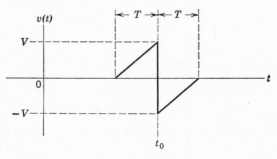

Fig. P6-10

6.50   The operations of harmonic analysis can be symbolized in the form

	Time Domain		Frequency Domain
Voltage	$v(t)$	$\longleftrightarrow$	$V(\omega)$
	$\downarrow$		$\downarrow$
Energy	$\psi(\tau)$	$\longleftrightarrow$	$\Psi(\omega)$

(a) The arrows indicate operations upon the functions. What do they stand for? Why are the vertical paths irreversible ?

(b) Suppose $v(t)$ is as shown in Fig. P6-10. Determine and sketch the energy density spectrum by the route $v(t) \rightarrow V(\omega) \rightarrow \Psi(\omega)$. Show that the alternative path $v(t) \rightarrow \psi(\tau) \rightarrow \Psi(\omega)$ leads to the same result.

(c) Which method seems more direct? If the time function $v(t)$ is derived from a random source such as noise, how can $\Psi(\omega)$, for a pulse signal, or $\Phi(\omega)$, for a power signal, be found conveniently?

6.51 Ohm's acoustic law states that any periodic stimulus is capable of being analyzed into a sum of sinusoidal components, each corresponding to a pure tone, sensible to the ear, having a pitch determined by its frequency. In testing the general applicability of this law, Mathes and Miller (*J. Acoust. Soc. Amer.*, 1947, Vol. 19, pp. 780–799) investigated the effect of phase on auditory judgments. One pair of signals they employed had the following waveforms:

$$v_1(t) = \cos(\omega_c t) + \tfrac{1}{2}\cos[(\omega_c - \omega_m)t] + \tfrac{1}{2}\cos[(\omega_c + \omega_m)t]$$

$$v_2(t) = \sin(\omega_c t) + \tfrac{1}{2}\cos[(\omega_c - \omega_m)t] + \tfrac{1}{2}\cos[(\omega_c + \omega_m)t]$$

With $\omega_c = 2000\pi$ (radians/second) and $\omega_m = 100\pi$ (radians/second), sketch the two waveforms for $0 \leq t \leq \tfrac{1}{50}$ second.

(a) Do *you* think they would sound the same?

(b) Would they have identical autocorrelation functions? Find their autocorrelation functions.

(c) Would they have identical power spectra? Find their power spectra.

6.52 Specify two distinctly different signals that have the same power-density or energy-density spectra. Do this for (a) pulse signals, (b) periodic signals, (c) random power signals.

6.53 Using the Fourier integral, find and plot (with significant dimensions indicated) the frequency spectrum of a normalized plate-current pulse of a class B amplifier. [$f_1(t) = \cos t$, for $-\pi/2 \leq t \leq \pi/2$, and $= 0$ elsewhere.] Present the answer in the form

$$F_1(\omega) = A \left[\frac{\sin(\omega + a)c}{(\omega + a)c} + \frac{\sin(\omega + b)c}{(\omega + b)c} \right] \qquad \begin{array}{l}(A, a, b, \text{ and } c \text{ to be} \\ \text{determined})\end{array}$$

Similarly, find and plot $F_2(\omega)$ for the pulse $f_2(t) = \sin t$, for $-\pi/2 \leq t \leq \pi/2$, and $= 0$ elsewhere.

Note that $f_1(t)$ is not exactly the derivative of $f_2(t)$. What changes or additions would you make in $f_1(t)$ so that it would be exactly $(d/dt)f_2(t)$? If this new function $f_3(t) = (d/dt)f_2(t)$, what is $F_3(\omega)$?

6.54 An impulse is something that happens in negligible time, goes very high, exhibits an area of 1, and has a Fourier transform equal to 1 (if it occurs at the origin of the time axis).

One possible approximation to the impulse is a rectangular pulse of height $1/\delta$ and duration δ. Several other possibilities are indicated below. Find the Fourier transform of each, and show that as δ approaches zero, the functions approach impulses and their transforms approach 1.

(a) $\quad f(t) = \begin{cases} \dfrac{1}{\delta}\left(1 - \left|\dfrac{t}{\delta}\right|\right), & |t| < \delta \\[2mm] 0, \text{ otherwise} \end{cases}$

(b) $f(t) = \dfrac{1}{\delta} \exp\left(-\dfrac{t}{\delta}\right) u_{-1}(t)$

(c) $f(t) = \dfrac{1}{\pi t} \sin\left(\dfrac{t}{\delta}\right)$

(d) $f(t) = \dfrac{1}{\sigma\sqrt{2\pi}} \exp\left(-\dfrac{t^2}{2\sigma^2}\right)$

6.55 The voltage waveforms shown in Fig. P6-11 are typical of those found in a homing-missile range-tracking radar which must automatically acquire a target after the missile has been launched.

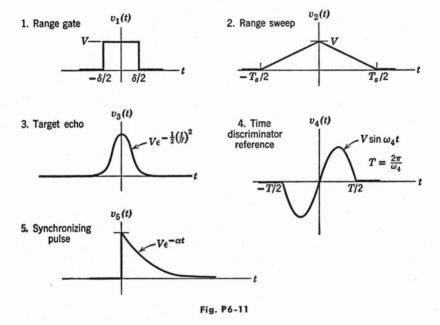

Fig. P6-11

(a)   Find and sketch, with dimensions, the voltage spectral-density function for each of the waveforms.

(b)   If you needed rough estimates of the frequency bandwidths of each of these signals, what values might you choose? Explain.

(c)   Determine and sketch, with dimensions, the autocorrelation function of each of the waveforms.

(d)   For each waveform find the energy-density spectrum from the results of part (a) and from the results of part (c). Compare.

6.56 Given $f_1(t) = u_{-1}(t)e^{-\alpha t}$, calculate, plot, and dimension:

(a) $f_2(t)$, the convolution of $f_1(t)$ with itself.

(b) $|F_2(\omega)|$, the magnitude of the transform of $f_2(t)$.

(c) $f_3(t)$, the autocorrelation function of $f_1(t)$.

(d) $F_3(\omega)$, the transform of $f_3(t)$.

(e)   Are parts (b) and (d) related? Why?

6.57 Find $F(\omega)$ for the waveform in Fig. P6-12. Sketch and dimension the energy-density spectrum $|F(\omega)|^2$.

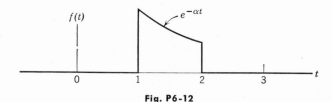

Fig. P6-12

6.58 Find the transforms of the pulse waveforms in Fig. P6-13 using only the transform of an impulse, together with appropriate transform properties.

Give a dimensioned sketch of the frequency spectrum in each case, plotting both magnitude and phase.

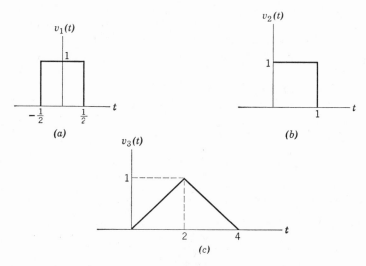

Fig. P6-13

6.59 Find and plot the Fourier transforms of the pulse waveforms shown in Fig. P6-14. How are the transforms related?

6.60 Three a-c voltage sources and three 1-ohm resistors are connected in a three-phase "delta" to supply commercial power as shown in Fig. P6-15. If $v(t)$ is a periodic triangular wave having a 200-volt peak-to-peak amplitude, compute the no-load (terminals A, B, and C open-circuited) average power dissipated in the resistances R. Compare this loss with that calculated using the powerman's rule of thumb that the fundamental and the third harmonic account for most of the loss.

6.61 In an attempt to produce approximate impulses, the output voltage of a square-wave generator is applied to a series RC circuit and a voltage $v(t)$ is measured across the resistance R. Find $v(t)$ and the Fourier series for $v(t)$.

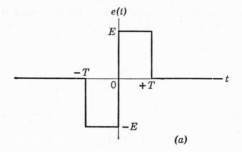

(a)

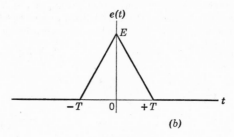

(b)

Fig. P6-14

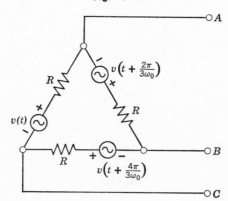

Fig. P6-15

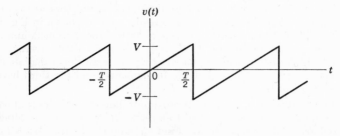

Fig. P6-16

Show that the series approaches that of a periodic impulse train as R is increased.

6.62 The sawtooth voltage waveform shown in Fig. P6-16 is periodic. Determine the Fourier series coefficients V_k.

6.63 Find the Fourier series for the output voltage $v(t)$ in Fig. P6-17.

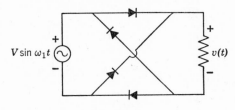

$V \sin \omega_1 t$ $v(t)$

Fig. P6-17

6.64 Vowel sounds are generated by periodically repeated impulsive excitation (from the vocal cords) of an acoustic resonator (the vocal tract). The output of the vocal tract when it is excited by *one* impulse is of the form $u_{-1}(t)e^{-\alpha t} \sin \omega_1 t$. The repetition frequency is $\omega_0/2\pi$. Typical values for $\omega_0/2\pi$, $\omega_1/2\pi$, and α/π are 100, 500, and 100 cycles per second respectively.

  (*a*) Calculate and sketch the power-density spectrum of the steady-state output signal.

  (*b*) Indicate how the spectrum in part (*a*) changes as the "vocal frequency" $\omega_0/2\pi$ changes from 100 to 125 cycles per second, keeping ω_1 and α constant.

  (*c*) Indicate how the spectrum in part (*a*) changes as the "formant frequency" $\omega_1/2\pi$ changes from 400 to 600 cycles per second, keeping ω_0 and α constant. This corresponds to a change in "vowel quality."

6.65 Voltage $v(t)$ is a periodic rectangular wave (even function) that remains alternately at $+E$ for T seconds and at $-E$ for $3T$ seconds.

  (*a*) Find and sketch $\phi(\tau)$, the autocorrelation function of $v(t)$.

  (*b*) Find the autocorrelation function of $v(t - t_1)$.

  (*c*) Find the coefficients Φ_k in the Fourier series for the autocorrelation function in part (*a*).

  (*d*) Find $\Phi(\omega)$, the Fourier transform of the autocorrelation function found in part (*a*). Show that this transform is the power-density spectrum of $v(t)$.

6.66 For the circuit and input waveform in Fig. P6-18, let $E_{bb} = 100$, and $\mu = E_{cc} = r_p = R_b = R_g = 10$, all in appropriate units.

  (*a*) Find Fourier-series expressions for the current delivered by E_{bb} and for the output voltage e_0.

  (*b*) Determine the average power delivered by E_{bb}, dissipated in R_b, and dissipated in the tube. (Average power dissipated in the tube = $\langle e_b i_b \rangle$.) Approximately how many terms of the Fourier series are needed to account for 90 per cent of the power in each case?

6.67 (*a*) Find the complex Fourier series for the periodic voltage wave indicated in Fig. P6-19.

  (*b*) Let $V_k = |V_k|e^{j\theta_k}$. Plot $|V_k|$ and $(\theta_k - \theta_0)$ versus ω. (For convenience of visualization, these plots may be shown as continuous curves, but emphasize the points $\omega = k\omega_1$ at which Fourier components exist.)

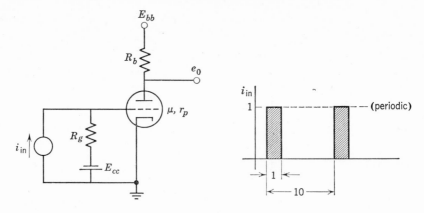

Fig. P6-18

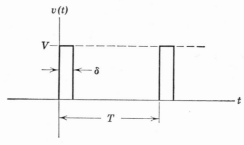

Fig. P6-19

(c)   Show that $V_{-k} = V_k^*$ for a real time function $v(t)$, and that therefore the $|V_k|$ curve is an even function and the $(\theta_k - \theta_0)$ curve is an odd function.

(d)   Show that V_k is real for a real even time function and imaginary for a real odd time function. What does this tell about the trigonometric series for real even and real odd time functions?

(e)   Shift the wave in Fig. P6-19 to the left by an amount $\delta/2$ and plot the corresponding V_k versus ω.

(f)   Briefly discuss the results of part (e) for the special case $\delta = T$.

(g)   Repeat part (f) for the limiting case in which δ becomes small and V becomes large, while the product $V\delta$ remains at the fixed value A.

6.68   Write the Fourier series for a periodic trapezoidal wave in which the flat regions have the same time duration as the regions of constant positive and negative slope separating the flat regions. The period is 1 millisecond and the peak-to-peak amplitude is 1 volt. Assume that the wave is centered on the time axis.

6.69   A relaxation oscillator generates the periodic capacitor-voltage waveform plotted in Fig. P6-20.

The time constant of the exponentials is τ. Find the time-average energy stored in the capacitor due to:

(a)   The zero-frequency component.

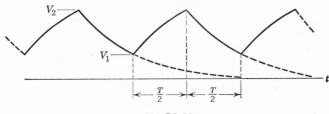

Fig. P6-20

(b) The fundamental components $\omega = \pm 2\pi/T$.

(c) The second-harmonic components $\omega = \pm 4\pi/T$.

(d) The third-harmonic components $\omega = \pm 6\pi/T$.

(e) The a-c part of the signal.

(f) How does the sum of parts (b), (c), and (d) compare with (e)? (Assume $T = K\tau$ and calculate for $K = \frac{1}{5}$, 1, and 5.)

6.70 The trapezoidal wave shown in Fig. P6-21 is periodic.

(a) Determine the Fourier coefficients V_k for $v(t)$.

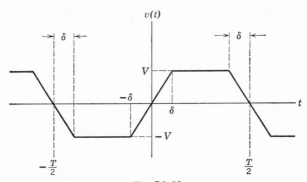

Fig. P6-21

(b) What characteristic of the waveshape accounts for the fact that only odd harmonics are present?

(c) State general conditions upon a periodic signal $v(t)$ such that its Fourier series has only odd-numbered harmonics.

6.71 Figure P6-22 is the output waveform of a simple rectifier circuit

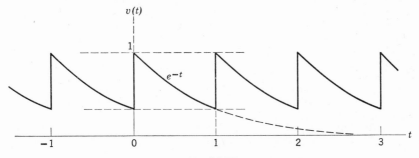

Fig. P6-22

with smoothing capacitor and resistor load. Find the complex Fourier coefficients of the waveform by direct integration. DO NOT approximate the waveform. Verify your answer by any less direct but simpler method which may suggest itself.

6.72 Given that the probability of finding N events in a time interval of T seconds is $[(\gamma T)^N e^{-\gamma T}]/N!$, find a probability-density function for the delay between two successive events. Specifically, find some $P(t)$ such that the probability that the time delay lies between t and $t + dt$ is $P(t)\,dt$.

6.73 The volume flow of air through the human vocal cords during the generation of vowels may be approximated by a nearly periodic sequence of narrow pulses of height A, width δ, and period T between pulses. Random

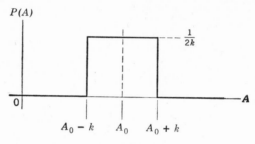

Fig. P6-23

influences, however, cause the amplitudes A of these pulses to fluctuate about a mean value A_0. Assume that the probability density $P(A)$ of amplitudes is rectangular, as shown in Fig. P6-23. Find the autocorrelation function and power spectrum of this pulse train. Assume $\delta \ll T$.

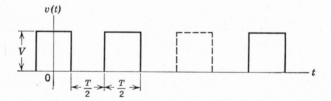

Fig. P6-24

6.74 A random voltage wave is made up of a string of rectangular pulses equally spaced in time. A typical segment of this wave is shown in Fig. P6-24.

As shown by the dashed lines in Fig. P6-24, some of the pulses are blanked out, and the probability that any given pulse is blanked out is $\frac{1}{2}$. The blanking of a pulse does not affect the probability of blanking any other pulse.

(a) Find the autocorrelation function of $v(t)$.

(b) From this correlation function, determine and sketch (in the time domain) the total periodic component of $v(t)$.

(c) What is the total power contained in the random component of $v(t)$?

(d) Determine and sketch the power-density spectrum of $v(t)$.

6.75 The power-density spectrum $\Phi(\omega)$ of a waveform $v(t)$ is shown in Fig. P6-25.
(a) Determine and sketch the autocorrelation function $\phi(\tau)$.
(b) What is the d-c power contained in $v(t)$?

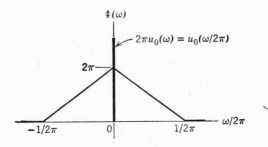

Fig. P6-25

(c) What is the a-c power contained in $v(t)$?

6.76 Figure P6-26 shows the autocorrelation function for an unpredictable wave $v_1(t)$.
(a) What is the mean power of the random (unpredictable) component of $v_1(t)$?
(b) What is the mean power of the periodic component of $v_1(t)$?

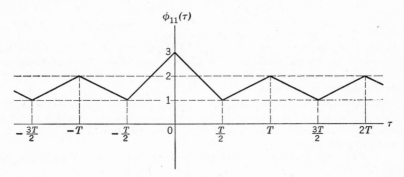

Fig. P6-26

(c) Sketch and dimension the periodic component of $v_1(t)$. Can this be found uniquely from $\phi_{11}(\tau)$? Why?
(d) Sketch the power-density spectrum $\Phi_{11}(\omega)$ and give as much information about it as you can obtain by inspection of $\phi_{11}(\tau)$.

6.77 A random voltage wave $v(t)$ consists of a string of rectangular pulses of duration $T/2$. The pulses can occur only at periodic intervals T, but some of the pulses are missing.
(a) Find the autocorrelation of $v(t)$.
(b) From this correlation function, determine and sketch (in the time domain) the total *periodic component* of $v(t)$.
(c) Determine and sketch the power-density spectrum of $v(t)$.

In parts (a), (b), and (c), consider two cases:

(1)   The erasure of pulses takes place independently and at random, with, on the average, one out of N pulses missing.

(2)   The erasure is random but *exactly one* pulse is missing in *each* of the adjacent time intervals of length NT.

6.78   Repeated bursts of tone are frequently used as sounds in psycho-acoustic experiments.   Consider the following two possible ways of generating such sounds:

(a)   The tone is generated with the same starting phase at the beginning of each burst, as depicted in Fig. P6-27.

(b)   A *continuous* tone is "blanked" or "gated" by a rectangular wave.   The frequency of the tone is not necessarily a multiple of the blanking frequency.

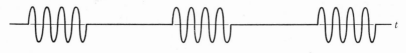

Fig. P6-27

Discuss the differences between the time functions and the spectra of these two signals.   Are both signals periodic?

6.79   A sinusoidal audio signal of frequency f is turned on abruptly for an integral number of cycles n and is then turned off abruptly.   Consider two cases:

(1)   The signal is turned on and off at the zero crossings.

(2)   The signal is turned on and off when the amplitude is a maximum.

Sketch the frequency spectrum for the two cases.

When a person listens to sound (2), he hears a "click" at the beginning and end of the sound, whereas for sound (1) this click is less pronounced. Explain this phenomenon in terms of the degree of spreading of energy to high frequencies in the spectrum.

6.80   An ideal "multiplier" has two input signals, $v_1(t)$ and $m(t)$, and its output signal is their product $v_2(t) = v_1(t)m(t)$.   Let the "modulating" or "sampling" signal $m(t)$ be a periodic train of very narrow pulses, with period T and pulse area $1/T$.

(a)   What set of different input cosine waves $v_1(t)$ all produce the same output signal?

(b)   If an input cosine wave $v_1(t)$ is known to have a frequency $\omega_1/2\pi < 1/2T$, can ω_1 be determined uniquely by inspection of the output signal?

(c)   If the input $v_1(t)$ is not a pure sinusoid, but rather a signal whose spectrum $V_1(\omega)$ is given by $1/|\omega|^2$ for $|\omega| < \omega_1$ and zero for $|\omega| > \omega_1$, plot the output spectrum $V_2(\omega)$.

(d)   In terms of the $V_2(\omega)$ spectrum in part (c), interpret the effect of sampling pulses that are not sufficiently narrow to justify an "ideal impulse" model of $m(t)$.

6.81   Let $f(t) = \frac{1}{2}[u_0(t) + u_0(t-1)]$ and define $f_n(t)$ as the function obtained by convolving $f(t)$ with itself n times (for example, $f_3 = f \otimes f \otimes f$).

(a)   Show that $f_n(t)$ is the probability-density function describing the probability of obtaining t tails in n independent tosses of an ideal coin.

(b) Let $F(\omega)$ and $F_n(\omega)$ be the Fourier transforms of $f(t)$ and $f_n(t)$ respectively. Show that $F_n(\omega) = e^{-jn\omega/2} \cos^n (\omega/2)$.

(c) Show that for large n, the function $\cos^n (\omega/2)$ is essentially a periodic train of relatively narrow Gaussian pulses. *Hint:* Examine the power-series expansion of $\log [\cos^n (\omega/2)]$.

(d) On the basis of the results in part (c), show that $f_n(t)$ is essentially a wide, delayed Gaussian pulse multiplied (sampled) by a periodic train of impulses.

(e) By carrying out the details show that, for large n, the mean (ensemble-average) number of tails t increases in proportion to n, whereas the rms deviation (the standard deviation)

$$\sigma = [\overline{(t - \bar{t})^2}]^{1/2}$$

is porpotrional to the square root of n.

(f) What is the interpretation of $f_n(t)$ if $F_n(\omega)$ is approximated by retaining only the lowest-frequency pulse, discarding the others located at $\omega = \pm 2\pi, \pm 4\pi, \cdots$?

(g) Show that, *for any positive* n, the mean-square deviation is given by $\sigma^2 = n/4$. *Hint:* Utilize the relationship between the second moment of a function and the second derivative of its Fourier transform, evaluated at zero ω. In this case, the pertinent function is $f_n[t + (n/2)]$.

6.82 Under a (complex) rotation of orthogonal co-ordinates in N-dimensional space, the components x_k of a vector x transform into new components

$$x_m' = \sum_{k=-n}^{n} x_k a_{km} \qquad (N = 2n + 1)$$

where a_{km} is interpreted as the "cosine of the complex angle" between co-ordinate axes k and m. For $a_{km} = (1/\sqrt{N}) \exp (j2\pi km/N)$, show that the inverse transformation is

$$x_i = \sum_{m=-n}^{n} a_{im}{}^* x_m'$$

Also show that the "length" of the vector is invariant $(\sum |x_m'|^2 = \sum |x_k|^2)$. You may use the fact that

$$\sum_{m=-n}^{n} e^{j2\pi(k-i)m/N} = \begin{cases} N, & \text{for } k = i \\ 0, & \text{for } k \neq i \end{cases}$$

Now, let the x_m' be the sample values $v(mT/N)$ of a periodic signal $v(t)$, let $x_k = V_k\sqrt{N}$, and show that in the limit of large N the two transformations above lead to the Fourier series for $v(t)$ and to the integral formula for the Fourier coefficients, respectively. Discuss the sampling theorem in the light of these results.

Transmission of Signals
Through
Linear Systems

7.1 Introduction

In the preceding chapter we found that a signal can be represented
either as a time function or as a frequency function, and that these
two descriptions are related through the Fourier integral. In this
chapter we ask the question, "What happens to the time waveform of a
signal, and what happens to its frequency spectrum, when that signal
passes through a linear transmission system?" In answering this
question we shall find out more about signals, and many elegant and
important properties of linear transmission systems will be brought to
light. The linear systems used as examples in this chapter are all
linear incremental models of electric or electronic circuits. However,
it should be remembered that the methods are generally applicable to
any physical system which can be approximated with satisfactory
accuracy by a linear model.

7.2 The Singularity Signals

Figure 7-1(a) shows a very simple linear "system" consisting of a
single ideal capacitor C driven by an ideal voltage source $v(t)$. Suppose
that we desire to find the current response due to the ideal voltage step

indicated in Fig. 7-1(b).   Even in this simple problem a dilemma immediately appears.   The current is proportional to the time derivative of
the voltage, but this derivative does not exist at the time origin where $v(t)$
is discontinuous.   Since physical reasoning indicates that some current
must flow in order to charge the capacitor, we conclude that the mathe-

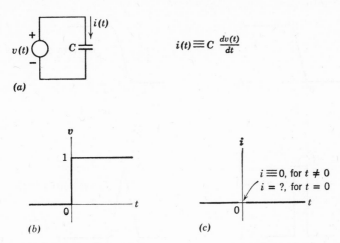

Fig. 7-1.   The differentiability dilemma, arising from idealization of the signal $v(t)$
driving an idealized system C.

matics gives an unsatisfactory picture.   The trouble arises simply
because we have idealized both the signal $v(t)$ and the system C.   By
unidealizing either the signal or the system we can regain a suitable
picture of current flow in the model.

Figure 7-2(a) shows one of many possible ways in which the unit
step signal may be "unidealized."   This approximation replaces the
discontinuity by a short interval of rapid but continuous rise.   The
function in Fig. 7-2(a), called the finite ramp, approaches the ideal
step as the ramp interval a becomes small.   The finite ramp is differentiable, as indicated in Fig. 7-2(b).   Apart from a vertical scale factor
equal to the value of the capacitance C, the function in Fig. 7-2(b)
represents the waveform of capacitor current.   As parameter a is allowed
to become small this waveform approaches a so-called impulse, a pulse
whose duration is very small but whose area is definite.   This matches
the physical necessity that a definite amount of charge must be supplied
to the capacitor in order to change its voltage from one fixed value to
another.

Here the nondifferentiable ideal step has been visualized as the
limiting form of a differentiable function, and we avoid trouble by agree-

ing not to carry out the limiting process until after the differentiation. Moreover, after differentiation, it is the limiting process, rather than the limit itself, which affords a usable physical picture. A current pulse of finite area and arbitrarily short, but nonzero, duration is a useful

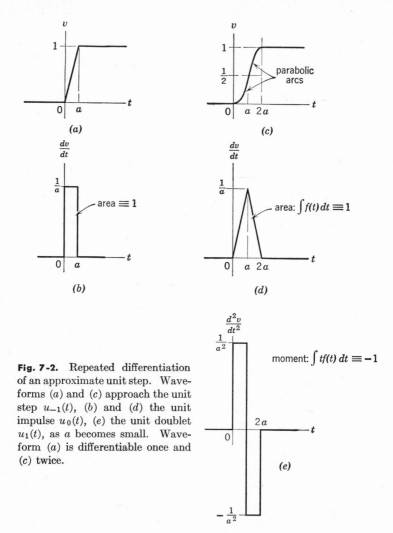

Fig. 7-2. Repeated differentiation of an approximate unit step. Waveforms (a) and (c) approach the unit step $u_{-1}(t)$, (b) and (d) the unit impulse $u_0(t)$, (e) the unit doublet $u_1(t)$, as a becomes small. Waveform (a) is differentiable once and (c) twice.

concept, whereas Fig. 7-2(b) becomes meaningless when we set the parameter a exactly equal to zero. To be sure, the main value of elementary calculus is that a limit quite beyond human comprehension can be understood in terms of the limiting process.

Figure 7-2(c) shows a smoother approximation to the ideal step. Here not only the function but also its first derivative is continuous. Such a signal is twice differentiable as shown in Fig. 7-2(d) and (e). Observe that in the limit of small a the interesting feature of the second derivative, Fig. 7-2(e), is that its *moment* has a definite value. The extension to higher orders of smoothing, permitting still further differentiation, is obvious but the bookkeeping becomes more complicated.

In analyzing those systems which differentiate the signal several times, it is often more convenient to "unidealize" the system rather than the signal. The approximate derivative of a function $v(t)$ is given by

$$\frac{\Delta v(t)}{\Delta t} = \frac{v(t) - v(t - a)}{a} \tag{7.1}$$

wherein a is some small but nonzero time interval. If $v(t)$ is a smooth function, then expression (7.1) approaches, by definition, the true derivative as a approaches zero. With parameter a small but nonzero, (7.1) gives us the "approximate" derivative of a discontinuous function. The *unit step* is defined as

$$u_{-1}(t) = \begin{cases} 0, & \text{for } t \leq 0 \\ 1, & \text{for } t > 0 \end{cases} \tag{7.2}$$

and its approximate derivative is, therefore, a rectangular pulse

$$p_0(t) = \frac{u_{-1}(t) - u_{-1}(t - a)}{a} \tag{7.3}$$

identical to that shown in Fig. 7-2(b). Higher approximate derivatives, also made up of rectangular pulses, may now be found by repetition of the process

$$p_{k+1} = \frac{p_k(t) - p_k(t - a)}{a}, \quad \text{for } k = 0, 1, 2, \cdots \tag{7.4}$$

The results are illustrated in Fig. 7-3. Figure 7-4 shows in detail the calculation of $p_3(t)$ by shifting and subtracting the function $p_2(t)$. The pulse functions $p_k(t)$ can be characterized in terms of their moments. The *nth* moment of p_k is given by

$$\int_{-\infty}^{\infty} t^n p_k(t)\, dt = \begin{cases} 0, & \text{for } n < k \\ (-1)^k k!, & \text{for } n = k \\ \text{order of } a^{n-k}, & \text{for } n > k,\ n + k \text{ odd} \\ 0, & \text{for } n > k,\ n + k \text{ even} \end{cases} \tag{7.5}$$

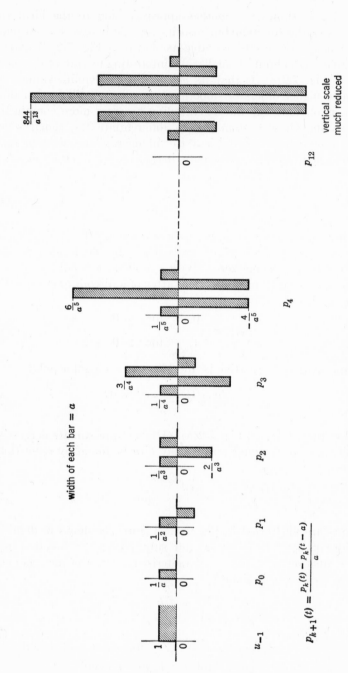

Fig. 7-3. Repeated approximate differentiation of a unit step.

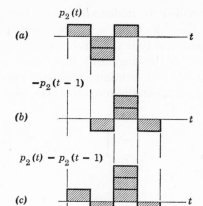

Fig. 7-4. Details of the approximate differentiation of $p_2(t)$.

where n and k are nonnegative integers. Hence the pulse function p_k has the property that only its kth moment is important for small a.

The higher derivatives of an ideal step can now be defined as the limit approached by the approximate derivative as a becomes arbitrarily small,

$$u_k(t) = \lim_{a \to 0} p_k(t), \qquad \text{for } k = 0, 1, 2, \cdots \tag{7.6}$$

For completeness we shall also define the set of functions obtained by successive integrations of a unit step

$$u_{-k}(t) = \frac{t^{k-1}}{(k-1)!}\, u_{-1}(t), \qquad \text{for } k = 1, 2, 3, \cdots \tag{7.7}$$

Relations (7.6) and (7.7) give us a complete set of functions including the unit step u_{-1}, the unit impulse u_0, and the unit doublet u_1, as well as the unit semi-infinite ramp u_{-2}, the parabolic ramp u_{-3}, and so forth. The recurrence formula relating two adjacent functions may be written either as

$$u_{k+1}(t) = \lim_{a \to 0} \frac{u_k(t) - u_k(t - a)}{a} \tag{7.8}$$

or as

$$\frac{d}{dt} u_{k-1}(t) = u_k(t) = \int_{-\infty}^{} u_{k+1}(t)\, dt \tag{7.9}$$

provided we understand that (7.9) is the result of a limiting process.

The functions $u_k(t)$ are usually called the singularity functions. A singularity is a point at which a function does not possess a derivative. Each of the singularity functions (or if not the function itself, then the function differentiated a finite number of times) has a singular point at the origin and is zero elsewhere.

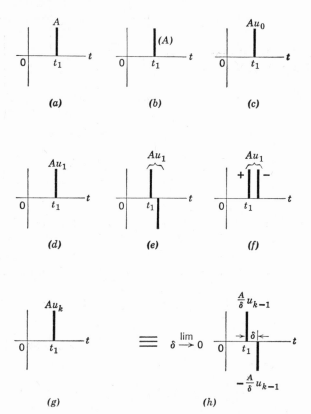

Fig. 7-5. Symbols for the singularity functions. (a), (b), (c) all denote $Au_0(t - t_1)$. (d), (e), (f) all denote $Au_1(t - t_1)$. (g) is the general symbol for $Au_k(t - t_1)$ and this is always equivalent to the limiting form (h).

In common usage an impulse of area A located at time t_1 is denoted by any of the symbols indicated in Fig. 7-5(a), (b), or (c). A doublet of negative moment A might be indicated by the single spike in (d) or by a pair of spikes, as in (e) and (f), to show that it is actually composed of two impulses located close together. In general, however, any one of the singularity functions having a coefficient A and a location t_1 is perhaps most conveniently symbolized by the spike in Fig. 7-5(g) with its proper name attached.   Function u_k is, of course, always equivalent to a doublet of functions u_{k-1}, as shown in (h).

For negative index k the functions u_k are bounded for finite t and need no special symbol.   Figure 7-6(a) shows the relative shapes and positions

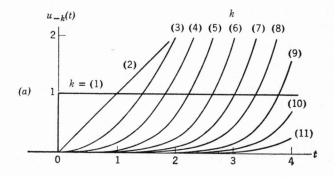

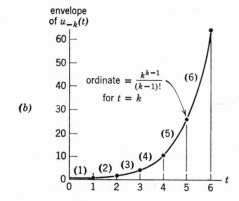

Fig. 7-6.   Character of the functions $u_{-k}(t)$.   (a) Detailed behavior.   (b) Envelope plot showing each function $u_{-k}(t)$ only in the interval $k - 1 < t < k$, wherein it lies above all the others.

of the first eleven functions.   Observe that u_{-2}, the ramp, lies above all of the other functions in the region between 1 and 2 on the time scale. Similarly, u_{-3} is larger than the others in the interval between 2 and 3. The bounding upper envelope of the family of functions is plotted in Fig. 7-6(b).

In contrast with negative-index singularity functions, those of non-negative index are truly singular and cannot be plotted.   In view of

(7.5) and (7.6), however, we have

$$\int_{-\infty}^{\infty} t^n u_k(t)\, dt = \begin{cases} 0, & \text{for } n \neq k \\ (-1)^k k!, & \text{for } n = k \end{cases} \tag{7.10}$$

where n and k are nonnegative integers. The function $u_k(t)$ possesses a kth moment but all other moments vanish. Statement (7.10) is, in fact, one simple way in which we could define the nonnegative-index singularity functions (with, of course, the usual interpretation of the limiting processes involved).

7.3   The Impulse Response of a Linear Transmission System

Figure 7-7(a) shows a transmission system having an input signal v_1 and an output signal v_2. In this chapter we shall be concerned with linear systems. A *linear system* is one for which the output response

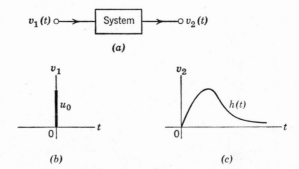

Fig. 7-7.   The impulse response of a transmission system.

due to the sum of two input signals is identically equal to the sum of the outputs due to each of these two input signals acting alone. Specifically, if $f_1(t)$ and $g_1(t)$ are any two input signals and $f_2(t)$ and $g_2(t)$ are the corresponding output signals, then the input signal

$$v_1 = a f_1(t) + b g_1(t) \tag{7.11}$$

yields the output signal

$$v_2 = a f_2(t) + b g_2(t) \tag{7.12}$$

for *any* a and b. It may happen, of course, that the system is excited not only by the *external* input v_1 but perhaps also by some *independent internal* input (such as a battery somewhere within an electric circuit). In this case, the system might exhibit an output even when no external input signal is applied. It is to be understood that the output v_2 in

(7.12) does *not* include the effects of *independent* internal excitation of the system. Instead, the v_2 we speak of here represents only that part of the total output caused by the external input v_1. In a linear system the total output is the sum of the separate outputs due to the external and internal excitations. When there is no *independent* internal excitation (as in the usual linear incremental model of an electronic circuit), the system is said to be homogeneous. A *homogeneous* system produces zero output when the external input is zero for all time. Henceforth, homogeneity is assumed unless otherwise specified.

When a unit impulse is applied at the input, as indicated in Fig. 7-7(b), we expect the system to respond with some definite output signal $h(t)$ which we shall call the *impulse response* of the system. The particular impulse response shown in Fig. 7-7(c) exhibits two characteristics which are worth mentioning at this point simply because we shall see them so

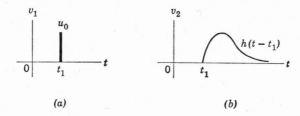

(a)   (b)

Fig. 7-8. The impulse response of a time-invariant transmission system for any value of t_1.

often. First, the impulse response vanishes for negative time. In other words, the system does *not* respond *before* it is excited by the input signal. This characteristic is usually referred to as *realizability*, since under normal circumstances we should not expect to be able to construct a prophetic device or circuit. Second, the impulse response settles toward zero for large positive time. In short, the system eventually forgets that we have excited it and once more sinks into a state of repose. This characteristic is sometimes referred to as *stability*. In this sense, a stable system is one which produces an appreciable output only when some input has been applied in the not-too-distant past. A precise definition of stability will be given later in the chapter.

Strictly speaking, the impulse response should be defined as

$$h(t) = \lim v_2(t), \qquad \text{as } v_1(t) \rightarrow u_0(t) \qquad (7.13)$$

Now let us specialize further. For a *time-invariant* system (sometimes called a constant-parameter system) the shape of the output wave is the same no matter when the input impulse is applied, as indicated in Fig. 7-8. More generally, if $f_1(t)$ is any input and $f_2(t)$ is the corresponding output, then the input signal

$$v_1 = f_1(t - t_1) \qquad (7.14)$$

yields the output

$$v_2 = f_2(t - t_1) \qquad (7.15)$$

for *any* t_1. In short, the properties of the system do not change with time.

We say that "superposition applies" in linear systems, meaning that a superposition of input signals produces a superposition of the corre-

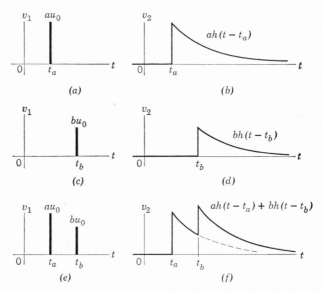

Fig. 7-9. Superposition of responses in a linear time-invariant system.

sponding outputs, as illustrated in Fig. 7-9. The superposition property is sometimes stated as a theorem for linear systems. However, superposability is simply another name for linearity and really does not deserve the status of a theorem. Excitations and responses may be superposed in a linear system, and a linear system is one in which excitations and responses may be superposed. Superposability and linearity are really the same thing.

7.4   The Superposition Integral

Once we know the response of a linear time-invariant system to an input pulse of short duration, formulation of the response due to any input follows directly. Figure 7-10(a) shows an arbitrary input signal waveform $v_1(t)$. Function $v_1(t)$ may be represented *exactly* as the superposition of adjacent narrow pulses, one of which is emphasized by shading in Fig. 7-10(a). The particular pulse upon which we concentrate attention here is located at t_1, has a width dt_1, and has (to the first differential order) an area equal to $v_1(t_1)\,dt_1$. Associated with this narrow pulse of infinitesimal area there is a corresponding infinitesimal contribution to the output signal $dv_2(t)$, as indicated in Fig. 7-10(b). The component $dv_2(t)$ is an infinitesimal replica of a shifted impulse-

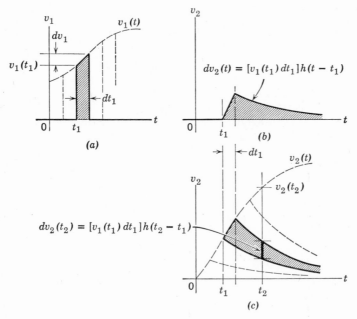

Fig. 7-10. Superposition of infinitesimal responses dv_2 due to infinitesimal input pulses $v_1(t_1)\,dt_1$.

response function. To find the total output signal $v_2(t_2)$ at some specific time t_2, it is only necessary to superpose the various infinitesimal outputs due to the various input pulses, as shown in Fig. 7-10(c). The summation of infinitesimals is by definition (not by analogy or by approximation, but by definition) the integral

$$v_2(t_2) = \int v_1(t_1) h(t_2 - t_1)\,dt_1 \tag{7.16}$$

This is called the *superposition integral*. Notice that three different time scales are involved: "input-signal time" t_1, "output-signal time"

t_2, and "system-memory time" $t_2 - t_1$. It is clear from Fig. 7-10(c) that the integration need be carried out only over those values of t_1 which are less than t_2. This is a consequence of the fact that the impulse response $h(t_2 - t_1)$ vanishes for negative values of its argument. In other words, a realizable system remembers the past, but does not "remember" the future.

The superposition integral (7.16) states that *the present value of the output signal is a weighted integral over the past history of the input signal*, weighted according to the impulse response, which here plays the role of a memory function for the system.

By giving a special name τ to the memory time $t_2 - t_1$, we can put the superposition integral in a different but equivalent form:

$$v_2(t_2) = \int h(\tau) v_1(t_2 - \tau) \, d\tau \tag{7.17}$$

The symbol τ is sometimes used as the dummy variable in both forms of the superposition integral, and the output-signal time is usually called t. With this notation we have

$$v_2(t) = \begin{cases} \displaystyle\int_{-\infty}^{\infty} v_1(\tau) h(t - \tau) \, d\tau & \text{(7.18)} \\[2em] \displaystyle\int_{-\infty}^{\infty} h(\tau) v_1(t - \tau) \, d\tau & \text{(7.19)} \end{cases}$$

$$v_2(t) = \begin{cases} \displaystyle\int_{-\infty}^{t} v_1(\tau) h(t - \tau) \, d\tau & \text{(7.20)} \\[2em] \displaystyle\int_{0}^{\infty} h(\tau) v_1(t - \tau) \, d\tau & \text{(7.21)} \end{cases} \quad \text{if } h(t) = 0 \text{ for } t < 0$$

$$v_2(t) = \begin{cases} \displaystyle\int_{0}^{t} v_1(\tau) h(t - \tau) \, d\tau & \text{(7.22)} \\[2em] \displaystyle\int_{0}^{t} h(\tau) v_1(t - \tau) \, d\tau & \text{(7.23)} \end{cases} \quad \begin{array}{l} \text{if } h(t) \text{ and } v_1(t) \text{ both vanish} \\ \text{for } t < 0 \end{array}$$

Observe that for a realizable system the integration need be carried only over the interval from minus infinity to t in "input time" (7.20) or from zero to infinity in "memory time" (7.21). Moreover, if the input signal begins at zero on the input-time scale (as we might specify if we were interested, for example, in the response of a system at rest to a suddenly applied excitation), then the limits of integration run from zero to t on either the input-time or memory-time basis of integration, (7.22) or (7.23).

One graphical interpretation of the superposition integral was given in Fig. 7-10. Figure 7-11 shows another graphical presentation which

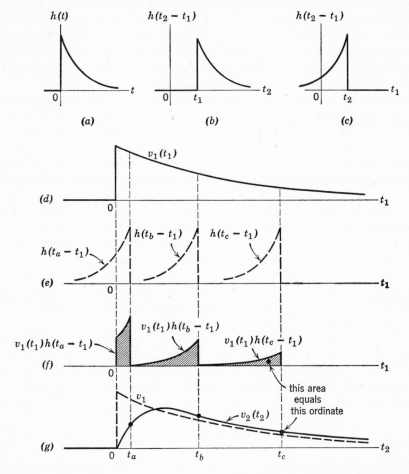

Fig. 7-11. Convolution of an impulse response (a) with an input signal (d), yielding the output signal (g).

aids in visualizing the operations involved. The impulse response (a) enters the superposition integral in the form of a weighting or memory function $h(t_2 - t_1)$. We can plot the memory function against t_2 with t_1 treated as a parameter (b) or, alternatively, we can think of $h(t_2 - t_1)$ as a function of the input time t_1 with output time t_2 playing the role of a parameter (c). Observe that the impulse-response-function shape appears reversed in Fig. 7-11(c) merely because of the way in which we have chosen to plot it. Plot (c) is the one we want here, since the integration is to be carried out over the input-time variable t_1. Now, given an input, Fig. 7-11(d), we multiply it by the memory function (e) to obtain the weighted input (f), and the area under the weighted input curve is the value of the output signal (g) at a specific output time, such as t_a, t_b, or t_c in Fig. 7-11. If we think of the multiplication and input-time integration as *instantaneous* operations, *then* we can imagine the memory function sliding along the input waveform and generating, as it goes, the successive instantaneous values of the output signal. The memory or weighting function is sometimes called a "scanning" function since the input is effectively "scanned" by an "operator" to produce the output. It is also referred to as a "window" function. The output (at a given time) is influenced only by that part of the input signal which can be "seen" through the "window," and the influence of the input is proportional to the height of the window.

The superposition integral provides the basis for a precise definition of stability. *Let us define a stable system as one for which the output signal is bounded for all bounded input signals.* To find the corresponding restrictions on the impulse response $h(t)$, first write

$$\left| v_1(t) \right| \leq M \tag{7.24}$$

where M is some positive real finite number. Substitution of (7.24) into the superposition integral (7.19) yields

$$\left| v_2(t) \right| \leq M \int_{-\infty}^{\infty} \left| h(\tau) \right| d\tau \tag{7.25}$$

from which it follows immediately that the necessary and sufficient condition for stability is

$$\int_{-\infty}^{\infty} \left| h(t) \right| dt < \infty \tag{7.26}$$

In other words, the system is stable if and only if the impulse response is "absolutely integrable."

7.5 Interpretation of the Superposition Integral as a Correlation Operation

The transmission of a signal through a linear system involves a weighted integration and can therefore be interpreted as a correlation operation. Such interpretation begins with a definition of the memory function of the linear system. The *memory function* $m(t)$ is defined as the present value of the output signal in response to a unit impulse input signal applied t seconds ago. Hence the memory function is simply the reversed impulse-response function

$$m(t) = h(-t) \tag{7.27}$$

and substitution into the superposition integral (7.20) yields

$$v_2(t) = \int_{-\infty}^{t} v_1(\tau) m(\tau - t) \, d\tau = \psi_{1m}(t) \tag{7.28}$$

For real memory functions (the usual situation of interest) the output signal is therefore recognizable as the crosscorrelation function of the input signal and the memory function, as indicated by the symbol $\psi_{1m}(t)$ in (7.28).

For simplicity, let "zero time" represent "the present," whence the present value of the output signal is given by the particularly simple expression

$$v_2(0) = \int_{-\infty}^{0} v_1(\tau) m(\tau) \, d\tau = \psi_{1m}(0) \tag{7.29}$$

Now, to reiterate the vector-space analogy presented in the preceding chapter, we can visualize the memory function and the input signal as vectors in multidimensional space, vectors whose orthogonal components are the sample values

$$m_k = \delta m(k\delta) \tag{7.30}$$

and

$$v_{1k} = v_1(k\delta) \tag{7.31}$$

In (7.30) and (7.31) parameter δ is the sampling interval and k is an integer. For small δ the summation

$$v_2(0) \approx \sum_{k=-\infty}^{0} v_{1k} m_k \tag{7.32}$$

approximates the integral (7.29). Hence the present value of the output-signal "vector" may be visualized as the inner product of the input-signal and memory "vectors,"

$$v_2 \approx v_1 \cdot m \tag{7.33}$$

The point is that every linear transmission system is itself a "correlator" whose output signal is an instantaneous measure of the extent to which the past input signal correlates with the memory function. For a physical interpretation of the approximation (7.32), see Fig. 8-35.

7.6   Convolution Algebra

The superposition integral is identified with the transmission of a signal through a linear system. Quite apart from this identification, the superposition integral represents a certain mathematical operation involving two functions. As such it has a name of its own: *convolution*. We say that two functions $f_1(t)$ and $f_2(t)$ are "convolved" to give a third function $f_3(t)$, and that $f_3(t)$ is the "convolution" of $f_1(t)$ and $f_2(t)$. In a discussion of convolution the following shorthand notation is convenient;

$$f_3(t) = f_1(t) \otimes f_2(t) \quad \text{means} \quad f_3(t) = \int_{-\infty}^{\infty} f_1(\tau) f_2(t - \tau) \, d\tau \quad (7.34)$$

This notation permits us to think of convolution as a special kind of multiplication, and therefore permits us to write the five fundamental laws of "convolution algebra" in the compact form

Addition association:

$$A + (B + C) \equiv (A + B) + C \tag{7.35}$$

Addition commutation:

$$A + B \equiv B + A \tag{7.36}$$

Convolution distribution:

$$A \otimes (B + C) \equiv (A \otimes B) + (A \otimes C) \tag{7.37}$$

Convolution association:

$$A \otimes (B \otimes C) \equiv (A \otimes B) \otimes C \tag{7.38}$$

Convolution commutation:

$$A \otimes B \equiv B \otimes A \tag{7.39}$$

where A, B, and C are arbitrary functions of time. These laws, happily indeed, are identical in form with the basic laws of ordinary algebra (involving ordinary numbers and ordinary multiplication).

The first three laws are self-evident, and the fifth was demonstrated previously in equations (7.18) and (7.19). It remains to examine the associative law for convolution (7.38). Relation (7.38) can be verified formally by writing the double convolution as a double integral over two dummy variables τ_1 and τ_2 and recognizing that the order in which the two integrations are carried out is immaterial. Alternatively, double convolution may be interpreted as the result of cascading two linear systems as shown in Fig. 7-12(a). The input signal v_1 is first convolved with the impulse response h_{12} of the first system to give v_2, and convolution of v_2 with the impulse response h_{23} of the second system yields the output signal v_3. Now suppose that a unit impulse is applied at the input as shown in Fig. 7-12(*b*). In this case the final output signal is, by definition, equal to the impulse response h_{13} of the complete system,

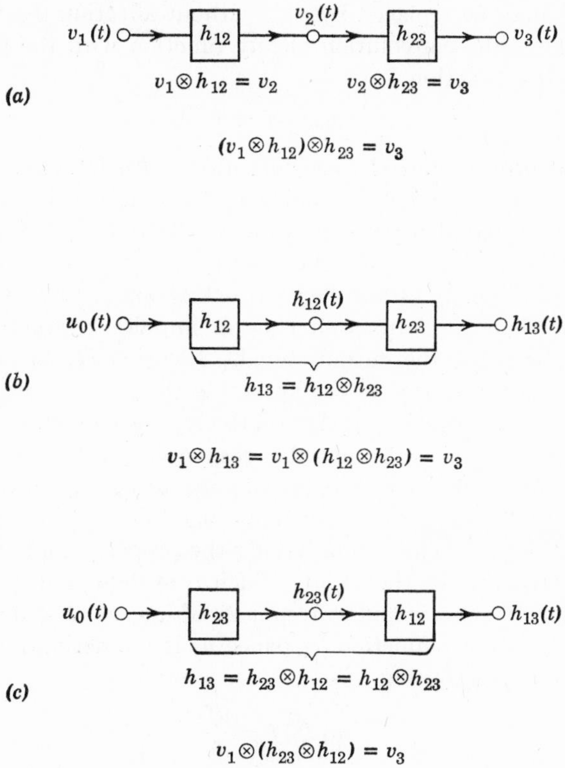
$v_1(t)$
h_{12}
$v_2(t)$
h_{23}
$v_3(t)$
$v_1 \otimes h_{12} = v_2$
$v_2 \otimes h_{23} = v_3$
(*a*)
$(v_1 \otimes h_{12}) \otimes h_{23} = v_3$
$u_0(t)$
h_{12}
$h_{12}(t)$
h_{23}
$h_{13}(t)$
(*b*)
$h_{13} = h_{12} \otimes h_{23}$
$v_1 \otimes h_{13} = v_1 \otimes (h_{12} \otimes h_{23}) = v_3$
$u_0(t)$
h_{23}
$h_{23}(t)$
h_{12}
$h_{13}(t)$
$h_{13} = h_{23} \otimes h_{12} = h_{12} \otimes h_{23}$
(*c*)
$v_1 \otimes (h_{23} \otimes h_{12}) = v_3$

Fig. 7-12. Interpretation of associativity and commutivity in convolution.

and h_{13} is evidently the convolution of h_{12} and h_{23}. The associative law then follows directly from the fact that the convolution of v_1 and h_{13} must yield the original output signal v_3.

Parts (*b*) and (*c*) of Fig. 7-12 illustrate the interpretation of the commutation law, which states in effect that linear systems in a cascaded chain may be rearranged or interchanged without affecting the over-all signal transmission. *Nonlinear* systems do not enjoy such flexibility of arrangement.

The singularity functions u_k play an especially simple but important role in convolution algebra. When the unit impulse u_0 is convolved with an arbitrary function f, we have

$$\int_{-\infty}^{\infty} f(\tau)u_0(t-\tau)\,d\tau = f(t)\int_{-\infty}^{\infty} u_0(t-\tau)\,d\tau = f(t) \qquad (7.40)$$

The integrand vanishes except in the neighborhood of τ equal to t. Hence, $f(\tau)$ may be replaced by $f(t)$ without affecting the value of the integral. Thus the convolution of any function with the unit impulse yields the same function

$$u_0 \otimes f = f \qquad (7.41)$$

The result is proved above by consideration of the integral, but we have already been through such reasoning in the detailed derivation of the superposition integral for linear systems. Therefore, a result such as (7.41) should be obvious from those simple properties of linear systems which we have already established. If in relation (7.41) we interpret u_0 as an input signal and function f as an impulse response, then their convolution must be the output signal. Relation (7.41) merely states that the impulse response of the system is the impulse response of the system. (Hardly surprising.) Alternatively, we can interpret f as an input signal and u_0 as an impulse response, whence relation (7.41) states the obvious result that if the impulse response is a unit impulse, then the output signal is an exact reproduction of the input.

Now consider a linear system having the property that the output is the time derivative of the input. Such a system is called an "ideal differentiator." The impulse response of an ideal differentiator is evidently the doublet function u_1 (since u_1 is the derivative of u_0) and it follows immediately that

$$u_1 \otimes f = \frac{df}{dt} \qquad (7.42)$$

Similarly, for an "ideal integrator" the impulse response must be u_{-1} and

$$u_{-1} \otimes f = \int_{-\infty}^{t} f\,dt \qquad (7.43)$$

In general, therefore,

$$u_k \otimes f = f^{(k)} \qquad (7.44)$$

where the parenthetical superscript k denotes the kth derivative of function f. A negative value of k indicates integration; for example, $f^{(-3)}$ means that f has been integrated three times, each time with the limits shown in (7.43).

In addition to differentiation and integration, another fundamental operation is time delay. If a linear system produces an output $f(t - t_0)$, which is a delayed replica of the input $f(t)$, then the impulse response of the "ideal delay" must be the shifted unit impulse $u_0(t - t_0)$. Hence,

$$u_0(t - t_0) \otimes f(t) = f(t - t_0) \tag{7.45}$$

We see, therefore, that the singularity functions convolve according to simple rules

$$u_0 \otimes u_0 = u_0 \tag{7.46}$$

$$u_1 \otimes u_1 = u_2 \tag{7.47}$$

$$u_{-1} \otimes u_1 = u_0 \tag{7.48}$$

$$u_j \otimes u_k = u_{j+k} \tag{7.49}$$

and that time delay accumulates when the functions are convolved,

$$u_j(t - t_1) \otimes u_k(t - t_2) = u_{j+k}(t - t_1 - t_2) \tag{7.50}$$

In other words, when a signal passes through a sequence of linear systems, experiencing some time delay in each, it will emerge with a total delay equal to the sum of the individual delays. Once again, this is hardly surprising, but it nevertheless deserves statement as the identity (7.50).

Another fundamental result of some interest is the following: If, for a given linear system h, an input v_1 produces an output v_2, then a new input signal which is the kth derivative of the original input will produce a new output which is the kth derivative of the original output. In short,

$$v_1^{(k)} \otimes h = v_2^{(k)} \tag{7.51}$$

Figure 7-13 offers the explanation. Let us cascade the original system (a) with an ideal differentiator u_1 as shown in (b). We can now interchange h and u_1 without affecting the over-all transmission, as indicated in (c). Hence the time derivative of v_1, when applied at the input of system h, must produce an output which is the time derivative of v_2. Furthermore, as illustrated in (d), the convolution of u_1 and h yields a new impulse response $h^{(1)}$. Thus differentiation of the output v_2 can be accomplished either by differentiating the input v_1 or by replacing the impulse response of the system by its derivative.

As a result of all this discussion we have the basic fact that orders of differentiation and time delays both accumulate under the operation of convolution, that is, under the operation of transmitting a signal through a succession of linear systems

$$f_1^{(j)} \otimes f_2^{(k)} = f_3^{(j+k)} \tag{7.52}$$

$$f_1^{(j)}(t - t_1) \otimes f_2^{(k)}(t - t_2) = f_3^{(j+k)}(t - t_1 - t_2) \tag{7.53}$$

Identity (7.52), which is a special case of (7.53), is *particularly useful in practical computations*. For example, suppose that function f_1 is continuous and piecewise linear. The first derivative of f_1 is a stairstep curve, and the second derivative is a discrete set of impulses. If we differentiate f_1 twice and integrate f_2 twice, their convolution is unchanged. The practical advantage is that the convolution of $f_1^{(2)}$ with $f_2^{(-2)}$ is much simpler to carry out than a direct convolution of f_1 with

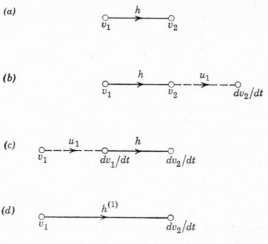

Fig. 7-13. Differentiation of the input produces differentiation of the output.

f_2, because the convolution of a delayed impulse with a function merely shifts the function and multiplies it by a constant. Even when f_1 is not piecewise linear and continuous, a piecewise-linear approximation may well be suitable for the accuracy required.

7.7   The Solution of Certain Convolution Equations

Figure 7-14 shows a simple transmission system containing a closed transmission path BC. If A, B, and C are constants [that is, if the impulse response of branch A is $Au_0(t)$, and similarly for B and C], then the transmission rules for linear signal-flow graphs yield, by inspection, the relationship between the input v_1 and the output v_3

$$v_3 = \frac{v_1 AB}{1 - CB} \tag{7.54}$$

On the other hand, if A, B, and C are the impulse responses of three linear systems, then the flow-graph rules must be modified, or rather reinterpreted, to accommodate convolution in the place of ordinary multiplication. In this case, the equations of the complete system become

$$v_2 = (v_1 \otimes A) + (v_3 \otimes C) \qquad (7.55)$$

and

$$v_3 = v_2 \otimes B \qquad (7.56)$$

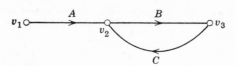

Fig. 7-14. A simple transmission system with feedback.

Elimination of v_2 by substitution yields

$$v_3 \otimes (u_0 - C \otimes B) = v_1 \otimes A \otimes B \qquad (7.57)$$

Now if only we had some way of "dividing" both sides of (7.57) by the "coefficient" of v_3, the problem would be solved. In convolution algebra, division will not have the same interpretation as in ordinary algebra. Let us use a double fraction line to denote this special operation

$$f_3(t) = \frac{f_1(t)}{f_2(t)} \quad \text{means} \quad f_1(t) = f_2(t) \otimes f_3(t) \qquad (7.58)$$

Given f_1 and f_2 we can "divide" f_1 by f_2 to obtain the unknown function f_3. By this we really mean that the unknown function f_3 must be so chosen that its convolution with f_2 yields f_1. Such "division" implies that we must solve an integral equation, for the unknown function f_3 lies within the convolution integral. With this symbolic notation the solution of the system problem posed in Fig. 7-14 is

$$v_3 = \frac{v_1 \otimes A \otimes B}{u_0 - (C \otimes B)} \qquad (7.59)$$

Comparison with (7.54) shows the similarity of form.

In the next few articles of this chapter we shall see how such problems can be dealt with very conveniently by transforming the signals and the system impulse responses into the frequency domain, where convolution is replaced by ordinary multiplication. Nevertheless, it is worthwhile at this point to take a brief look at what can be done directly in the time domain.

Consider first the system shown in Fig. 7-15(a). The branch running from v_2 to v_3 is an ideal integrator whose impulse response is u_{-1}. Branches a and b are ideal amplifiers. Their impulse responses are au_0 and bu_0, respectively. When a unit impulse is applied at the input (node 1), the output v_3 immediately jumps from zero to the new value a. Following this initial excitation, the input vanishes and the subsequent time variation of v_3 is governed by the integrator, u_{-1}, and the feedback

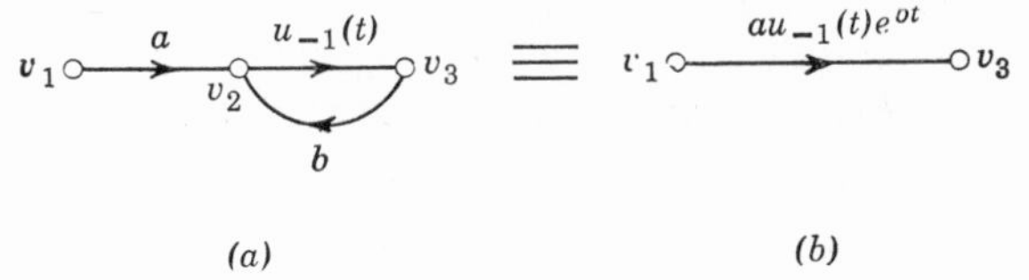

(a)   (b)

Fig. 7-15. An integrator u_{-1} with feedback b has an exponential impulse response $u_{-1}e^{bt}$.

branch, b. Since v_3 is the integral of v_2 it follows that v_2 must be the time rate of change or growth rate of v_3. Also, because of the presence of branch b, we see that the growth rate of v_3 is proportional to v_3. Thus $v_3(t)$ is immediately recognizable as an exponential function, that function whose rate of growth is proportional to its value. In short, the integral equation

$$v_3(t) = b \int v_3(t)\, dt \tag{7.60}$$

has the familiar solution of the form

$$v_3(t) \sim e^{bt} \tag{7.61}$$

On the basis of these considerations we see that the system in Fig. 7-15(a) is equivalent to a single transmission branch having the impulse response indicated in Fig. 7-15(b).

Next consider the system shown in Fig. 7-16(a). The branch having an exponential impulse response is replaceable by an integrator with feedback as indicated in (b). The two feedback paths may then be combined in parallel (c) and the result is recognizable as the single equivalent branch (d).

The two examples illustrated in Figs. 7-15 and 7-16 are important in their own right because these particular forms occur so often in the flow-graph representations of linear communication, measurement, and control systems. They also point the way to the analysis of more general systems containing integrators. Analysis of a linear transmission system having lumped parameters is really the same thing as the analysis of a signal flow graph containing integrators. Although such representation is by no means restricted to electrical systems we can cite electric networks as an example; the flow graph of a lumped-parameter electric network can be constructed so as to contain a number of integrators equal to the number of (independent) capacitor voltages plus the number of (independent) inductor currents in the network.

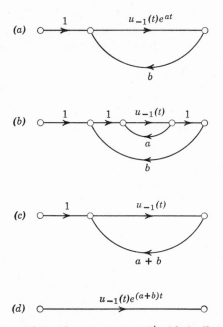

Fig. 7-16. An exponential impulse response $u_{-1}e^{at}$ with feedback b has an over-all exponential impulse response $u_{-1}e^{(a+b)t}$.

Consider an arbitrary flow graph containing three integrators. The flow-graph rules lead to an impulse response of the general form

$$\frac{v_2}{v_1} = \frac{A_0 u_0 + A_1 u_{-1} + A_2 u_{-2} + A_3 u_{-3}}{u_0 - B_1 u_{-1} - B_2 u_{-2} - B_3 u_{-3}} \tag{7.62}$$

in which the A_k and B_k are constants. This follows from the fact that no path or loop in the flow graph can contain more than three integrators, and the convolution of three integrators is, of course, u_{-3}. No matter what the form of the original flow graph, the impulse response (7.62) can be synthesized as the particular flow graph shown in Fig. 7-17(a). Moreover, the denominator of (7.62) may be factored to obtain

$$\frac{v_2}{v_1} = \frac{A_0 u_0 + A_1 u_{-1} + A_2 u_{-2} + A_3 u_{-3}}{(u_0 - b_1 u_{-1}) \otimes (u_0 - b_2 u_{-1}) \otimes (u_0 - b_3 u_{-1})} \tag{7.63}$$

where the b_k are constants, perhaps complex, dependent upon the B_k. The fraction (7.63) can then be recast as a sum of simpler fractions

$$\frac{v_2}{v_1} = a_0 u_0 + \frac{a_1 u_{-1}}{u_0 - b_1 u_{-1}} + \frac{a_2 u_{-1}}{u_0 - b_2 u_{-1}} + \frac{a_3 u_{-1}}{u_0 - b_3 u_{-1}} \quad (7.64)$$

The transformation from (7.63) to (7.64) is called a *partial-fraction expansion*. Calculation of the new constants a_k in terms of the b_k and A_k proceeds as follows: First collect the terms of (7.64) over a common

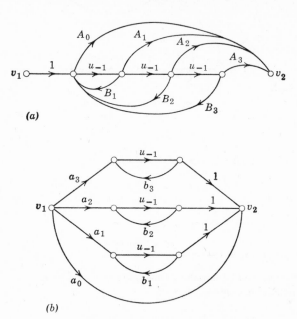

(a)

(b)

Fig. 7-17. Two general forms for systems containing integrators.

denominator. In the resulting numerator the coefficient of u_{-r} will be some linear combination of the quantities a_k and this must equal A_r. Thus we have a set of simultaneous linear equations giving the A_r in terms of the a_k and these equations can be solved to find the a_k in terms of the known A_r.

Expression (7.64) is identifiable as the impulse reponse of the flow graph in Fig. 7-17(b). In this way, the general analysis problem suggested by (7.62) can be broken into a number of simpler problems which we already know how to solve. The elementary result given in Fig. 7-15 and the partial-fraction expansion are, in combination, a powerful tool for the analysis of linear systems with lumped parameters.

7.8   Complex Exponential Signals

We have seen that one convenient way of studying a linear system is to apply a unit impulse at the input and then observe the resulting output signal. From such data we can, with the aid of the superposition integral, calculate the response of that system to an arbitrary input signal. In addition to the unit impulse (or the unit step, which is simply related to the unit impulse) there is another basic input signal of primary interest in the study of linear systems. This signal is the exponential. If we assume that the input signal is exp (σt) for all time, past, present, and future, then we can verify by direct substitution into the superposition integral that the corresponding output signal will be H exp (σt) for all time, past, present, and future. In short, an exponential input produces an exponential output having the same exponential coefficient σ. The parameter H will, in general, be different for different values of the exponential coefficient σ and, as it turns out, the properties of the linear system under test are completely determined by the function $H(\sigma)$. Thus, the function $H(\sigma)$ is just as valid and complete a description of the linear system as is the impulse-response function $h(t)$. If either $H(\sigma)$ or $h(t)$ is known, then the output can be calculated for any specified input. Unless the reader has some familiarity with functions of a complex variable it may seem even more surprising that everything we have said above also applies when the real number σ is replaced by a complex number s. The question now arises, "What is meant by exp (st) when s is a complex number?" Our first problem is to define the complex exponential signal exp (st) and to relate it to the real signals which appear in the physical world.

Let us begin by defining the "complex frequency"

$$s = \sigma + j\omega \qquad (7.65)$$

and its complex conjugate, denoted by an asterisk,

$$s^* = \sigma - j\omega \qquad (7.66)$$

in which σ and ω are real quantities and j is the square root of -1. Each of the quantities s, σ, and ω has the dimensions of inverse time, and this is really the only excuse for referring to s as a "frequency." Although it would be logical, perhaps, to call σ the "real frequency" and ω the "imaginary frequency," such names would be entirely contrary to present common usage. As a matter of fact, wide current usage suggests that we call ω the "real frequency." As for σ, various names have been used, among them "growth parameter" and "negative-damping coefficient." We shall try to avoid such difficulties in this chapter by using the symbols as much as possible rather than their names. However, it is tempting to suggest another name for s. Instead of "complex frequency" we can refer to s as the "complex rate" or simply the "rate" of the exponential signal. This comes, of course, from the fact that s has to do with the rate (the "compound interest" rate) at which the exponential is growing or decreasing. Thus σ and ω are respectively the "real rate" and "imaginary rate." Moreover, this does not interfere with the use of the term "frequency" as a synonym for the "imaginary rate" ω.

So much for nomenclature. Now back to the business of developing a suitable definition for the complex exponential. The total differential of s is simply

$$ds = d\sigma + j\,d\omega \tag{7.67}$$

and the square of s is

$$s^2 = \sigma^2 - \omega^2 + j2\sigma\omega \tag{7.68}$$

Next consider the total differential of the square of s. This can be computed from the right-hand portion of (7.68) since we know how to differentiate functions of real variables. The result is

$$d(s^2) = 2\sigma\,d\sigma - 2\omega\,d\omega + j2\omega\,d\sigma + j2\sigma\,d\omega \tag{7.69}$$

and this is recognizable as

$$d(s^2) = 2(\sigma + j\omega)(d\sigma + j\,d\omega) \tag{7.70}$$

Now, dividing (7.70) by ds we obtain

$$\frac{d(s^2)}{ds} = 2s \tag{7.71}$$

Relation (7.71) suggests that in differentiating certain functions of a complex variable we can use the same rules of calculus which apply to functions of a real variable. To find the derivative of a higher power of s we first write

$$\frac{d(s^n)}{ds} = \frac{d}{ds}[s(s^{n-1})] = s^{n-1} + s\frac{d}{ds}(s^{n-1}) \tag{7.72}$$

Differentiation of the product of two functions follows the usual rules even when we are not sure how to differentiate one of the two functions in the product. Hence, relation (7.72) allows us to proceed by induction. It follows from (7.72) that if the usual differentiation rule holds for a given power of s then the same rule applies to the next higher power. Since we have already established the validity of the usual rule for s^2, it therefore must hold for all higher powers of s. Thus,

$$\frac{d(s^n)}{ds} = ns^{n-1} \tag{7.73}$$

In view of (7.73) we can apply the ordinary rules of calculus to any function of s which is defined by a power series in s (with normal precautions about convergence of the series). Such functions are said to be "analytic." Every analytic function of the complex variable s possesses a unique derivative, is differentiable by the ordinary rules of calculus, and is expandable as a power series in s. Examples of analytic functions are $\cos(s)$, $\log(s)$, and $1/s$. The function $1/s$ cannot be expanded in a series about the origin, for at the origin this function is singular. Nevertheless, $1/s$ can be expanded in a Taylor series about some point other than the origin, and this fact is sufficient evidence of its analyticity. One simple example of a nonanalytic function is

$$|s| = \sqrt{\sigma^2 + \omega^2} \tag{7.74}$$

The absolute value $|s|$ cannot be represented as a power series in the variable s.

The meaning of the complex exponential function can now be made clear. The complex exponential function is *defined* by the series

$$\exp(st) \equiv e^{st} = \sum_{k=0}^{\infty} \frac{(st)^k}{k!} \tag{7.75}$$

This particular series converges for all finite values of s and t. Separation of s into its real and imaginary parts yields

$$e^{st} = e^{\sigma t}(e^{j\omega t}) = e^{\sigma t} \sum_{k=0}^{\infty} \frac{(j\omega t)^k}{k!} \tag{7.76}$$

and a knowledge of the power series for the functions $\cos \omega t$ and $\sin \omega t$ allows us to make the identifications

$$\cos \omega t = \frac{e^{j\omega t} + e^{-j\omega t}}{2} \tag{7.77}$$

and

$$\sin \omega t = \frac{e^{j\omega t} - e^{-j\omega t}}{j2} \tag{7.78}$$

From (7.76), (7.77), and (7.78) we find

$$e^{st} = e^{\sigma t}(\cos \omega t + j \sin \omega t) \tag{7.79}$$

Also

$$e^{\sigma t} \cos \omega t = \frac{e^{st} + e^{s*t}}{2} \tag{7.80}$$

$$e^{\sigma t} \sin \omega t = \frac{e^{st} - e^{s*t}}{j2} \tag{7.81}$$

Having related exp (st) to the more familiar trigonometric and exponential functions of the real variables ωt and σt, we are in a better position to see how it behaves. A complete plot of exp (st) versus time would require a three-dimensional space: one co-ordinate for time and one each for the real and imaginary parts of the function. In three-dimensional space the curve would appear as a "helix" whose diameter varies exponentially with distance along the axis of the "helix." How-

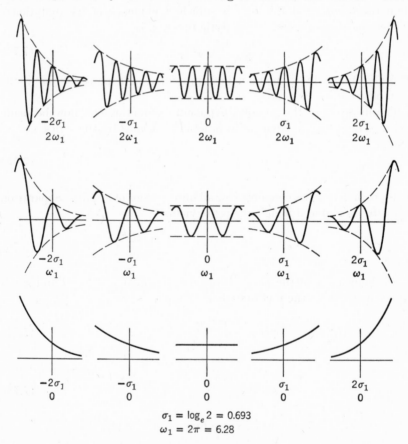

$$\sigma_1 = \log_e 2 = 0.693$$
$$\omega_1 = 2\pi = 6.28$$

Fig. 7-18. Real part of the time function exp (st) for various σ and ω.

ever, the real part of the function can be plotted in two dimensions, as in Fig. 7-18, for various values of the complex parameter s. Specification of s requires the designation of two real numbers: the values of σ and ω. It is exceedingly convenient to think of σ and ω as rectangular coordinates in a plane, as shown in Fig. 7-19.

Each point in the plane is associated with a specific value of the complex number s. This complex plane is usually called the "complex s-plane" or "complex-frequency plane" or, more simply, the "s-plane."

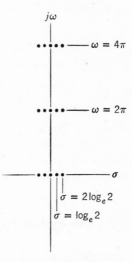

Thus far we have stated without proof that in a linear (and time-invariant) system an exponential input signal exp (st), having a complex rate s, produces an exponential output signal in which the complex rate is actually the same as that of the input. We have also described the complex exponential signal in detail by expressing its real and imaginary parts in terms of familiar functions of real variables. The question remains, "Of what possible interest are complex signals when only real signals exist in nature?" One way of parrying this question is to adopt the concept that complex signals do exist in nature, but always in complex-conjugate pairs whose sum

Fig. 7-19. Locations in the complex s-plane associated with the waveforms of Fig. 7-18.

is real. To the next question, "Then why not work with real signals rather than complex exponentials?", we answer simply, "Because it is usually more convenient to work with complex exponential signals."

Let v_{1r} be a *real* input signal. We know that the system will respond with some *real* output signal v_{2r}. Also let v_{1i} be some other possible real input signal for which v_{2i} is the corresponding real output. By superposition, therefore, an input signal $v_1 = v_{1r} \pm jv_{1i}$ must produce the output $v_{2r} \pm jv_{2i}$. In short, if an input v_1 produces an output v_2, then its complex conjugate v_1^* must produce the output v_2^*. This property of "real" linear systems is known as "conjugate symmetry." In view of the conjugate symmetry property it is really no more difficult to follow a *pair* of complex-conjugate exponential signals through the system than it is to follow a *single* complex exponential signal. Thus we can work with a single complex exponential signal, temporarily ignoring its complex-conjugate twin, provided we understand that the corresponding real signal in the physical world is merely the real part of the complex signal appearing in our calculations. The special case $s = j\omega$ is, of course, the basis for the impedance concept in steady-state a-c circuit analysis.

The general complex exponential signal can be written as

$$Ve^{st} = |V|e^{\sigma t}[\cos{(\omega t + \phi)} + j \sin{(\omega t + \phi)}] \qquad (7.82)$$

in which

$$V = |V|e^{j\phi} = |V|\,(\cos\phi + j \sin\phi) \qquad (7.83)$$

is the so-called "complex amplitude" of the signal. The corresponding physical (real) signal is

$$\text{Re}\,[Ve^{st}] = \tfrac{1}{2}[(Ve^{st}) + (Ve^{st})^*] = |V|e^{\sigma t}\cos{(\omega t + \phi)} \qquad (7.84)$$

The (real part of the) complex exponential signal represents a generalization of the familiar steady-state sinusoidal wave, a generalization in which the amplitude of the wave may either remain constant ($\sigma = 0$), grow exponentially with time (σ positive), or decay exponentially with time (σ negative).

7.9   The System Function H(s)

Substitution of the complex exponential input signal

$$v_1(t) = V_1 e^{st} \qquad (7.85)$$

into the superposition integral

$$v_2(t) = \int_{-\infty}^{\infty} h(\tau)v_1(t - \tau)\,d\tau \qquad (7.86)$$

gives

$$v_2(t) = \int_{-\infty}^{\infty} h(\tau)V_1 e^{s(t-\tau)}\,d\tau \qquad (7.87)$$

Removing from the integral that part not dependent upon τ, we have

$$v_2(t) = V_1 e^{st}\int_{-\infty}^{\infty} h(\tau)e^{-s\tau}\,d\tau \qquad (7.88)$$

The remaining integral is defined as the *system function* or *transmission function*

$$H(s) = \int_{-\infty}^{\infty} h(t)e^{-st}\,dt \qquad (7.89)$$

For real $h(t)$, it is apparent that $H(s)$ is "conjugate symmetric," that is, $H(s^*) = H^*(s)$. From (7.88) and (7.89) we see that the output signal is an exponential having the same complex rate s as the input signal

$$v_2(t) = H(s)V_1e^{st} \tag{7.90}$$

When the system input signal is a *single complex exponential for all time*, the striking fact is that $H(s)$ is simply the *quotient* of the output and input signals

$$H(s) = \frac{v_2(t)}{v_1(t)} \tag{7.91}$$

For input waveforms other than the complex exponential we should not, in general, expect the *quotient* of the output and input signals to be *independent* of time. Relation (7.91) may, in fact, be taken as a simple definition of the system function, with the clear understanding that such a definition makes sense only for an input signal of the form exp (st).

The output signal is of the form

$$v_2(t) = V_2e^{st} \tag{7.92}$$

and this brings us to what is perhaps the simplest interpretation of the system function: the quotient of the complex amplitudes of the output and input signals

$$H(s) = \frac{V_2}{V_1} \tag{7.93}$$

Thus only ordinary multiplication, rather than convolution, is required in the process of following a complex exponential signal through a sequence of linear systems.

The integral (7.89) defines an analytic function $H(s)$. For example, if

$$h(t) = u_{-1}(t)e^{-t} \tag{7.94}$$

then

$$H(s) = \int_0^\infty e^{-(s+1)t}\, dt \tag{7.95}$$

and this can be written as

$$H(s) = \lim_{t \to \infty} \left[\frac{1 - e^{-(s+1)t}}{s + 1} \right] \tag{7.96}$$

In the limit

$$H(s) = \begin{cases} \dfrac{1}{s + 1}, & \text{for } \sigma > -1 \tag{7.97} \\[2mm] \infty, & \text{for } \sigma < -1 \tag{7.98} \end{cases}$$

Thus the *formula* $1/(s + 1)$ is a valid representation of the *function*

$H(s)$ *only* within the "region of validity" or "region of convergence" lying to the right of the vertical line $\sigma = -1$ in the s-plane. We often equate the formula and the function

$$H(s) = \frac{1}{s+1} \tag{7.99}$$

for convenience of notation, but this is always done with the tacit understanding that the equality is valid only in certain regions of the s-plane.

The failure of the formula to represent the function everywhere is not a mere mathematical difficulty. Let an input signal

$$v_1(t) = e^{st} \tag{7.100}$$

be applied to the system defined by (7.94). Substitution into the superposition integral shows that

$$v_2(t) = \begin{cases} \dfrac{e^{st}}{s+1}, & \text{for } \sigma > -1 & (7.101) \\[2ex] \infty, & \text{for } \sigma \le -1 & (7.102) \end{cases}$$

Hence, the output $v_2(t)$ is equal to $v_1(t)/(s+1)$ only when σ is greater than -1. For σ less than or equal to this critical value, the output signal is actually infinite for all finite t.

The system function of a realizable stable system has special properties. Since the $h(t)$ of a realizable system vanishes for negative t, we have, from (7.89),

$$|H(s)| \le \int_0^\infty |h(t)| e^{-\sigma t}\, dt \tag{7.103}$$

If the system is also stable, it follows from (7.26) and (7.103) that

$$|H(s)| < \infty, \qquad \text{for all } \sigma \ge 0 \tag{7.104}$$

Hence the integral defining a realizable stable system function converges in the entire right-half s-plane, including the $j\omega$ axis and the point at infinity. If the impulse response is known to be stable, but is not necessarily realizable, then all we can say about the system-function integral is that it converges on the $j\omega$ axis.

In the special case $s = j\omega$, the system function becomes $H(j\omega)$, the Fourier transform of the impulse response $h(t)$. For stable systems, this Fourier integral converges for all ω. Having started with the definition of the system function $H(s)$, we shall, for consistency, refer to the Fourier transform of $h(t)$ as $H(j\omega)$ rather than $H(\omega)$. The distinction is only a matter of notation.

7.10 Correlation of Input and Output Signals

In the next few articles we shall be concerned with the general properties of realizable stable systems. When we concentrate attention upon the $j\omega$ axis, the system function $H(s)$ becomes $H(j\omega)$ and is then sometimes referred to as the "frequency response" of the system. For the present it will be sufficient to think of $H(j\omega)$ as simply the Fourier transform of the impulse response $h(t)$.

The frequency response $H(j\omega)$ of a linear system may be found experimentally by applying an (approximate) impulse u_0 at the input and recording the output $h(t)$, from which $H(j\omega)$ can then be computed. A step input u_{-1}, often more convenient in practice, produces an output $h^{(-1)}(t)$ whose derivative is again the impulse response. Alternatively, a sinusoidal input of adjustable frequency permits direct determination of $H(j\omega)$ as the quotient of the complex amplitudes of the complex exponential representations of the input and output sinusoids.

It might at first appear that a more complicated input signal, any input signal other than an impulse (or step) or sinusoid, would greatly complicate the problem of determining the system properties from the recorded input and output signals. Such is not the case; at least it is not the case if we admit correlation as an acceptable computational operation. The argument proceeds as follows. Suppose that

$$v \quad \text{means} \quad v(t) \tag{7.105}$$

$$v' \quad \text{means} \quad v^*(-t) \tag{7.106}$$

so that the crosscorrelation function of the output and input signals can be written as

$$\psi_{21} = v_2 \otimes v_1' \tag{7.107}$$

We assume here that the system is realizable and stable and that the input, and therefore the output, is a pulse signal (one having finite energy). The input v_1, output v_2, and system impulse response h are related by the convolution

$$v_2 = v_1 \otimes h \tag{7.108}$$

Substitution of (7.108) into (7.107) yields

$$\psi_{21} = (v_1 \otimes h) \otimes v_1' = (v_1 \otimes v_1') \otimes h \tag{7.109}$$

which is recognizable as

$$\psi_{21} = \psi_{11} \otimes h \tag{7.110}$$

Now, if the autocorrelation function ψ_{11} of the input signal is, *in com-*

parison with h, a relatively narrow "window" function, then we can treat ψ_{11} as an impulse in (7.110) to obtain

$$\psi_{11} \otimes h \approx \Psi_{11} h \qquad (7.111)$$

where Ψ_{11} is a constant equal to the area of the impulse. Hence

$$\psi_{21} \approx \Psi_{11} h \qquad (7.112)$$

which tells us that the shape of the impulse response is the same as that of the crosscorrelation function ψ_{21}, a function that can be computed directly from the recorded input and output signals.

Another result of interest is the relationship between the input and output autocorrelation functions, ψ_{11} and ψ_{22}. First observe that $v_2' = v_1' \otimes h'$, so that

$$\psi_{22} = (v_1 \otimes h) \otimes (v_1' \otimes h') = (v_1 \otimes v_1') \otimes (h \otimes h')$$
$$(7.113)$$

Now define

$$\psi_{hh} = h \otimes h' \qquad (7.114)$$

whence

$$\psi_{22} = \psi_{11} \otimes \psi_{hh} \qquad (7.115)$$

This tells us that the autocorrelation function of a signal can be followed through a succession of linear systems in exactly the same way as the signal itself, provided the impulse response of each block in the complete system is replaced by its autocorrelation function ψ_{hh}.

In the frequency domain, convolution is replaced by ordinary multiplication, with the result that Fourier transformation of (7.110) gives

$$\Psi_{21}(\omega) = \Psi_{11}(\omega)H(j\omega) \qquad (7.116)$$

The statement that ψ_{11} is a narrow pulse is the same as the statement that the energy-density spectrum $\Psi_{11}(\omega)$ is broad and flat. The approximation (7.112) is equivalent to the assumption that $\Psi_{11}(\omega)$ is essentially constant over the significant frequency range occupied by $H(j\omega)$. The other correlation relationship (7.115) becomes, in the frequency domain,

$$\Psi_{22}(\omega) = \Psi_{11}(\omega) \left| H(j\omega) \right|^2 \qquad (7.117)$$

In other words, the output energy-density spectrum is the product of the input energy-density spectrum and the squared magnitude of the frequency-response function of the system.

All of the above results apply to power signals as well as energy signals. The appropriate relationships are obtained by replacing ψ with ϕ and $\Psi(\omega)$ with $\Phi(\omega)$ throughout. Such replacement does not include ψ_{hh} and Ψ_{hh}, because the impulse response of a stable system has the character of a pulse signal.

Relation (7.110) has important practical consequences. Suppose, for example, that we are interested in some portion of an automatically controlled oil refinery, say that portion whose input signal is the control voltage on a valve-adjustment servomechanism and whose output signal is the temperature of the fluid in a mixing chamber somewhere down the line of equipment. Suppose this system operates as an approximately linear signal transmission system within the expected ranges of signal variation. We want to obtain the steady-state frequency response $H(j\omega)$ for use in a study of system performance under some proposed change in plant operation. A direct calculation of the response function $H(j\omega)$ is difficult or impossible, so that an experimental determination is required. However, to shut down the plant for sinusoidal-input-signal testing would be prohibitively expensive. Moreover, the frequency range of interest runs from 1 to 1000 cycles per day, so that a sinusoidal-signal experiment might take several days to reach steady-state equilibrium at each of the test frequencies on the low end of the range. Fortunately, plant records are available and, upon running the data through a small computer programmed for correlation, we find that ψ_{11} is a relatively narrow pulse in comparison with the function ψ_{21}. Hence the approximation (7.112) is good and the desired impulse response $h(t)$ is in our hands. The point is that *the transmission properties of the system have been determined without making special tests or in any way interrupting the normal operation of the system.* Even when the approximation (7.112) does not hold, $H(j\omega)$ may still be obtainable from the recorded signal data. We can return to (7.110) and its frequency-domain counterpart (7.116). With $\Psi_{21}(\omega)$ and $\Psi_{11}(\omega)$ known, $H(j\omega)$ is determined by (7.116). The determination is accurate so long as $\Psi_{11}(\omega)$ does not become too small within the frequency range of interest for $H(j\omega)$. In short, the input-signal spectrum must cover the significant frequency range of $H(j\omega)$.

7.11 Signal Matching

As stated previously, the output signal of a linear system is the cross-correlation of the input signal with the memory function of the system. If we choose a system whose memory function has the same waveshape as that of the input signal, then the output signal is, apart from a possible constant multiplier, simply the autocorrelation function of the input signal. Such a system is said to be "matched" to the input signal.

A possible exploitation of the "matching" technique is illustrated in Fig. 7-20. Consider an impulse signal v_0 which is to be transmitted to some receiving point v_2. The physical transmission path is represented by the first block in the diagram and is characterized by a memory function m_0. Suppose that the transmission path badly distorts the pulse signal, as indicated by the irregular waveform of v_1 (alternatively, we may imagine that the signal has been *purposely* distorted by a filter m_0 *before* actual distortionless transmission, for some purpose such as confusion of an enemy). In an attempt to recuperate the original impulsive waveform we might employ a "matched filter" m at the receiving station. If the distorted signal v_1 is sufficiently "noiselike" in character, that is, if it has much the appearance and character of a sample of a broad-spectrum random signal, then its autocorrelation function ($\psi_{11} = v_2$) approximates an impulse, as indicated in Fig. 7-20.

The two filters m_0 and m in Fig. 7-20 are said to be a "matched pair" and the extent to which the output v_2 approximates an impulse is simply the extent to which the autocorrelation function of the memory function m_0 approximates a unit impulse. However, the more fundamental point to be made here is that for any given $m_0(t)$, and for a *fixed integral square* $m(t)$, the *maximum possible peak* value of the output signal v_2 is obtained by matching m to m_0, that is, by choosing an m whose *reversed* waveform is the same as that of m_0. This result is apparent from the vector-space interpretation of the time functions involved. A fixed integral square m corresponds to a vector of fixed length. The inner product or correlation of vector v_1 with vector m is obviously a maximum when vector m is rotated to the same direction as v_1 in the vector space.

When a signal v_1 contains not only the desired message or information s_1 but also some unavoidable additive broad-spectrum noise n_1, the matching technique may be exploited to maximize the output signal-to-noise ratio at a specified instant of time. Let

$$v_1 = s_1 + n_1 \qquad (7.118)$$

and

$$v_2 = s_2 + n_2 \qquad (7.119)$$

where s_2 is that part of v_2 produced by s_1 acting alone. Specifically,

$$s_2 = s_1 \otimes h \qquad (7.120)$$

$$n_2 = n_1 \otimes h \qquad (7.121)$$

Assume that the input noise n_1 has a known autocorrelation function ϕ_{11}. The Fourier transform of ϕ_{11} is

$$\Phi_{11}(\omega) = \text{power-density spectrum of } n_1 \qquad (7.122)$$

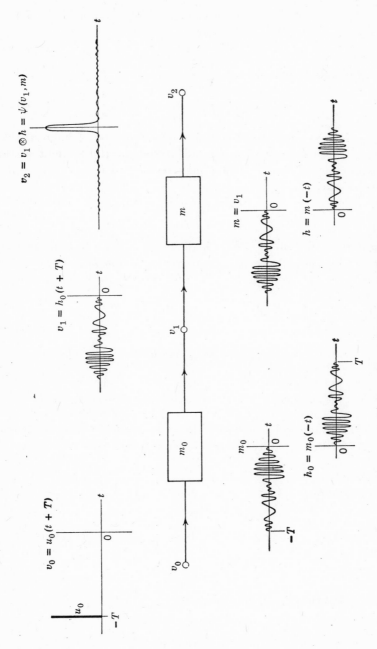

Fig. 7-20. A matched transmission system.

Similarly,

$$\Phi_{22}(\omega) = \text{power-density spectrum of } n_2 \qquad (7.123)$$

Now, since

$$\Phi_{22}(\omega) = |H(j\omega)|^2 \Phi_{11}(\omega) \qquad (7.124)$$

we can integrate to obtain

$$\int \Phi_{22}(\omega) \frac{d\omega}{2\pi} = \int |H(j\omega)|^2 \Phi_{11}(\omega) \frac{d\omega}{2\pi} \qquad (7.125)$$

If $\Phi_{11}(\omega)$ is essentially flat over the frequency region of interest, that frequency range embracing nearly all of the spectral content of the system function $H(j\omega)$, then Φ_{11} may be treated as a constant and (7.125) becomes

$$\int \Phi_{22}(\omega) \frac{d\omega}{2\pi} = \Phi_{11} \int |H(j\omega)|^2 \frac{d\omega}{2\pi} \qquad (7.126)$$

The integral on the left of (7.126) is the total power in the output-noise spectrum and is therefore equal to the average output-noise power. The integral on the right is recognizable as the energy of the impulse response

$$\int |H(j\omega)|^2 \frac{d\omega}{2\pi} = \int h^2 \, dt = \int m^2 \, dt \qquad (7.127)$$

Hence

$$\langle n_2{}^2 \rangle = \Phi_{11} \int m^2 \, dt \qquad (7.128)$$

Thus, for a given input noise n_1 having a flat power-density spectrum of height Φ_{11}, and a memory function m having a *fixed* integral-square value, the mean-square output noise (that is, the average noise power) is *independent* of the shape of the memory function. So much for the noise. As for the signal, the superposition integral gives

$$s_2(t) = \int s_1(\tau) h(t - \tau) \, d\tau \qquad (7.129)$$

With s_1 and h real and

$$h(\tau) = m(-t) \qquad (7.130)$$

the superposition integral can be rewritten as the crosscorrelation integral of s_1 and m

$$s_2(t) = \int s_1(\tau) m(\tau - t) \, d\tau \qquad (7.131)$$

The associated correlation efficiency is

$$0 \leq \frac{[s_2(t)]^2}{\left[\int s_1{}^2 \, dt\right]\left[\int m^2 \, dt\right]} \leq 1 \qquad (7.132)$$

and the efficiency takes on its maximum value, unity, when $m(t)$ is chosen to have the same waveshape as $s_1(t)$,

$$m(t) = Ks_1(t) \tag{7.133}$$

where K is an arbitrary scale factor. Moreover, the maximum of $s_2(t)$ occurs at the origin. From (7.131) through (7.133), therefore,

$$[s_2(0)]^2 = (s_2{}^2)_{\max} = \left[\int s_1{}^2 \, dt\right]\left[\int m^2 \, dt\right] \tag{7.134}$$

We are now in a position to compute the output signal-to-noise ratio in terms of the input-signal energy and the input-noise spectral power density (which also has the dimensions of energy). The quotient of (7.134) and (7.128) gives the desired ratio

$$\frac{\int s_1{}^2 \, dt}{\Phi_{11}} = \frac{(s_2{}^2)_{\max}}{\langle n_2{}^2 \rangle} \tag{7.135}$$

Thus,

$$\frac{\text{input-signal energy}}{\text{input-noise spectral power density}} = \frac{\text{peak output-signal power}}{\text{average output-noise power}} \tag{7.136}$$

In other words, a matched filter is the optimum linear system for the extraction of an energy signal from additive flat-spectrum noise, provided the peak output signal-to-noise power ratio is taken as the figure of merit or criterion for "detectability" of the signal.

When the input-noise spectrum is not flat over the frequency range of interest, we can precede filter m by a preliminary linear system m_p, whose frequency-response curve is chosen to compensate for the shape of $\Phi_{11}(\omega)$. Specifically, we choose $H_p(j\omega)$ so that the product $\Phi_{11}(\omega)|H_p(j\omega)|^2$ is flat over the range of interest. The output-noise spectrum of m_p is therefore flat and m may be adjusted to match the modified signal. Consequently, the cascade combination of m_p and m, taken as a unit, comprises the general optimum linear filter for maximization of the peak signal-to-noise power ratio.

In the language of audible sounds, the performance of a matched transmission system can be described very simply. With reference to Fig. 7-20, an input "click" (v_0) produces a soft "hiss" or "swish" (v_1) and the job of the matching filter (m) is to "pull the signal together" once again to produce a final output "click" (v_2).

A variation on the same theme is afforded by a filter m_0 whose impulse response h_0 is a "whistle" of *increasing* pitch and duration T. The impulse response h of the matching filter m would sound like a "whistle" of *decreasing* pitch and duration T. In effect, m_0 delays the "high-frequency" energy in v_0 more than the "low-frequency" energy. The matching filter m then does the opposite, so that each frequency component experiences the same total delay and the "click" reappears at the output of m.

7.12   Real and Imaginary Parts of a Realizable Stable Frequency-Response Function

As a consequence of the property that $h(t)$ vanishes for negative t, the real and imaginary parts of a realizable stable $H(j\omega)$ are strongly related. In fact, given the real part $H_r(j\omega)$, the imaginary part $jH_i(j\omega)$ is *uniquely determined*, and vice versa.

To obtain the relationship between $H_r(j\omega)$ and $H_i(j\omega)$ we can construct an arbitrary $H(j\omega)$ by superposition (addition) of certain elementary functions. Let $f(t)$ stand for the impulse response of some elementary realizable system and let $F(j\omega)$ be the corresponding frequency response. Stability is tacitly assumed, for otherwise the transform $F(j\omega)$ would have no meaning. Multiplication of $f(t)$ by $\exp(j\omega_1 t)$ destroys neither realizability nor stability so that $F(j\omega - j\omega_1)$, the Fourier transform of $f(t) \exp(j\omega_1 t)$, is also a realizable function. Now consider a weighted sum of many such elementary functions, each having a different ω_1,

$$H(j\omega) = \int_{-\infty}^{\infty} F(j\omega - j\omega_1)g(\omega_1)\,d\omega_1 \qquad (7.137)$$

where $g(\omega_1)$ is a real weighting factor. Function $g(\omega_1)$ must be even, for otherwise the $h(t)$ associated with $H(j\omega)$ would not be purely real. Since a sum of realizable system functions is itself a realizable system function, it follows that the $H(j\omega)$ in (7.137) is realizable, provided the integral converges.

To continue, let us choose the elementary impulse response

$$f(t) = \frac{1}{\pi} u_{-1}(t)e^{-\alpha t} \qquad (7.138)$$

wherein α is a *positive* real constant. Thus

$$F(s) = \frac{1}{\pi(\alpha + s)}, \qquad \text{for } \sigma > -\alpha \qquad (7.139)$$

$$F(j\omega) = \frac{1}{\pi(\alpha + j\omega)} \qquad (7.140)$$

and

$$F_r(j\omega) = \frac{\alpha}{\pi(\alpha^2 + \omega^2)} \tag{7.141}$$

$$F_i(j\omega) = \frac{-\omega}{\pi(\alpha^2 + \omega^2)} \tag{7.142}$$

$$F(j\omega) = F_r(j\omega) + jF_i(j\omega) \tag{7.143}$$

Substitution into (7.137) yields

$$H_r(j\omega) = \frac{1}{\pi} \int_{-\infty}^{\infty} \frac{\alpha g(\omega_1)}{\alpha^2 + (\omega_1 - \omega)^2} d\omega_1 \tag{7.144}$$

$$H_i(j\omega) = \frac{1}{\pi} \int_{-\infty}^{\infty} \frac{(\omega_1 - \omega)g(\omega_1)}{\alpha^2 + (\omega_1 - \omega)^2} d\omega_1 \tag{7.145}$$

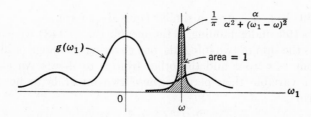

Fig. 7-21.   The factors in the integrand of equation (7.144).

The integrand factors of (7.144) are sketched in Fig. 7-21. If the integral (7.144) converges, then as α becomes small $g(\omega_1)$ is effectively convolved with a unit impulse. In the limit of small α, therefore,

$$H_r(j\omega) = g(\omega) \tag{7.146}$$

$$H_i(j\omega) = \frac{1}{\pi} \int_{-\infty}^{\infty} \frac{g(\omega_1)}{\omega_1 - \omega} d\omega_1 \tag{7.147}$$

or

$$H_i(j\omega) = \frac{1}{\pi} \int_{-\infty}^{\infty} \frac{H_r(j\omega_1)}{\omega_1 - \omega} d\omega_1 \tag{7.148}$$

Any difficulties with integration across the point $\omega_1 = \omega$ can be resolved by returning to (7.145) and treating α as a positive number, small but nonzero. Repeating the entire process with a pure imaginary (rather than real) function $f(t)$, and with an odd (rather than even) function $g(\omega_1)$, we find the complementary result

$$H_r(j\omega) = -\frac{1}{\pi} \int_{-\infty}^{\infty} \frac{H_i(j\omega)}{\omega_1 - \omega} d\omega_1 \tag{7.149}$$

Relations (7.148) and (7.149) are called Hilbert transforms, after the mathematician who introduced them. They tell us the aforementioned remarkable fact that the imaginary (or real) part of a realizable frequency-response function is completely determined when the real (or imaginary) part is specified. For example, knowledge of $R(j\omega)$, the resistive part of a passive impedance function $Z(j\omega)$, automatically fixes the reactive component $X(j\omega)$.

Incidentally, since $H_i(j\omega)$ is an odd function, we can write

$$H_i(j\omega) = \tfrac{1}{2}[H_i(j\omega) - H_i(-j\omega)] \tag{7.150}$$

whereupon substitution of (7.148) into (7.150) yields an equivalent form of (7.148)

$$H_i(j\omega) = \frac{1}{\pi} \int_{-\infty}^{\infty} \frac{\omega_1 H_r(j\omega_1)}{\omega_1^2 - \omega^2} \, d\omega_1 \tag{7.151}$$

and (7.149) has, of course, a similar equivalent form.

For a better understanding of the meaning of (7.148) we can express (7.145) as the sum of two integrals, one covering the range of integration on ω_1 from $-\infty$ to ω and the other from ω to $+\infty$. An elementary change of variable then permits these two integrals to be combined in the form

$$H_i(j\omega) = \frac{2}{\pi} \int_0^\infty \left(\frac{\omega_1^2}{\alpha^2 + \omega_1^2}\right) q(\omega_1) \, d\omega_1 \tag{7.152}$$

where

$$q(\omega_1) = \frac{g(\omega + \omega_1) - g(\omega - \omega_1)}{2\omega_1} \tag{7.153}$$

Function $q(\omega_1)$ has the geometric interpretation indicated in Fig. 7-22. The value of $q(\omega_1)$ is the slope of a chord drawn between the two points $\omega + \omega_1$ and $\omega - \omega_1$ on the g curve. For any fixed ω this slope will vary with ω_1, defining the function $q(\omega_1)$. If (7.152) converges, then in the limit of small α we have

$$H_i(j\omega) = \frac{2}{\pi} \int_0^\infty q(\omega_1) \, d\omega_1 \tag{7.154}$$

A reactance function, such as the transfer impedance of a lossless network (when treated as the limiting form of a lossy network), has a real part on the $j\omega$ axis consisting entirely of impulses. Although a reactance function is formally unstable the Hilbert transform gives the proper imaginary part. This is to be expected, since the elementary function (7.139), from which the Hilbert transformation was deduced, becomes a reactance functon in the limit of small α. In fact, (7.139) is the impedance of a simple parallel RC circuit. Allowing α to approach zero through positive values is equivalent to making the positive conductance $(1/R)$ arbitrarily small.

Reactance functions which become infinite at infinite ω are exceptions. Consider the reactance function

$$\frac{1 + s^2}{s} = \frac{1}{s} + s \tag{7.155}$$

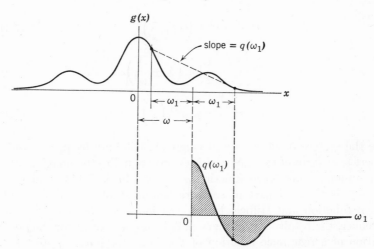

Fig. 7-22. A geometrical interpretation of the Hilbert transform.

If we treat this as "almost stable," the limiting form of a realizable stable function, then on the $j\omega$ axis the function can be expressed as

$$\pi u_0(\omega) + \left(\frac{1}{j\omega} + j\omega\right) \tag{7.156}$$

Application of the Hilbert transformation to the real part yields only the portion $1/j\omega$ of the imaginary part and does not show the other portion $j\omega$ coming from the term s. Another example is offered by the system

$$h(t) = u_0(t) - u_1(t) - u_{-1}(t)e^{-t} \tag{7.157}$$

$$H(s) = -\frac{s^2}{1 + s} = \frac{s}{1 + s} - s \tag{7.158}$$

$$H_r(j\omega) = \frac{\omega^3}{1 + \omega^2} \tag{7.159}$$

$$H_i(j\omega) = -\frac{\omega^3}{1 + \omega^2} = \frac{\omega}{1 + \omega^2} - \omega \tag{7.160}$$

As indicated in (7.158), this function can be expressed as the algebraic sum of a stable function $s/(1 + s)$ and a reactance function s. Hilbert transformation of the real part (7.159) gives only that portion $\omega/(1 + \omega^2)$ of the imaginary part arising from the stable portion $s/(1 + s)$. As a final example, let us take the almost-stable system

$$h(t) = u_{-1}(t) \left(\frac{1 - e^{-t}}{t} \right) \tag{7.161}$$

$$H(s) = \log \left(1 + \frac{1}{s} \right) \tag{7.162}$$

$$H_r(s) = \frac{1}{2} \log \left(1 + \frac{1}{\omega^2} \right) \tag{7.163}$$

$$H_i(s) = -\tan^{-1} \left(\frac{1}{\omega} \right) \tag{7.164}$$

Here the system function is well behaved at infinite frequency and the Hilbert transform of the real part is exactly equal to the imaginary part.

In summary, any even function $g(\omega)$ for which (7.144) and (7.145) converge is the real part of some realizable stable (or almost-stable) system function and Hilbert transformation gives the imaginary part. Moreover, the resulting imaginary part is unique except for the possible addition of a reactance function of the form $a_1 s + a_3 s^3 + a_5 s^5 + \cdots$, which is infinite only at infinite frequency.

7.13 The Real Part Integral

The Hilbert integrals (7.148) and (7.149) permit us to deduce special results of great practical interest. One such result is that the high-frequency character of $H_i(j\omega)$ controls the area under the curve $H_r(j\omega)$. To obtain this result first multiply both sides of (7.148) by ω. After such multiplication the integrand contains a factor $\omega/(\omega - \omega_1)$. If ω is sufficiently large the factor may be replaced by unity without appreciable effect upon the value of the integral. In other words, we may assume that ω is considerably larger than ω_1 throughout the significant range of integration. Hence, in the limit,

$$\lim_{\omega \to \infty} [-\omega H_i(j\omega)] = \frac{1}{\pi} \int_{-\infty}^{\infty} H_r(j\omega_1) \, d\omega_1 \tag{7.165}$$

The limit in (7.165) is also related to $h(0+)$, the value of the impulse response $h(t)$ for a vanishingly small but positive value of t. To see this, remember that $h(t)$ is the inverse Fourier transform of $H(j\omega)$

$$h(t) = \int_{-\infty}^{\infty} H(j\omega)e^{j\omega t}\frac{d\omega}{2\pi} \qquad (7.166)$$

Since $h(t)$ is real, the even part of $h(t)$ is the inverse transform of the real part of $H(j\omega)$,

$$h_e(t) = \int_{-\infty}^{\infty} H_r(j\omega)e^{j\omega t}\frac{d\omega}{2\pi} \qquad (7.167)$$

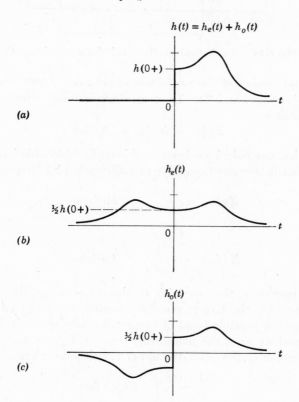

Fig. 7-23. The even and odd parts of an impulse response.

Now, by inspection of Fig. 7-23 and relation (7.167), we have

$$h(0+) = 2h_e(0+) = \frac{1}{\pi}\int_{-\infty}^{\infty} H_r(j\omega)\,d\omega \qquad (7.168)$$

Hence

$$\lim_{\omega\to\infty}[-\omega H_i(j\omega)] = h(0+) = \frac{2}{\pi}\int_{0}^{\infty} H_r(j\omega_1)\,d\omega_1 \qquad (7.169)$$

Notice that in (7.169) the lower limit of integration is now zero and the integral has been multiplied by 2. This simplification is permissible because $H_r(j\omega)$ is an even function of ω.

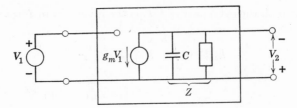

Fig. 7-24. A unilateral amplifier with shunt capacitance C.

As an illustration of the usefulness of relation (7.169) consider the amplifier shown in Fig. 7-24. The total shunt impedance in the amplifier output circuit is

$$Z(j\omega) = R(j\omega) + jX(j\omega) \tag{7.170}$$

Suppose that our only knowledge of this realizable stable impedance is the fact that it becomes capacitive at sufficiently high frequencies

$$Z(j\omega) \to \frac{1}{j\omega C}, \qquad \text{for large } \omega \tag{7.171}$$

or

$$X(j\omega) \to -\frac{1}{\omega C}, \qquad \text{for large } \omega \tag{7.172}$$

Suppose, moreover, that we wish to choose or design the network Z so as to provide the largest possible amount of voltage amplification over the widest possible band of frequencies, and that within this frequency band we want the phase shift between V_2 and V_1 to be small.

In the light of (7.169), (7.170), and (7.172) it follows immediately that

$$\frac{1}{C} = \frac{2}{\pi} \int_0^\infty R(j\omega)\, d\omega \tag{7.173}$$

The "in-phase" voltage amplification of the amplifier will be (for a fixed g_m) proportional to the resistive component R of the impedance Z, and the resistance integral in (7.173) is therefore a criterion or figure of merit for the design of impedance Z. The larger this integral, the better the amplifier. For a given value of the resistance integral we can, of course, design the impedance function Z so as to obtain either a large amount of voltage gain over a narrow band of frequencies or a small voltage gain over a wider band of frequencies. Observe, however, that the shunt capacitance C fixes the total "gain-bandwidth product" of the amplifier.

Parameter g_m really should be brought into the picture since the gain can be increased by raising g_m just as well as by raising R. By inspection of Fig. 7-24 (the polarity of the output voltage V_2 has been chosen to eliminate a minus sign in the gain expression) the voltage gain or voltage amplification is

$$\frac{V_2}{V_1} = g_m Z(j\omega) = H(j\omega) \tag{7.174}$$

Thus the "gain-bandwidth product" of the amplifier is fixed by the value of g_m/C,

$$\frac{g_m}{C} = \frac{2}{\pi} \int_0^\infty H_r(j\omega)\, d\omega \tag{7.175}$$

and, under the conditions specified in this problem, the quantity g_m/C becomes an important practical figure of merit.

The connection of an additional external passive network across the output terminals of the amplifier cannot decrease C nor increase g_m. External loading can, of course, increase the value of R at some frequencies but, since the resistance integral is fixed, this must be accompanied by a decrease of R at other frequencies. In other words, the frequency response curve H_r (or R) can be moved about and reshaped by redesigning Z but the area under the curve must remain constant. If, for example, we tune the amplifier by adding an inductance across the output terminals, then the phenomenon of resonance increases the gain at some relatively high frequency at the expense of gain at the lower frequencies. The main point is that a knowledge of relation (7.173) or (7.175) rescues the designer from a futile search for some magical network Z, in the attempt to meet specifications set by someone unaware of the theoretical limitations.

7.14 Gain and Phase

The word "gain" is sometimes used rather loosely as a synonym for "voltage amplification" or "current amplification." In its more precise usage the term "gain" has a specific meaning: the logarithm of the magnitude of the system function. Let the system function be written in complex polar form,

$$H(j\omega) = |H(j\omega)| e^{j\theta(\omega)} \tag{7.176}$$

whence the *gain* associated with this system function is

$$G(\omega) = \log |H(j\omega)| \tag{7.177}$$

and $\theta(\omega)$ is called the *phase* or *phase angle*. The gain and phase are the real and imaginary parts of the logarithm of the frequency-response function

$$\log H(j\omega) = G(\omega) + j\theta(\omega) \tag{7.178}$$

and it follows from the conjugate symmetry of $H(s)$ that

$$G(-\omega) = G(\omega) \tag{7.179}$$

and

$$\theta(-\omega) = -\theta(\omega) \tag{7.180}$$

When a system function is represented as the product of two or more simpler functions, the gain (and phase) curve of the more complicated system function is obtainable by simple addition of the gain (and phase) curves of the individual system-function factors. Specifically, if

$$H(s) = H_1(s)H_2(s) \tag{7.181}$$

then

$$G(\omega) = G_1(\omega) + G_2(\omega) \tag{7.182}$$

$$\theta(\omega) = \theta_1(\omega) + \theta_2(\omega) \tag{7.183}$$

Before we go on to more detailed discussion of gain and phase curves, a word about notation is necessary. As derived from (7.176), the expression for $G(\omega)$ in (7.177) implies the use of natural logarithms. The units of the natural logarithmic scale are called nepers.

$$\left(\frac{x_2}{x_1}\right)_{\text{nepers}} = \log_e\left(\frac{x_2}{x_1}\right) \tag{7.184}$$

where numbers x_1 and x_2 are the input and output signal amplitudes in a transmission system. If we say that "x_2 is 6 nepers above x_1," we mean that the transmission system has a gain equal to 6 nepers. In practice, other logarithmic scales are often more convenient. The "decilog" scale is defined by

$$\left(\frac{x_2}{x_1}\right)_{\text{decilogs}} = 10\log_{10}\left(\frac{x_2}{x_1}\right) \tag{7.185}$$

For example, if x_2 is one hundred times larger than x_1, then we say that "x_2 is 20 decilogs above x_1." The decilog scale makes no distinction as to the physical units of quantities x_1 and x_2. Many people prefer to work instead with the "decibel" scale:

$$\left(\frac{x_2}{x_1}\right)_{\text{decibels}} = \begin{cases} 20 \log_{10}\left(\dfrac{x_2}{x_1}\right), & \text{if } x_1 \text{ and } x_2 \text{ are both voltage} \\ & \text{(or both current)} \end{cases} \tag{7.186}$$

$$\begin{cases} 10 \log_{10}\left(\dfrac{x_2}{x_1}\right), & \text{if } x_1 \text{ and } x_2 \text{ are both power} \end{cases} \tag{7.187}$$

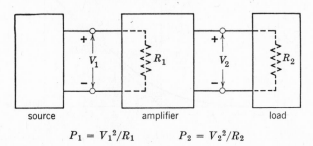

$$P_1 = V_1{}^2/R_1 \qquad P_2 = V_2{}^2/R_2$$

Fig. 7-25. A transmission system (amplifier) having input resistance R_1 and load resistance R_2.

The motivation for the decibel scale becomes clear when we consider an amplifier such as the one shown in Fig. 7-25. By inspection of the diagram, the ratio of output power to input power is (in decibels)

$$\left(\frac{P_2}{P_1}\right)_{\text{decibels}} = 10 \log_{10}\left(\frac{V_2{}^2 R_1}{V_1{}^2 R_2}\right) = 20 \log_{10}\left(\frac{V_2}{V_1}\right) - 10 \log_{10}\left(\frac{R_2}{R_1}\right) \tag{7.188}$$

Now, if the input resistance R_1 and the load resistance R_2 are identical, as they often are in actual cascaded transmission systems, then

$$\left(\frac{P_2}{P_1}\right)_{\text{decibels}} = \left(\frac{V_2}{V_1}\right)_{\text{decibels}} \tag{7.189}$$

Thus we can speak of the amplifier gain in decibels without bothering to state whether we mean the power gain or the voltage gain, for the number is the same in either case.

Figure 7-26 shows the gain and phase curves corresponding to the elementary system function $H(s) = 1 + s$. The "idealized semi-infinite ramp gain" curve and the corresponding phase curve are plotted as dashed lines for comparison. The phase curves can be calculated from the corresponding gain curves by means of the integral

$$\theta(\omega) = \frac{1}{\pi} \int_{-\infty}^{\infty} \frac{G(\omega_1)}{\omega_1 - \omega} \, d\omega_1 \tag{7.190}$$

which is the same Hilbert-transform relationship as that between the real and imaginary parts of $H(j\omega)$. Given $G(\omega)$, the Hilbert integral defines $\theta(\omega)$ such that the function $\log H(j\omega) = G(\omega) + j\theta(\omega)$ has all the analytic properties of a realizable stable system function. If $\log H(s)$

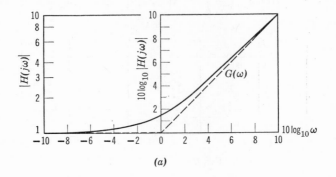

(a)

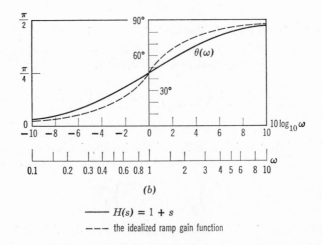

(b)

——— $H(s) = 1 + s$

– – – the idealized ramp gain function

Fig. 7-26. Universal gain (a) and phase (b) curves.

is realizable and stable, then so are $H(s)$ and $1/H(s)$, for if $|\log H(s)|$ is bounded for nonnegative σ, then so are $|H(s)|$ and $|1/H(s)|$. In short, the *real part* of any realizable system function is *also* the *gain* of some *other* realizable system function, and the corresponding phase is therefore its Hilbert transform.

As mentioned previously, the Fourier integral, and hence the Hilbert integral, apply not only to stable system functions but also to some "almost-stable" system functions: functions whose defining integrals converge in the interior of the right-half s-plane and almost everywhere on the $j\omega$ axis, that is, everywhere except at certain isolated values of ω. Such functions are properly visualized as limiting forms of stable functions.

For a real even function $g(\omega)$, the condition

$$\int_0^\infty \frac{|g(\omega)|}{1 + \omega^2} \, d\omega < \infty \qquad (7.191)$$

is sufficient to insure the existence of its Hilbert transform. The mathematicians Paley and Wiener have shown that this condition is not only sufficient but *also necessary*. A system whose gain function violates the Paley-Wiener criterion has an impulse response extending forever into the past. We would need to shift such an impulse response an unlimited distance to the right along the time axis in order to make it realizable.

The Gaussian impulse response $h(t) = \exp(-t^2)$ is an example. The corresponding frequency-response function $H(j\omega)$ is also a real Gaussian curve. Hence the corresponding gain is parabolic in ω and the phase is identically zero. This system is, of course, formally unrealizable. For a large positive shift T, the impulse response $h(t - T)$ becomes "approximately" realizable, in the sense that only a small portion of the impulse-response energy now lies in the negative-time region. The phase function is now $-\omega T$, rather than zero, and a better "approximation" to realizability requires a still larger slope in the phase curve. Hilbert transformation of the parabolic gain function gives, of course, infinite phase at all nonzero ω, which is just another way of saying that the phase function diverges when we demand strict realizability from a system whose gain violates the Paley-Wiener criterion.

Given $G(\omega)$, the Hilbert transformation fixes $\theta(\omega)$, and thereby determines the associated function $H(j\omega) = \exp[G(\omega) + j\theta(\omega)]$. This function is not unique. There are always other realizable functions having the same gain but a different phase. To see this, consider a realizable system function whose *magnitude* is a constant K on the $j\omega$ axis. Such functions are called *flat* or *all-pass* functions. An "all-pass" system "passes" signals at all frequencies without relative change in the signal amplitudes. The simplest example of a flat system is $h(t) = Ku_0(t)$, $H(s) = K$, $G(\omega) = \log K$, for which the Hilbert transform gives the correct phase $\theta(\omega) = 0$. However, we can also cite the examples

$$h(t) = K[u_0(t) - 2u_{-1}(t)e^{-t}] \qquad (7.192)$$

$$H(s) = K\left(1 - \frac{2}{1+s}\right) = K\left(\frac{1-s}{1+s}\right) \qquad (7.193)$$

$$G(\omega) = \log K \qquad (7.194)$$

$$\theta(\omega) = -2\tan^{-1}\omega \qquad (7.195)$$

and

$$h(t) = Ku_0(t-a) \qquad (7.196)$$

$$H(s) = Ke^{-as} \qquad (7.197)$$

$$G(\omega) = \log K \qquad (7.198)$$

$$\theta(\omega) = -a\omega \qquad (7.199)$$

Now let H_h be a system function determined by Hilbert transformation of a gain function, and let H be any other realizable system function having the same gain. Then the quotient

$$H_f = H/H_h \qquad (7.200)$$

gives a flat function H_f with zero gain $[|H_f(j\omega)| = 1]$. Function H_f will certainly be realizable because $\log H_h$, and consequently H_h and $1/H_h$, are realizable, and the product of two such functions is likewise realizable. Thus

$$H = H_h H_f \qquad (7.201)$$

$$G(\omega) = G_h(\omega) \qquad (7.202)$$

$$\theta(\omega) = \theta_h(\omega) + \theta_f(\omega) \qquad (7.203)$$

The phase function of a flat system has special properties without which the result (7.203) would have little significance. In particular, the phase $\theta_f(\omega)$ of a realizable flat system function is a *nonincreasing* function of the frequency ω. Hence $H_h(j\omega)$ is a *minimum-phase* function; any *other* realizable function having the *same gain* must accumulate *phase lag* (negative phase shift) at a greater rate as ω proceeds from $-\infty$ to $+\infty$.

It may appear to be contradictory that the Hilbert transformation gives a unique $H_i(j\omega)$ from $H_r(j\omega)$, whereas the determination of $\theta(\omega)$ from $G(\omega)$ is not unique. The key lies in the following observation: Although possession by $\log H$ of all the properties of a realizable system function makes H and $1/H$ automatically realizable, the realizability of H does *not* mean that $\log H$ necessarily has such properties. The flat function $H_f = (1-s)/(1+s)$ is realizable but its logarithm becomes infinite in the right-half s-plane at the point $s = 1$. Hence $\log H_f$ cannot be both stable and realizable, and since stability is understood throughout this discussion, unrealizability is the only alternative. This example shows that we should not expect a (nontrivial) flat function to arise from Hilbert transformation of a gain, since the function $\log H = G + j\theta$ so determined is automatically realizable.

The nonincreasing character of $\theta_f(\omega)$ is suggested by the examples (7.196) and (7.199). For a more general argument about the phase of a flat function, first observe that if

$$|H_f(j\omega)|^2 = H_f(j\omega)H_f{}^*(j\omega) = H_f(j\omega)H_f(-j\omega) = 1 \quad (7.204)$$

then

$$H_f{}^2(j\omega) = \frac{H_f(j\omega)}{H_f(-j\omega)} \quad (7.205)$$

or

$$H_f{}^2(s) = \frac{H_f(s)}{H_f(-s)} \quad (7.206)$$

Many system functions of interest fall into the category of rational functions: quotients of polynomials in s,

$$H(s) = \frac{b_0 + b_1 s + b_2 s^2 + \cdots + b_n s^n}{a_0 + a_1 s + a_2 s^2 + \cdots + a_n s^n} \quad (7.207)$$

and many nonrational system functions may be suitably approximated by a rational function. In view of (7.206), a flat rational function must have the form

$$H_f(s) = \frac{a_0 - a_1 s + a_2 s^2 - a_3 s^3 + \cdots + a_n s^n}{a_0 + a_1 s + a_2 s^2 + a_3 s^3 + \cdots + a_n s^n} \quad (7.208)$$

The polynomials in (7.208) can be factored to obtain

$$H_f(s) = \frac{(s_1 + s)(s_2 + s) \cdots (s_n + s)}{(s_1 - s)(s_2 - s) \cdots (s_n - s)} \quad (7.209)$$

where $s_1, s_2, \cdots, s_n$ are the zeros of the denominator polynomial. For real $h_f(t)$ we have $H_f(s^*) = H_f{}^*(s)$, with the consequent restriction that the zeros are either real or occur in complex-conjugate pairs. Let s_1 and s_2 be such a pair:

$$s_1 = -\alpha_1 + j\omega_1$$
$$s_2 = -\alpha_1 - j\omega_1 \quad (7.210)$$

The constant α_1 must be positive, for otherwise $H_f(s)$ would become infinite in the right-half s-plane, making $H_f(s)$ either unstable or unrealizable. Interchanging the first two factors in the numerator of (7.209) and substituting (7.210), we find

$$H_f(j\omega) = \left[\frac{\alpha_1 - j(\omega - \omega_1)}{\alpha_1 + j(\omega - \omega_1)}\right]\left[\frac{\alpha_1 - j(\omega + \omega_1)}{\alpha_1 + j(\omega + \omega_1)}\right] \cdots \left[\frac{s_n + j\omega}{s_n - j\omega}\right] \quad (7.211)$$

Thus a rational H_f is a product of elementary flat functions, each similar in character to the earlier example (7.193). Each elementary factor exhibits nonincreasing phase, so that $\theta_f(\omega)$ must have the same property.

Incidentally, to any θ_f we can always add a constant $\pm n\pi$, where n is an integer, reflecting the fact that multiplication of any $H(s)$ by $\exp(\pm jn\pi) = (-1)^n$ does not change the character of $H(s)$.

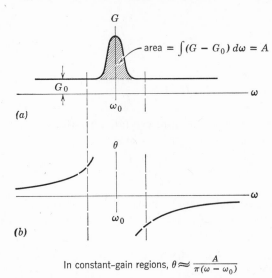

In constant-gain regions, $\theta \approx \dfrac{A}{\pi(\omega - \omega_0)}$

Fig. 7-27. The effect of a "gain bump" upon the phase in a surrounding constant-gain plateau.

Now back to minimum-phase systems. On the basis of the Hilbert transformation, it is fairly easy to deduce certain elementary properties of the gain-phase relationship. For example, the phase in a region is roughly proportional to the slope of the gain curve in that region. We can also see that if gain variation occurs only in a restricted region of the $j\omega$ axis, as indicated in Fig. 7-27 (a), then the phase in the neighboring constant-gain regions is roughly inversely proportional to the distance away from that region, as shown in Fig. 7-27 (b).

The gain curves in Fig. 7-26(a) have the associated minimum-lag phase curves shown in (b). Figure 7-28 presents basic variations on the universal gain curves, obtained by shifting, scaling, reversing, or inverting the broken-line curves in Fig. 7-26. With the aid of the universal gain and phase curves we can find the phase function associated with a given gain function by the simple process illustrated in Fig. 7-29. Suppose that the given gain function is first approximated

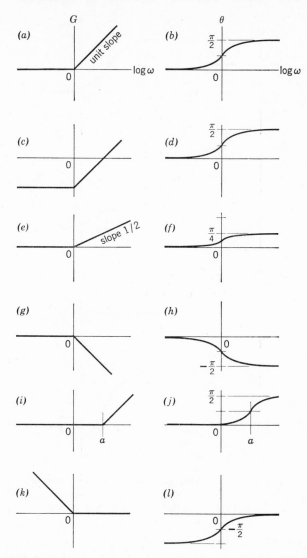

Fig. 7-28. Basic variations on the universal gain and phase curves.

by the piecewise-linear curve shown in Fig. 7-29(g). The piecewise-linear approximation is recognizable as the sum of the three elementary gain curves indicated in (a), (c), and (e), and the corresponding elementary phase curves, therefore, are those shown in (b), (d), and (f). Hence the desired phase curve is the sum of the three elementary phase

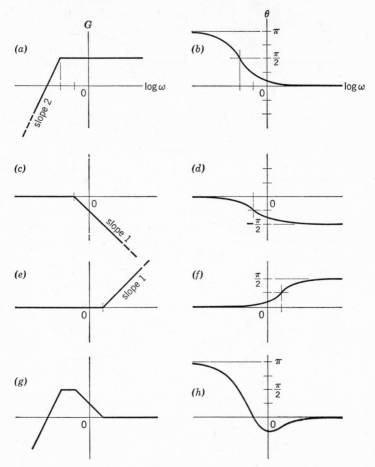

Fig. 7-29. The superposition of basic gain curves (*a*), (*c*), (*e*) to give a piecewise-linear approximation (*g*) of an arbitrary gain curve. Superposition of the basic phase curves (*b*), (*d*), (*f*) then yields the associated phase curve (*h*).

curves as indicated in Fig. 7-29(*h*). *Such superposition of elementary gain and phase curves is an extremely useful process in the practical analysis and design of linear transmission systems.*

7.15   Carrier Delay and Envelope Delay

When a signal $f(t)$ is passed through a transmission system, its waveform is, in general, distorted by the system. However, if the frequency spectrum of the signal is restricted to a region within which the gain is essentially constant and the phase is essentially a linear function of ω, then the output signal will be a delayed but undistorted replica of the input. In order to examine the details of this effect let us first expand the function $\log H(s)$ in a power series about some point s_0, so that

$$H(s) = e^{a_0 + a_1(s-s_0) + a_2(s-s_0)^2 + \cdots} \tag{7.212}$$

Now suppose that within the region of interest the first two terms of the series are a suitable approximation. Also suppose that s_0 is purely imaginary. Under these conditions we can rewrite (7.212) in the equivalent form

$$H(j\omega) = A_0 e^{-j\omega_0 t_0 - j(\omega - \omega_0)t_1} \tag{7.213}$$

where constants A_0, ω_0, and t_0 are real. If we insist that gain be independent of frequency in the region of interest, then the constant t_1 must also be real. The associated gain and phase are

$$G(\omega) = \log A_0 \tag{7.214}$$

and

$$\theta(\omega) = -\omega_0 t_0 - (\omega - \omega_0)t_1 \tag{7.215}$$

Now consider an input signal

$$v_1(t) = f(t)e^{j\omega_0 t} \tag{7.216}$$

whose frequency spectrum $V_1(\omega)$ is restricted to the region of interest near ω_0. It follows that

$$V_2(\omega) = V_1(\omega)H(j\omega) = A_0 e^{-j\omega_0(t_0 - t_1)} V_1(\omega)e^{-j\omega t_1} \tag{7.217}$$

from which we can identify the inverse Fourier transform

$$v_2(t) = A_0 e^{-j\omega_0(t_0 - t_1)} v_1(t - t_1) \tag{7.218}$$

Finally, substitution of (7.216) into (7.218) gives

$$v_2(t) = A_0 f(t - t_1)e^{j\omega_0(t - t_0)} \tag{7.219}$$

Thus we see that the original input "modulation" signal $f(t)$ and the input "carrier-frequency" wave $\exp(j\omega_0 t)$ are both delayed by the system, but each may be delayed by a different amount. The point is that the time delays

$$t_0 = -\left[\frac{\theta}{\omega}\right]_{\omega = \omega_0} = \text{carrier delay} \tag{7.220}$$

and

$$t_1 = -\left[\frac{d\theta}{d\omega}\right]_{\omega = \omega_0} = \text{envelope delay} \tag{7.221}$$

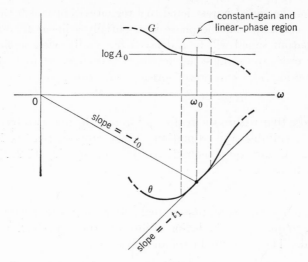

Fig. 7-30. Carrier delay (t_0) and envelope delay (t_1) in a region of constant gain and linear phase.

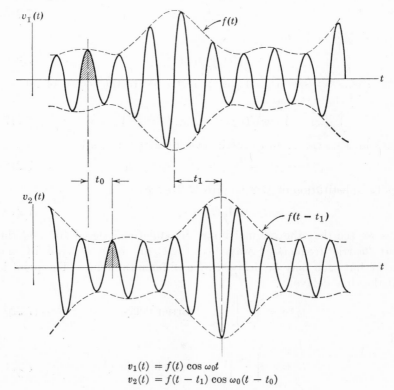

$$v_1(t) = f(t) \cos \omega_0 t$$
$$v_2(t) = f(t - t_1) \cos \omega_0(t - t_0)$$

Fig. 7-31. Carrier delay (t_0) and envelope delay (t_1).

are easily obtainable by inspection of the gain and phase curves, as shown in Fig. 7-30. The real (physical) input and output signals are plotted in Fig. 7-31 for comparison. Incidentally, Fig. 7-31 shows t_0 and t_1 both positive, whereas the particular curves in Fig. 7-30 are associated with a positive t_0 and a negative t_1, purely for convenience of illustration.

Since phase is the Hilbert transform of gain, the carrier delay and envelope delay of a minimum-phase transmission system are fixed by the shape of the gain curve. This leads to the observation that the character of the entire gain curve, including frequency regions outside that occupied by the signal spectrum, is important in determining the delay suffered by the signal.

7.16   Exponential Transforms

The system-function integral (7.89) is a general operation which may be applied to any function $f(t)$ to give a corresponding transform function $F(s)$. If we write

$$F(s) = \int_{-\infty}^{\infty} f(t)e^{-st}\, dt \qquad (7.222)$$

then $F(s)$ is said to be the "exponential transform" or "bilateral Laplace transform" of $f(t)$. The mathematician Laplace is credited with having introduced such transforms in his studies of heat flow and related problems. The integral itself is called the "exponential transformation" or "bilaterial Laplace transformation." (The unilateral Laplace transformation has zero, rather than minus infinity, as the lower limit of integration.) The exponential transformation can be applied to signals $v(t)$ as well as to system-impulse responses $h(t)$; the letter f is used here rather than v or h in order to avoid any implication of restricted application. As noted before, the transformation (7.222) is a generalization of the Fourier integral, to which it reduces for zero σ, that is, for s equal to $j\omega$.

The question of convergence of the integral immediately arises. If we can find some real positive finite number M such that

$$|f(t)| \leq \begin{cases} Me^{bt}, & \text{for } t \geq 0 \\ Me^{at}, & \text{for } t \leq 0 \end{cases} \qquad (7.223)$$

then the integral converges for all values of σ greater than b and less than a. Parts (i) and (j) of Fig. 7-32 serve as a graphical interpretation of condition (7.223). For any time function whose absolute value falls below the tent-shaped curve in Fig. 7-32(i), the transformation con-

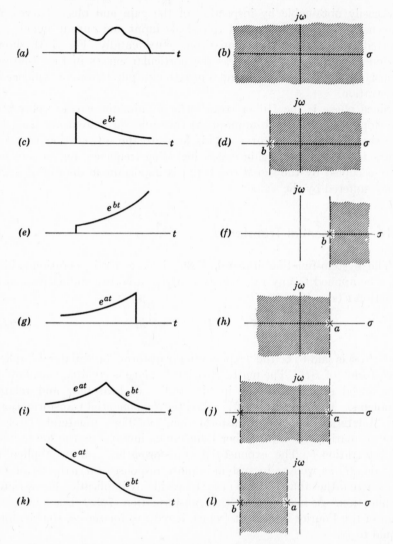

Fig. 7-32. Some simple time functions $f(t)$ and the regions of convergence (shown shaded in the complex s-plane) of their exponential transforms $F(s)$.

verges in (at least) that vertical strip of the s-plane shown shaded in Fig. 7-32(j). These conditions follow directly once we observe that

$$|F(s)| \leq \int_{-\infty}^{\infty} |f(t)| \, e^{-\sigma t} \, dt \leq M \left[\int_{-\infty}^{0} e^{(a-\sigma)t} \, dt + \int_{0}^{\infty} e^{(b-\sigma)t} \, dt \right] \quad (7.224)$$

Hence $F(s)$ is assuredly finite only if a exceeds b, and then only if σ lies between a and b.

Figure 7-32 shows the regions of convergence for a few simple time functions. A function such as (a), which vanishes outside some finite time interval, has a convergent transformation for all finite values of σ. Convergence of the transformation for all finite σ does not necessarily imply that the time function vanishes outside some finite time interval, however; the Gaussian function $\exp(-t^2)$ is an example.

The function in Fig. 7-32(e), when visualized as an impulse response, is realizable but unstable. That in Fig. 7-32(g) is unrealizable but stable. Observe that in the special case $a = b$ their exponential transforms have the same "formula,"

$$u_{-1}(t)e^{bt} \leftrightarrow \frac{1}{s-b}, \qquad b < \sigma \qquad\qquad (7.225)$$

$$u_{-1}(-t)e^{at} \leftrightarrow -\frac{1}{s-a}, \qquad \sigma < a \qquad\qquad (7.226)$$

although their regions of convergence are quite different. For example, if a and b are both positive, the transform in (7.226) is meaningful on the $j\omega$ axis ($\sigma = 0$), but that in (7.225) is not.

The impulse function $u_0(t)$ deserves attention at this point. The unit impulse is unbounded and hence does not lend itself directly to the convergence test (7.223). However, a suitable approximation to u_0, such as a Gaussian pulse, has a convergent transform for all finite σ and this condition holds as the Gaussian pulse is allowed to become taller and slimmer. In the limit, the transform of u_0 converges for all σ. The transforms of the higher-order singularity functions also converge for finite σ but become infinite for infinite s, as will be shown in the next article by direct calculation of the transforms.

The exponential transformation converts an impulse response $h(t)$ into a system function $H(s)$ and a knowledge of H allows us to find, by simple multiplication, the output signal due to a complex exponential input signal. When the input signal is not an exponential, but rather some arbitrary transformable function $v_1(t)$, we can multiply its transform $V_1(s)$ by $H(s)$ to find the transform of the output signal $V_2(s)$. The problem then is to find the time function $v_2(t)$ corresponding to the transform $V_2(s)$. It may happen (and it does happen in very many problems of interest) that $V_2(s)$ is identifiable from a table of known transforms, either with or without the aid of some preliminary operation such as partial-fraction expansion. On the other hand, it is possible to formulate the inverse transformation as an explicit integral operation.

To obtain the inverse transformation, we can first rewrite (7.222) as

$$F(\sigma + j\omega) = \int_{-\infty}^{\infty} f(\tau)e^{-(\sigma+j\omega)\tau}\,d\tau \qquad (7.227)$$

Now we form the integral

$$\int_{-\infty}^{\infty} F(\sigma + j\omega)e^{(\sigma+j\omega)t-a^2\omega^2}\,d\omega$$

$$= \int_{-\infty}^{\infty}\int_{-\infty}^{\infty} f(\tau)e^{(\sigma+j\omega)(t-\tau)-a^2\omega^2}\,d\tau\,d\omega \qquad (7.228)$$

$$= \int_{-\infty}^{\infty} f(\tau)e^{\sigma(t-\tau)}\left[\int_{-\infty}^{\infty} e^{j\omega(t-\tau)-a^2\omega^2}\,d\omega\right]d\tau \qquad (7.229)$$

$$= \int_{-\infty}^{\infty} f(\tau)e^{\sigma(t-\tau)}\left[\frac{\sqrt{\pi}}{a}\,e^{-(t-\tau)^2/4a^2}\right]d\tau \qquad (7.230)$$

The bracketed expression in (7.229) is a standard definite integral whose value appears bracketed in (7.230). In the limit of small a the Gaussian function in (7.230) becomes an impulse located at the point t on the τ scale. Assuming that (7.230) converges, we have

$$\int_{-\infty}^{\infty} F(\sigma + j\omega)e^{(\sigma+j\omega)t}\,d\omega = \int_{-\infty}^{\infty} f(\tau)[2\pi u_0(t - \tau)]\,d\tau \qquad (7.231)$$

The right side of (7.231) is just equal to $2\pi f(t)$, so that

$$f(t) = \int_{-\infty}^{\infty} F(\sigma + j\omega)e^{(\sigma+j\omega)t}\,\frac{d\omega}{2\pi} = \int_{-j\infty}^{+j\infty} F(s)e^{st}\,\frac{ds}{2\pi j} \qquad (7.232)$$

Relation (7.232) represents the *inverse exponential transformation*. In the second of the two alternative forms it is to be understood that $ds = d(j\omega) = j\,d\omega$ and that the integration is carried out upward along a constant-σ line in the complex s-plane. The choice of σ depends, of course, upon the region of convergence of the integral (7.222) defining $F(s)$. Unless σ lies in this region of convergence, the inverse transformation of the "formula" $F(s)$ will not yield the original time function $f(t)$.

No matter what the chosen value of σ, we can always convert the problem to an equivalent one in which σ is effectively equal to zero. To see this, first define

$$F_\sigma(j\omega) = F(\sigma + j\omega) \qquad (7.233)$$

$$f_\sigma(t) = f(t)e^{-\sigma t} \qquad (7.234)$$

With such notation (7.227) and (7.232) reduce to the Fourier transformation pair

$$F_\sigma(j\omega) = \int_{-\infty}^{\infty} f_\sigma(t)e^{-j\omega t}\, dt \tag{7.235}$$

$$f_\sigma(t) = \int_{-\infty}^{\infty} F_\sigma(j\omega)e^{j\omega t}\, \frac{d\omega}{2\pi} \tag{7.236}$$

From a limited viewpoint, therefore, one could say that the introduction of the complex variable s is merely a device which permits us to handle a larger class of time functions in terms of the Fourier integral.

7.17   Some Fundamental Properties of Exponential Transforms

A number of useful transform pairs are listed below, with their regions of convergence indicated by the inequalities involving σ.

$$f(t) \leftrightarrow F(s), \qquad\qquad\qquad \sigma' < \sigma < \sigma'' \tag{7.237}$$

$$f(t - t_0)e^{s_0 t} \leftrightarrow F(s - s_0)e^{-t_0(s-s_0)}, \qquad \sigma' + \sigma_0 < \sigma < \sigma'' + \sigma_0 \tag{7.238}$$

$$f(t/a) \leftrightarrow |a|\, F(as), \qquad\qquad \sigma'/a < \sigma < \sigma''/a \tag{7.239}$$

$$df(t)/dt \leftrightarrow sF(s), \qquad\qquad \sigma' < \sigma < \sigma'' \tag{7.240}$$

$$\int_{-\infty}^{t} f(\tau)\, d\tau \leftrightarrow \frac{1}{s} F(s), \qquad\qquad (0, \sigma') < \sigma < \sigma'' \tag{7.241}$$

$$f^{(k)}(t) \leftrightarrow s^k F(s), \qquad\qquad \sigma' < \sigma < \sigma''$$
$$\text{also } 0 < \sigma \text{ for } k \text{ negative} \tag{7.242}$$

$$(-t)^k f(t) \leftrightarrow F^{(k)}(s), \qquad\qquad \sigma' < \sigma < \sigma'' \tag{7.243}$$

$$f_1(t) \otimes f_2(t) \leftrightarrow F_1(s)F_2(s), \qquad (\sigma_1', \sigma_2') < \sigma < (\sigma_1'', \sigma_2'') \tag{7.244}$$

$$f_1(t)f_2(t) \leftrightarrow F_1(s) \otimes F_2(s), \qquad \sigma_1' + \sigma_2' < \sigma < \sigma_1'' + \sigma_2'' \tag{7.245}$$

$$u_k(t) \leftrightarrow s^k, \qquad\qquad\qquad \text{all } \sigma \ (k \geq 0) \tag{7.246}$$

$$u_{-1}(t)\, \frac{t^{k-1}}{(k-1)!} \leftrightarrow s^{-k}, \qquad\qquad 0 < \sigma \ (k \geq 1) \tag{7.247}$$

$$e^{s_0 t} \leftrightarrow 2\pi u_0(\omega - \omega_0), \qquad\qquad \sigma = \sigma_0 \tag{7.248}$$

$$1 \leftrightarrow 2\pi u_0(\omega), \qquad\qquad\qquad \sigma = 0 \tag{7.249}$$

$$\frac{t}{2|t|} \leftrightarrow \frac{1}{j\omega}, \qquad\qquad \sigma = 0 \qquad\qquad (7.250)$$

Most of the above follow directly from the forms of the direct and inverse exponential transformations.

Relation (7.243) states that

$$\frac{d^k F(s)}{ds^k} = \int_{-\infty}^{\infty} (-t)^k f(t) e^{-st} \, dt \qquad\qquad (7.251)$$

and this leads to the subsidiary result that the kth moment of $f(t)$ is related to the kth derivative of $F(s)$ at the origin in the complex s-plane,

$$(-1)^k \left[\frac{d^k F(s)}{ds^k} \right]_{s=0} = \int_{-\infty}^{\infty} t^k f(t) \, dt \qquad\qquad (7.252)$$

For an explanation of s-plane convolution (7.245), let us start with the known transform pair

$$f_2(t) e^{s_0 t} \leftrightarrow F_2(s - s_0) \qquad\qquad (7.253)$$

and construct the weighted sum of a large number of such pairs, all having the same σ_0 but different ω_0. The weighted sums are given by the integrals

$$f_2(t) \int_{-\infty}^{\infty} e^{s_0 t} \left[F_1(s_0) \frac{d\omega_0}{2\pi} \right] \leftrightarrow \int_{-\infty}^{\infty} F_2(s - s_0) \left[F_1(s_0) \frac{d\omega_0}{2\pi} \right] \quad (7.254)$$

The integral on the left is recognizable as $f_1(t)$ so that

$$f_1(t) f_2(t) \leftrightarrow \int_{\sigma_0 - j\infty}^{\sigma_0 + j\infty} F_1(s_0) F_2(s - s_0) \frac{ds_0}{2\pi j} \qquad\qquad (7.255)$$

The integration is to be carried out upward along a constant-σ_0 line in the complex s_0 plane. If $F_1(s)$ converges between $\sigma_1{}'$ and $\sigma_1{}''$ and if $F_2(s)$ converges between $\sigma_2{}'$ and $\sigma_2{}''$, then the integrand $F_1(s_0) F_2(s - s_0)$ converges within the vertical strip

$$(\sigma_1{}', \sigma - \sigma_2{}'') < \sigma_0 < (\sigma_1{}'', \sigma - \sigma_2{}') \qquad\qquad (7.256)$$

in the complex s_0 plane, the overlapping portion of the two strips $\sigma_1{}' < \sigma_0 < \sigma_1{}''$ and $\sigma - \sigma_2{}'' < \sigma_0 < \sigma - \sigma_2{}'$. Such a strip evidently does not exist unless

$$\sigma_1{}' + \sigma_2{}' < \sigma < \sigma_1{}'' + \sigma_2{}'' \qquad\qquad (7.257)$$

The convolution in (7.245) is to be interpreted as the integral in (7.255) with the restriction (7.256) as to the path of integration.

To find the transform of a singularity function (7.246) we can first express the exponential function as the power series

$$e^{-st} = 1 - st + \frac{(st)^2}{2!} - \frac{(st)^3}{3!} + \cdots \tag{7.258}$$

and then utilize what we already know about the moments of a singularity function. In particular, $u_k(t)$ possesses only a kth moment, as stated previously in (7.10). Substitution of (7.258) into the transformation yields, therefore,

$$\int_{-\infty}^{\infty} u_k(t)e^{-st}\,dt = \frac{(-s)^k}{k!} \int_{-\infty}^{\infty} t^k u_k(t)\,dt = s^k \tag{7.259}$$

The transform of a constant is formally divergent for all values of σ. However, by means of a suitable limiting process, the transform can be interpreted as an impulse function along the $j\omega$ axis, as indicated in (7.249). To see this, consider the transform pairs

$$u_{-1}(t)e^{-at} \leftrightarrow \frac{1}{a+s}, \qquad -a < \sigma \tag{7.260}$$

$$u_{-1}(-t)e^{at} \leftrightarrow \frac{1}{a-s}, \qquad \sigma < a \tag{7.261}$$

whose sum

$$e^{-a|t|} \leftrightarrow \frac{2a}{a^2 - s^2}, \qquad -a < \sigma < a \tag{7.262}$$

approaches unity for all t as parameter a becomes small. For small values of a, the region of convergence in the s-plane is a narrow vertical strip including the $j\omega$ axis. Since a is to be made arbitrarily small, our examination of the transform function will be restricted to the $j\omega$ axis. Thus

$$e^{-a|t|} \leftrightarrow \frac{2a}{a^2 + \omega^2}, \qquad \text{for } \sigma = 0 \tag{7.263}$$

The area under the transform curve is 2π for all positive a. Hence, in the limit of small a we have (7.249).

Half the difference of (7.260) and (7.261) gives a function that can be made to approach the odd-symmetric step, a time function whose value is $-1/2$ for negative t and $+1/2$ for positive t

$$\frac{t}{2|t|} e^{-a|t|} \leftrightarrow \frac{-s}{a^2 - s^2}, \qquad -a < \sigma < a \tag{7.264}$$

Again, for small a the transform converges only in a narrow vertical strip enclosing the $j\omega$ axis. Once more we restrict our attention to the $j\omega$

axis, and we see that (7.264) approaches (7.250) in the limit of small a. The transform of $u_{-1}(t)$ is $1/s$ and, as σ approaches zero from the positive side, we find that $1/s$ approaches $\pi u_0(\omega) + (1/j\omega)$. This result is in accord with the fact that $u_{-1}(t)$ is just equal to (7.250) plus half of (7.249).

7.18 Contour Integration

The inverse exponential transformation involves integration along a contour in the complex s-plane, in particular, integration upward along any straight vertical line lying within the vertical strip of convergence of the direct transform $F(s)$. One of the most beautiful results of the theory of analytic functions, a result attributed to the mathematician Cauchy, is that *the shape of the contour can be altered without affecting the value of the integral*. As a consequence of this result, the properties of the inverse transformation can be explained with great simplicity and unity.

In preparation for the discussion of contour integration, we must define what is meant by a *pole* and its *residue*. Consider, for example, the stable function

$$e^{-|t|} \leftrightarrow \frac{2}{1 - s^2}, \qquad -1 < \sigma < 1 \tag{7.265}$$

The transform can be rewritten as

$$\frac{2}{1 - s^2} = \frac{-2}{(s + 1)(s - 1)} = \frac{1}{s + 1} - \frac{1}{s - 1} \tag{7.266}$$

It is obvious from (7.265) that the function $2/(1 - s^2)$ becomes infinite when s is set equal to either $+1$ or -1. We say that the function has *poles* at the two points $s_1 = -1$ and $s_2 = +1$ in the complex s-plane. In general, $F(s)$ has a *simple pole* of *residue* K_p at the point s_p if

$$F(s) \to \frac{K_p}{s - s_p} \qquad \text{as } s \to s_p \tag{7.267}$$

The partial-fraction expansion (7.266) shows the residues explicitly. In general, the residue can therefore be evaluated as the limit

$$K_p = \lim_{s \to s_p} (s - s_p)F(s) \tag{7.268}$$

The poles of (7.266) are indicated in Fig. 7-33(a). For a stable function having several poles, the width of the convergent strip is limited by the poles nearest to the $j\omega$ axis on the left and on the right.   If the function is both stable and realizable, of course, the poles are necessarily restricted to the left side of the $j\omega$ axis.

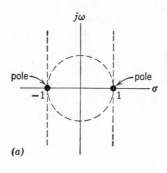

(a)

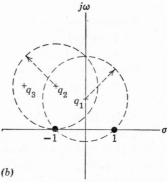

(b)

Fig. 7-33. Domains of an analytic function. (a) Vertical strip of convergence of the transform $F(s)$ of a stable $f(t)$, and circle of convergence of its series expansion. (b) Extension of $F(s)$ over the s-plane by analytic continuation.

The direct transformation defines an analytic function $F(s)$ which can be expanded in a Taylor series about some chosen point s_0,

$$F(s) = \sum_{k=0}^{\infty} \frac{F^{(k)}(s_0)}{k!} (s - s_0)^k \qquad (7.269)$$

where

$$F^{(k)}(s) = \frac{d^k F(s)}{ds^k} \qquad (7.270)$$

The Taylor series converges within a circle whose radius is the distance from s_0 to the nearest pole.   For example, the function (7.266), when expanded about the origin ($s_0 = 0$), has the Taylor-series representation

$$\frac{2}{1 - s^2} = 2(1 + s^2 + s^4 + s^6 + \cdots), \qquad |s| < 1 \qquad (7.271)$$

which converges within the unit circle shown in Fig. 7-33(a).

Had we expanded the function about some other point, such as q_1 in Fig. 7-33(b), the circle of convergence would have extended slightly beyond the boundaries of the vertical strip shown in Fig. 7-33(a). The Taylor series about point q_1 defines an analytic function everywhere within the associated circle of convergence, and therefore implicitly specifies all the derivatives of the function at any other point q_2 within the circle. Thus the coefficients in the Taylor-series expansion about point q_2 are specified and this new series defines the function over a still wider area of the s-plane: the area of the q_1 circle plus the additional area covered by the q_2 circle in Fig. 7-33(b). As before, the series about point q_2 determines the series about any other point q_3 with the q_2 circle. By this process, called *analytic continuation*, a function originally defined only within a vertical strip can be continued or extended over the entire complex s-plane. To continue a function whose "formula" $F(s)$ is given in closed analytic form, we do not need to carry out the arithmetic of successive series expansions. Instead, we merely use the same formula but no longer restrict its range of validity to a vertical strip. Analytic continuation provides rigorous justification for speaking of the "value" of a function anywhere in the s-plane when that function was originally defined by an integral convergent only in a restricted region.

Our next job is to show that the definite integral of a function, carried out along a path lying within the circle of convergence of a series expansion of that function, is dependent only upon the location of the end points of the path and not upon the shape of the contour joining them. First consider the two points s_1 and s_2 whose quotient is

$$\frac{s_2}{s_1} = e^{\gamma} \tag{7.272}$$

where γ is a complex constant. Let the path between these two points be a segment of a logarithmic spiral in the s-plane, with the spiral focus at the origin. Thus,

$$\frac{s}{s_1} = e^{\gamma x} \tag{7.273}$$

where s is a point on the path and x is a real variable. As x runs from 0 to 1, point s moves along the path from s_1 to s_2, as shown in Fig. 7-34(a). For simplicity, and without loss of generality, we may assume that the circle of convergence is centered at the origin, so that each term in the series expansion of the function is simply a power of s. If s_1 and s_2 both lie within the circle of convergence, then this specified path is also con-

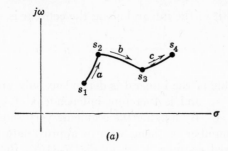

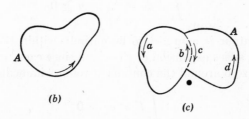

Fig. 7-34.   Paths of integration in the complex s-plane.

tained within the circle.   Now observe that

$$\frac{ds}{s_1} = \gamma e^{\gamma x}\, dx \tag{7.274}$$

and form the integral

$$\int_{s_1}^{s_2} s^n\, ds = \gamma s_1^{n+1} \int_0^1 e^{(n+1)\gamma x}\, dx \tag{7.275}$$

$$= s_1^{n+1}\left[\frac{e^{(n+1)\gamma}}{n+1} - 1\right] \tag{7.276}$$

The integral on the right of (7.275) is an ordinary real-variable integral containing a complex constant, and it can be evaluated immediately as indicated in (7.276).   Substitution of (7.272) gives

$$\int_{s_1}^{s_2} s^n\, ds = \frac{s_2^{n+1} - s_1^{n+1}}{n+1}, \qquad n \geq 0 \tag{7.277}$$

The result (7.277) is just what we would expect on the basis of the rules of ordinary real-variable calculus.   For a path consisting of a continuous succession of logarithmic-spiral segments, such as the path abc in

Fig. 7-34(a), the value of the integral along the contour is

$$\int_{abc} s^n \, ds = \frac{s_4^{n+1} - s_1^{n+1}}{n+1}, \qquad n \geq 0 \tag{7.278}$$

Observe that the value of the integral is dependent only upon the end-point values s_1 and s_4, and is therefore independent of the locations of the points s_2 and s_3. By making the segments very short and using a sufficiently large number of them, we can approximate any desired contour. For a closed contour A, as in Fig. 7-34(b), the end points coincide and we have

$$\int_A s^n \, ds \equiv 0, \qquad n \geq 0 \tag{7.279}$$

Since the contour is assumed to lie entirely within the circle of convergence of a series expansion of $F(s)$, and since each term of the series integrates to zero around the contour, it follows immediately that

$$\int_A F(s) \, ds \equiv 0 \tag{7.280}$$

An apparent dilemma arises in Fig. 7-34(c), where the black dot represents a pole of the function being integrated. Here the contour A cannot be enclosed in a circle without at the same time enclosing the pole. However, contour A can be visualized as the juxtaposition of two separate contours ab and dc, and each of these can be enclosed by a circle of convergence through proper choice of the expansion point. Since the integrations along segments b and c are equal and opposite, the integral around ab plus the integral around cd is just equal to the integral around contour A. Hence the result (7.280) applies to any closed contour within which the function is analytic, in other words, to any contour whose interior is free of singularities such as poles.

When the contour contains poles, the integral does not, in general, vanish. Let us examine the integral around a small circle centered at a pole s_p, as illustrated in Fig. 7-35(a). In the neighborhood of the pole, the function has the simple form indicated in (7.267). Let

$$s - s_p = re^{j\phi} \tag{7.281}$$

where r is constant. Thus

$$ds = jre^{j\phi} \, d\phi \tag{7.282}$$

$$F(s) = \frac{K_p}{r} e^{-j\phi} \tag{7.283}$$

and

$$\int_P F(s)\, ds = jK_p \int_0^{2\pi} d\phi \tag{7.284}$$

$$\int_P F(s)\, ds = j2\pi K_p \tag{7.285}$$

Now consider a closed contour C containing two poles, as shown in Fig. 7-35(b). Contour A in Fig. 7-35(c) is the same as contour C,

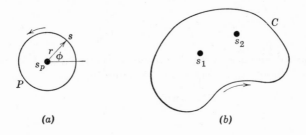

(a)   (b)

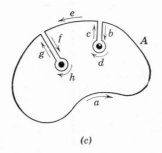

(c)

Fig. 7-35.   Integration on a contour enclosing poles.

except for the intrusion of two narrow corridors which serve to exclude the poles from the interior of A. If the path segments b and c are very close together, then the integrations along segments b and c cancel as do those along f and g. Hence we have

$$\int_A = \int_C + \int_d + \int_h \tag{7.286}$$

Since contour A contains no poles, (7.286) becomes

$$0 = \int_C F(s)\, ds - j2\pi K_1 - j2\pi K_2 \tag{7.287}$$

The contributions from the small circular segments d and h are negative, rather than positive as in (7.285), because d and h are clockwise integrations whereas the integration in Fig. 7-35(a) was counterclockwise. Thus the value of a counterclockwise closed-contour integral is just $2\pi j$ times the sum of the residues of those poles lying within the contour:

$$\int_C F(s)\,\frac{ds}{2\pi j} = \sum_i K_i \qquad (7.288)$$

The inverse exponential integral is

$$f(t) = \int_V F(s)e^{st}\,\frac{ds}{2\pi j} \qquad (7.289)$$

taken upward along a vertical contour V lying within the convergence strip of the direct transform $F(s)$. Assume that

$$F(s) \to 0 \qquad \text{as } s \to \infty \qquad (7.290)$$

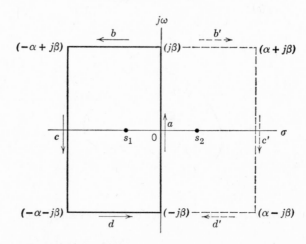

Fig. 7-36. Contours for evaluation of the inverse exponential transformation.

Now let us examine the rectangular closed contour $abcd$ in Fig. 7-36. For a very large rectangle, integration along the vertical segment a approximates the inverse transformation (7.289). Integration along segment b produces a limited contribution; as a consequence of the form of (7.289) we have

$$2\pi \left| \int_b \right| \le F_m \int_0^{-\infty} e^{\sigma t}\,d\sigma = F_m/t, \qquad \text{for } t > 0 \qquad (7.291)$$

wherein F_m is the maximum magnitude of $F(s)$ on segment b (or d).

Similarly, segment c of the closed contour contributes a limited amount to the value of the contour integral

$$2\pi \left| \int_c \right| \le F_m e^{-\alpha t} \int_{-\beta}^{\beta} d\omega = 2F_m \beta e^{-\alpha t}, \qquad \text{for } t > 0 \qquad (7.292)$$

In view of assumption (7.290), F_m becomes arbitrarily small as the rectangular contour is expanded in size. In the limit of large α and β, therefore, integration along the path bcd contributes nothing to the value of the closed-contour integral and the inverse transformation (7.289) may be replaced by integration around the closed contour $abcd$ without altering the result $f(t)$.

For negative t the contribution from path bcd in Fig. 7-36 is no longer negligible. However, a rectangle extending to the right rather than to the left may now be employed. For negative t the integral along the path $b'c'd'$ in Fig. 7-36 is, for a large rectangle, negligible. As a consequence of these considerations, we have

$$f(t) = \begin{cases} \left(\sum_i K_i e^{s_i t} \right)_{\text{left}}, & t > 0 & (7.293) \\ \left(- \sum_k K_k e^{s_k t} \right)_{\text{right}}, & t < 0 & (7.294) \end{cases}$$

The K_i are the residues at the poles of $F(s)$ to the left of the inverse-transform contour V, and the K_k are the residues at the poles lying to the right. The factor $\exp(s_i t)$ appears in (7.293) because $F(s) \exp(st)$ is the integrand of the inverse transform. If function $F(s)$ has a residue K_i at a pole s_i, then the function $F(s) \exp(st)$ must have a residue $K_i \exp(s_i t)$ at the pole. A minus sign is present in (7.294) because the contour $ab'c'd'$ runs clockwise in Fig. 7-36 whereas integration along contour $abcd$ takes place in a counterclockwise direction.

For a simple illustration of the residue law, let us return to the stable but unrealizable function

$$f(t) = e^{-|t|} \leftrightarrow F(s) = \frac{2}{1 - s^2}, \qquad -1 < \sigma < 1 \qquad (7.295)$$

whose poles and residues are

$$\begin{aligned} s_1 &= -1, & K_1 &= 1 \\ s_2 &= 1, & K_2 &= -1 \end{aligned} \qquad (7.296)$$

Here, the $j\omega$ axis may be taken as the inverse-transformation contour V, so that s_1 is to the left and s_2 to the right. The residue law, (7.293) and (7.294), gives

$$f(t) = \begin{cases} e^{-t}, & t > 0 \\ e^{t}, & t < 0 \end{cases} \qquad (7.297)$$

which, of course, matches the time function in (7.295). The next example is the realizable but unstable function

$$u_{-1}(t)[e^{-t} - e^t] \leftrightarrow \frac{2}{1 - s^2}, \qquad \sigma > 1 \qquad (7.298)$$

Here the poles and their residues are exactly the same as for (7.295) but the inverse-transformation contour V must now be located to the right of s_2. Hence, both poles are on the left and the residue law yields the proper time function. The unstable and unrealizable function

$$u_{-1}(-t)[e^t - e^{-t}] \leftrightarrow \frac{2}{1 - s^2}, \qquad \sigma < -1 \qquad (7.299)$$

is the third and final example. Here $F(s)$ is exactly the same as in the two previous examples, but its region of convergence now lies to the left of s_1, so that both poles are on the right and both are therefore associated with a time function that is nonzero only for negative values of t. The point is that $F(s)$ does not determine the inverse transform $f(t)$ uniquely unless the location of the inverse-transformation contour is also specified. Specifically, *the inverse transformation returns us to the original time function only if the inverse-transformation contour is located within a vertical strip of convergence of the direct transformation.*

In the foregoing discussion we have assumed that $F(s)$ approaches zero for sufficiently large values of s. When this is not the case, the function $F(s)$ is said to be "improper." For example, the almost-stable function

$$\frac{s^2}{s + 2} = s - \frac{2s}{s + 2} = s - 2 + \frac{4}{s + 2}, \qquad \sigma > -2 \quad (7.300)$$

is obviously improper. However, we can express a complicated improper function as the sum of a simpler improper part and a proper part. The function (7.300) becomes, for very large s, the simpler improper function s. Subtraction of s from the function leaves the remainder $-2s/(s + 2)$ which, unfortunately, is also improper. This remainder is equal to -2 for very large s. Extracting the value -2, we find a new remainder $4/(s + 2)$ that is proper. When $F(s)$ is a quotient of polynomials in s, as in (7.300), the expansion to a proper remainder is merely a process of arithmetical "long division." The simple improper function $(s - 2)$ in (7.300) is immediately recognizable as the transform of $u_1(t) - 2u_0(t)$ and the proper remainder is then susceptible to inverse transformation by the residue law.

An item of unfinished business remains. If, in the neighborhood of point s_p, the function $F(s)$ is inversely proportional to the nth power of $(s - s_p)$, then $F(s)$ is said to have an nth-order pole at s_p. A first-order pole is sometimes referred to as a "simple" pole. An nth-order pole can be visualized as the result of a limiting process in which n different simple poles are allowed to congregate or coalesce at the same point in the s-plane. Since the residue law that we have derived here applies only to simple poles, such a limiting process may be used to find the inverse transform of a function having a higher-order pole. For example, the realizable function

$$F(s) = \frac{1}{(s + a)(s + b)}, \qquad \sigma > (-a, -b) \qquad (7.301)$$

has the simple poles and residues

$$s_1 = -a, \qquad K_1 = 1/(b - a)$$
$$s_2 = -b, \qquad K_2 = 1/(a - b) \qquad (7.302)$$

so that

$$f(t) = \frac{e^{-at} - e^{-bt}}{b - a} u_{-1}(t) = e^{-at}\left[\frac{1 - e^{-(b-a)t}}{b - a}\right] u_{-1}(t) \quad (7.303)$$

Now, as b approaches a we have

$$\lim_{b \to a} F(s) = \frac{1}{(s + a)^2}, \qquad \sigma > -a \qquad (7.304)$$

$$\lim_{b \to a} f(t) = te^{-at}u_{-1}(t) \qquad (7.305)$$

The general result is covered by (7.238) and (7.247).

7.19   The One-Pole Transmission

For complex exponential signals, the energy-storage elements in a lumped-parameter time-invariant linear system satisfy a complex form of Ohm's law. Hence, the linear differential equations relating time signals in various parts of the system may be replaced by complex algebraic equations relating the complex amplitudes of the exponential signals. A simple but very important class of lumped linear systems are those containing only one energy-storage element.

Figure 7-37(a) shows one such system together with (b) a suitable flow-graph model, (c) the impulse response, and (d) the step response. If, on the other hand, analysis of the system is carried out for a complex exponential input signal rather than an impulse or a step, we have the situation shown in Fig. 7-37(e). In the flow graph (f) the integrator

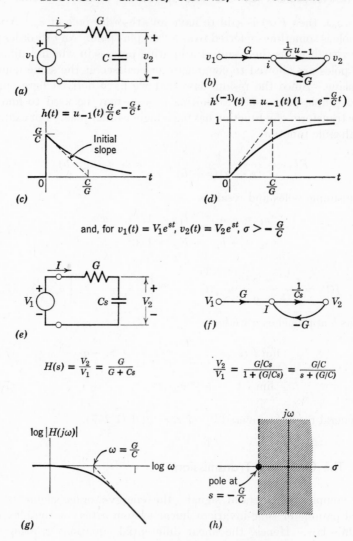

Fig. 7-37. Analysis of a simple RC circuit.

u_{-1}/C is replaced by the admittance $1/Cs$. Figure 7-37(g) shows the gain curve and (h) indicates the shaded region of the s-plane within which the system-function integral converges. The whole purpose of Fig. 7-37 is to emphasize the close relationship between the impulse or step response, the gain curve, and the pole position. The same quantity G/C, or its reciprocal, appears as the significant dimension in parts (c), (d), (g), and (h) of Fig. 7-37. The "transient response" of the system, (c) or (d), and the "frequency response" of the system, (g), are both controlled by the location of the pole in the complex s-plane (h).

The general model of a one-pole system (a circuit containing a single inductance or capacitance or a flow graph containing a single integrator or differentiator) is shown in Fig. 7-38. The model (a) is conveniently represented as the combination of two parts: the capacitor C and the

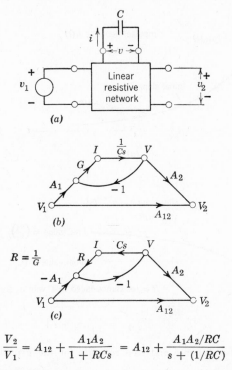

(a)

(b)

(c)

$$\frac{V_2}{V_1} = A_{12} + \frac{A_1 A_2}{1 + RCs} = A_{12} + \frac{A_1 A_2/RC}{s + (1/RC)}$$

Fig. 7-38. An arbitrary linear system containing one lumped energy-storage element, that is, one integrator.

remaining portion of the system, which is purely resistive. The flow graph (b) is a convenient representation of the system equations. This flow graph states three things. First, the current I is equal to $V_1 A_1 G$ minus VG. This is merely a statement of Thévenin's theorem at the capacitor terminals. Quantity $V_1 A_1$ is the open-circuit voltage at the capacitor terminals, G is the output conductance at these terminals, and $V_1 A_1 G$ is therefore the short-circuit current. In short, the resistive network fixes I when V_1 and V are specified. Similarly, the specification of V_1 and V fixes the output voltage V_2, as indicated by the flow-graph branches A_2 and A_{12}. Finally, the flow graph also states that V must equal $1/Cs$. Another form of the graph, obtained by inverting the loop, is that shown in Fig. 7-38(c). Here we have the capacitor voltage V expressed as the difference of the open-circuit voltage V_1A_1 and the voltage drop IR in the effective output resistance R at the capacitor terminals.

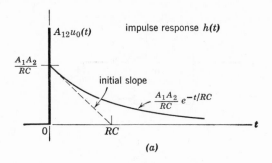

(a)

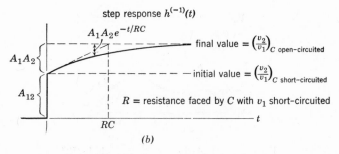

(b)

Fig. 7-39. Impulse response and step response for the general system shown in Fig. 7-38.

The system function V_2/V_1 is obtainable by inspection of either form of the flow graph. In terms of the general model in Fig. 7-38, the special example considered previously in Fig. 7-37 has A_{12} equal to zero and A_1A_2 equal to unity. Figure 7-39 shows the impulse response and step response of the general one-pole system. Observe that the step response of the one-pole system is completely determined by three resistive (no-pole) measurements: the value of the transmission when C is open-circuited, the value of the transmission when C is short-circuited, and the value of the resistance R faced by the capacitor.

The transmission expression given in Fig. 7-38 can be collected over a common denominator to obtain a function of the form

$$H(s) = K \frac{s + a}{s + b} \tag{7.306}$$

where K, a, and b are real constants. Expression (7.306) is the general one-pole system function for a lumped-parameter system. The function has a so-called *zero* at the point $s = -a$ and a pole at the point $s = -b$

$$H(-a) = 0, \qquad H(-b) = \infty \tag{7.307}$$

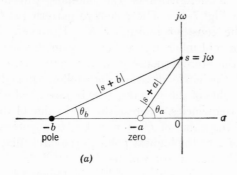

(a)

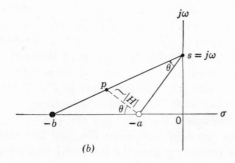

(b)

Fig. 7-40. The s-plane vector diagram for a one-pole function.

The magnitude and phase of H are placed in evidence by the polar form of (7.306)

$$|H(s)| \, e^{j\theta} = K \frac{|s + a| e^{j\theta_a}}{|s + b| e^{j\theta_b}} = K \frac{|s + a|}{|s + b|} \, e^{j(\theta_a - \theta_b)} \tag{7.308}$$

which leads to the s-plane vector diagram shown in Fig. 7-40. To study the magnitude and phase of $H(j\omega)$, let s be a point on the $j\omega$ axis as indicated in Fig. 7-40(a). It follows that the phase θ is the angle between the two vectors drawn from the pole and from the zero to point s. Moreover, if we construct another vector from the zero to point p as indicated in Fig. 7-40(b), such that the angle between this vector and the negative-real axis is also equal to θ, then we have two similar triangles with a common vertex located at the pole. The proportionality of sides of the similar triangles tells us that the length of the new vector (from zero to point p) is proportional to the magnitude of the system function. As point s moves up or down the $j\omega$ axis, point p describes a curve, which proves to be a circle. Such a curve, called a "circle diagram," is often a very convenient way of depicting the character of $H(j\omega)$.

The general characteristics of the one-pole transmission function are displayed in Fig. 7-41. The pole-zero pattern (a) does not tell us the value of the constant multiplier K. However, if the pole-zero pattern and the multiplier K are both specified, then the important dimensions of the step response (d), the gain curve (g), the phase curve (j), and the circle diagram (m) follow immediately. Notice that the initial value of the step response is associated with the value of H at very high frequencies, whereas the final value of the step response is a measure of the value of H at very low frequencies. Observe also that the value of ω at the highest point of the circle diagram is fixed by the location of the pole in the s-plane.

Parts (b), (e), (h), (k), and (n) of Fig. 7-41 show what happens when the zero lies to the left of the pole. Relocating the zero to the right of the pole, but this time also to the right of the $j\omega$ axis, we have the situation described in Fig. 7-41(c), (f), (i), (l), and (o). In contrast with Fig. 7-41(m) and (n), the circle diagram (o) spans the origin in the complex H-plane, with the result that as ω proceeds from 0 to $+\infty$ the phase θ changes by an amount π. The functions in Fig. 7-41(a) and (b) are minimum-phase whereas (c) is nonminimum-phase.

Figure 7-41 emphasizes the fact that the pole-zero pattern (plus a knowledge of the constant multiplier K), and the transient response (step or impulse response), and the gain and phase curves (or, for a minimum-phase function, the gain curve alone), and the circle diagram (including a knowledge of the critical frequency $\omega = b$), are merely different ways of presenting exactly the same information. If any one is given, the others follow. The ability to convert this information easily from one form to another is a great help in linear systems analysis. Suppose, for instance, that we wish to sketch the gain curve of a certain single-energy-storage amplifier circuit, and suppose that the circuit is such that the high-frequency gain, the low-frequency gain, and the time constant of the step response are all easily obtainable by inspection of the circuit. The time constant gives us the location of the pole, and this immediately locates one of the break points on the piecewise-linear approximation of the gain curve [in Fig. 7-41 (g), the point log a], whence projection along a line of unity slope gives the other break point (log b). In short, the quickest route to a frequency-response curve may possibly

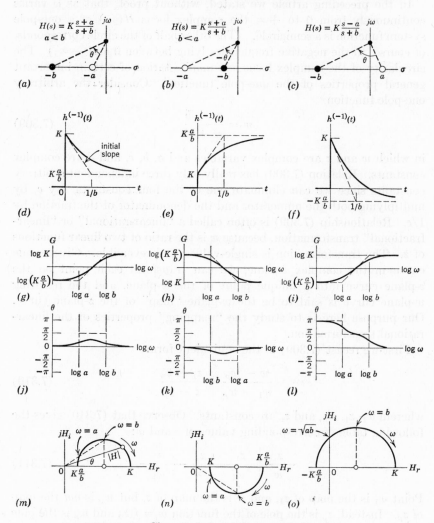

Fig. 7-41. Characteristics of the one-pole function.

lie along a detour through the transient characteristics of the system. The key which connects the transient response with the frequency response is the pole-zero pattern of the system function.

7.20   Circle Diagrams

In the preceding article we stated, without proof, that as ω varies continuously from 0 to $+\infty$ the complex locus $H(j\omega)$ of a one-pole system function is a semicircle. (The other half of the circle corresponds, of course, to the negative frequencies lying between 0 and $-\infty$.) The circularity of the complex locus is a manifestation of certain important general properties of the one-pole function. Consider the arbitrary one-pole function

$$w = \frac{az + b}{cz + d} \tag{7.309}$$

in which w and z are complex variables and a, b, c, and d are complex constants. Relation (7.309) has really only three independent arbitrary constants since we can eliminate one of the four constants, say c, by multiplying both the numerator and the denominator of the fraction by $1/c$. Relationship (7.309) is often called a "linear-rational" or "linear-fractional" transformation, because w is the ratio of two linear functions of z. The transformation is single-valued and reversible. Given some curve in the complex z-plane, we can transform each point on the z-plane curve into a unique point of the w-plane, and the resulting w-plane curve is said to be the w-plane "map" of the z-plane curve. Our purpose here is to study the "mapping" properties of the linear-rational transformation.

First we recast (7.309) in the equivalent form

$$\frac{w - w_p}{w_1 - w_p} = \frac{z_1 - z_p}{z - z_p} \tag{7.310}$$

wherein w_1, z_1, w_p, and z_p are constants. Observe that (7.310) gives the following table of corresponding values of z and w:

$$\begin{array}{c|ccc} z & z_1 & z_p & \infty \\ \hline w & w_1 & \infty & w_p \end{array} \tag{7.311}$$

Point w_1 is the map of z_1, and w is the map of z, but w_p is *not* the map of z_p. Instead, z_p is the pole of the function $w = f(z)$ and w_p is the pole of the inverse function $z = g(w)$. Relation (7.310) contains four complex constants but two of these, z_1 and w_1, are related through (7.309) and are therefore not independent. Hence equation (7.310), like (7.309), has really only three independent arbitrary constants.

Form (7.310) is convenient because it lends itself to the simple geometrical interpretation shown in Fig. 7-42. The complex z-plane triangle $z_p z z_1$ and the complex w-plane triangle $w_p w_1 w$ must be similar, since the sides $(z - z_p, z_1 - z_p)$ are in the same proportion as the sides $(w_1 - w_p, w - w_p)$ and the included angles [in equation (7.310), the complex angles of each of the fractions] are equal. Notice that z and w_1 are corresponding vertices of the similar triangles, as are z_1 and w (*not* z_1 and w_1, or z and w).

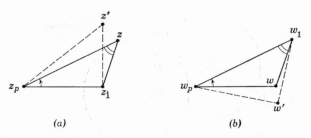

Fig. 7-42. Similar triangles in the complex z- and w-planes.

We are now in a position to *construct* the w-plane map of any z-plane curve. First locate the fixed points z_p and w_p. Now choose any convenient point z_1 and compute its w-plane map w_1. Once we have located the four points z_p, w_p, z_1, and w_1, a z-plane curve can be mapped point by point into the w-plane by *geometrical construction* of similar triangles. When point z in Fig. 7-42(a) moves along some curve to a new position z', point w in Fig. 7-42(b) must move to the new location w' in such a way as to maintain the similarity of triangles.

The basic mapping characteristics of the linear-rational transformation are embodied in the statement that the two triangles shown in Fig. 7-42 are similar. We shall now investigate the special cases in which the z-plane curve to be mapped is a circle or a straight line. For this we shall need, in addition to the similar-triangle property, the plane-geometry theorem stated in Fig. 7-43. To find the w-plane map of a z-plane circle, first choose z_1 to be the center of the circle, as shown in Fig. 7-44(a). Next, compute w_1 from the transformation and locate w_1 in the w-plane, as shown in (b). Now let z be any point on the circumference of the circle, so that the quotient r_2/r_1 remains fixed as z moves around the circle. It follows from the similar-triangle property that R_2/R_1 is equal to r_2/r_1 and therefore constant, whence the geometry theorem gives us the result that point w must also move on a circle. Thus *a z-plane circle maps into a w-plane circle.* To locate the center of the w-plane circle, draw a line from z_p tangent to the z-plane circle, as in Fig. 7-44(c), and call the point of tangency z'. The corresponding w-plane triangle is $w_p w_1 w'$, as in (d). Since the maximum value of angle α must be the same in both planes, it follows that the center of the circle can be located by erecting the perpendicular $w'o$ as shown in Fig. 7-44(d). Incidentally, Fig. 7-44 contains the essential elements of a proof for part of the geometry theorem stated in Fig. 7-43. For a proof, assume that the w-plane locus (b) is a circle and locate its

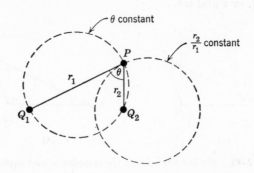

Fig. 7-43. A geometry theorem regarding the locus of a moving point P relative to fixed points Q_1 and Q_2: The locus is a circle if either θ or r_2/r_1 is fixed.

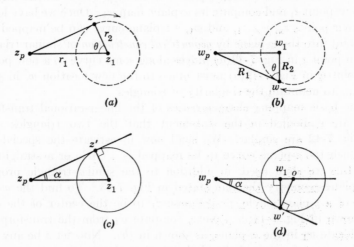

Fig. 7-44. Transformation of a circle.

center as in (d). Next, observe that the triangles w_pow and w_pww_1 are similar for any point w on the circumference of the circle. Thus $w_po:ow$ is the same proportion as $w_pw:ww_1$, which means that R_2/R_1 is constant for a properly located w-plane circle, and this is the same as saying that the locus is a circle if R_2/R_1 is constant.

Next we shall use the similar-triangle property and the geometry theorem to find the w-plane map of a straight line in the z-plane.   Let z_1 be the foot of the perpendicular dropped from z_p upon the given straight line, as illustrated in Fig. 7-45(a), and let point z move along the straight line as shown.   In the w-plane, Fig. 7-45(b), vertex w of the similar triangle must move so as to maintain a right angle at that

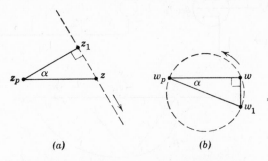

(a)   (b)

Fig. 7-45.   Transformation of a straight line.

vertex.   Hence, according to the geometry theorem, the w-plane map is a circle.   Moreover, for this particular choice of z_1, the line $w_p w_1$ is a *diameter* of the w-plane circle.

Returning to Fig. 7-41(a) and (m), we recognize $s_p = b$, $s_1 = 0$, $H_p = K$, and $H_1 = Ka/b$.   Thus the H-plane map of the $j\omega$ axis is a circle, and the points Ka/b and K are end points of a diameter.

7.21   An Illustrative Example—A Feedback Integrator

Figure 7-46 shows an amplifier having capacitive plate-to-grid feedback (a), its linear incremental model (b), and an appropriate flow graph (c).   This amplifier produces an a-c output signal which approximates the integral of the a-c input time function $e_1(t)$.   Since the circuit contains a single energy-storage element C, the transmission from e_1 to e_2 is governed by a one-pole system function.

The operation of the circuit can be explained as follows.   Let us first remove the source e_1 and the resistance R_1 and apply a step voltage directly across the grid terminals e.   In particular, assume that the voltage e in Fig. 7-47(a) is a positive step of height E_0.   When the step occurs, the capacitor voltage temporarily remains at the value zero, with the result that the entire step E_0 appears initially across the resistance R_2.   Hence the initial value of the input current i_1 is that shown in Fig. 7-47(c).   The steady-state value of current i_1 is evidently zero since the series capacitor blocks the flow of direct current.   To find

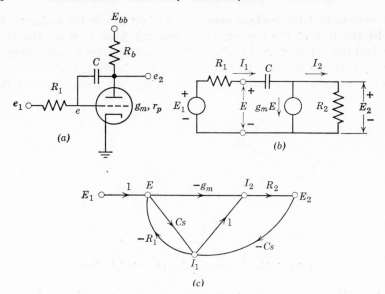

(a)

(b)

(c)

Fig. 7-46.   The Miller integrator.

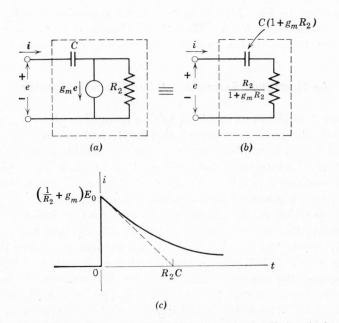

(a)

(b)

(c)

Fig. 7-47.   The Miller effect.   (a) The Miller circuit.   (b) The equivalent input circuit.   (c) The response i to an input voltage step of height E_0.

the time constant of the current waveform, we observe that voltage e and current $g_m e$ are both constant after the step occurs, and we can set voltage e and current $g_m e$ both equal to zero to find the incremental resistance faced by C. With e short-circuited and the current source $g_m e$ open-circuited, the circuit reduces to a simple loop containing capacitance C and resistance R_2, whence the time constant is obviously equal to $R_2 C$, as indicated in Fig. 7-47(c). *With respect to the relationship between e and i*, the circuit shown in Fig. 7-47(b) is entirely equivalent to that in (a), since both have exactly the same current response to an input voltage step. This equivalent input circuit places in evidence the "Miller effect": the relatively large effective input capacitance in series with a very small resistance. Inspection of Fig. 7-47(b) shows that the grid-to-plate capacitance C is effectively aggravated by a factor $(1 + A)$, where A is the magnitude of the low-frequency grid-to-plate voltage amplification E_2/E. The factor $(1 + A)$ is roughly equal to the voltage across the capacitor per unit of voltage applied at the grid. Now, for a sufficiently large source resistance R_1 in Fig. 7-46, the signal e will be much smaller than e_1 and we can make the approximations

$$i_1 \approx e_1/R_1 \tag{7.312}$$

$$e \approx \frac{1}{(1 + A)C} \int i_1 \, dt \tag{7.313}$$

$$e_2 \approx -Ae \tag{7.314}$$

so that the a-c output signal approximates the integral of the input signal,

$$e_2(t) \approx \frac{-A}{(1 + A)R_1 C} \int e_1(t) \, dt \tag{7.315}$$

For an exact analysis of the transmission, let us turn to the system function, which has the form

$$H(s) = \frac{E_2}{E_1} = K \frac{s - s_z}{s - s_p} \tag{7.316}$$

At very high frequency the capacitance C in Fig. 7-46(b) becomes a short circuit, and we find by inspection of the circuit

$$H(\infty) = \frac{G_1}{G_1 + G_2 + g_m} = \frac{R_2}{R_1 + R_2 + g_m R_1 R_2} = K \tag{7.317}$$

Next, to locate the zero s_z, let $e_1(t)$ be a complex exponential signal of complex amplitude E_1. The number s_z is that value of s for which the output voltage E_2 is equal to zero. If we assume that E_2 vanishes, then the voltage across C is just equal to E. Moreover, no current can flow in resistance R_2, with the result that $g_m E$ must be just equal to the capacitor current. Hence,

$$Cs_z E = g_m E \tag{7.318}$$

and

$$s_z = g_m/C \tag{7.319}$$

or

$$H(g_m/C) = 0 \tag{7.320}$$

It remains to locate the pole s_p. An indirect attack turns out to be the simplest one here. At zero frequency the capacitance becomes an open circuit. By inspection of Fig. 7-46(b), and at the same time by setting s equal to zero in (7.316), we find

$$H(0) = -g_m R_2 = Ks_z/s_p \tag{7.321}$$

which is easily solved for s_p

$$s_p = Ks_z/H(0) = \frac{-1}{(R_1 + R_2 + g_m R_1 R_2)C} \tag{7.322}$$

Figure 7-48 shows the pole-zero pattern. As g_m becomes large the zero moves off to infinity and the pole approaches the origin. In the limit of large g_m we would have, of course, an ideal integrator with a pole at the origin and no zero in the finite complex plane. The effect upon the circle diagram [see Fig. 7-41(o), with $a \gg b$] of increasing g_m is to increase the diameter of the circle and at the same time bring the infinite-frequency point closer to the origin. In the limit, the complex locus approaches the imaginary axis. For values of g_m attainable in practice the pole can be made to lie much closer to the s-plane origin than the zero. The circuit will behave like an integrator at those frequencies for which vector r_1 in Fig. 7-48 is not too far from vertical and vector r_2 is not too far from horizontal, a middle range of frequencies bounded roughly by $\omega_1 = 1/R'C$ and $\omega_2 = g_m/C$. The gain curve is just like that in Fig. 7-41(h), with ω_1 and ω_2 taking the place of the constants b and a. (The gain-versus-log-frequency curve for an ideal integrator would be an infinite straight line having a slope of -1.) The step response is plotted in Fig. 7-49.

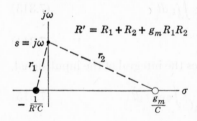

Fig. 7-48. The pole-zero pattern of the integrator circuit.

Relations (7.316), (7.317), (7.319), and (7.322) give us the complete expression for the system function. To verify this result, let us return to Fig. 7-46(c), which shows a suitable flow graph for the Miller circuit.

Construction of the graph begins with the three horizontal branches, after which I_1 can be expressed as the difference $(E - E_2)Cs = ECs - E_2Cs$. The graph is then completed by adding the two branches which state that I_1 contributes to I_2 and also reduces E by an amount equal to the voltage I_1R_1. By inspection of the graph, the system function is

$$\frac{E_2}{E_1} = \frac{(Cs - g_m)R_2}{1 + (R_1 + R_2 + g_mR_1R_2)Cs} \tag{7.323}$$

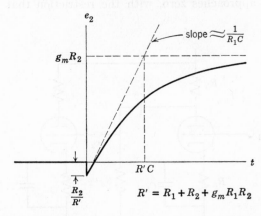

Fig. 7-49.   Response of the integrator circuit to a unit negative step input voltage $e_1 = u_{-1}(t)$.

The apparent input admittance at the grid can be found by setting R_1 equal to zero in the flow graph,

$$Y_{\text{grid}} = \left(\frac{I_1}{E_1}\right)_{R_1=0} = \frac{(1 + g_mR_2)Cs}{1 + R_2Cs} \tag{7.324}$$

Finally, the output admittance faced by R_2 can be recognized as the negative of the transmission from E_2 to I_2, as computed with flow-graph branch R_2 removed,

$$Y_{\text{out}} = -\left(\frac{I_2}{E_2}\right)_{R_2=0} = \frac{(1 + g_mR_1)Cs}{1 + R_1Cs} \tag{7.325}$$

7.22   The Two-Pole Transmission

A two-pole system function has the general form

$$H(s) = K\frac{(s - a_1)(s - a_2)}{(s - b_1)(s - b_2)} \tag{7.326}$$

exhibiting zeros at a_1 and a_2 and poles at b_1 and b_2. It is not necessary to have both zeros in the finite part of the s-plane. For example, if one of the zeros lies at infinity, then the form becomes

$$H(s) = K' \frac{(s - a_1)}{(s - b_1)(s - b_2)} \tag{7.327}$$

Form (7.327) is obtainable from (7.326) by allowing a_2 to approach infinity as K approaches zero, with the restriction that the product

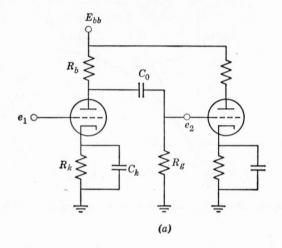

(a)

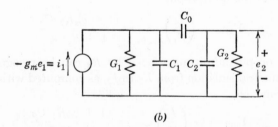

(b)

Fig. 7-50. The RC-coupled amplifier (a) and the incremental model for one stage (b).

$-Ka_2$ remains at the constant value K'. Since most practical transmission systems have negligible transmission at arbitrarily high frequencies, we can expect many system functions of interest to have fewer zeros than poles in the finite portion of the s-plane.

As one illustration of the two-pole system function, we shall consider the RC-coupled amplifier shown in Fig. 7-50(a). Assuming the bypass capacitance C_k to be so large as to have negligible reactance at all frequencies of interest, we can reduce the problem to the linear incremental model indicated in Fig. 7-50(b). Here G_1 is the conductance of the parallel combination of plate resistance r_p and plate load resistance R_b, whereas G_2 is simply the conductance of the grid-leak resistor R_g. Capacitances C_1 and C_2 represent the small stray and interelectrode capacitances present in the circuit. For a good approximation to the actual situation, C_1 should include the grid-to-plate capacitance of the first tube as well as the plate-to-cathode capacitance, and C_2 should include not only the grid-to-cathode capacitance of the second tube, but also the grid-to-plate capacitance, which is, of course, aggravated by the Miller effect.

By inspection of the circuit in Fig. 7-50(b) we find

$$Z(s) = \frac{E_2}{I_1} = \frac{C_0 s}{(C_1 s + G_1)(C_2 s + G_2) + C_0 s[(C_1 + C_2)s + G_1 + G_2]} \tag{7.328}$$

This can be rewritten as

$$Z(s) = \frac{C_0 s}{(C_1 C_2 + C_0 C_1 + C_0 C_2)(s + \omega_1)(s + \omega_2)} \tag{7.329}$$

where

$$\omega_1 + \omega_2 = \frac{C_1 R_1 + C_2 R_2 + C_0(R_1 + R_2)}{(C_1 C_2 + C_0 C_1 + C_0 C_2)R_1 R_2} \tag{7.330}$$

and

$$\omega_1 \omega_2 = \frac{1}{(C_1 C_2 + C_0 C_1 + C_0 C_2)R_1 R_2} \tag{7.331}$$

Further condensation leads to the compact expression

$$Z(j\omega) = \frac{1}{\left[\dfrac{1}{R_1}\left(1 + \dfrac{C_2}{C_0}\right) + \dfrac{1}{R_2}\left(1 + \dfrac{C_1}{C_0}\right) \right]\left[1 + j\left(\dfrac{\dfrac{\omega}{\omega_2} - \dfrac{\omega_1}{\omega}}{1 + \dfrac{\omega_1}{\omega_2}} \right) \right]} \tag{7.332}$$

The character of the frequency dependence stands out even more clearly when we introduce the quantities R_m, K_0, and x to obtain

$$Z(j\omega) = \frac{R_m}{1 + jK_0\left(x - \dfrac{1}{x}\right)} \tag{7.333}$$

where

$$R_m = \frac{1}{\frac{1}{R_1}\left(1 + \frac{C_2}{C_0}\right) + \frac{1}{R_2}\left(1 + \frac{C_1}{C_0}\right)} \tag{7.334}$$

$$x = \frac{\omega}{\sqrt{\omega_1\omega_2}} \tag{7.335}$$

$$K_0 = \frac{1}{\sqrt{\omega_2/\omega_1} + \sqrt{\omega_1/\omega_2}} \tag{7.336}$$

Quantity x is a normalized frequency variable. When x takes the value unity (or minus unity) the impedance $Z(j\omega)$ is purely real and equal to the so-called "mid-band" resistance R_m. Parameter K_0 is a measure of the relative width of the frequency interval over which Z remains approximately equal to R_m. The smaller the value of K_0, the larger is the "bandwidth" of Z.

The critical frequencies ω_1 and ω_2 appearing in (7.329) can be calculated from relations (7.330) and (7.331). It is simpler to work with the reciprocals $1/\omega_1$ and $1/\omega_2$

$$\frac{1}{\omega_1} + \frac{1}{\omega_2} = C_1R_1 + C_2R_2 + C_0(R_1 + R_2) \tag{7.337}$$

$$\frac{1}{\omega_1\omega_2} = [C_1C_2 + C_0(C_1 + C_2)]R_1R_2 \tag{7.338}$$

In practice, the shunt capacitances C_1 and C_2 are usually considerably smaller than the coupling capacitance C_0. If C_1 and C_2 are relatively small, then from (7.334) we can make the approximation

$$R_m \approx \frac{R_1R_2}{R_1 + R_2} \tag{7.339}$$

Moreover (with C_1 and C_2 relatively small), we might expect ω_1 and ω_2 to have widely different values. Let ω_1 denote the smaller of the two frequencies ω_1 and ω_2 and make the trial assumption that the terms $1/\omega_2$, C_1R_1, and C_2R_2 are negligible in (7.337). Thus

$$\frac{1}{\omega_1} \approx C_0(R_1 + R_2) \tag{7.340}$$

Substitution of (7.340) into (7.338) then yields

$$\frac{1}{\omega_2} \approx (C_1 + C_2)R_m \tag{7.341}$$

which verifies the trial assumption that ω_1 is much smaller than ω_2. If a closer approximation is required, we can now recompute the value of $1/\omega_1$ from (7.337), using the value of $1/\omega_2$ given by (7.341). So long as ω_1 and ω_2 differ by a factor of at least 10 or so, such a successive-approximations procedure is rapidly convergent and therefore a convenient

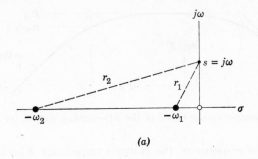

(a)

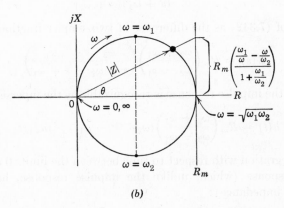

(b)

Fig. 7-51. The pole-zero pattern (a) and the circle diagram (b), for the RC-coupling circuit.

way of obtaining the numerical values of ω_1 and ω_2. However, the first approximations (7.339), (7.340), and (7.341) usually suffice in practice.

Figure 7-51(a) shows the pole-zero pattern of the RC-coupling circuit, with a zero at the origin and two poles located on the negative real axis. Because of the form of expression (7.332) or (7.333), the impedance function $Z(j\omega)$ has a complex locus which, like that of a one-pole function, is a circle. However, as indicated in Fig. 7-51(b), the frequency scale along the circle is not the same as that of the one-pole function. The corresponding frequency response curve is plotted in Fig. 7-52. Frequencies ω_1 and ω_2 are referred to as the "3-decibel" points or "half-power" points of the curve, since at these points the squared magnitude of the impedance drops to half its maximum value.

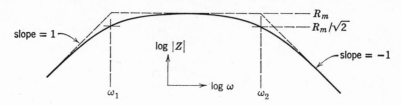

Fig. 7-52. Frequency-response curve of the RC-coupling circuit, for $\omega_1 \ll \omega_2$.

To find the step response of the transfer impedance $Z(s)$ let us first rewrite (7.329) in the form

$$Z(s) = \frac{R_m(\omega_1 + \omega_2)s}{(s + \omega_1)(s + \omega_2)} \qquad (7.342)$$

Expansion of (7.342) as the difference of two simpler fractions yields

$$Z(s) = R_m \left(\frac{\omega_2 + \omega_1}{\omega_2 - \omega_1}\right)\left(\frac{\omega_2}{s + \omega_2} - \frac{\omega_1}{s + \omega_1}\right) \qquad (7.343)$$

from which the impulse response is recognizable as the inverse transform

$$h(t) = R_m \left(\frac{\omega_2 + \omega_1}{\omega_2 - \omega_1}\right)(\omega_2 e^{-\omega_2 t} - \omega_1 e^{-\omega_1 t})u_{-1}(t) \qquad (7.344)$$

Finally, integration with respect to time between the limits 0 and t gives the step response (which, unlike the impulse response, has the dimensions of impedance):

$$z(t) = R_m \left(\frac{\omega_2 + \omega_1}{\omega_2 - \omega_1}\right)(e^{-\omega_1 t} - e^{-\omega_2 t})u_{-1}(t) \qquad (7.345)$$

Thus a unit step of input current produces the output voltage waveform shown in Fig. 7-53. We can see from relations (7.340) and (7.341) that the shunt capacitances C_1 and C_2 prevent the step response from rising instantaneously and that the coupling capacitance C_0 produces the droop indicated in Fig. 7-53. For zero C_1 and C_2 and infinite C_0 the step response would itself become an ideal step of height A. The initial rise rate of the step response can be found either by setting t equal to zero in (7.344) or by differentiating (7.345) with respect to time and then setting t equal to zero.   The result is

$$\text{per-unit initial rise rate} = (\omega_2 + \omega_1)R_m = \frac{1}{C_1 + C_2 + (C_1C_2/C_0)} \quad (7.346)$$

The initial rise rate is, of course, controlled by the values of capacitance in the circuit of Fig. 7-50(b) and is independent of the conductances G_1

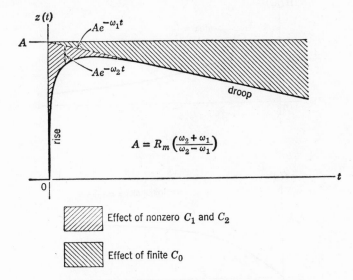

Fig. 7-53.   Step response of the RC-coupling circuit.

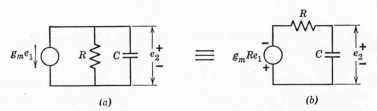

Fig. 7-54.   The high-frequency approximation for the RC-coupling circuit.

and G_2. This is to be expected, since the capacitor voltages are all zero *immediately* following the application of the step current and conductances G_1 and G_2 therefore carry no initial current.

When only the high-frequency behavior of the RC-coupled amplifier is of interest, we can ignore C_0 (that is, set C_0 equal to infinity), thereby reducing the circuit to the simpler form shown in Fig. 7-54(a). Here R is the parallel combination of G_1 and G_2 and C is the sum of C_1 and C_2.

The input and output voltages e_1 and e_2 are related by the system function $H = g_m Z$ where Z is simply the parallel combination of R and C. The magnitude of the system function is plotted in Fig. 7-55(a) against a linear, rather than a logarithmic, frequency scale. The maximum transmission $g_m R$ multiplied by the upper-half-power fre-

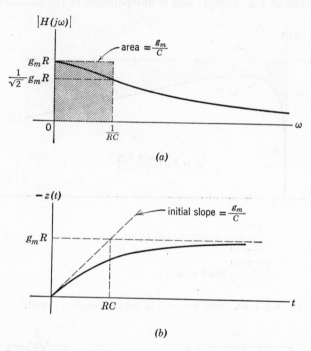

Fig. 7-55. Finite gain-bandwidth product (a) and finite initial rise rate (b), due to nonzero shunt capacitance.

quency $1/RC$ gives an area g_m/C which is often referred to as the gain-bandwidth product of the circuit. Figure 7-55(b) illustrates the fact that this gain-bandwidth product is also the initial slope of the step-response curve. Thus the "large-frequency" and the "small-time" responses of the voltage amplifier are both entirely controlled by the transconductance of the tube and the shunt capacitance of the circuit.

7.23 The Resonant Two-Pole Transmission

Passive RC circuits (those made up of positive resistances and capacitances) give rise to impedance functions whose poles are always located on the negative real axis of the s-plane. The same is true for passive *RL* circuits. However, if either *inductance* or *unilateral transconductance* (such as the g_m of a vacuum-tube model) is added in the proper way to an *RC* circuit, then the poles of the system function are no longer *necessarily* restricted to the negative real axis. Because of the conjugate symmetry of system functions, any poles not on the negative real axis must occur in conjugate complex pairs. When such a pole pair

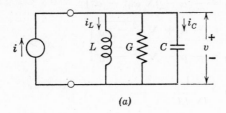

(a)

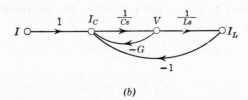

(b)

Fig. 7-56. The parallel-tuned circuit (a) and its flow graph (b) containing the two integrators $1/Cs$ and $1/Ls$.

lies in the left half of the s-plane, but fairly close to the $j\omega$ axis, we say that the system function exhibits *resonance*. If the poles move into the right half-plane, then the system is *unstable* and becomes an *oscillator*.

Consider first the addition of inductance to an *RC* circuit as shown in Fig. 7-56(a). The associated two-integrator flow graph of the system equations is indicated in Fig. 7-56(b). By inspection of either the circuit or the flow graph, we obtain the impedance function

$$\frac{V}{I} = Z = \frac{1}{G + Cs + (1/Ls)} = \frac{1/Cs}{1 + (G/Cs) + (1/LCs^2)} \quad (7.347)$$

which can then be put in the form

$$Z = \frac{s/C}{s^2 + (G/C)s + (1/LC)} \quad (7.348)$$

and the denominator factored to give

$$Z = \frac{s/C}{(s - s_1)(s - s_2)} \tag{7.349}$$

wherein

$$s_1 = -\alpha + j\sqrt{\omega_0{}^2 - \alpha^2} \left.\vphantom{\sqrt{\omega_0{}^2 - \alpha^2}}\right\} \tag{7.350}$$
$$s_2 = -\alpha - j\sqrt{\omega_0{}^2 - \alpha^2} \left.\vphantom{\sqrt{\omega_0{}^2 - \alpha^2}}\right\} \quad \alpha < \omega_0 \tag{7.351}$$

$$s_1 = -\alpha + \sqrt{\alpha^2 - \omega_0{}^2} \left.\vphantom{\sqrt{\alpha^2 - \omega_0{}^2}}\right\} \tag{7.352}$$
$$s_2 = -\alpha - \sqrt{\alpha^2 - \omega_0{}^2} \left.\vphantom{\sqrt{\alpha^2 - \omega_0{}^2}}\right\} \quad \alpha > \omega_0 \tag{7.353}$$

$$\omega_0 = \frac{1}{\sqrt{LC}} \tag{7.354}$$

$$\alpha = \frac{G}{2C} \tag{7.355}$$

The pole positions s_1 and s_2 are related to the convenient parameters ω_0 and α by the equations

$$s_1 s_2 = \omega_0{}^2 \tag{7.356}$$

and

$$\tfrac{1}{2}(s_1 + s_2) = -\alpha \tag{7.357}$$

Figure 7-57 shows the pole-zero pattern of the system function, and Figs. 7-58 and 7-59 illustrate the geometrical interpretation of relations (7.356) and (7.357). If ω_0 is held fixed and α is allowed to increase from zero, the poles move toward each other along the circular locus shown in Fig. 7-58. When α becomes equal to ω_0, the poles meet on the negative real axis. At this point the system function is said to be "critically damped," because the oscillatory or resonant character of its impulse response then disappears. A further increase in α causes the poles to separate once more as indicated in Fig. 7-59, and the system is said to be "overdamped." With increasing α, one pole moves inward toward the origin and the other moves outward toward infinity along the negative real axis. During the entire motion of the two poles depicted in Figs. 7-58 and 7-59, the product of their distances from the origin remains equal to the square of ω_0.

Notice that in the overdamped case the pole-zero pattern is the same as that of the RC-coupled amplifier shown in Fig. 7-51(a). Now, just as in eq. (7.333), we can put the impedance function in a standard form

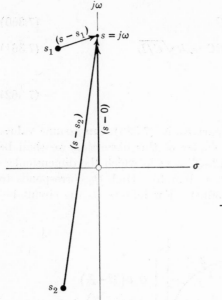

Fig. 7-57. The vector factors of the function $\dfrac{(s-0)}{(s-s_1)(s-s_2)}$.

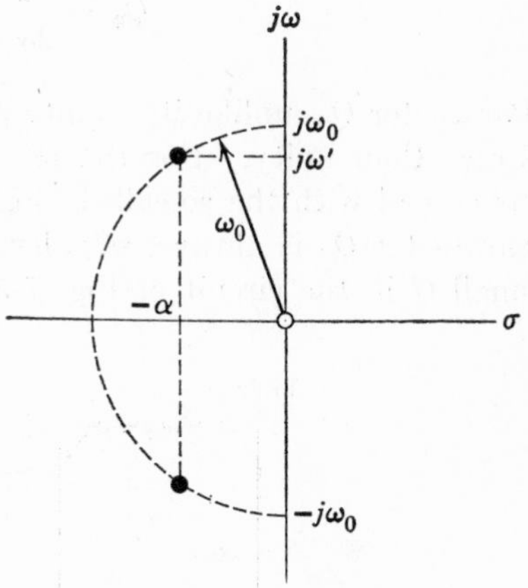

Fig. 7-58. The underdamped pole-zero pattern.

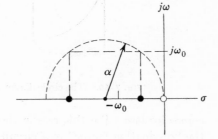

Fig. 7-59. The overdamped pole-zero pattern.

suitable for interpretation as a circle diagram

$$Z(s) = \frac{R}{1 + Q_0 \left(\dfrac{s}{\omega_0} + \dfrac{\omega_0}{s} \right)} \qquad (7.358)$$

and

$$Z(j\omega) = \frac{R}{1 + jQ_0 \left(\dfrac{\omega}{\omega_0} - \dfrac{\omega_0}{\omega} \right)} \qquad (7.359)$$

where

$$R = 1/G \tag{7.360}$$

$$Q_0 = \omega_0 RC = R\sqrt{C/L} \tag{7.361}$$

or

$$Q_0 = \frac{\omega_0}{2\alpha} \tag{7.362}$$

Parameter Q_0, unlike its counterpart K_0 in (7.333), can assume values larger than unity. For the remainder of this discussion we shall be concerned with the so-called "high-Q" case in which the dimensionless parameter Q_0 is always, say, larger than 10. High Q_0 corresponds to small G in the circuit of Fig. 7-56(a). For infinite Q_0 the circuit be-

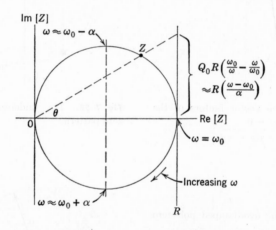

Fig. 7-60. The circle diagram for the parallel-tuned circuit.

comes lossless. For this reason the reciprocal $1/Q_0$ is sometimes called the "dissipation factor" of a circuit, and Q_0 itself is often referred to as the "quality factor" of a nearly lossless system.

Expression (7.359) leads directly to the circle diagram shown in Fig. 7-60. For the high-Q case the motion of point Z around the circle with increasing ω is controlled primarily by the vector $(s - s_1)$ in Fig. 7-57. High Q means that s_1 and s_2 are close to the $j\omega$ axis, and the interesting variations of the function $Z(j\omega)$ take place in a relatively small region of the axis near $j\omega_0$. Within this small region we can replace the slowly varying vectors $(s - s_2)$ and $(s - 0)$ by the constant values $j2\omega_0$ and $j\omega_0$, respectively, without appreciable error. In other words, near resonance Z behaves like a one-pole function. Figure 7-61 shows the points $(\omega_0 + \alpha)$ and $(\omega_0 - \alpha)$ at which the magnitude of the vector

$(j\omega - s_1)$ increases to $\sqrt{2}$ times its minimum value. Thus the band-width $\Delta\omega$ of the function $Z(j\omega)$ is very nearly equal to 2α in the high-Q case, as indicated by the resonance curve in Fig. 7-62. The normalized

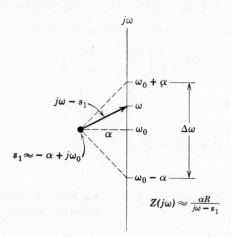

Fig. 7-61. The neighborhood of the point $j\omega_0$ on the $j\omega$ axis.

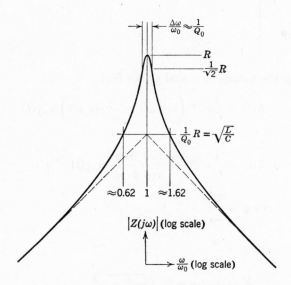

Fig. 7-62. The resonance curve of a tuned circuit.

bandwidth $\Delta\omega/\omega_0$ is very nearly equal to the inverse of Q_0 and is con-veniently identifiable as twice the angle (in radians) between the pole and the $j\omega$ axis, as shown in Fig. 7-63.

The impulse response of the resonant two-pole function may be found by rewriting (7.349) as the difference of two one-pole functions

$$Z(s) = \frac{1}{C}\left[\frac{s_2}{(s_2 - s_1)(s - s_2)} - \frac{s_1}{(s_2 - s_1)(s - s_1)}\right] \qquad (7.363)$$

from which the inverse transform is recognizable as

$$h(t) = \frac{1}{C}\left[\frac{s_2 e^{s_2 t} - s_1 e^{s_1 t}}{s_2 - s_1}\right] u_{-1}(t) \qquad (7.364)$$

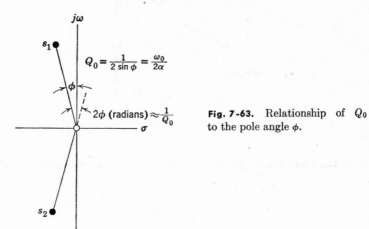

Fig. 7-63. Relationship of Q_0 to the pole angle ϕ.

Substituting the values of s_1 and s_2, we find

$$h(t) = \frac{1}{C} e^{-\alpha t}\left(\cos \omega' t - \frac{\alpha}{\omega'}\sin \omega' t\right) u_{-1}(t) \qquad (7.365)$$

or

$$h(t) = \frac{1}{C} e^{-\alpha t}\frac{\cos (\omega' t + \phi)}{\cos \phi} u_{-1}(t) \qquad (7.366)$$

$$\cos \phi = \frac{\omega'}{\omega_0} \qquad (7.367)$$

$$\sin \phi = \frac{\alpha}{\omega_0} \qquad (7.368)$$

$$\omega' = \omega_0 \cos \phi = \sqrt{\omega_0^2 - \alpha^2} \qquad (7.369)$$

wherein ω' and ϕ are quantities which have already been shown in Figs. 7-58 and 7-63. The impulse response is plotted in Fig. 7-64.

With the current source in Fig. 7-56(a) replaced by the transconductance of a unilateral amplifying device, the circuit becomes the model of a tuned voltage amplifier, as shown in Fig. 7-65. The voltage amplification is just equal to the product of g_m and the impedance Z about which we have been talking. The resonance curve of the tuned amplifier

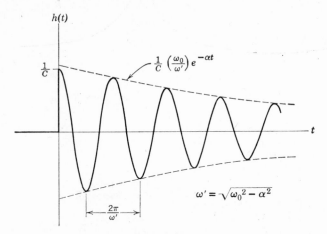

$h(t)$

$\frac{1}{C}$

$\frac{1}{C}\left(\frac{\omega_0}{\omega'}\right)e^{-\alpha t}$

t

$\omega' = \sqrt{\omega_0{}^2 - \alpha^2}$

$\frac{2\pi}{\omega'}$

Fig. 7-64. Impulse response of the parallel-tuned circuit.

is plotted in Fig. 7-66(a). Comparison with Fig. 7-55(a) shows that the gain-bandwidth product g_m/C is unchanged by the addition of the tuning inductance L, provided Q_0 is high enough to validate the approxi-

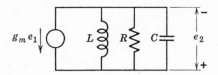

Fig. 7-65. The basic tuned amplifier model.

$g_m e_1$ L R C e_2

mations indicated in Fig. 7-66(a). These approximations are equivalent to ignoring the presence of the conjugate pole lying near $-j\omega_0$ in the s-plane.

Figure 7-66(b) shows the response of a high-Q amplifier to a suddenly applied resonant-frequency sinusoid. The broken-line envelope of the growing oscillations is sometimes referred to as the "build-up" curve of the amplifier. As we might expect, the time constant of the build-up curve is $2RC$, the reciprocal of α. Thus the build-up curve of the parallel RLC circuit is the same as the step-response curve of an RC circuit having the same R, but twice as much C, as the tuned circuit.

For a justification of Fig. 7-66(b) first reconsider the system function

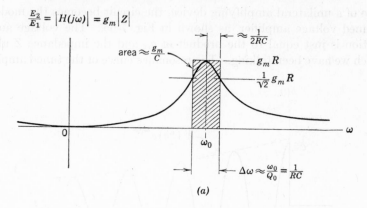

$$\frac{E_2}{E_1} = |H(j\omega)| = g_m|Z|$$

area $\approx \frac{g_m}{C}$

$\approx \frac{1}{2RC}$

$g_m R$

$\frac{1}{\sqrt{2}} g_m R$

ω_0

$\Delta\omega \approx \frac{\omega_0}{Q_0} = \frac{1}{RC}$

(a)

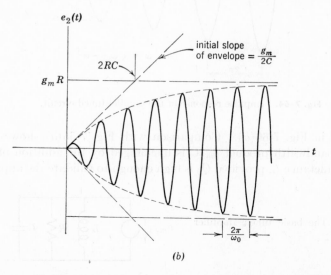

$e_2(t)$

initial slope of envelope $= \frac{g_m}{2C}$

$2RC$

$g_m R$

$\frac{2\pi}{\omega_0}$

(b)

Fig. 7-66. "Build-up" in a resonant system. (a) Resonance curve showing gain-bandwidth product g_m/C and (b) response to an input $e_1(t) = u_{-1}(t) \cos \omega_0 t$.

of the untuned amplifier

$$H(s) = \frac{\alpha}{s + \alpha}, \qquad h(t) = u_{-1}(t)\alpha e^{-\alpha t} \qquad (7.370)$$

Here $H(s)$ is normalized to unity at zero frequency, for convenience. The output voltage function $V_2(s)$ is the product of $H(s)$ and the input voltage function $V_1(s)$. For an input step

$$V_1(s) = \frac{1}{s}, \qquad v_1(t) = u_{-1}(t) \qquad (7.371)$$

we have, therefore,

$$V_2(s) = \frac{\alpha}{s(s+\alpha)} = \frac{1}{s} - \frac{1}{s+\alpha} \qquad (7.372)$$

The pole pattern of $V_2(s)$ is indicated in Fig. 7-67(a). The corresponding time function is

$$v_2(t) = u_{-1}(t)(1 - e^{-\alpha t}) \qquad (7.373)$$

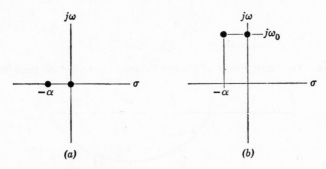

Fig. 7-67. The pole pattern for suddenly applied excitation at the resonant frequency.

Now consider the application of the hypothetical complex signal

$$V_1(s) = \frac{1}{s - j\omega_0}, \qquad v_1(t) = u_{-1}(t)e^{j\omega_0 t} \qquad (7.374)$$

to a high-Q tuned amplifier. This signal has frequency components concentrated mainly in the neighborhood of the resonance frequency ω_0 and represents negligible excitation at the conjugate resonance lying at the negative of ω_0. Hence, we can ignore the conjugate pole and approximate the system function as

$$H(s) = \frac{\alpha}{s + \alpha - j\omega_0}, \qquad h(t) = [u_{-1}(t)\alpha e^{-\alpha t}]e^{j\omega_0 t} \qquad (7.375)$$

By analogy with (7.372) above we have

$$V_2(s) = \frac{1}{s - j\omega_0} - \frac{1}{s + \alpha - j\omega_0} \qquad (7.376)$$

which has the shifted pole pattern shown in Fig. 7-67(b). Shifting the frequency function is equivalent to multiplication of the corresponding time function by a complex exponential. Thus

$$v_2(t) = u_{-1}(t)(1 - e^{-\alpha t})e^{j\omega_0 t} \qquad (7.377)$$

represents the response to the complex exponential input (7.374). The waveform in Fig. 7-66(b) is, of course, the real part of (7.377), the response to an input which is the real part of (7.374).

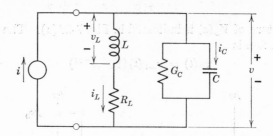

Fig. 7-68. The tuned circuit with series inductor loss and shunt capacitor loss.

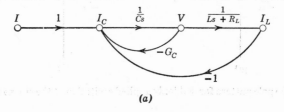

(a)

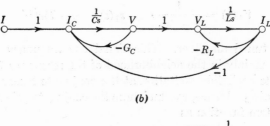

(b)

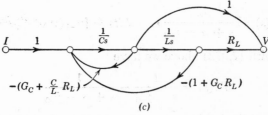

(c)

Fig. 7-69. Flow graphs for the tuned circuit.

In practice, the Q of a tuned circuit is often limited by series resistance in the inductor rather than by shunt conductance of the capacitor. Figure 7-68 shows the general circuit containing both types of loss, R_L and G_C. In order to account for R_L, the flow graph in Fig. 7-56 can be modified as shown in Fig. 7-69(a) and (b). The transmission from I to V can also be represented as the standard form (c) presented previously in Fig. 7-17(a).

Pole locations are controlled entirely by the feedback loops in the flow graph. The two feedback loops in Fig. 7-56(b) gave rise to the values of ω_0 and α indicated in (7.354) and (7.355). Now, by inspection of the corresponding feedback loops in Fig. 7-69(c) we find that the required modifications of ω_0 and α are

$$\omega_0 = \sqrt{(1 + G_C R_L)/LC} \tag{7.378}$$

and

$$\alpha = \frac{1}{2}\left(\frac{G_C}{C} + \frac{R_L}{L}\right) \tag{7.379}$$

Hence

$$Q_0 = \frac{\omega_0}{2\alpha} = \frac{1 + G_C R_L}{G_C\sqrt{L/C} + R_L\sqrt{C/L}} \tag{7.380}$$

$$\frac{1}{Q_0} = \frac{G_C}{\omega_0 C} + \frac{R_L}{\omega_0 L} \tag{7.381}$$

The quantities

$$R_0 = \sqrt{L/C}, \qquad G_0 = \sqrt{C/L} \tag{7.382}$$

appearing in (7.380) are called the "characteristic resistance" R_0 and the "characteristic conductance" G_0 of the tuned circuit. In terms of the characteristic conductance and resistance we can define

$$\frac{1}{Q_C} = \frac{G_C}{G_0} \tag{7.383}$$

and

$$\frac{1}{Q_L} = \frac{R_L}{R_0} \tag{7.384}$$

and if we ignore the small term

$$G_C R_L = \frac{1}{Q_C Q_L} \tag{7.385}$$

in (7.380), then

$$\frac{1}{Q_0} \approx \frac{1}{Q_C} + \frac{1}{Q_L} \tag{7.386}$$

As mentioned previously, the reciprocal of Q_0 is a measure of relative power loss in the circuit. Relation (7.386) states in effect that the total loss is the sum of the losses in the capacitor and in the inductor.

The pole-zero pattern of the tuned-circuit impedance is shown in Fig. 7-70. The addition of R_L in series with L shifts the poles to the left by an amount $R_L/2L$. This effect can be accounted for by an approximate equivalent circuit in which the inductor remains lossless and the shunt conductance G_C is replaced by a new *equivalent shunt conductance*

$$G_C' = G_C + G_0{}^2 R_L \tag{7.387}$$

In other words, inductor resistance can be transferred to the capacitor where it appears as an equivalent conductance $G_0{}^2 R_L$. Such an equivalent circuit does not, of course, account for the two minor effects of R_L: the shift of the zero slightly to the left of the origin and the slight in-

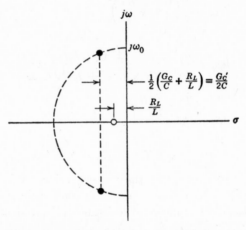

Fig. 7-70. Pole-zero pattern of the tuned circuit with loss in the capacitor and in the inductor.

crease in ω_0 due to the small term $G_C R_L$ in (7.378). Under conditions of high Q the resonance curve of the approximate equivalent circuit matches the actual resonance curve quite closely except at very low frequencies.

7.24   Resonance in an RC-Coupled Feedback Circuit

As already mentioned, the phenomenon of resonance is not confined to circuits in which two different types of energy-storage elements are present. As an illustration of this fact Fig. 7-71(*a*) shows an inductance-less circuit whose voltage-transfer function E_3/E_0 exhibits a sharp resonance for properly chosen values of the circuit parameters.

The circuit consists of two voltage-amplifier stages with a portion B of the output signal e_3 fed back in series with the input signal e_0. The circuit model leads directly to the flow graph of Fig. 7-71(b), where A_1, A_2, a, and b are convenient parameters dependent upon the values of the circuit elements. Quantities A_1, a, and b have the dimensions of frequency whereas A_2 and B are dimensionless.

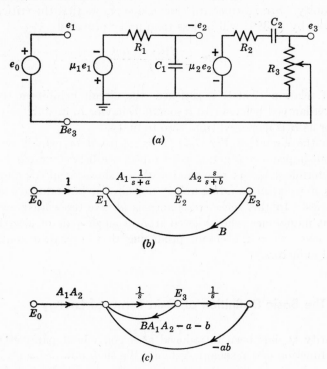

Fig. 7-71. Resonance without inductance.

The system function can be written by inspection of the flow graph and rearranged in the form

$$\frac{E_3}{E_0} = \frac{A_1 A_2 s}{s^2 + (a + b - BA_1A_2)s + ab} \tag{7.388}$$

After division of both the numerator and the denominator by s^2, this expression is recognizable as the transmission from E_0 to E_3 in the flow graph of Fig. 7-71(c). Comparison with Fig. 7-56(b) brings out the analogy with the parallel-tuned circuit. The system in Fig. 7-71(c) becomes resonant when the parameter B is adjusted for sufficiently small feedback around the first integrator. For the special value

$$B = \frac{a + b}{A_1 A_2} \tag{7.389}$$

this feedback branch vanishes, leaving only the larger feedback loop containing both integrators, and the system oscillates with infinite Q at a frequency ω_0 equal to $\sqrt{ab}$. Incidentally, quantity B is the transfer ratio of the output potentiometer in Fig. 7-71(a) and therefore cannot exceed unity. Straightforward calculation shows that the critical value of B given by (7.389) will be less than unity provided

$$\mu_1\mu_2 \geq \frac{R_1C_1 + R_2C_2}{R_3C_2} \qquad (7.390)$$

Thus, if relation (7.390) is satisfied, the circuit exhibits a transition from overdamped behavior to resonant behavior to unstable oscillatory behavior as B is increased from zero to unity.

When the circuit of Fig. 7-71(a) is adjusted to exhibit resonance, its output-impedance function (the impedance between ground and the output terminal e_3, as measured with e_0 short-circuited) necessarily exhibits a resonance and therefore appears to be inductive at some frequencies. In this sense, resonance is always associated with some apparent inductance when viewed from a single pair of electrical terminals, even when the circuit producing that resonance contains no physical inductors.

7.25 The Basic Definition of Q in Terms of Energy

Quantity Q_0 has been introduced as a convenient parameter in the system function of a resonant system. We shall now *define* Q_0 in terms of energy in the system and show that this basic physical definition leads, in the high-Q case, to the other interpretations which have already been introduced.

Suppose that a resonant system is excited by a resonant-frequency sinusoidal input signal which persists for a time long enough to allow the system to reach steady-state equilibrium. Suppose now that the input signal is suddenly removed, leaving the system thereafter isolated from the rest of the world. Henceforth, we can expect all of the system variables including the output signal to vary with time at the same frequency ω_0 and the same damping rate α. The output signal has the complex exponential representation

$$v(t) = e^{(-\alpha+j\omega_0)t} \qquad (7.391)$$

If the system is highly resonant, the oscillations will be nearly sinusoidal in the sense that the amplitude of oscillation decreases only very slightly from one oscillation to the next. In an oscillatory physical system we know that average energy storage anywhere in the system (averaged over 1 cycle of the oscillation) is proportional to the square of the amplitude of the voltage or current (or force or velocity) in that part of the system. Since the amplitudes of all system variables are decreasing at the same rate as the amplitude of the output signal, we can write

$$\text{stored energy} = W \approx K|v|^2 = Ke^{-2\alpha t} \tag{7.392}$$

where K is a constant of proportionality dependent upon the values of the system parameters and the relative amplitudes of the system variables. Now, since the system is isolated and cannot transfer energy to or from its environment, we must have

$$\text{power dissipated} = -\frac{dW}{dt} \approx 2\alpha W \tag{7.393}$$

For our present purposes the internal power dissipation is more conveniently expressed as

$$\text{energy dissipated per radian} = -\frac{dW}{d(\omega_0 t)} \approx \frac{2\alpha}{\omega_0} W \tag{7.394}$$

We can now *define* the "quality factor" Q_0 of the resonant system as

$$Q_0 = \frac{\text{stored energy}}{\text{energy dissipated per radian}} \approx \frac{\omega_0}{2\alpha} \tag{7.395}$$

This matches the previous interpretation of Q_0 as the quotient of the resonant frequency ω_0 and the bandwidth 2α.

One further interpretation of Q_0, not previously mentioned, has to do with the rate of change of phase with frequency. In the neighborhood of resonance the system function can be approximated by

$$H(j\omega) \approx \frac{H_m}{1 + j2Q_0\left(\dfrac{\omega - \omega_0}{\omega_0}\right)} \tag{7.396}$$

and for values of ω very close to ω_0, we have

$$\theta(j\omega) \approx -2Q_0\left(\frac{\omega - \omega_0}{\omega_0}\right) \tag{7.397}$$

Hence

$$Q_0 \approx -\frac{1}{2}\left[\frac{d\theta}{d\left(\dfrac{\omega}{\omega_0}\right)}\right]_{\omega=\omega_0} = -\frac{1}{2}\left[\frac{d\theta}{d\log\omega}\right]_{\omega=\omega_0} \tag{7.398}$$

Thus the value of Q_0 is conveniently obtainable from the phase curve when the phase curve is plotted on a logarithmic frequency scale.

The various interpretations of Q_0 are not in general compatible unless the value of Q_0 is sufficiently large, say greater than 10 or 20. In any conflict of interpretations the energy definition takes precedence.

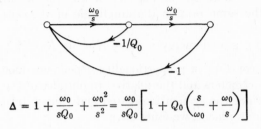

$$\Delta = 1 + \frac{\omega_0}{sQ_0} + \frac{\omega_0^2}{s^2} = \frac{\omega_0}{sQ_0}\left[1 + Q_0\left(\frac{s}{\omega_0} + \frac{\omega_0}{s}\right)\right]$$

Fig. 7-72. The normalized two-integrator flow graph of a resonant system.

For comparison with the flow graphs of resonance systems given earlier, Fig. 7-72 shows the basic two-integrator system with the parameters ω_0 and Q_0 placed in evidence. The determinant Δ of this flow graph (which must appear in the denominator of every transmission function arising from such a graph) is identifiable as the standard algebraic expression involving Q_0, and this identification justifies the branch transmissions shown in the flow graph.

7.26   The Flat Low-Pass Transmission

The circuit in Fig. 7-73(a) and its dual (b) have transmission functions H exhibiting two poles but no zeros in the finite s-plane. From the flow graph (c), we have

$$H(s) = \frac{1/LCs^2}{1 + (G/Cs) + (1/LCs^2)} \tag{7.399}$$

or

$$H(s) = \frac{\omega_0^2}{s^2 + 2\alpha s + \omega_0^2} = \frac{s_1 s_2}{(s - s_1)(s - s_2)} \tag{7.400}$$

$$s_1 = -\alpha + j\sqrt{\omega_0^2 - \alpha^2}$$
$$s_2 = -\alpha - j\sqrt{\omega_0^2 - \alpha^2} \tag{7.401}$$

$$\omega_0^2 = 1/LC = s_1 s_2 \tag{7.402}$$

For α positive but not too large, the function has a pair of conjugate complex poles located as in Fig. 7-74. The only zero of the function is a second-order zero located at infinity, since $H(s)$ is proportional to

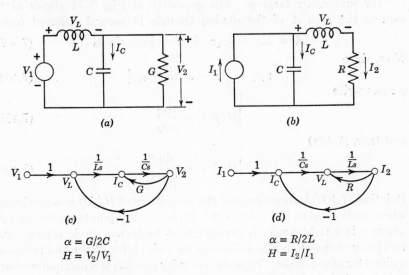

(a)   (b)

(c) -1 (d) -1

$\alpha = G/2C$ $\alpha = R/2L$

$H = V_2/V_1$ $H = I_2/I_1$

Fig. 7-73. System function with no zeros in the finite s-plane.

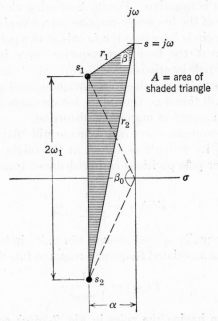

A = area of shaded triangle

Fig. 7-74. An angle β related to $|H(j\omega)|$.

s^{-2} for sufficiently large s. The geometry of Fig. 7-74 allows us to express the area A of the shaded triangle in several different forms

$$A = \alpha\omega_1 = \tfrac{1}{2}r_1r_2 \sin \beta = \tfrac{1}{2}s_1s_2 \sin \beta_0 \qquad (7.403)$$

Now, since

$$r_1r_2 = \left|(s - s_1)(s - s_2)\right| \qquad (7.404)$$

we can write

$$\left|H(j\omega)\right| = \frac{s_1s_2}{r_1r_2} \qquad (7.405)$$

and from (7.403)

$$\left|H(j\omega)\right| = \frac{\sin \beta}{\sin \beta_0} \qquad (7.406)$$

Relation (7.406) informs us that the magnitude of $H(j\omega)$ is a maximum when angle β takes the value $\pi/2$. To locate the points on the $j\omega$ axis where β is a right angle, it is convenient to draw a circle through the two poles as shown in Fig. 7-75, with the poles lying at the end points of a diameter of the circle. Thus $\sin \beta$ is unity and $|H|$ is a maximum where the circle intersects the $j\omega$ axis, as in Fig. 7-75(c). When the circle lies away from the $j\omega$ axis, as in (a), $|H|$ is a maximum at the origin and its second derivative is negative. For an osculating circle, as in (b), the second derivative of the frequency-response curve vanishes at the origin. Finally, when the circle intersects the $j\omega$ axis at two points, as in (c), the second derivative of the frequency-response curve is positive at the origin. Thus, the pole locations in Fig. 7-75(b) give a frequency-response function that is as flat as possible in the neighborhood of zero frequency, and the system will therefore transmit a low-frequency signal spectrum with a minimum amount of amplitude distortion.

The frequency-response curve can be made still "flatter," in the sense that still more of its derivatives vanish at the origin, by adding more poles. The proper pole positions can be deduced from an examination of the function

$$F(s) = \frac{1}{1 + (-s^2)^n} \qquad (7.407)$$

whose poles are equally spaced around the unit circle, as indicated in Fig. 7-76(a). The associated frequency-response function is

$$F(j\omega) = \frac{1}{1 + \omega^{2n}} \qquad (7.408)$$

A system function having the poles in Fig. 7-76(a) could not be both stable and realizable, for some of the poles lie in the right-half s-plane. However, a realizable system having only the left-half-plane poles of

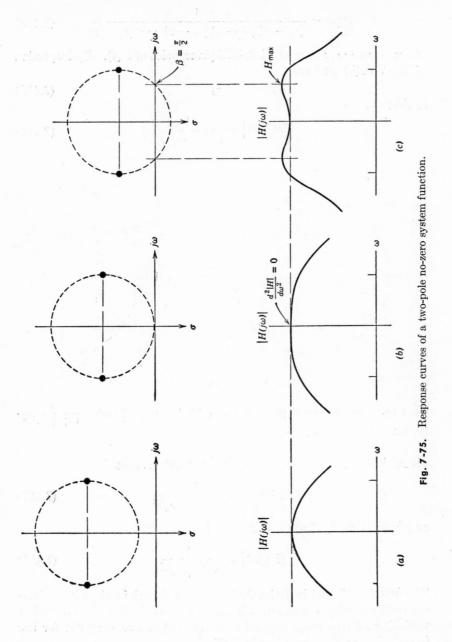

Fig. 7-75. Response curves of a two-pole no-zero system function.

$F(s)$, as shown in (b), is evidently stable. The function has the form

$$H(s) = \frac{1}{(s_1 - s)(s_2 - s)(s_3 - s) \cdots (s_n - s)} \qquad (7.409)$$

where $s_1, s_2, \cdots, s_n$ are the left-half-plane poles of $F(s)$. By inspection of Fig. 7-76(b) we have

$$|s_k - s| = r_k \qquad (7.410)$$

so that

$$|H(j\omega)| = \frac{1}{r_1 r_2 r_3 \cdots r_n} \qquad (7.411)$$

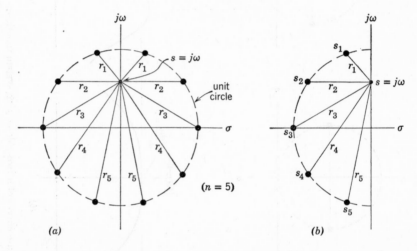

Fig. 7-76. The Butterworth pole pattern. (a) Pole pattern of $F(s) = \dfrac{1}{1 + (-s^2)^n}$. (b) Pole pattern of $H(s)$.

Meanwhile, the symmetry of Fig. 7-76(a) tells us that

$$F(j\omega) = \frac{1}{(r_1 r_2 r_3 \cdots r_n)^2} \qquad (7.412)$$

and from (7.408), (7.411), and (7.412)

$$|H(j\omega)| = \frac{1}{\sqrt{1 + \omega^{2n}}} \qquad (7.413)$$

The function (7.408) is obviously very flat at the origin, since its reciprocal (and therefore the function itself) has all derivatives up to $2n - 1$ vanishing at zero frequency. Hence, (7.413) is also very flat for low frequencies, as illustrated in Fig. 7-77.

The flat low-pass function in Fig. 7-77 is called a *Butterworth function* of order n. There are several other useful flat low-pass functions, each based upon a different "flatness" criterion and each having, therefore, a different pole pattern. However, Fig. 7-76(a) and relation (7.412) give the general idea. For a distribution of poles around a closed contour, the magnitude of the associated function $F(s)$ remains relatively constant as the point s moves about within the contour, because any displacement of point s increases some of the distances r_k and decreases

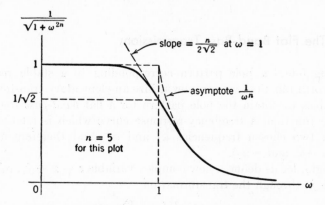

Fig. 7-77.   The Butterworth flat low-pass function.

others. As point s moves outside and away from the contour, however all of the distances r_k increase and $F(s)$ rapidly becomes smaller in magnitude.

An electrical analogy is often useful, both for the value of another viewpoint and for rapid experimental determination of a frequency-response curve from a given pole pattern. Suppose that the s-plane is covered by a uniform sheet of conducting material and let a unit current be injected, by means of a small probe, into the conducting sheet at each of the pole positions. (To close the circuit, the total injected current is extracted from the sheet at some point far away in comparison to the dimension of the pole pattern. In effect, current is injected at poles and extracted at zeros.) Apart from an additive constant, the electric potential at any point in the conducting plane is proportional to the sum of the logarithms of the distances from that point to the current-injection points. Similarly, the logarithm of $|H|$ is proportional to the sum of the logarithms of the distances r_k. Hence the gain function $G(j\omega) = \log |H|$ is directly identifiable as the electric potential in the experiment described above.

To reiterate, for any $F(s)$ having a pole pattern symmetric about both the σ axis and the $j\omega$ axis, we can extract a realizable stable function $H(s)$ by associating the left-half-plane poles of $F(s)$ with $H(s)$ and the right-half-plane pole with $H(-s)$. Thus,

$$H(s)H(-s) = F(s) = F(-s) \tag{7.414}$$

and since

$$H(-j\omega) = H^*(j\omega) \tag{7.415}$$

we have

$$|H(j\omega)|^2 = F(j\omega) \tag{7.416}$$

7.27   The Flat Band-Pass Transmission

Having found a pole pattern corresponding to a stable realizable Butterworth function, we can now utilize an elementary transformation of variables to obtain the pole pattern for a flat *band-pass* frequency-response function, a frequency-response curve which is relatively flat between two chosen frequencies ω_1 and ω_2 (and therefore also flat between $-\omega_1$ and $-\omega_2$).

To begin, let us define a new complex variable $z = x + jy$, related to $s = \sigma + j\omega$ through the transformation

$$z = \frac{1}{2}\left(s + \frac{1}{s}\right) \tag{7.417}$$

Any specified point in the s-plane maps into a unique point of the z-plane, according to (7.417). In the reverse direction, the mapping is double-valued,

$$s = z \pm \sqrt{z^2 - 1} \tag{7.418}$$

An arbitrary point z maps into two different points in the s-plane. It is apparent from (7.417) or (7.418) that the imaginary axes in the z- and s-planes map onto each other. Along the imaginary axes, the transformation takes the form

$$\left.\begin{aligned} y &= \frac{1}{2}\left(\omega - \frac{1}{\omega}\right) \\[6pt] \omega &= y \pm \sqrt{1 + y^2} \end{aligned}\right\}, \quad \text{for } z = jy, \quad s = j\omega \tag{7.419}$$

The character of the z-to-s transformation can be visualized with the aid of Fig. 7-78. As a point traces the path $ADEC$ in the z-plane, corresponding points move along the correspondingly designated path segments in the s-plane. Similarly, the semicircular path B in Fig. 7-78(a) maps into the two distorted semicircles B in the s-plane (b).

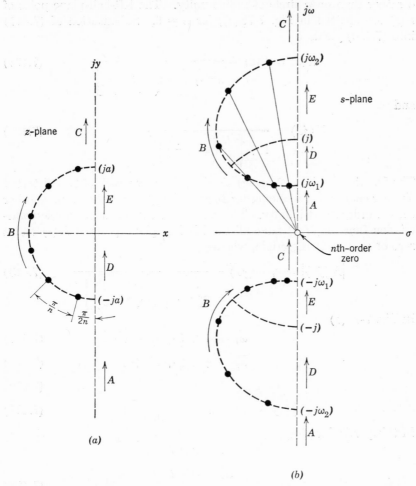

Fig. 7-78. Transformation from z to $s = z \pm \sqrt{z^2 - 1}$, showing the pole-zero patterns of (a) a flat low-pass function, and (b) the corresponding flat band-pass function $(a = 1/\sqrt{2}$ for this plot).

Incidentally, the real axis in the z-plane maps into a unit-radius circle in the s-plane, two small segments of which are indicated in Fig. 7-78(b).

Now, to generate the desired band-pass transmission function, take the auxiliary function

$$F(z) = \frac{1}{1 + [-(z/a)^2]^n} \qquad (7.420)$$

This is the same as (7.407), except that the poles lie on a circle of radius

a rather than on a circle of radius unity. The left-half-plane poles of $F(z)$ are spotted in Fig. 7-78(a), for $n = 6$. Substitution of (7.417) into (7.420) yields

$$K(s) \equiv F(z) = \frac{s^{2n}}{s^{2n} + \left[-\left(\dfrac{s^2 + 1}{2a}\right)^2\right]^n} \qquad (7.421)$$

and

$$K(j\omega) = \frac{1}{1 + \left[\dfrac{1}{2a}\left(\omega - \dfrac{1}{\omega}\right)\right]^{2n}} \qquad (7.422)$$

The function $K(s)$ has $2n$ poles distributed around each of two distorted circular contours, a zero of order $2n$ at the origin, and, therefore, another zero of order $2n$ at infinity. To proceed, let the realizable stable transmission function $H(s)$ have all the left-half-plane poles of $K(s)$ and a zero of order n at the origin, whence

$$|H(j\omega)| = \sqrt{K(j\omega)} = \frac{1}{\sqrt{1 + \left[\dfrac{1}{2a}\left(\omega - \dfrac{1}{\omega}\right)\right]^{2n}}} \qquad (7.423)$$

In Fig. 7-78(b)

$$\omega_1 = +\sqrt{1 + a^2} - a \qquad (7.424)$$

$$\omega_2 = +\sqrt{1 + a^2} + a \qquad (7.425)$$

$$\omega_1 \omega_2 = 1 \qquad (7.426)$$

$$\tfrac{1}{2}(\omega_2 - \omega_1) = a \qquad (7.427)$$

In this particular plot,

$$a = 0.707$$

$$\omega_1 = 0.517$$
$$\qquad\qquad\qquad\qquad\qquad (7.428)$$
$$\omega_2 = 1.93$$

$$\omega_2/\omega_1 = 3.73$$

The value of parameter a determines the locations of the left-half-plane poles of $F(z)$, as indicated in Fig. 7-78(a). These pole locations can then be mapped into the s-plane according to (7.418). Incidentally, radial lines from the origin can be drawn through pairs of s-plane poles, as shown in Fig. 7-78(b), and for each such pair the product of their distances from the origin is unity.

The band-pass response curve given by (7.423) is relatively flat in the frequency band lying between ω_1 and ω_2 in the same sense that the low-pass function in Fig. 7-77 is flat for values of ω between -1 and $+1$. For larger or smaller values of the parameter a, the bandwidth increases or decreases, but the general character of the response curve remains the same. However, as illustrated in Fig. 7-79, the character of the pole pattern may change completely. As a consequence of (7.417) or (7.418), we have the approximations

$$s \approx z \pm j, \qquad \text{for } |z| \ll 1 \qquad (7.429)$$

and

$$s \approx (2z)^{\pm 1}, \qquad \text{for } |z| \gg 1 \qquad (7.430)$$

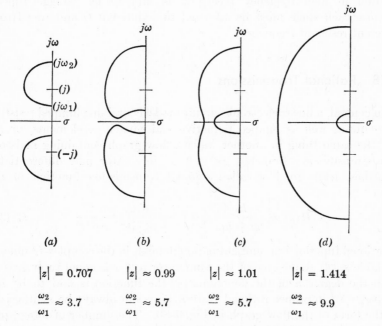

(a)	(b)	(c)	(d)
$\|z\| = 0.707$	$\|z\| \approx 0.99$	$\|z\| \approx 1.01$	$\|z\| = 1.414$
$\dfrac{\omega_2}{\omega_1} \approx 3.7$	$\dfrac{\omega_2}{\omega_1} \approx 5.7$	$\dfrac{\omega_2}{\omega_1} \approx 5.7$	$\dfrac{\omega_2}{\omega_1} \approx 9.9$

Fig. 7-79. Pole contours for various bandwidths.

For very small bandwidths (ω_2/ω_1 close to unity) the poles lie on two small semicircles spanning the positive-frequency and negative-frequency pass bands. For a large bandwidth (ω_2/ω_1 at least several times larger than a critical value, which is approximately 5.7) the poles lie on one small and one large semicircle, as suggested in Fig. 7-79(d).

The flat band-pass transmission function can be factored to obtain the form

$$H(s) = \left[\frac{s}{(s - s_1)(s - s_1{}^*)} \right] \left[\frac{s}{(s - s_2)(s - s_2{}^*)} \right] \cdots \left[\frac{s}{(s - s_n)(s - s_n{}^*)} \right]$$

$$(7.431)$$

where the s_k are the upper-left-quarter-plane poles shown in Fig. 7-78(b). Each of the bracketed factors has the same functional form as the voltage-transfer function of an ideal transconductance driving a parallel resonant circuit. Thus one way to synthesize a flat band-pass transmission is to construct a chain or cascade of such tuned stages. The resulting amplifier, a type often used for intermediate-frequency amplification in high-frequency receivers, is said to be "stagger-tuned" because each stage must be adjusted to a different Q and tuned to a different resonant frequency.

7.28 Rational Transmissions

In general, a linear electronic circuit model containing lumped resistive elements as well as lumped inductive and capacitive elements, or (to say the same thing in another way) a flow graph containing real-constant-transmission branches as well as integrator and differentiator branches, leads to a so-called *rational* transmission function of the form

$$H(s) = \frac{k_0 + k_1 s + \cdots + k_{n+r} s^{n+r}}{b_0 + b_1 s + \cdots + b_{n-1} s^{n-1} + s^n} \qquad (7.432)$$

A rational function is a quotient of polynomials in the complex-frequency variable s. If the degree of the numerator $n + r$ is equal to or greater than the degree n of the denominator, the function is said to be *improper*. An improper rational transmission can always be synthesized in the form of the flow graph in Fig. 7-80. The number of integrators (s^{-1}) in the flow graph is equal to the degree of the numerator polynomial and the number of differentiators (s) in cascade at the output is equal to r. The transmission function shown in Fig. 7-80 can be put in the form (7.432) by multiplying both the numerator and the denominator by s^n.

Long division of the denominator of (7.432) into the numerator gives a simple improper function (a polynomial of degree r) plus a proper remainder

$$H(s) = c_0 + c_1 s + \cdots + c_r s^r + \frac{a_0 + a_1 s + \cdots + a_{n-1} s^{n-1}}{b_0 + b_1 s + \cdots + b_{n-1} s^{n-1} + s^n} \qquad (7.433)$$

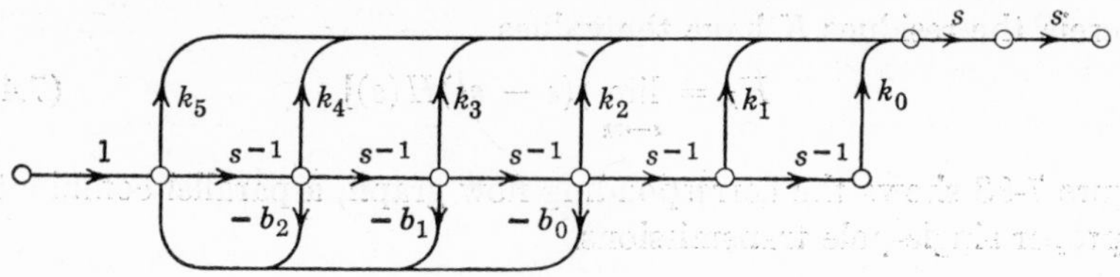

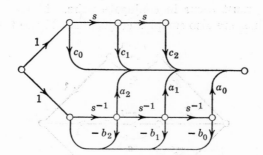

$$H(s) = \frac{k_0 s^{-3} + k_1 s^{-2} + k_2 s^{-1} + k_3 + k_4 s + k_5 s^2}{b_0 s^{-3} + b_1 s^{-2} + b_2 s^{-1} + 1}$$

Fig. 7-80. An improper rational transmission.

The corresponding flow graph is indicated in Fig. 7-81. Here the required number of differentiators is the same, but the number of integrators is now n rather than $n + r$. For a proper transmission function

$$H(s) = \frac{a_0 + a_1 s + \cdots + a_{n-1} s^{n-1}}{b_0 + b_1 s + \cdots + b_{n-1} s^{n-1} + s^n} \tag{7.434}$$

$$H(s) = c_0 + c_1 s + c_2 s^2 + \frac{a_0 s^{-3} + a_1 s^{-2} + a_2 s^{-1}}{b_0 s^{-3} + b_1 s^{-2} + b_2 s^{-1} + 1}$$

Fig. 7-81. An improper rational transmission expressed as the sum of a simple improper function and a proper function.

the flow graph is as shown in Fig. 7-82, a form to which the previous flow graph reduces when the coefficients c_k vanish.

The denominator polynomial can be factored to place the poles in evidence:

$$H(s) = \frac{a_0 + a_1 s + \cdots + a_{n-1} s^{n-1}}{(s - s_1)(s - s_2) \cdots (s - s_n)} \tag{7.435}$$

whereupon partial-fraction expansion gives the form

$$H(s) = \frac{K_1}{s - s_1} + \frac{K_2}{s - s_2} + \cdots + \frac{K_n}{s - s_n} \tag{7.436}$$

wherein the residues K have the values

$$K_k = \lim_{s \to s_k} [(s - s_k)H(s)] \tag{7.437}$$

Figure 7-83 shows the corresponding flow graph, a parallel combination of proper single-pole transmissions.

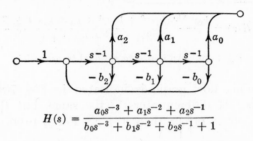

$$H(s) = \frac{a_0 s^{-3} + a_1 s^{-2} + a_2 s^{-1}}{b_0 s^{-3} + b_1 s^{-2} + b_2 s^{-1} + 1}$$

Fig. 7-82. A proper rational transmission.

The coefficients a_k and b_k and (7.434) are presumably real so that complex poles must occur in conjugate pairs. Moreover, the corresponding residues are also complex conjugates. Hence the pole pair in

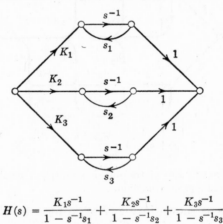

$$H(s) = \frac{K_1 s^{-1}}{1 - s^{-1} s_1} + \frac{K_2 s^{-1}}{1 - s^{-1} s_2} + \frac{K_3 s^{-1}}{1 - s^{-1} s_3}$$

Fig. 7-83. Partial-fraction expansion of a proper rational transmission.

Fig. 7-84(a) can be combined to obtain the equivalent form shown in Fig. 7-84(b).

Alternatively, the numerator of (7.435) can be factored to place the transmission function in the form

$$H(s) = A \left[\frac{s - s_1'}{s - s_1} \right] \left[\frac{s - s_2'}{s - s_2} \right] \cdots \left[\frac{s - s_{n-1}'}{s - s_{n-1}} \right] \left[\frac{1}{s - s_n} \right] \tag{7.438}$$

The individual bracketed factors, or combinations of two or more bracketed factors, may be synthesized as stages of amplification and the entire function is then recognizable as a cascaded chain of amplifier stages, provided the interconnection of stages does not alter the trans-

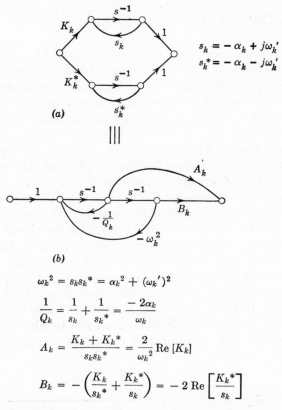

$$s_k = -\alpha_k + j\omega_k'$$
$$s_k^* = -\alpha_k - j\omega_k'$$

(a)

(b)

$$\omega_k^2 = s_k s_k^* = \alpha_k^2 + (\omega_k')^2$$

$$\frac{1}{Q_k} = \frac{1}{s_k} + \frac{1}{s_k^*} = \frac{-2\alpha_k}{\omega_k}$$

$$A_k = \frac{K_k + K_k^*}{s_k s_k^*} = \frac{2}{\omega_k^2}\operatorname{Re}[K_k]$$

$$B_k = -\left(\frac{K_k}{s_k^*} + \frac{K_k^*}{s_k}\right) = -2\operatorname{Re}\left[\frac{K_k^*}{s_k}\right]$$

Fig. 7-84.   Equivalent forms for a two-pole proper transmission function.

mission functions of the individual stages.   There are many other ways in which a system function can be broken into simple parts for convenient representation as a block diagram or flow graph.   Partial-fraction expansion (7.436), factoring (7.438), and continued-fraction expansion are examples.   The point is that the representation of a transmission function as a flow graph provides a convenient picture that often facilitates visualization and discussion of the system characteristics.   The construction of a suitable flow graph from the system function may also be thought of as the first step in the synthesis of an electronic system intended to realize a given function. Different equivalent forms of the flow graph suggest different system configurations. From the viewpoint of analysis, the flow graph represents an "analog-computer program" or "model" of the actual physical system.

7.29   The One-Pole All-Pass Transmission

We have already seen that the time function $f(t - T)$, a delayed replica of the function $f(t)$, has the exponential transform $\exp(-sT)$, the so-called ideal-delay transmission function. The ideal-delay function is a suitable model for many physical processes, for example, the transmission of a sound wave (of sufficiently small amplitude and frequency) through air or the transmission of electromagnetic radiation through space from one point to another. The transmission of electric waves through space or along guiding conductors is a subject more properly approached through the medium of field theory. However, in order to provide some basis for the concept of ideal delay in electric or electronic system models, this article and the following article will be devoted to the development of ideal delay from the circuit standpoint.

The ideal-delay frequency-response function $\exp(-j\omega T)$ has the same magnitude at all frequencies. In other words, ideal delay is one special type of all-pass function. In preparation for the synthesis of an ideal-delay system, let us first consider the all-pass lattice shown in Fig. 7-85(a). The lattice is recognizable as a bridge circuit that has been redrawn to place the input and output terminal pairs in convenient locations. By inspection of the circuit configuration, we can write

$$H(s) = \frac{V_2}{V_1} = \frac{\dfrac{1}{(Ls)^2} - (Cs)^2}{\left(\dfrac{1}{Ls} + Cs\right)^2 + G\left(\dfrac{2}{Ls} + 2Cs\right)} \qquad (7.439)$$

The numerator and denominator have common factors so that the system function reduces to

$$H(s) = \frac{\dfrac{1}{Ls} - Cs}{\dfrac{1}{Ls} + Cs + 2G} \qquad (7.440)$$

Now let

$$\alpha = 1/\sqrt{LC}, \qquad G_0 = \sqrt{C/L} \qquad (7.441)$$

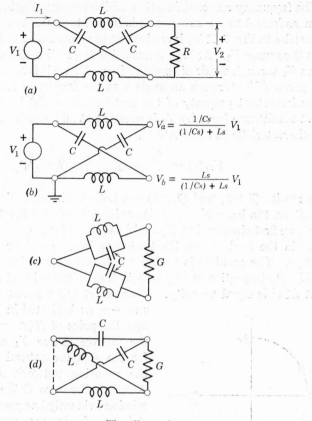

Fig. 7-85.   The all-pass lattice.

In terms of these parameters, the system function becomes

$$H(s) = \frac{\alpha^2 - s^2}{\alpha^2 + \left(\dfrac{2\alpha G}{G_0}\right)s + s^2} = \frac{(\alpha - s)(\alpha + s)}{\alpha^2 + \left(\dfrac{2\alpha G}{G_0}\right)s + s^2} \qquad (7.442)$$

Now set the load conductance G equal to the characteristic conductance G_0 of the lattice, and cancel another common factor to obtain the simple form

$$H(s) = \left(\frac{\alpha - s}{\alpha + s}\right), \qquad \text{for } G = G_0 \qquad (7.443)$$

$$H(j\omega) = \frac{1 - j(\omega/\alpha)}{1 + j(\omega/\alpha)} = e^{-j2\tan^{-1}(\omega/\alpha)} \qquad (7.444)$$

The frequency-response function exhibits constant gain and the phase changes from 0 to $-\pi$ as ω proceeds from 0 to $+\infty$. At low frequencies the lattice in Fig. 7-85(a) is equivalent to a direct connection of the load R to the source V_1. At high frequencies, the lattice effectively connects V_1 to V_2 through a pair of crossed wires. Hence it is not surprising that the phase shifts through an angle π as the frequency increases from 0.

An important property of the matched $(G = G_0)$ lattice is that the input admittance faced by V_1 is constant at all frequencies and equal to the characteristic conductance G_0

$$Y_{11}(s) = \frac{I_1}{V_1} \equiv G_0, \qquad \text{for } G = G_0 \qquad (7.445)$$

The results (7.443) and (7.445) can both be deduced directly from the circuit on the basis of physical considerations. To locate the zeros of $H(s)$, we first observe that V_2 vanishes if $H(s)$ is zero. Hence no current flows in the load R and the load may be removed as shown in Fig. 7-85(b). The problem is to find a value of s for which V_a and V_b are equal. By inspection of Fig. 7-85(b) the desired value of s must be such that LCs^2 is equal to unity. Hence $H(s)$ has zeros at the points $+\alpha$ and $-\alpha$, as indicated in Fig. 7-86. To find the poles of $H(s)$ we short-circuit the voltage source V_1 and then look for the complex natural frequencies of the resulting network shown in Fig. 7-85(c). For zero G the lattice transmission evidently has poles at the points $+j\alpha$ or $-j\alpha$ in the complex s-plane, and as G is increased from zero the two poles move together along a circle of radius α as indicated in Fig. 7-86. When G reaches the value G_0 the two poles and the zero coalesce at the point $-\alpha$, leaving a single pole as in (7.443). Now, to identify the input admittance, we can exploit the fact that the zeros of the input admittance are the natural complex frequencies of the network with V_1 open-circuited, for at these frequencies I_1 must vanish. The poles of the input admittance are the natural frequencies of the network when V_1 is short-circuited, for at these frequencies I_1 may exist even when V_1 vanishes. With V_1 open-circuited, the upper-left L and C may be interchanged, as in Fig. 7-85(b), without altering the natural behavior of the network. After this interchange the potentials at the two left-hand nodes will be the same and these two nodes may be short-circuited

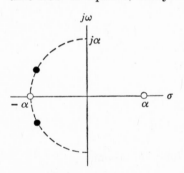

Fig. 7-86. The pole-zero pattern of the unmatched lattice.

together, as indicated by the dashed line in Fig. 7-85(d). Thus G is in series with $2C$ and $L/2$. In Fig. 7-85(c), conductance G is effectively in parallel with $2L$ and $C/2$. With G equal to G_0, the networks (c) and (d) are duals having exactly the same natural complex frequencies.

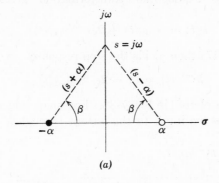

(a)

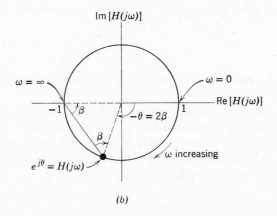

(b)

Fig. 7-87. The pole-zero pattern (a) and the circle diagram (b) of the all-pass lattice.

Hence the zeros of the input admittance coincide with the poles, which is just another way of saying that the input admittance is a constant. This constant must be G_0, as can be seen by evaluating the input admittance at zero frequency.

The pole-zero pattern and circle diagram of the matched lattice are shown in Fig. 7-87. As indicated in (b), the phase θ is very simply related to the angle of the line between the pole and the point of observation $s = j\omega$ in the s-plane. The lattice transmission (7.443) can be rewritten as

$$H(s) = -1 + \frac{2\alpha}{s + \alpha} \tag{7.446}$$

whereupon inverse exponential transformation gives the impulse response

$$h(t) = -u_0(t) + 2\alpha e^{-\alpha t} u_{-1}(t) \tag{7.447}$$

Integration of (7.447) then yields the step response

$$h^{(-1)}(t) = (1 - 2e^{-\alpha t})u_{-1}(t) \tag{7.448}$$

And this function is plotted in Fig. 7-88. For small values of t the lattice effectively connects the input to the output through a pair of crossed

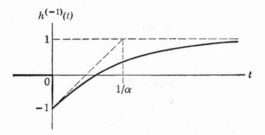

Fig. 7-88. Step response of the all-pass lattice.

wires, since the capacitor voltages cannot change instantaneously. Accordingly, the step response has an initial value of -1. For large values of t the inductances provide a direct connection between input and output and this is reflected in the fact that the step response approaches a final value of $+1$.

7.30 The Exponential Transmission—Ideal Delay

Using the all-pass lattice as a building block, we can now approach the ideal-delay transmission. For convenience let the element values of the lattice be normalized as shown in Fig. 7-89(a). Since the input admittance of the matched lattice is unity, we can cascade a number of lattice sections, as indicated in Fig. 7-89(b), without changing the voltage transmission function of each section. Hence the transmission from V_0 to V_n is just the product of the transmissions of the n individual sections

$$\frac{V_n}{V_0} = H_n(s) = \left[\frac{1 - (s/2n)}{1 + (s/2n)}\right]^n \tag{7.449}$$

As n becomes arbitrarily large, several things happen. First, the transmission function $H_n(s)$ approaches an exponential

$$H_n(s) \to e^{-s}, \qquad \text{as } n \to \infty \qquad (7.450)$$

This follows from the mathematical *definition* of exp (x) as the limit approached by the nth power of $1 + (x/n)$ as n becomes large. Second,

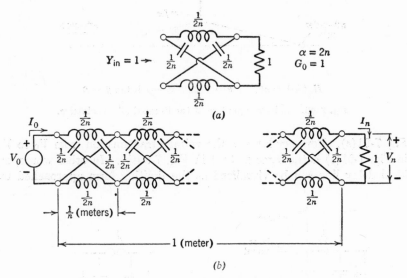

Fig. 7-89. The iterated all-pass lattice.

the pole and zero of $H_n(s)$ increase in order and move farther apart in the s-plane, as shown in Fig. 7-90. For any chosen finite frequency $j\omega$, the angle β becomes arbitrarily small for sufficiently large n, so that $\tan \beta$ may be replaced by β and the phase function $\theta(j\omega)$ approaches linearity. The larger we make n, the larger is the frequency region over which θ remains very nearly proportional to ω. Third, the individual lattice sections become arbitrarily narrow, as indicated in Fig. 7-91 (a). In the limit of large n, the cascade of lattices may be visualized as a continuous structure characterized by a certain amount of continuous distributed series inductance and shunt capacitance per unit of length. Such a structure is called a uniform lossless *transmission line* or *delay line*.

For large n, the current and voltage relationships in the network are not altered appreciably if the two connecting wires in Fig. 7-91 (a) are uncrossed, as shown in (b). After this modification, symmetry tells us that the electric potential is constant along the horizontal axis of symmetry, and the mid-points of the vertical capacitor wires therefore may be short-circuited together without disturbing the operation of the circuit. With a central "ground line" or "short-circuiting bar" in place, the upper half of the network takes the form of a ladder, as shown in

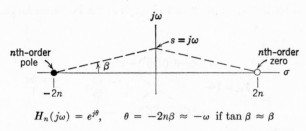

$$H_n(j\omega) = e^{j\theta}, \qquad \theta = -2n\beta \approx -\omega \text{ if } \tan \beta \approx \beta$$

Fig. 7-90. Pole-zero pattern of the iterated all-pass lattice.

Fig. 7-91(c). For very large n, the voltage transmission from V_0 to V_n in Fig. 7-91(c) is the same as that in Fig. 7-89(b). In other words, an ideal delay line can be visualized as the limiting form approached by

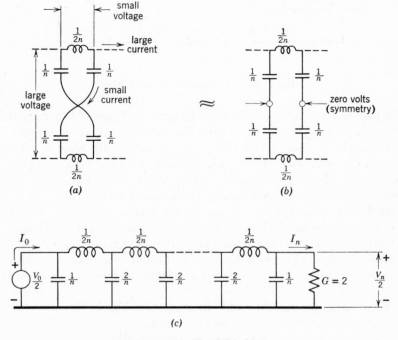

Fig. 7-91. The LC ladder.

either a cascade of lattices or a cascade of ladder sections. The ladder-network representation is said to be "unbalanced" or "common grounded," because the input and output have a common ground-reference terminal. Conversely, the lattice representation is said to be "balanced."

In Fig. 7-89(b) the network has total series inductance and total shunt capacitance both equal to unity, and the time delay through the network is 1 second. By cascading two such networks, we would have twice as much series inductance, twice as much shunt capacitance, and also twice as much time delay. Hence, for an ideal delay line of arbitrary length

$$H(s) = e^{-sT} \tag{7.451}$$

$$R_0 = 1/G_0 = \sqrt{L/C} \tag{7.452}$$

and the total time delay T is given by

$$T = \sqrt{LC}$$

$$L = \text{total series inductance} \tag{7.453}$$

$$C = \text{total shunt capacitance}$$

When an ideal delay line (R_0, T) is driven from the left, as shown in Fig. 7-92(a), and matched at the right end with a load resistance equal to the characteristic resistance R_0, the output voltage $v_2(t)$ is a delayed replica of the input voltage $v_1(t)$. In this case it is convenient to think of a "wave" traveling along the line from left to right. We shall call this the "plus" wave and designate the associated currents and voltages by the superscript indicated in Fig. 7-92(a). When the primary generator E_2 is located at the right and the matched load R_0 at the left, as in Fig. 7-92(b), we have a "minus" wave. Here the opposite reference polarity is convenient for the currents. By superposition of the sources E_1 and E_2 in (a) and (b), we have the system shown in Fig. 7-92(c). With drives applied at both ends, both plus and minus waves exist on the line, as indicated by the flow graph (d) of the relationships among the system variables. Since total voltage is the sum of the plus and minus voltages, we can write

$$V_1 = V_1{}^+ + V_1{}^- = \tfrac{1}{2}E_1 + \tfrac{1}{2}e^{-sT}E_2 \tag{7.454}$$

and the associated time signal (the inverse exponential transform) is

$$v_1(t) = \tfrac{1}{2}e_1(t) + \tfrac{1}{2}e_2(t - T) \tag{7.455}$$

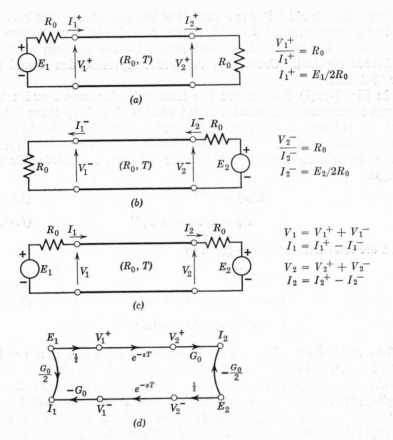

Fig. 7-92. Superposition of "plus" and "minus" waves on a delay line.

7.31   Reflection of Waves

When a transmission line terminates in some impedance Z different from the characteristic resistance R_0, as shown in Fig. 7-93(a), both plus and minus waves are necessary in order to satisfy conditions at the termination. With reference to Fig. 7-93(a), we can write

$$V = V^+ + V^- \qquad (7.456)$$

$$I = I^+ - I^- \qquad (7.457)$$

$$\frac{V^+}{I^+} = \frac{V^-}{I^-} = R_0 \qquad (7.458)$$

$$\frac{V}{I} = Z \qquad (7.459)$$

The above equations can be solved to find the reflection coefficient Γ

$$\Gamma = \frac{V^-}{V^+} = -\frac{I^-}{I^+} \tag{7.460}$$

The reflection coefficient is defined as the quotient of the complex amplitudes of the *reflected* and *incident* waves. In this particular example, the wave incident upon the load Z is a plus wave arriving from

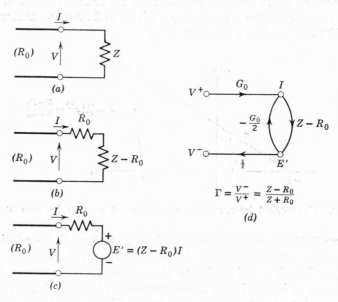

Fig. 7-93. Reflection at an unmatched termination.

the left along the transmission line. Unless the load Z is matched to R_0, a certain portion of the incident signal will be reflected as a minus wave traveling to the left away from the load.

From (7.456) through (7.459) we have

$$Z = \frac{V^+ + V^-}{I^+ - I^-} = R_0 \frac{1 + (V^-/V^+)}{1 - (V^-/V^+)} \tag{7.461}$$

so that

$$\frac{Z}{R_0} = \frac{1 + \Gamma}{1 - \Gamma} \tag{7.462}$$

Solution of (7.462) for the value of the reflection coefficient gives

$$\Gamma = \frac{(Z/R_0) - 1}{(Z/R_0) + 1} = \frac{Z - R_0}{Z + R_0} \tag{7.463}$$

It is apparent from (7.463) that the reflection coefficient vanishes when the load Z is matched. Also observe that Γ takes the value unity for infinite Z (an open circuit) and minus unity for zero Z (a short circuit).

For an explanation of the wave-reflection process, first replace Z by the equivalent series combination shown in Fig. 7-93(b), which can be interpreted as indicated in (c). We now have a circuit resembling the right-hand end of that in Fig. 7-92(c). The flow graph in Fig. 7-93(d) is the same as before, except for addition of the branch $Z - R_0$ to insure the proper value of the voltage source E'. The flow-graph transmission from V^+ to V^- verifies relation (7.463).

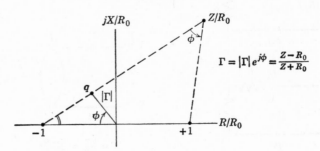

Fig. 7-94. Geometrical interpretation of the transformation between Γ and Z.

Figure 7-94 shows a geometrical interpretation of the relationship between Γ and Z. Given any point Z/R_0 in the complex Z-plane, we can draw two lines from this point to the points $+1$ and -1, and the included angle ϕ is identifiable as the complex angle of Γ. A line from the origin to point q in Fig. 7-94, making the angle ϕ with the negative real axis, has a length equal to the magnitude of Γ. Since (7.463) is a linear rational transformation from Z to Γ, it follows that circles (or straight lines) in the Z-plane must map into circles or straight lines in the Γ-plane, and vice versa. For example, if Z is purely imaginary in Fig. 7-94, then point q must lie on a circle of unit radius centered at the origin. For a purely lossless load impedance Z we should expect the amplitude of the reflected wave to equal that of the incident wave, for none of the incident power carried by the plus wave can be dissipated by the load. Similarly, the right half of the Z-plane transforms into the interior of the unit circle in the Γ-plane, in accordance with the physical reasoning that the wave amplitude (and therefore the power) reflected from a passive load termination cannot exceed the amplitude of the incident wave.

Thus far we have spoken about the reflection coefficient at the load terminals. The reflection-coefficient definition also applies to the opposite end of the transmission line, as indicated in Fig. 7-95. The relationship between Γ_1 (at the left end) and Γ_2 (at the right end) is very simple. By inspection of the flow graph in Fig. 7-95(b), we find

$$\Gamma_1 = \Gamma_2 e^{-2sT} \tag{7.464}$$

From this we can compute the input impedance Z_1 presented at the left end of the line. First let

$$Z_1 = \frac{V_1}{I_1}, \qquad Z_2 = \frac{V_2}{I_2} \tag{7.465}$$

whence

$$\frac{Z_1}{R_0} = \frac{1 + \Gamma_1}{1 - \Gamma_1} = \frac{1 + \Gamma_2 e^{-2sT}}{1 - \Gamma_2 e^{-2sT}} \tag{7.466}$$

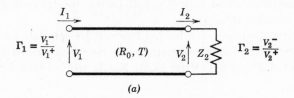

(a)

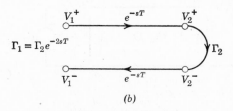

(b)

Fig. 7-95. The reflection coefficient at the input of a terminated line.

and substitution for Γ_2 in terms of Z_2 then gives

$$\frac{Z_1(s)}{R_0} = \frac{Z_2 \cosh{(sT)} + R_0 \sinh{(sT)}}{Z_2 \sinh{(sT)} + R_0 \cosh{(sT)}} \tag{7.467}$$

For steady-state sinusoidal operation, this reduces to

$$\frac{Z_1(j\omega)}{R_0} = \frac{Z_2 + jR_0 \tan{(\omega T)}}{jZ_2 \tan{(\omega T)} + R_0} \tag{7.468}$$

The impedance of a length of line short-circuited at the far end is, therefore,

$$Z_1(j\omega) = jR_0 \tan{(\omega T)}, \qquad \text{for } Z_2 = 0 \tag{7.469}$$

At low frequency, $\tan{(\omega T)}$ may be replaced by ωT so that

$$Z_1(j\omega) \approx jR_0\omega T = j\omega L \tag{7.470}$$

The result (7.470) is to be expected since at low frequencies the shunt capacitance of the short-circuited transmission line is negligible and the line behaves like a simple loop having a total series inductance L. Similarly, for a length of line open-circuited at the far end,

$$Z_1(j\omega) = \frac{R_0}{j \tan (\omega T)}, \quad \text{for } Z_2 = \infty \quad (7.471)$$

Again at low frequency,

$$Z_1(j\omega) \approx \frac{R_0}{j\omega T} = \frac{\sqrt{L/C}}{j\omega\sqrt{LC}} = \frac{1}{j\omega C} \quad (7.472)$$

At low frequency the open-circuited line is effectively a simple capacitor whose capacitance is, of course, equal to the total shunt capacitance of the transmission line.

The input impedance of a loaded line can be computed analytically from (7.468). The same calculation can be accomplished graphically with the aid of Fig. 7-94. First locate Z_2/R_0 and construct the point q

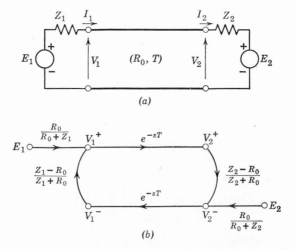

(a)

(b)

Fig. 7-96. A line mismatched at both ends.

corresponding to Γ_2. For s equal to $j\omega$, the transformation from Γ_2 to Γ_1 involves only rotation of the point q about the origin through an angle $2\omega T$, after which Z_1/R_0 can be reconstructed from Γ_1, again by the similar-triangle relationship indicated in Fig. 7-94. Special charts are available for such calculations, showing either circles of constant Γ-magnitude and Γ-phase in the Z-plane or circles of constant R and X in the Γ-plane. The former are usually called impedance charts and the latter are referred to as Smith charts.

To summarize the preceding discussion, Fig. 7-96(a) shows a transmission line driven at each end by a source whose associated impedance is not necessarily equal to the characteristic resistance of the line. The accompanying flow graph (b) specifies the relationships between the plus and minus wave amplitudes and the source voltages. The voltages and currents in the circuit are, of course, simple sums and differences of the corresponding plus and minus voltages or currents.

7.32 Wave Launching

In many communications problems the ideal transmission line is often a suitable model for certain portions of the signal transmission path. The signal arriving at a receiving point via such a path may contain noise or other contaminating signals not present in the original trans-

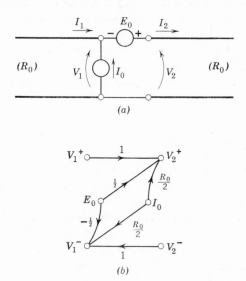

(a)

(b)

Fig. 7-97. A "wave launcher."

mitted signal. In the model, we may wish to insert auxiliary sources to account for such effects. Figure 7-97(a) shows a transmission line of indefinite length into which a voltage source E_0 has been *inserted* and across which a current source I_0 has been *attached*. This pair of sources can be adjusted to launch outgoing waves in either or both directions along the line. Alternatively, the pair of sources can be adjusted to absorb or "capture" any specified pair of incident waves approaching from the left and from the right. In this problem the independent quantities are $V_1{}^+$, $V_2{}^-$, E_0, and I_0, and the dependent quantities or "effects" are $V_1{}^-$ and $V_2{}^+$. The flow graph in Fig. 7-97(b) can be constructed by superposition of the component effects due to each of the independent quantities acting alone. For example, if E_0 and I_0 both vanish, then the voltage source is a short circuit, the current is an open circuit, and incident waves are not disturbed in passing through the neighborhood. In short, a series voltage source or a shunt current source is "transparent" to the incident waves. This accounts for the uppermost and lowermost branches in the flow graph. Now suppose that $V_1{}^+$, $V_2{}^-$, and I_0 are all zero, but E_0 is not. In this case, the source E_0 is effectively connected in series with two resistances R_0, one on the left and one on the right; and it follows that $V_2{}^+ = E_b/2$ and $V_1{}^- = -E_0/2$. Hence, the voltage source E_0, acting alone, launches waves to the right and to the left of opposite polarity. On the other hand, the current source I_0, acting alone, launches waves in opposite directions of equal amplitudes and polarities. By inspection of the flow graph, we can see that making $E_0/I_0 = R_0$ insures that a wave will be launched only to the right. Changing the sign of either E_0 or I_0 reverses the picture and results in a wave transmitted only toward the left. So much for the launching of outgoing waves. To absorb incoming waves we need only adjust E_0 and I_0 to give zero values for $V_2{}^+$ and $V_1{}^-$ in the flow graph.

7.33   A Lumped Attenuator

Another problem of interest is the design of a "pad" or "attenuator." An ideal attenuator is a resistive network inserted into the transmission line and so designed as to produce no reflection of an incident wave. One purpose of an attenuator is to reduce the severity of multiple reflections between the ends of the transmission system, thereby effectively isolating one end from the other and avoiding instability or some other undesirable effect of interaction or coupling. The attenuator shown in Fig. 7-98(a) is laterally symmetric. The characteristic resistance R_0 is here taken as unity for simplicity. As viewed from the left, the attenuator is a resistance R_a in series with the parallel combination of R_b and $R_a + 1$. For no reflection, therefore, we must set

$$\frac{V_1}{I_1} = 1 = R_a + \frac{(1 + R_a)R_b}{1 + R_a + R_b} \tag{7.473}$$

which can be solved to obtain

$$R_b = \frac{1}{2}\left(\frac{1}{R_a} - R_a\right) \tag{7.474}$$

The transmission A of the attenuator can be found by allowing a plus wave to approach from the left. Since the attenuator "matches" the line, we have $I_1 = I_1^+$, $V_1 = V_1^+$, and the same for I_2 and V_2. The current transmission I_2^+/I_1^+ is equal to the voltage transmission

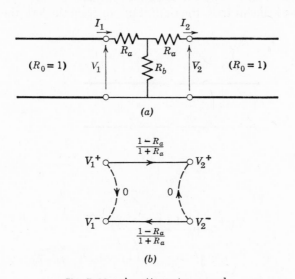

(a)

(b)

Fig. 7-98.   An attenuator or pad.

V_2^+/V_1^+ and is somewhat easier to evaluate in this particular problem. The current I_1 divides between R_b and $R_a + 1$ in inverse proportion to the resistance. Hence

$$A = \frac{V_2^+}{V_1^+} = \frac{I_2^+}{I_1^+} = \frac{R_b}{1 + R_a + R_b} = \frac{1 - R_a}{1 + R_a} \qquad (7.475)$$

and this yields the flow graph in Fig. 7-98(b).

7.34   Discontinuities in Characteristic Resistance

A situation occurring frequently in transmission-line systems is that shown in Fig. 7-99(a). Here the transmission line is continuous, but the characteristic resistance changes suddenly from R_0 in region 1 to the new value R_0' in region 2. With a wave V_1^+ incident from the left, we have the reflection coefficient Γ indicated in Fig. 7-99(b). For the calculation of the reflection coefficient, R_0' acts like a load impedance connected to the left-hand portion of the line. Just to the left of the discontinuity, the total voltage is $V_1^+ + V_1^-$. Just to the right of the discontinuity, the total voltage is $V_2{}^+$ (we are temporarily assuming no $V_2{}^-$). Since the total voltage must be continuous across the boundary between the two regions of different characteristic resistance, it follows that the transmission from $V_1{}^+$ to $V_2{}^+$ must be just equal to unity plus the reflection coefficient, as indicated by the uppermost branch in Fig. 7-99(b). Now, with a wave incident from the right, but not from the left, the quantities

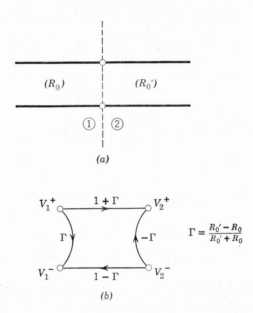

Fig. 7-99. A discontinuity in the characteristic resistance.

R_0 and R_0' interchange their roles, so that the reflection from $V_2{}^-$ to $V_2{}^+$ is just the negative of that relating $V_1{}^+$ and $V_1{}^-$. The point is that the scattering (reflection and transmission) of waves by a discontinuity in characteristic resistance is completely described by a single parameter Γ in the flow graph of Fig. 7-99(b).

Now consider two such discontinuities in characteristic resistance, as indicated in Fig. 7-100(a). The numbers 1 and 2 will be used as subscripts to designate voltages and currents immediately to the left and to the right of the first discontinuity and similarly with subscripts 3 and 4 in the neighborhood of the second discontinuity. The flow graph in Fig. 7-100(b) allows us to evaluate, by inspection, the over-all transmission and reflection of the combination of discontinuities. With a wave incident only from the left ($V_4{}^- = 0$), we find the over-all reflection coefficient

$$\frac{V_1^-}{V_1^+} = \Gamma + \frac{(1 + \Gamma)(1 - \Gamma)\Gamma' e^{-2j\omega T}}{1 + \Gamma\Gamma' e^{-2j\omega T}} \tag{7.476}$$

which simplifies to the form

$$\frac{V_1^-}{V_1^+} = \frac{\Gamma + \Gamma' e^{-2j\omega T}}{1 + \Gamma\Gamma' e^{-2j\omega T}} \tag{7.477}$$

The line section (R_0', T) is usually called a transformer. A transformer can be sandwiched between two line sections of different characteristic

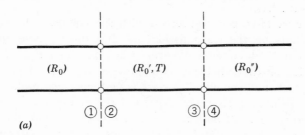

(a)

(b)

$$\Gamma = \frac{R_0' - R_0}{R_0' + R_0}, \qquad \Gamma' = \frac{R_0'' - R_0'}{R_0'' + R_0'}$$

Fig. 7-100. A transformer.

resistance so as to eliminate reflections at certain frequencies. Since the quantities Γ and Γ' in (7.477) are real, the numerator of (7.477) can vanish only if Γ and Γ' are either equal or opposite. Consider

$$\Gamma' = \Gamma \tag{7.478}$$

The numerator of (7.477) then vanishes at frequencies for which

$$e^{-2j\omega T} = -1 \tag{7.479}$$

If Γ and Γ' are equal, then R_0 and R_0' must be in the same ratio as R_0' and R_0''. Hence,

$$R_0' = \sqrt{R_0 R_0''} \tag{7.480}$$

Finally, to satisfy (7.479) we must have

$$\omega = \pm \frac{\pi}{2T}, \qquad \pm \frac{3\pi}{2T}, \qquad \pm \frac{5\pi}{2T}, \qquad \cdots \qquad (7.481)$$

At the specific frequencies given in (7.481), the transformer is said to match the line R_0'' into the line R_0 and a wave incident from either direction passes from one line through the transformer to the other line without any net reflection. There are, of course, multiple reflections within the transformer, but for incident excitation from only one direction, the waves in regions 1 and 4 are traveling either both to the right or both to the left.

Thus far we have been concerned with the voltages and currents at discrete points on the transmission line and the relationships among these currents and voltages have been specified in terms of the time delay or "transit time" between two points on the line. Thus, although the concept of the "traveling" wave has perhaps been implied by some of the discussion, we have not expressed the voltages and currents as continuous functions of both time and distance. For our purpose here, the distance scale is arbitrary and we may assume, without loss of generality, that the velocity of wave propagation is unity. Hence a plus wave $v^+(t, x)$ can be written as $v^+(t - x)$, and a minus wave $v^-(t, x)$ takes the form $v^-(t + x)$, where x is the distance along the line measured positively toward the right from some specified origin. By fixing t we can plot a wave pattern as a function of the distance x, or by fixing x (as we have been doing all along) the voltage wave becomes purely a function of time. For a sinusoidal wave, the *wavelength* is to be interpreted as the period of the sinusoid when that sinusoid is plotted as a function of x for fixed t. As frequency increases, the wavelength decreases in inverse proportion. The reason for this digression is that the concept of wavelength allows us to describe the matching transformer in terms of its length rather than its delay time. At the smallest frequency specified in (7.481), the matching transformer has a length equal to one-quarter of a wavelength. At any given frequency, the transformer "matches" the two lines if its length is any odd multiple of one-quarter wavelength.

For a vanishing numerator in (7.477), the other possibility is

$$\Gamma' = -\Gamma \qquad (7.482)$$

$$e^{-2j\omega T} = 1 \qquad (7.483)$$

To insure (7.482) we must have

$$R_0 = R_0'' \qquad (7.484)$$

and the frequencies satisfying (7.483) are

$$\omega = 0, \qquad \pm \frac{\pi}{T}, \qquad \pm \frac{2\pi}{T}, \qquad \pm \frac{3\pi}{T}, \qquad \cdots \qquad (7.485)$$

In this case the length of the transformer is an integer multiple of one-half wavelength. To see the same result from a slightly different viewpoint, return to Fig. 7-95 and set s equal to $j\omega$. If Γ_1 is equal to Γ_2 in Fig. 7-95, then the line section shown can be inserted into another line without causing over-all reflection. The lowest frequency at which this happens is, of course, zero. At the first nonzero frequency for which Γ_1 and Γ_2 are equal, the delay time T of the line must be just one-half of the time period ($T = \pi/\omega$), so that the round trip along the line section and back again takes exactly one cycle of the periodic wave.

Either of the two types of transformers, (7.478) or (7.482), acts as a selective frequency filter whose Q becomes large as the quotient R_0'/R_0 is made either large or small in comparison to unity. The transformer acts as a rejection filter, one that transmits an incident wave at certain frequencies but reflects waves at all other frequencies.

7.35   Scattering Coefficients

Figure 7-101 (a) shows an arbitrary coupling between two lines. The coupling is completely described by the two reflection coefficients Γ_{11} and Γ_{22} and the two transmission coefficients Γ_{12} and Γ_{21} indicated in (b). The set of parameters Γ_{jk} are called *scattering coefficients*. When n different transmission lines are connected together in some manner in a common junction, the coupling among them is described by a scattering matrix having n rows and n columns. The value of the traveling-wave and scattering-matrix description of a system is that it facilitates visualization of energy flow within the system. For example, the power carried by the traveling wave V_1^+ is just the squared magnitude of V_1^+ multiplied by the characteristic conductance G_0. It is sometimes convenient to normalize the system equations as illustrated in Fig. 7-101 (c), so that the squared magnitudes of the node signals in the flow graph are directly identifiable as the powers carried by waves. Strictly speaking, the scattering coefficients should be thought of as the branch transmissions in a normalized diagram, such as that in Fig. 7-101 (c).

When both a plus wave and a minus wave are present on a transmission line, the concept of "power carried by a traveling wave" is meaningful and convenient only if the amount of power associated with one wave is unaffected by the presence of the other wave. In short, as we shall now show, plus and minus traveling waves are orthogonal. To see this, select any point on a transmission line (perhaps one end of the line) and compute the total complex power

$$VI^* = (V^+ + V^-)(I^+ - I^-)^* \tag{7.486}$$

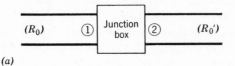

(a)

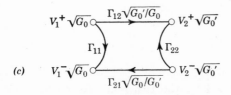

(b)

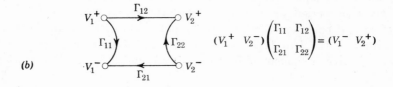

(c)

Fig. 7-101. Scattering coefficients for an arbitrary junction.

where V and I are the rms values of the complex amplitudes of the voltage and the current at a single frequency [or, perhaps, the voltage-density and current-density spectra of pulse-type signals $v(t)$ and $i(t)$; in which case VI^* is an energy-density spectrum, the spectrum of their crosscorrelation function]. In terms of the reflection coefficient Γ and the characteristic conductance G_0, (7.486) becomes

$$VI^* = |V^+|^2 G_0 (1 + \Gamma)(1 - \Gamma^*) \tag{7.487}$$

The real and imaginary components of power are P_r and P_i,

$$VI^* = P_r + jP_i \tag{7.488}$$

The quantity P_r is, of course, the time-average real power crossing the specified point on the transmission line from the left toward the right. Now define the "plus" and "minus" powers,

$$P^+ = V^+(I^+)^* = |V^+|^2 G_0 \tag{7.489}$$

$$P^- = V^-(I^-)^* = |V^-|^2 G_0 = |\Gamma|^2 P^+ \tag{7.490}$$

whence it follows directly that

$$P_r + jP_i = P^+[1 - |\Gamma|^2 + (\Gamma - \Gamma^*)] \qquad (7.491)$$

Hence

$$P_r = P^+(1 - |\Gamma|^2) = P^+ - P^- \qquad (7.492)$$

$$P_i = 2\,\text{Im}\,[\Gamma] = 2|\Gamma|\sin\phi \qquad (7.493)$$

where

$$\Gamma = |\Gamma|e^{j\phi} \qquad (7.494)$$

Relation (7.492) demonstrates the orthogonality of plus and minus waves. The net power flowing to the right is simply the difference of the power carried toward the right by the plus wave and the power carried toward the left by the minus wave.

The convenience of scattering coefficients for power calculations can be illustrated by formulating general criteria for passivity and lossless-ness. A junction box having n different transmission-line entries (all having unity characteristic resistance, for simplicity) is characterized by an n-by-n scattering matrix Γ whose elements are Γ_{jk}. In this general case [in contrast to the notation in Fig. 7-101(b)], it is convenient to let V_j^+ be the wave *incident* upon the junction from the jth transmission line. Similarly, V_j^- is the reflected or scattered wave traveling *away* from the junction along the jth line. Thus the row vectors V^+ and V^- stand for incident and scattered waves, respectively, and the behavior of the multi-entry junction is described by the *matrix* equation $V^+\Gamma = V^-$. The net average power incident upon the junction is the product of V^+ with its conjugate transposition (a column vector). Thus, *incident* average power is $(V^+)(V^+)_t{}^* = |V_1|^2 + |V_2|^2 + \cdots + |V_n|^2$, and the net average power *entering* the junction is $P = (V^+)(V^+)_t{}^* - (V^-)(V^-)_t{}^*$. Substitution of $V^+\Gamma$ for V^- gives the quadratic form

$$P = (V^+)[I - \Gamma\Gamma_t{}^*](V^+)_t{}^* \qquad (7.495)$$

wherein I is the unit matrix. The junction is passive if and only if P is nonnegative for all possible choices of the complex row vector V^+. Hence, as in the analogous discussion of power and passivity in Chapter 2, the *passivity* criterion is that the hermitian matrix $[I - \Gamma\Gamma_t{}^*]$ must be positive definite. If the junction box is to be lossless, then P must vanish for all possible choices of V^+. Hence all elements of the matrix $[I - \Gamma\Gamma_t{}^*]$ must also vanish, and we have the particularly simple condition for losslessness,

$$\Gamma\Gamma_t{}^* = I = \text{unit matrix} \qquad (7.496)$$

If the system obeys reciprocity, then $\Gamma_{jk} = \Gamma_{kj}$ and the transposition subscript t may be omitted in (7.496).

7.36   A System Containing Random-Phase Transmissions

In the previous chapter, we saw that although a stationary random process does not have a meaningful voltage-density spectrum, its power-density spectrum is nevertheless significant and useful. Let us examine an elementary system whose properties are random. As we shall see,

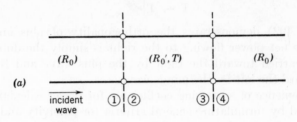

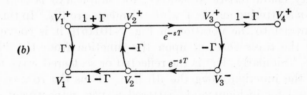

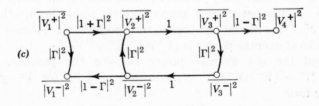

Fig. 7-102. Scattering of power by an inserted section of indefinite length.

the squared magnitudes of the scattering coefficients may be significant even when the scattering coefficients themselves are not. To proceed, suppose that a line section R_0' is inserted between two lines having the same characteristic resistance R_0, different from that of the inserted section, as shown in Fig. 7-102(a). From the associated flow graph (b) we find the transmission to be

$$\frac{V_4^+}{V_1^+} = \frac{(1 - \Gamma^2)e^{-j\omega T}}{1 + (\Gamma^2 e^{-j2\omega T})} \tag{7.497}$$

This assumes the time delay T of the section is known. Suppose, however, that T is not known accurately, so that the phase of the minus wave arriving at V_2^- from V_3^- might be anywhere in the range from 0 to 2π, relative to the incident wave V_1^+. For instance, when a light wave passes through a sheet of glass, the wavelength of the radiation is so short compared with the thickness of the glass that a crude measurement of the thickness of the glass will determine that thickness only within a tolerance of many wavelengths. With respect to the phase of multiple reflections within the glass, we might as well assume the thickness to be completely random. Exactly the same situation arises when the thickness is known accurately but not the frequency of the radiation, or when the radiation is distributed over a frequency spectrum of sufficient width. Let the two signals entering node V_2^+ in Fig. 7-102(b) be called A and $B \exp(j\theta)$, so that their relative phase is just θ. We are really faced with an ensemble of different signals B whose phase angles are uniformly distributed over the complete angle space 2π. The ensemble average of the sum $A + B \exp(j\theta)$ is, of course, just equal to A. However, when the phase is random, power adds. Specifically

$$\overline{|V_2^+|^2} = \overline{|A + Be^{j\theta}|^2} = \frac{1}{2\pi} \int_0^{2\pi} |A + Be^{j\theta}|^2 \, d\theta \tag{7.498}$$

$$= \frac{1}{2\pi} \int_0^{2\pi} [(A + B \cos\theta)^2 + (B \sin\theta)^2] \, d\theta \tag{7.499}$$

$$= A^2 + B^2 \tag{7.500}$$

Hence the equations relating time-average power in the various waves are linear and can be expressed in the form of the flow graph in Fig. 7-102(c). Remember that the bar over a squared magnitude denotes the ensemble average taken over the randomly distributed different possible values of the round-trip transit angle $2\omega T$. By inspection of the "power-scattering" flow graph we find the power-transmission ratio

$$\overline{|V_4^+|^2} / \overline{|V_1^+|^2} = \frac{|1 - \Gamma^2|^2}{1 - |\Gamma|^4} \tag{7.501}$$

This is a true power ratio because regions 1 and 4 in Fig. 7-102(a) have the same characteristic resistance. In this particular example Γ is real and no greater than unity in magnitude, so that the result (7.501) reduces to

$$\overline{|V_4^+|^2} / \overline{|V_1^+|^2} = \frac{1 - \Gamma^2}{1 + \Gamma^2} \tag{7.502}$$

Since the inserted line section is lossless, the power reflection need not be calculated separately in this particular problem. It is only necessary to subtract the result (7.502) from unity to obtain

$$\overline{|V_1{}^-|^2} \big/ \overline{|V_1{}^+|^2} = \frac{2\Gamma^2}{1 + \Gamma^2} \tag{7.503}$$

7.37 A "Pulse-Forming" Transmission-Line System

For another illustration or application of the theory, we shall take the "pulse-forming" line shown in Fig. 7-103(a). The transit times and

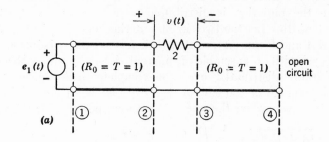

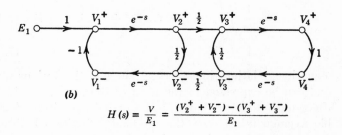

$$H(s) = \frac{V}{E_1} = \frac{(V_2{}^+ + V_2{}^-) - (V_3{}^+ + V_3{}^-)}{E_1}$$

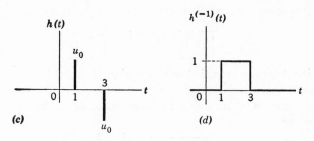

Fig. 7-103. A pulse-forming line.

characteristic resistances have been normalized to unity for simplicity. In practice, the line is charged to a certain voltage and allowed to reach static equilibrium, after which the left-hand end is suddenly short-circuited. As it turns out, this produces a square pulse at the terminals $v(t)$. The experimental conditions can be duplicated in the model by applying an input voltage $e_1(t)$ that is equal to -1 for negative time and equal to 0 for positive time. Since the addition of a constant to e_1 obviously does not affect $v(t)$, we might just as well let $e_1(t)$ be 0 for all negative time and $+1$ for positive time. In other words, $v(t)$ is the response to a unit step applied at e_1. For convenience, we can find the impulse response, rather than the step response, and then integrate the result. Since V is just the total voltage V_2 minus the total voltage V_3, we can write the transmission function from E_1 to V by inspection of the flow graph in Fig. 7-103(b). The result is

$$H(s) = \frac{V}{E_1} = \frac{e^{-s}(1 - \frac{1}{2}e^{-2s}) + \frac{1}{2}(1 - \frac{1}{2}e^{-2s}) + \frac{1}{4}e^{-3s} - \frac{1}{2}e^{-s} - \frac{1}{2}e^{-3s}}{1 + \frac{1}{4}e^{-4s} - \frac{1}{4}e^{-4s}}$$

(7.504)

Many terms cancel, leaving the simple result

$$H(s) = \frac{V}{E_1} = e^{-s} - e^{-3s}$$

(7.505)

so that the impulse response is immediately recognizable as the two impulses in Fig. 7-103(c). Integration then gives the step response (d).

The simplicity of the result suggests that we look for a simpler explanation. Let us return to the flow graph and apply a unit impulse at the input. After 1 second the impulse reaches the node $V_2{}^+$ where it immediately produces two half-size impulses, one at $V_3{}^+$ and one at $V_2{}^-$. These two half-size impulses pass around the two smaller feedback loops in the flow graph, one of them returning to $V_2{}^+$ with a change of sign and the other returning to $V_3{}^-$ without any alteration of its algebraic sign. At that moment, 3 seconds after the initial application of the input impulse, two equal and opposite half-size impulses reach the points $V_2{}^+$ and $V_3{}^-$ and their superposed effects cancel to produce *nothing* at the points $V_3{}^+$ and $V_2{}^-$. Following this cancellation all signals have disappeared and the system remains quiet forever after.

7.38   A Potentially Unstable Transmission-Line System

For another example, we shall consider the simple but interesting system shown in Fig. 7-104(a). This system becomes interesting when we permit negative as well as positive values for the terminating resistances R_1 and R_2. If, say, R_1 is negative, then the reflection coefficient due to R_1 at the left end of the line will be greater than unity in magnitude. A pulse signal launched toward the left will reflect from R_1 as a pulse of larger amplitude traveling to the right. If R_2 is also negative, then reflection at the right end will increase the size of the

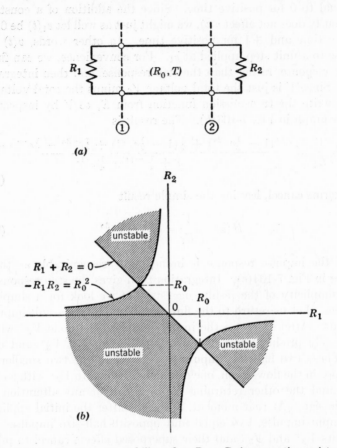

Fig. 7-104. Regions of instability when R_1 or R_2 is a negative resistance.

pulse still further. Hence the signal reflects back and forth, becoming exponentially larger in proportion to the number of reflections. The system is unstable since it generates growing oscillations independent of external excitation (apart from some initial disturbance, such as noise, sufficient to set the unstable process in motion). If, however, R_2 is positive and sufficiently large, we might expect that the small reflection coefficient at the right-hand end would overcome the large reflection coefficient at the left-hand end so as to result in multiple reflections that eventually die out with time. The problem is not quite that simple. Not only the relative values of R_1 and R_2 must be considered, but also the characteristic resistance R_0. In particular, the reflection coefficients at the two ends of the lines are

$$\Gamma_1 = \frac{R_1 - R_0}{R_1 + R_0}, \qquad \Gamma_2 = \frac{R_2 - R_0}{R_2 + R_0} \tag{7.506}$$

and to prevent net growth after two reflections (one at each end), we must have

$$|\Gamma_1 \Gamma_2|^2 < 1, \qquad \text{for stability} \tag{7.507}$$

To locate the boundaries of the region of stability, we shall replace the inequality in (7.507) by an equality. Moreover, the reflection coefficients are real for resistive terminations so that the boundary between stability and instability is specified by the condition

$$\Gamma_1 \Gamma_2 = \pm 1 \tag{7.508}$$

Substitution of (7.506) into (7.508) yields the two constraints

$$R_1 + R_2 = 0 \tag{7.509}$$

$$R_1 R_2 = -R_0{}^2 \tag{7.510}$$

giving the stability diagram shown in Fig. 7-104(b). For R_1 very nearly equal to R_0 and R_2 very nearly equal to the negative of R_0, the stability or instability of the system is somewhat indeterminate. This situation corresponds to nearly zero reflection at one end of the line and nearly an infinite reflection coefficient at the other, so that the value of the product $\Gamma_1 \Gamma_2$ is somewhat in doubt. Observe that for a fixed positive value of R_1 there is a single region of negative R_2 for which the system oscillates. Moreover, if R_2 takes some fixed negative value, then there is a single limited positive region of R_1 for which the system remains stable.

The stability diagram becomes somewhat less mysterious when we consider the character of the diagram in the two limiting cases of very large R_0 and very small R_0, as shown in Fig. 7-105. For very large R_0, the transmission line approaches a simple series inductance L, as in (a), and the stability diagram assumes the simple form shown in (b). A series RL circuit is evidently stable if and only if the total series resistance is positive. On the other hand, a very small characteristic resistance means that the transmission line behaves like a shunt capacitance, as in Fig. 7-105(c). A parallel RC circuit is stable if and only if the net shunt conductance (the parallel combination of R_1 and R_2) is positive. The shunt-conductance condition verifies the limiting form of the stability diagram indicated in (d).

In certain electronic-oscillator analysis problems, the circuit can be reduced to a model containing one positive resistance, one negative resistance, and certain energy storage elements L or C. In terms of lumped energy storage elements (especially if more than two such elements are present), the computations leading to a stability diagram may be quite tedious and, what is worse, inconvenient to interpret.

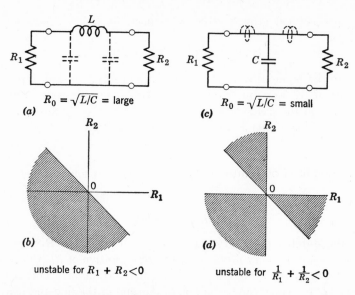

Fig. 7-105. Dependence of stability upon type of energy storage.

However, if energy storage in the system can be approximated by the simple transmission-line model in Fig. 7-104(a), then the simple and symmetrical stability diagram in Fig. 7-104(b) describes the character of the oscillator circuit. The point is that one transmission-line section (implying, as it does, a continuous distribution of L and C) is much simpler to analyze than a network containing, say, one lumped inductance and two lumped capacitances. Moreover, the transmission line may be a closer approximation to the physical situation.

7.39   Some General Remarks About Systems Containing Ideal-Delay Elements

Linear signal-transmission systems containing parts or elements that produce ideal delay are characterized by flow graphs in which branch transmissions of the form exp $(-sT)$ appear. If all flow-graph branch transmissions have the same delay time T (or all are integer multiples of some smallest delay time), the flow graph can be put in various standard forms, just as was done for a flow graph containing integrators or differentiators.   Partial-fraction expansion then leads to simple

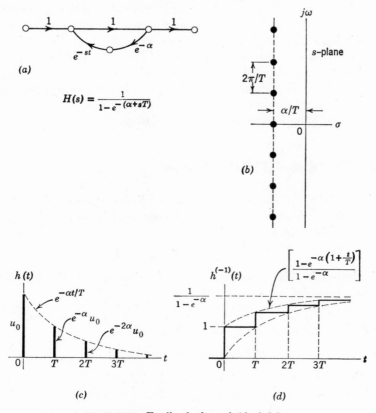

$$H(s) = \frac{1}{1 - e^{-(\alpha + sT)}}$$

(a)

(b)

(c)

(d)

Fig. 7-106. Feedback through ideal delay.

subsystems, each containing only a single ideal-delay branch.   Hence much of the character of systems containing ideal delays can be appreciated from the simple example given in Fig. 7-106.   Here the flow graph (a) has an ideal-delay branch within the feedback loop, which leads to a transmission function in which the ideal-delay function appears in the denominator.   Remembering that the fraction can be written as the sum of an infinite geometric series, we have

$$H(s) = \frac{1}{1 - e^{-(\alpha + sT)}} = 1 + e^{-(\alpha + sT)} + e^{-2(\alpha + sT)} + e^{-3(\alpha + sT)} + \cdots \quad (7.511)$$

whence the inverse exponential transformation (the impulse response) is immediately identifiable as

$$h(t) = u_0(t) + e^{-\alpha}u_0(t - T) + e^{-2\alpha}u_0(t - 2T) + \cdots \quad (7.512)$$

Figure 7-106(b) shows the pole pattern of the system function (in this particular example, there are no zeros in the finite s-plane). Parts (c) and (d) of Fig. 7-106 show the impulse response and step response of the transmission. Just as a single integrator in a feedback loop led to an exponential impulse response, so a single ideal delay within a feedback loop leads to an impulse response consisting of an infinite string of impulses, decreasing exponentially in size. For many problems it is actually simpler to work with models containing ideal delay than with models containing integrators or differentiators.

7.40   The "Binomial" Delay System

Figure 7-107(a) shows an elementary linear system whose transmission properties can be given interesting and important interpretations. The impulse response is

$$h_1(t) = \tfrac{1}{2}[u_0(t) + u_0(t - 1)] \quad (7.513)$$

as indicated in Fig. 7-107(f). By inspection of (a), the frequency-response function is

$$H_1(j\omega) = \tfrac{1}{2}(1 + e^{-j\omega}) \quad (7.514)$$

and this can be rewritten as

$$H_1(j\omega) = e^{-j(\omega/2)} \cos (\omega/2) \quad (7.515)$$

reflecting the fact that $h(t + 0.5)$, that is, $h(t)$ shifted 0.5 second to the left, is an even function. Apart from the linear phase factor $\exp(-j\omega/2)$, associated with 0.5-second time delay, the frequency response is the real cosine wave plotted in (k).

With two such systems in cascade, (b), the flow graph has one path containing no delay, two different paths containing one delay branch, and one path containing both delay branches. The corresponding impulse response $h_2(t)$ shown in (g) is the convolution of $h_1(t)$ with itself and the system function is therefore $H_1{}^2$, as indicated by Fig. 7-107(l). For a cascade of six elementary systems, as in (c), there will be, for example, fifteen different paths in the flow graph containing exactly two delay branches, and the impulse response shown in (h) therefore has an impulse of area $\tfrac{15}{64}$ located at the point $t = 2$. The areas of the impulses in $h_6(t)$ are simply the coefficients in the binomial expansion

$$H_6(j\omega) = [\tfrac{1}{2}(1 + e^{-j\omega})]^6$$
$$= \frac{1 + 6e^{-j\omega} + 15e^{-j2\omega} + 20e^{-j3\omega} + 15e^{-j4\omega} + 6e^{-j5\omega} + e^{-j6\omega}}{2^6}$$

$$(7.516)$$

As the number of stages in the cascade is increased, the frequency response

$$H_n(j\omega) = e^{-jn(\omega/2)} \cos^n (\omega/2) \qquad (7.517)$$

begins to assume a special shape, as indicated in (l), (m), and (n). Except at the frequencies $\omega/2\pi = 0, \pm 1, \pm 2, \cdots$, where the transmission retains unity value, the spectrum "melts away" as ordinates less than unity are raised to higher powers. For large n the spectrum becomes a periodic train of narrow pulses, as in (n). A system having a frequency response of this type is sometimes called a "comb filter." Expansion of $\log [\cos (\omega/2)]$ in a power series yields

$$\cos^n (\omega/2) = e^{-n\left(\frac{\omega^2}{8} + \frac{\omega^4}{192} + \cdots\right)} \qquad (7.518)$$

For large n and $-\pi < \omega < \pi$,

$$\cos^n (\omega/2) \approx e^{-n\frac{\omega^2}{8}} = e^{-\frac{1}{2}\left(\frac{\sqrt{n}}{2}\omega\right)^2} \qquad (7.519)$$

because, for large n and $-\pi < \omega < \pi$, the function (7.518) is appreciably different from zero only for small values of ω. As a result of (7.519), each of the pulses in Fig. 7-107(n) not only becomes narrow as n is allowed to increase, but also approaches a Gaussian shape.

If the system (d) were followed by a suitable low-pass filter, as in (e), then only the lowest-frequency "tooth" of the "comb" would remain, as indicated in (o). The associated system function is

$$H_f(j\omega) = e^{-j\frac{n\omega}{2}} e^{-\frac{1}{2}\left(\frac{\sqrt{n}}{2}\omega\right)^2} \qquad (7.520)$$

and the corresponding impulse response (j) is the inverse Fourier transform, and therefore also a Gaussian pulse,

$$h_f(t) = \sqrt{\frac{2}{n\pi}} e^{-\frac{1}{2}\left[\frac{t-(n/2)}{\sqrt{n}/2}\right]^2} \qquad (7.521)$$

Sampling the function $h_f(t)$ with a periodic impulse train would yield the sampled signal (i) and would return us to the comb spectrum (n). To say the same thing another way, the comb spectrum (n) is recognizable as the *convolution* of a *narrow* Gaussian pulse with a periodic impulse train; hence $h_n(t)$ must be the *product* of a *wide* Gaussian pulse

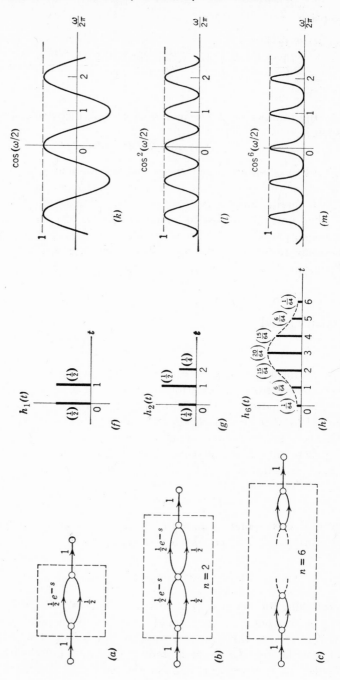

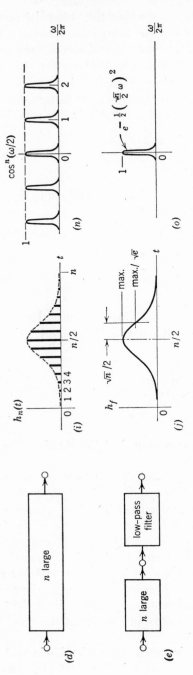

Fig. 7-107. A cascade whose impulse response is a binomial distribution of impulses.

and a periodic impulse train. Thus, we see that the "binomial array" of impulses in (h) approaches a "Gaussian array" for large n. The "envelope" curve in (i), a dashed curve whose height specifies the areas of the impulses, has a relative width indicated by the Gaussian standard deviation $\sqrt{n}/2$. For any positive n, large or small, it is convenient to define the width of the impulse-response function $h_n(t)$ in terms of the second moment of $h_n(t)$ about the "center of gravity" $n/2$. In particular,

$$\left(\frac{w}{2}\right)^2 = \frac{\int h_n[t + (n/2)]t^2\,dt}{\int h_n(t)\,dt} \qquad (7.522)$$

where w is the "width." To evaluate (7.522), we can return to the fact that $H_n(j\omega)$ is the Fourier transform of $h_n(t)$. Thus,

$$\int h_n(t)\,dt = H_n(0) = 1 \qquad (7.523)$$

and

$$\int h_n(t + \tfrac{1}{2}n)t^2\,dt = -\frac{d^2}{d\omega^2}[e^{jn\omega/2}H_n(j\omega)]_{\omega=0} \qquad (7.524)$$

The function within brackets is $\cos^n(\omega/2)$ and the negative of its second derivative, evaluated at zero frequency, is simply $n/4$. Hence, for any positive n,

$$\left(\frac{w}{2}\right)^2 = \frac{n}{4} \qquad (7.525)$$

or

$$w = \sqrt{n} \qquad (7.526)$$

The half-width $(w/2) = \sqrt{n}/2$ is, for large n, just the standard deviation of the Gaussian "envelope" curve.

Having analyzed the "binomial" transmission system, we can now relate the results directly to certain other systems of interest. Consider, first, the *probabilistic* linear system described in Fig. 7-108. As denoted by the dashed-line branches, the input is connected to *one* of the two solid-line branches, but we cannot predict *which* one. The probability of either connection existing is $p = \tfrac{1}{2}$. Hence the impulse response $h(t)$ may be *either* a unit impulse at the origin, as in (b), *or* a unit impulse delayed 1 second, as in (c). The two impulse-response functions, (b) and (c), constitute the *ensemble* of different possibilities. Since the two are equally likely, we weight them equally in computing the *ensemble average* or *mean* impulse response (d).

The mean impulse response of this particular probabilistic system happens to be the same as the impulse response in Fig. 7-107(f). Moreover, it is easy to see that the mean impulse response of n such prob-abilistic systems in cascade is the same as the $h_n(t)$ described in Fig. 7-107, *provided* the systems are *independent*, that is, provided the n random connections are chosen independently.   In the nonprobabilistic cascade, there are 2^n different paths through the flow graph, each corresponding to one of the 2^n equally probable ways in which the probabilistic cascade may be connected.   Hence any of the linear systems in Fig. 7-107 serves as an *ensemble-average model* of the corre-

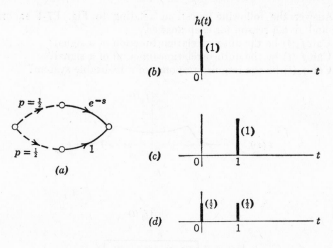

Fig. 7-108.   A probabilistic system.

sponding probabilistic system.   Convolution, Fourier transformation, and ensemble averaging are all linear operations; the ensemble averaging can therefore be carried out either before or after the other two operations without affecting the result.   For example, the spectrum in Fig. 7-107 (n) is just the average of the different spectra produced by the ensemble of different possible systems, each system in the ensemble representing one possible set of connections in the probabilistic cascade.

It is now only a short step to the coin-toss problem.   The *probability-density function* for the number of tails in n independent tosses of an ideal coin is immediately recognizable as the function $h_n(t)$, *provided* we now think of h as a probability density and t as the *number of tails* (not seconds—tails.).   Time is no longer involved, but the *occurrence* of a certain number of tails in the ensemble of all possible head-tail sequences is *analogous* to the occurrence of a certain number of delay branches in the ensemble of all possible flow-graph paths.   In the coin-toss problem, we speak of the rms deviation from the average number of tails, and this deviation is identical to the "half-width" $w/2 = \sqrt{n}/2$ calculated above.   Interpreting $h_n(t)$ as the probability-density function for t tails in n tosses of an ideal coin, we see that "the number of tails approaches half the number of tosses for large n," by which we mean that in Fig. 7-107(i) the ratio of the rms deviation $(\sqrt{n}/2)$ to the mean value $(n/2)$ becomes arbitrarily small as n increases.

PROBLEMS

7.1   Answer the following questions relating to Fig. P7-1 as briefly as possible and give a reason for each answer.
(a)   Can $f_1(t)$ be the autocorrelation function of a signal?
(b)   Can $f_2(t)$ be the autocorrelation function of a signal?
(c)   Can $f_2(t)$ be the impulse response of a realizable system?

(a)

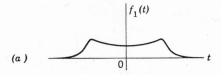

(b)

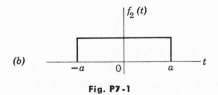

Fig. P7-1

7.2   A scheme for viewing high-speed transients is shown in Fig. P7-2.

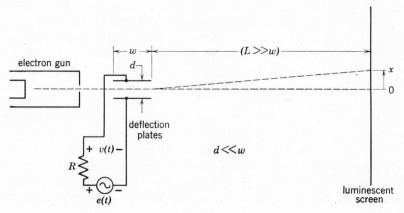

Fig. P7-2

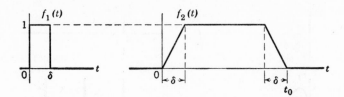

Fig. P7-3

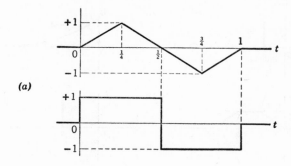

(a)

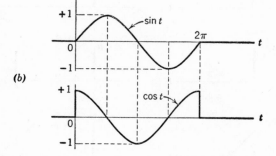

(b)

(c)

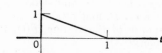

Fig. P7-4

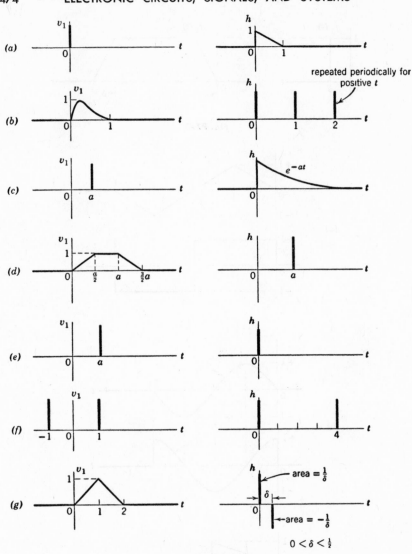

Fig. P7-5

The field in the deflection plates is uniform and fringing may be ignored. Electrons leave the gun with a velocity v_0, and strike the screen at point x.

(a) For $R = 0$ and $e(t) = Eu_{-1}(t)$, find $x(t)$.

(b) Find the impulse response of the system, $h(t)$, treating $e(t)$ as the excitation and $x(t)$ as the response.

(c) Now let $R \neq 0$. If the capacitance of the deflection plates is C and $e(t) = Eu_{-1}(t)$, find $x(t)$. (Assume $RC \approx w/v_0$.)

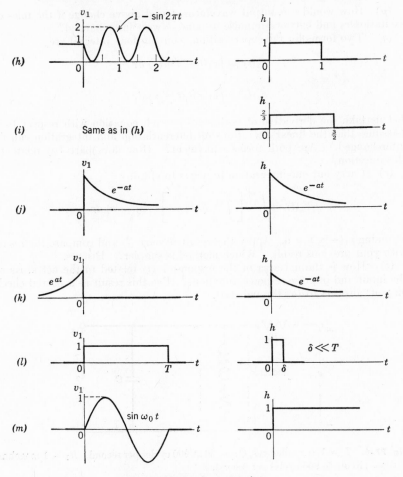

Fig. P7-5 (continued)

(*d*) In the light of part (*b*), discuss the effectiveness of this system for viewing high-speed transients.

7.3 Convolve $f_1(t)$ and $f_2(t)$ in Fig. P7-3.

7.4 Convolve the pairs of pulse signals shown in Fig. P7-4.

7.5 Find the output waveforms $v_2(t)$ for each of the v_1 and h pairs shown in Fig. P7-5(*a*) through (*m*). In each case, $v(t)$ is the input and $h(t)$ is the system impulse response. All impulses are of unit area, unless otherwise specified.

(*n*) Discuss the limiting form in (*g*) as $\delta \to 0$. How is the response related to the excitation?

(*o*) Describe the operation involved in each of the transmissions, wherever a simple description is possible. For example, (*d*) is delay.

(*p*) How would the output waveforms found above change if the roles of excitation v_1 and network impulse response h were interchanged?

(*q*)   Two forms for the superposition (convolution) integral are

$$v_2(t) = \int v_1(t - \tau)h(\tau)\, d\tau$$

$$v_2(t) = \int v_1(\tau)h(t - \tau)\, d\tau$$

Let us take the derivative of both sides of each equation with respect to t. (Assume that the linear operations of differentiation and integration can be interchanged.)   Are both forms equivalent?   How does part (*n*) relate to this question?

(*r*)   Carry out one integration by parts to obtain

$$v_2(t) = \int_{-\infty}^{\infty} \left[\int_{-\infty}^{t} h(x)\, dx \right] v_1'(t - \tau)\, d\tau$$

assuming $v_1(-\infty) = 0$.   Apply this result to part (*l*) and compare the result with your previous result.   Which method is simpler?   Discuss.

(*s*)   How is the net area of the response $v_2(t)$ related to the net areas of the input and impulse-response functions?   Use this result as a partial check on your answers to (*a*) through (*m*).

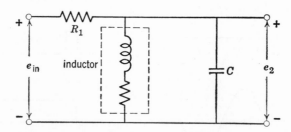

Fig. P7-6. $L = 100$ millihenrys, $Q_L = 30$ at 900 cycles per second. $R_1 = 1$ megohm, C tunes circuit to 900 cycles per second.

7.6   For the circuit in Fig. P7-6:

(*a*)   Find $H(j\omega) = E_2(j\omega)/E_{in}(j\omega)$. Plot $\log_{10}|H(j\omega)|$ versus $\log_{10}\omega$ from 10^2 to 10^4 cycles per second.

(*b*)   Find the amplitude spectrum, $|V_k|$, of a periodic square wave whose period is 10 milliseconds and whose peak-to-peak amplitude is 20 volts. Superimpose the plot on that of part (*a*).

(*c*)   Find the amplitude spectrum of the response, $e_2(t)$, when $e_{in}(t)$ is the square wave in part (*b*). Also superimpose this plot on that of part (*a*).

(*d*)   If $e_2(t)$ is measured on an ideal true-rms voltmeter, discuss the use of the circuit and meter combination as a wave analyzer.   Compare the measured value of output with the value of the corresponding Fourier-series harmonic amplitude.

7.7   A linear system has an impulse response $h(t) = \epsilon^{-t}u_{-1}(t)$.   The input is $v_1(t) = \epsilon^{\sigma t}$ *for all t, past, present, and future, and σ is real. Plot the present output $v_2(0)$ versus σ. Hint: Direct application of the superposition integral* shows that, for this type of input, $v_2(t) = H(\sigma)v_1(t)$, where $H(s)$ is the system function. Remember that $H(s)$ is defined by an integral that does not, in general, converge for all σ.

7.8 A linear transmission system has a frequency response $H(j\omega)$ which can be approximated by the idealized "low-pass" characteristic

$$H(j\omega) = \begin{cases} e^{-j\omega t_0}, & \text{for } |\omega| \leq \omega_0 \\ 0, & \text{for } |\omega| > \omega_0 \end{cases}$$

wherein $\omega_0 t_0 = 3\pi$. This characteristic has a corresponding impulse response $h(t)$ that is "almost realizable" in the sense that only a small portion of the energy of $h(t)$ lies in the negative-time region.

A rectangular pulse $v_1(t)$ of unit height and duration $10\pi/\omega_0$ is applied to the input of the system. Basing your explanation upon the visualization of $h(t)$ as a "window function" scanning $v_1(t)$ to produce the output $v_2(t)$, discuss the distortion suffered by the leading and trailing edges of the rectangular pulse during transmission through the system. Undertake the minimum amount of actual computation sufficient to obtain a reasonably good picture of $v_2(t)$. For example, you may employ reasonable estimates of areas under portions of a curve in lieu of analytical integration.

7.9 The response of a linear system to the input $i(t) = \exp(j\omega t)$ is $r(t) = H(j\omega) \exp(j\omega t)$, where $H(j\omega)$ is the frequency response of the system. The superposition or convolution integral, on the other hand, relates $i(t)$ to $r(t)$ by

$$r(t) = \int h(\tau) i(t - \tau)\, d\tau$$

where $h(t)$ is the response of the system to a unit impulse occurring at time $t = 0$. From this information, show that the frequency-response function is the Fourier transform of the impulse response.

7.10 With reference to Fig. P7-7, a sine wave $e_1(t) = 10 \sin \omega_1 t$ is applied to an amplifier having a piecewise-linear transfer curve. The output of the

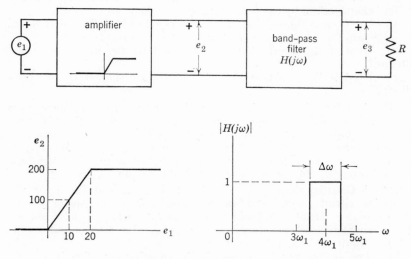

Fig. P7-7

amplifier is applied to a band-pass filter centered at frequency $4\omega_1$. The pass band of the filter $(\Delta\omega)$ is $<2\omega_1$. Determine the power delivered to the load $R = 10,000$ ohms.

7.11 A linear filter (amplifier), characterized by an impulse response $h(t) = u_{-1}(t)t \exp(-t)$, is excited by an input signal $v_1(t) = u_{-1}(t) \exp(-t)$.

(a) Find the output signal $v_2(t)$, carrying out your calculations in the time domain.

(b) Find the voltage-density spectrum $V_1(\omega)$.

(c) Find the system function $H(j\omega)$.

(d) From (b) and (c) find the output voltage-density spectrum $V_2(\omega)$.

(e) Compare (d) with the output voltage-density spectrum computed from (a).

(f) Find the autocorrelation function $\psi_{11}(\tau)$.

(g) Find the autocorrelation function $\psi_{hh}(\tau)$ of $h(t)$.

(h) Compute $\psi_{22}(\tau)$ from (f) and (g).

(i) Compare (h) with the $\psi_{22}(\tau)$ computed from (a).

(j) From $\psi_{11}(\tau)$, find the energy-density spectrum $\Psi_{11}(\omega)$.

(k) From $\psi_{22}(\tau)$, find the energy-density spectrum $\Psi_{22}(\omega)$.

(l) From $\psi_{hh}(\tau)$, find $\Psi_{hh}(\omega)$.

(m) Verify that $\Psi_{hh}(\omega) = |H(j\omega)|^2$.

(n) Compute $\Psi_{22}(\omega)$ from $\Psi_{11}(\omega)$ and $\Psi_{hh}(\omega)$ and compare with (k).

(o) Repeat the entire problem, with suitable changes of notation (ϕ instead of ψ in appropriate places) for an input $v_1(t)$ consisting of a periodic impulse train.

(p) Repeat part (o) for an input $v_1(t)$ consisting of broad-spectrum noise. In this case omit parts of the problem that are not pertinent.

7.12 A signal $v_1(t)$ generated by a stationary random process is the input to a linear filter. The probability-density function $P(v_1)$, the autocorrelation function $\phi_{11}(\tau)$, and the filter impulse response $h(t)$ are known.

(a) What can you say about the filter output signal $v_2(t)$?

(b) Repeat (a) with the linear filter replaced by an amnesic nonlinear "filter" characterized by the transfer curve $v_2 = f(v_1)$.

(c) For (a) and (b), consider the special case in which $P(v_1)$ is Gaussian, $\phi_{11}(\tau) = \exp(-|\tau|)$, $h(t) = u_0(t) + u_0(t - 10)$, and $f(x) = x^2$.

(d) What if the linear filtering is followed by the nonlinear amnesic filtering?

(e) What if the nonlinear amnesic filtering is followed by the linear filtering?

7.13 A voltage signal $v(t)$ is known to have a nonzero mean-square value and its autocorrelation function is found to be $\phi(t) = \exp(-|t|)$. This signal drives a voltage amplifier having an input impedance R_1, a load impedance R_2, and an impulse response $h(t) = u_0(t) - 2u_{-1}(t) \exp(-t)$. What is the average signal power delivered to the load R_2? Is the autocorrelation function of the output voltage the same as that of the input voltage?

7.14 A Gaussian-shape pulse signal $v_1(t)$ is applied at the input of a square-law circuit whose instantaneous output $v_2(t)$ is the square of $v_1(t)$. The square-law circuit is followed by a linear filter whose impulse response is approximately a delayed Gaussian-shape pulse. The filter output is $v_3(t)$.

(a) Describe $v_3(t)$ and its spectrum.

(b) How are the results modified if the squaring operation is preceded by the filter instead of being followed by the filter?

7.15   (a) If the autocorrelation function of a random process is

$$\phi_{11}(\tau) = e^{-\alpha|\tau|}$$

where α is a positive constant, and if signals from this process are passed through a stable filter having an impulse response

$$h(t) = e^{-\beta t}u_{-1}(t)$$

what is the output-input crosscorrelation function, $\phi_{21}(\tau)$?

  (b)   If α is large compared to β, what can be said about $\phi_{21}(\tau)$?

7.16   The transform of the crosscorrelation function of two signals is sometimes called the "complex-power" or "co-power" spectrum, in contrast with the real "power" spectrum which results when the two signals are the same.

A voltage $v(t)$, derived from a noise source, is applied to the terminals of a linear network and the resulting current at that same terminal pair is $i(t)$. The *cross*correlation function $\phi(\tau) = \langle i(t)v^*(t - \tau)\rangle$ of i and v has a Fourier transform $\Phi(\omega)$ which is, in general, not purely real.   Discuss the relationship between the complex-power density spectrum $\Phi(\omega)$ and

  (a)   average power dissipated in the network,

  (b)   energy pulsating into and out of the network.

Hint: First relate the co-power spectrum to the admittance $Y(j\omega)$ of the network and the power spectrum of $v(t)$.

  (c)   Consider the special case $i(t) = v(t - 1)$ and also

  (d)   the case $i(t) = dv(t)/dt$.

  (e)   How do you interpret the results if $v(t) = \cos \omega_1 t$?

  (f)   What if $v(t) = \exp(j\omega_1 t)$?

7.17   A lossless LC circuit, with $L = C = 1$, is driven (in parallel) by the current

$$i(t) = \begin{cases} 0, & t < 0 \\ 1, & 0 \le t < \pi \\ 2, & \pi \le t < 2\pi \\ 1, & 2\pi \le t < 3\pi \\ 0, & 3\pi \le t \end{cases}$$

and responds with a voltage $v(t)$.

  (a)   Compute the autocorrelation and crosscorrelation functions, $\psi_{ii}(\tau)$, $\psi_{vv}(\tau)$, and $\psi_{vi}(\tau)$.

  (b)   Interpret the results.

7.18   In electronic processing of electrophysiological potentials evoked by an external stimulus (Fig. P7-8), it is sometimes desirable to compute the crosscorrelation function between the responses and a train of impulses located at the times of stimulus presentation.   Some physiologists call the result an

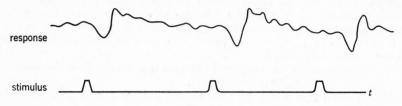

response

stimulus

Fig. P7-8

average response. In what way is this crosscorrelation function an average? How might a comparison of the results for various stimulus timings tell us something about the linearity or nonlinearity of the electrophysiological system?

7.19   White noise (a signal from a stationary random process whose power-density spectrum is broad and flat) is passed through a linear system whose impulse response is $h(t) = u_0(t) + u_0(t - 1)$. In effect, the system adds the noise to a delayed replica of itself. The following argument is proposed: "Since the noise is uncorrelated with its delayed replica, the sum of the two (the output signal of the linear system) is therefore white (flat-spectrum) noise having twice the spectral power density of the input signal." Find the flaws, if any, in this argument.

7.20   (*a*) Show that for the pulse signals $v_1(t)$ and $v_2(t)$, the associated energy-density spectra are related as follows:

$$\Psi_{11}(\omega)\Psi_{22}(\omega) = |\Psi_{12}(\omega)|^2$$

where the "co-energy-density" spectrum $\Psi_{12}(\omega)$ is the Fourier transform of the crosscorrelation function $\psi_{12}(\tau)$.

(*b*)   Interpret this result for the special case in which $v_1(t)$ is the *voltage* and $v_2(t)$ is the *current* at the terminals of a one-terminal-pair network.

(*c*)   Show that if v_1 and v_2 are power signals, generated by stationary random processes, the equality above (applied to power spectra rather than energy spectra) becomes an inequality.

(*d*)   What if v_1 is a power signal and v_2 is a pulse signal?

(*e*)   What if v_1 and v_2 are periodic?

7.21   Show that for a *complex* signal $v(t)$ having a Fourier transform $V(\omega)$,

$$v(-t) \leftrightarrow V(-\omega)$$

$$v^*(t) \leftrightarrow V^*(-\omega)$$

$$v^*(-t) \leftrightarrow V^*(\omega)$$

7.22   As an approximate model of a radar echo signal, take a positive rectangular pulse $v_1(t)$ occupying the time interval between $t = 9$ and $t = 10$. Because of random orientation of the target, the pulse has an amplitude probability density $P_1(v)$. Assume that independent stationary random noise $n_1(t)$ is unavoidably added to the echo, so that the total received signal is $v_2(t) = v_1(t) + n(t)$. The probability-density function for the noise is $P_n(v)$.

(*a*)   What is the probability-density function $P_2(v)$ of v_2?

(*b*)   Suppose that in a number of different experiments, each consisting of a single observation of v_2 at the time $t = 9.5$, the noise is always present but the target may be either present or absent, with probabilities p and $1 - p$, respectively. Let us set a "decision threshold," A, such that we will guess the target to be present if $v_2 > A$ and guess it to be absent if $v_2 < A$. Formulate the probability p_m of guessing wrong when the target is actually present (miss probability).

(*c*)   Formulate the probability p_f of guessing wrong when the target is actually absent (false-alarm probability).

(*d*)   Given $P_n(v)$, $P_2(v)$, and p, can you suggest a reasonable basis for setting the value A? This may depend upon an arbitrary judgment as to the "cost" of missing a target as compared to the "cost" of a false alarm.

(e) From a *single* observation of $v_2(9.5)$, what is your best guess as to the presence or absence of the target, without regard to the "costs" mentioned above?

(f) Investigate the specific case in which $p = 0.1$, $P_n(v) = 1 - |v|$ for $v < 1$, and $P_1(v) = u_0(v - 1)$. Plot curves of p_m and p_f versus A.

(g) Discuss the problem of making a best guess based upon n observations, rather than one observation as in (e).

7.23 Let $s(t)$ be a signal of the form shown in Fig. P7-9 and let $n(t)$ be broad-band noise with constant spectral power density N, which has been added to the signal.

(a) Sketch the impulse response of a linear filter designed to maximize the output signal-to-noise power ratio at a specified time $t_0 < T$.

(b) Repeat (a) but for $t_0 > T$. Explain your result.

(c) Sketch the output *signal* as a function of time for (a) and (b).

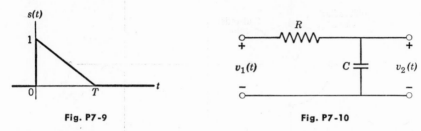

Fig. P7-9 Fig. P7-10

7.24 What input voltage signal, $v_1(t)$, in Fig. P7-10 will give a $v_2(t)$ that is the autocorrelation function of $v_1(t)$?

7.25 Consider the following alternative derivation of the Hilbert transform. If $h(t)$ is a realizable impulse response, it vanishes for negative t and we may write

$$h(t) = u_{-1}(t)h(t)$$

Take the exponential transform of both sides of this equation and equate the real and imaginary parts of the resulting expression. The final result will be the two Hilbert transform relationships between the real and imaginary parts of a realizable system function. In solving this problem, it will pay to keep in mind that the integral defining the transform of a unit step $u_{-1}(t)$ converges only in the right-half s-plane.

7.26 Each $R(j\omega)$ shown below is the real part of a complex function whose real and imaginary parts are related by the Hilbert transform. Find the corresponding imaginary part.

(a) $R(j\omega) = \cos \omega$

(b) $R(j\omega) = \begin{cases} 1, & |\omega| \leq 1 \\ 0, & |\omega| > 1 \end{cases}$

(c) $R(j\omega) = 1/(1 + \omega^2)$

In parts (a) and (c), $R(j\omega)$ is to be interpreted as a limiting form of the real part of a well-behaved (stable and realizable) system function.

7.27 Suppose that $f(t)$ is any real function and $g(t)$ is the Hilbert transform of $f(t)$,

$$g(t) = \frac{1}{\pi} \int_{-\infty}^{\infty} \frac{f(\tau)}{\tau - t} \, d\tau$$

Now define a complex function $z(t)$ as

$$z(t) = f(t) + jg(t)$$

(a)   What is the Fourier transform, $Z(\omega)$, of $z(t)$ in terms of the Fourier transform, $F(\omega)$, of $f(t)$?

(b)   Evaluate $\int |z(t)|^2 \, dt$ in terms of $\int |f(t)|^2 \, dt$.

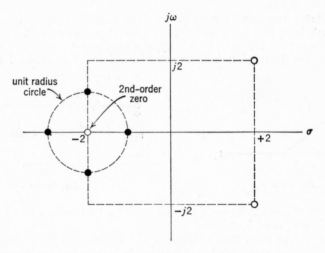

Fig. P7-11

7.28   A transmission system has a system function, $H(s)$, characterized by the pole-zero plot in Fig. P7-11.

(a)   Is this system minimum phase?   Why?

(b)   If the answer to (a) is no, split $H(s)$ into two factors,

$$H(s) = H_m(s)H_f(s)$$

where $H_m(s)$ is minimum phase and $H_f(s)$ is a flat (all-pass) transmission. In answering this question, only the pole-zero plots of $H_m(s)$ and $H_f(s)$ are required.   Assume $H(\infty) = 1$.

7.29   A real $f(t)$ has the associated "gain" function $G(\omega) = \log |F(j\omega)| = -|\omega|$.   Find $f(t)$ if $f(t)$ is known to be

(a)   an even function of time,

(b)   an odd function of time.

7.30   Let $h(t)$ be a realizable impulse response which is equal to t for $0 < t < T$, as indicated in Fig. P7-12; the behavior of $h(t)$ for $t > T$ is not known.

If the Fourier transform of $h(t)$ is known to have linear phase $\theta(\omega)$ with

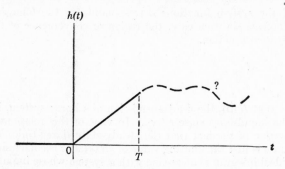

Fig. P7-12

slope $-T$ at all frequencies, what is the behavior of $h(t)$ for $t > T$? Repeat for the case in which the phase slope is twice as great; $\theta(\omega) = -2T\omega$.

7.31 A linear amplifier consists of three cascaded stages, each with a different impulse response, as shown in Fig. P7-13.
(a) Find the output for a single impulse input.
(b) Sketch the approximate curve of gain versus log frequency.
(c) Sketch the approximate curve of phase versus log frequency.

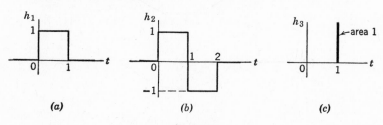

Fig. P7-13

7.32 Find the exponential transforms of the following time functions. Indicate the region of convergence of each transform.
(a) $u_{-1}(t)e^{-t}$
(b) $u_{-1}(-t)e^{t}$
(c) e^{-t}
(d) $u_{-1}(t)[e^{t} + e^{-t}]$
(e) $e^{t} + e^{-t}$

7.33 Let $f(t)$ be a time function having the properties

$$\int_{-\infty}^{\infty} |f(t)| e^{-2t}\, dt < \infty$$

$$f(t) = -f(-t), \qquad \text{i.e., } f \text{ is odd}$$

(a) Exhibit a rational function with two poles in the finite s-plane which could be the exponential transform of $f(t)$.
(b) Does $f(t)$ have a Fourier transform? Why?

7.34 Find the system functions corresponding to the following impulse responses. Indicate, in each case, the region of convergence of the integral defining the system function.

(a) $u_{-1}(t)e^{at}$

(b) $u_{-1}(t)\cos\omega t$

(c) $u_{-1}(t)$

(d) $u_{-1}(t)te^{at}$

7.35 Show that $H(0)$, the d-c transmission of a linear system, is the (net) area under the impulse-response curve. In view of this relationship, give a simple explanation of the fact that the steady-state (large-time) value of the impulse response is just the limiting value of $sH(s)$ as s becomes small. *Hint:* Consider an ideal integrator in cascade with a system whose impulse response has finite nonzero area.

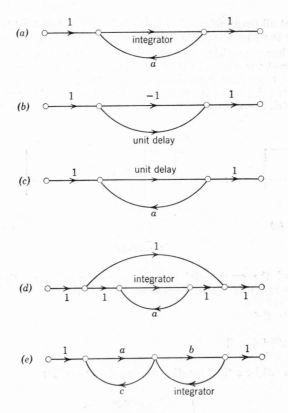

Fig. P7-14

7.36 (a) Find the impulse responses for the systems represented by the flow graphs in Fig. P7-14.

(b) Sketch and dimension the pole-zero pattern of each transmission function.

7.37 Find the exponential transforms of the following time functions:

(a) $u_{-1}(t)e^{-\alpha t}\sin\beta t$

(b) $u_{-1}(t)te^{-\alpha t}\sin\beta t$

(c) $u_{-1}(t - t_1)e^{-\alpha t}\sin\beta t$

(d) $u_{-1}(t)e^{-\alpha t}\cos\beta t$

7.38 Compare the *Fourier* transform of the signal $v_1(t) = u_{-1}(t)\exp(-\alpha t)$, in the limit of small positive α, with the *exponential* transform of the signal $v_2(t) = u_{-1}(t)$, in the limit of small positive σ, where $s = \sigma + j\omega$ is the complex frequency appearing in the exponential transformation. Show that in each case the resulting frequency function contains a real impulse.

7.39 Find the phase function, $\theta(\omega)$, corresponding to the $h(t)$ given in Fig. P7-15. *Hint:* Exploit symmetry!

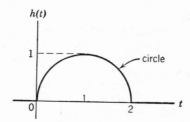

Fig. P7-15

7.40 Find the *realizable* impulse responses corresponding to the following system functions

(a) $H(s) = \dfrac{s + \alpha}{(s + \alpha)^2 + \beta^2}$

(b) $H(s) = \dfrac{e^{-\alpha s}}{\beta + s}$

7.41 A linear system has an impulse response $h(t)$, an input signal $f_1(t)$, and an output $f_2(t)$, as indicated in Fig. P7-16. Let

$$h(t) = te^{-t}u_{-1}(t)$$

(a) If $f_1(t) = e^{-t}u_{-1}(t)$, what is $f_2(t)$?

(b) If $f_1(t) = e^{-2t}$ for *all* time, what is $f_2(t)$?

(c) If $f_1(t) = e^{-t/2}$ for *all* time, what is $f_2(t)$?

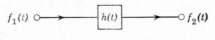

Fig. P7-16

In each case, solve first by application of the superposition integral; then relate the result to that obtained with the aid of exponential transform concepts.

7.42 The exponential transform of a unit step $u_{-1}(t)$ is the function $1/s$. The inverse exponential transformation gives, of course, 0 for t negative and 1 for t positive. Now consider the special case $t = 0$ and show that the inverse transformation leads to the value $1/2$. Do this by direct integration along each of the following contours:

(a) A vertical contour lying just to the *right* of the $j\omega$ axis.

(b) A contour consisting of three portions, the first from $-j\infty$ to $-j\omega_0$ along the negative $j\omega$ axis, the second around a small semicircle of radius ω_0 lying to the right of the origin and centered on the origin, and the third along the positive $j\omega$ axis from $j\omega_0$ to $j\infty$.

(c) Why is the Cauchy residue theorem not useful in the special case $t = 0$?

(d) Does the following simple interpretation

$$\lim_{a \to \infty} \left[\int_{-ja}^{ja} \frac{1}{s} \frac{ds}{2\pi j} = \left[\frac{\log s}{2\pi j} \right]_{-ja}^{ja} \right]$$

yield the proper result?

7.43 For the given input and output time functions, find the system function, $H(s)$, and the impulse response, $h(t)$. In each case, specify the regions of convergence of the exponential transforms $E_i(s)$, $E_0(s)$, and $H(s)$.

(a) $e_i(t) = u_{-1}(t),$ $e_0(t) = u_{-2}(t)$

(b) $e_i(t) = u_{-1}(t),$ $e_0(t) = u_{-1}(t - t_0)$

(c) $e_i(t) = u_0(t),$ $e_0(t) = u_{-1}(t) \cos t$

(d) $e_i(t) = u_{-1}(t) \sin t,$ $e_0(t) = u_{-1}(t)$

(e) $e_i(t) = u_{-1}(t)e^{-t},$ $e_0(t) = u_{-2}(t)$

(f) $e_i(t) = u_{-1}(-t)e^{t},$ $e_0(t) = e^{-t}$

7.44 The real impulse response $h(t)$ of a realizable stable linear system is known to have a discontinuity of height $h(0+)$ at the time origin. Consider the integral of the system function $H(s)$ around a closed contour in the complex s-plane, a contour that runs up the $j\omega$ axis from $-j\omega_0$ to $+j\omega_0$ and returns along a semicircle of radius ω_0 lying to the right. Evaluate the two portions of the integration in the limit of large ω_0 and show that $h(0+)$ determines the value of the real-part integral

$$\int_{-\infty}^{\infty} H_r(j\omega) \, d\omega$$

What is the physical interpretation of $h(0+)$ when $H(s)$ is a driving-point impedance?

7.45 For the triode amplifier in Fig. P7-17:

(a) Using a linear incremental model, find $h(t)$ in the time domain.

(b) Find the Fourier transform, $H(j\omega)$, and the exponential transform, $H(s)$, of $h(t)$.

(c) Sketch the gain of the amplifier in decibels versus $\log \omega$, showing critical frequencies, amplitudes, and slopes.

(d) For $e_1(t) = -2u_{-1}(t) \exp(-500t)$, find $E_2(s)$ and plot its pole-zero pattern in the s-plane.

(e) For the $e_1(t)$ in part (d), find and sketch $e_2(t)$.

7.46 (a) Find and plot the impulse response of the network shown in Fig. P7-18(a). The input is an ideal voltage source v_1 and the output is the open-circuit voltage v_2.

(b) Find the response to a unit step.

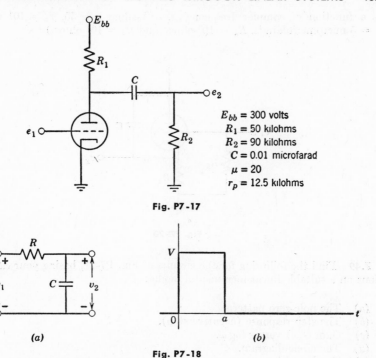

E_{bb} = 300 volts
R_1 = 50 kilohms
R_2 = 90 kilohms
C = 0.01 microfarad
μ = 20
r_p = 12.5 kilohms

Fig. P7-17

(a)

(b)

Fig. P7-18

(c) Find the response of the network to the voltage pulse shown in Fig. P7-18(b). Plot for $a = 0.2T$ and $a = 5T$. ($T = RC$; normalize your time scale in units of T for plotting purposes.)

(d) Repeat with a resistance R_0 in series with the capacitor. In this case let $T = (R + R_0)C$.

(e) For part (d), also sketch and dimension the pole-zero pattern of the system function, the circle diagram, the gain versus log ω curve, and the phase versus log ω curve.

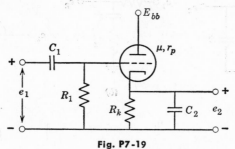

Fig. P7-19

7.47 Find the response of the circuit in Fig. P7-19 to a small negative voltage step.

7.48 Find the voltage amplification of the cathode follower (Fig. P7-20) as a function of complex frequency s. (Assume $\mu = 50$, $r_p = 10^4$ ohms, $C = 5$ micromicrofarads, $R_k = 10^3$ ohms, and $R_g = 10^6$ ohms.)

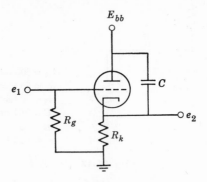

Fig. P7-20

7.49 Find the following for the circuits of Fig. P7-21, basing your calculations on a suitable linear incremental model:

(a)   The pole-zero pattern.
(b)   The step response (negative step).
(c)   Gain $G(\omega)$ versus $\log \omega$.
(d)   The circle diagram.
(e)   The impulse response.
(f)   What is the *impulse* response of the actual circuit, as contrasted with that of the linear incremental model?

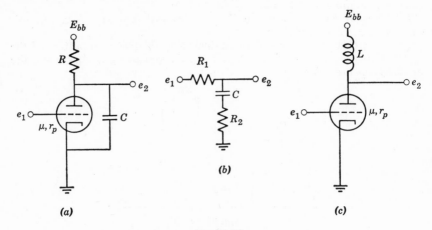

Fig. P7-21

7.50 A possible method of low-frequency compensation of an amplifier is illustrated in Fig. P7-22. Grid biasing is not indicated in the circuit, but assume that the grid operates at a negative potential.

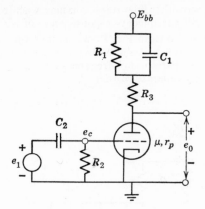

Fig. P7-22

(a) Find $H_1(s) = \dfrac{E_0(s)}{E_c(s)}$ in the form $A\left(\dfrac{s+a}{s+b}\right)$.

(b) Find $H_2(s) = \dfrac{E_0(s)}{E_1(s)}$ in the form $A\left(\dfrac{s+a}{s+b}\right)\left(\dfrac{s}{s+c}\right)$.

(c) What is the value of C_1 which allows $H_2(s)$ to have just one pole and one zero?

(d) Plot on the same graph $\log |H_2(j\omega)|$ versus $\log \omega$ for $C_1 = 0$ and for the value of C_1 obtained in part (c).

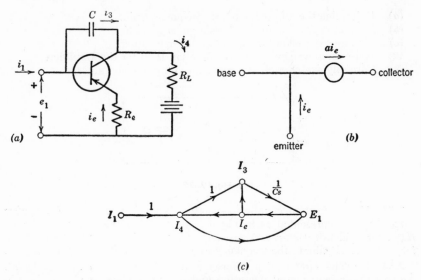

Fig. P7-23

7.51 For the amplifier in Fig. P7-23(a), and using the elementary linear transistor model in (b), find the input impedance $Z(s) = E_1/I_1$. Employ the flow graph (c) or any other flow graph you may wish to construct. Sketch and dimension the log-log frequency-response curve of $|Z(j\omega)|$.

7.52 For the circuit shown in Fig. P7-24, assume that $R_{g2}C_{g2}$ is very large so that the effect of insufficient screen bypassing can be neglected. In the following parts assume that the low-frequency cutoff ω_1 and high-frequency cutoff ω_2 are sufficiently separate so that

$$\omega_1 \ll \sqrt{\omega_1\omega_2} \ll \omega_2$$

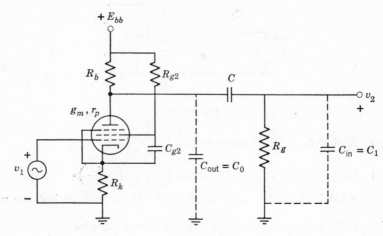

Fig. P7-24

(a) Determine the approximate mid-frequency gain.
(b) Find an expression for the low-frequency cutoff.
(c) Find an expression for the high-frequency cutoff.
(d) Write an approximate system function $H(s)$ for the amplifier.
(e) Carefully sketch and label the gain and phase characteristics.

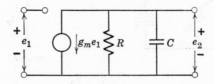

Fig. P7-25

7.53 If the effect of coupling capacitors is ignored, a pentode amplifier stage may be represented as in Fig. P7-25(a). Find the transfer function, $H(s)$, for n identical stages in cascade. Sketch the gain and phase curves for n stages. Evaluate the frequency at which the "3-decibel" point occurs.

7.54 (a) The circuit of a transistor amplifier is shown in Fig. P7-26. Assume linear incremental operation and use the transistor model given in Fig. P7-26 to determine the transfer function $H(s) = [E_2(s)]/[E_1(s)]$. The transformer has a turns ratio $n:1$, a coefficient of coupling k, and a primary self-inductance L_1 henrys. Neglect transformer losses. *Hint:* Remember that a practical transformer looks "ideal" over some appropriately chosen mid-band frequency range. Thus high-frequency and low-frequency limitations can be treated separately.

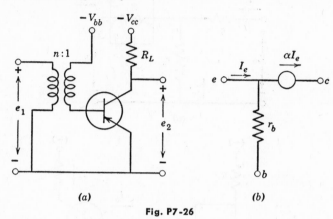

Fig. P7-26

(b) Let $R_L = 10$ kilohms, $n = 3$, $L_1 = 1$ henry, $r_b = 200$ ohms, $k = 0.995$, $\alpha = 0.98$. Show the location of the poles and zeros of $H(s)$ in the s-plane.

(c) On graph paper, plot $|H(j\omega)|$ in decibels versus $\log \omega$, and plot the phase of $H(j\omega)$ in degrees versus $\log \omega$. Consider the range: 2×10^2 to 2×10^6 radians per second.

(d) Consider an incremental signal $e_1(t) = Eu_{-1}(t)$. Compute, sketch, and dimension the resulting $e_2(t)$ versus t for $0 < t < 20$ milliseconds. Use the numerical values given in part (b).

7.55 (a) Using the incremental transistor model shown in Fig. P7-27(a), find the current amplification $H(j\omega) = I_c/I_b$ of the circuit in (b). Capacitance C_c is the equivalent collector capacitance and

$$a(\omega) = \frac{a_0}{1 - j(\omega/\omega_{co})}$$

where ω_{co} is the "α-cutoff" frequency. Let $\omega_{co} = 20$ megacycles, $a_0 = 0.9$, $r_b = 200$ ohms, $r_e = 10^3$ ohms, $r_c = 5$ megohms, $C_c = 10$ micromicrofarads.

(b) What is the maximum allowable value of R_L if a 1-megacycle bandwidth is desired? (Considering the last stage only.)

(c) What is the maximum bandwidth attainable? (Last stage only.)

(d) Outline a method for determining the over-all amplification of the two-stage amplifier,

$$H_1(j\omega) = I_c/I_{b1}$$

7.56 A voltage amplifier with a transformer-coupled output is shown in Fig. P7-28(a). Capacitance C is very large. The amplifier performance can be approximated by the linear incremental circuit shown in Fig. P7-28(b), where $L_2 \gg L_1$ and $L_2 \gg L_3$.

(a) Show that the transfer function $H(s) = [E_2(s)]/[E_1(s)]$ can be written

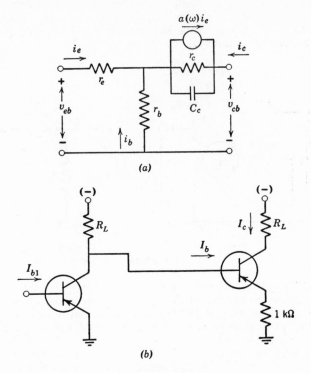

(a)

(b)

Fig. P7-27

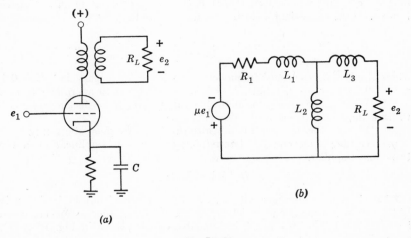

(a)

(b)

Fig. P7-28

in the form

$$H(s) = \frac{Ks}{(s - s_1)(s - s_2)}$$

and find the values of the constants K, s_1, and s_2.

(b)   Plot the frequency response of the amplifier ($\log |H(j\omega)|$ versus $\log \omega$) and physically interpret the manner in which the frequency response is limited at low and high frequencies.

(c)   Sketch the response of the circuit to a unit step voltage.

7.57   For a high-Q parallel RLC circuit ($Q > 10$), it is possible to approximate the impedance $Z(j\omega)$, for frequencies in the vicinity of the resonant frequency, by the form

$$Z(j\omega) \approx \frac{K_1}{1 + jK_2(\omega - \omega_0)}$$

Find K_1 and K_2 in this approximate expression.

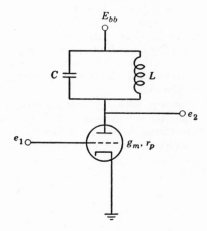

Fig. P7-29

7.58   The circuit in Fig. P7-29 is often used as a band-pass amplifier.

(a)   Determine the system function $H(s) = [E_2(s)]/[E_1(s)]$.

(b)   Determine and sketch the step response, $h^{(-1)}(t)$. Assume a high-Q circuit and linear operation.

7.59   Given the differential equation

$$\frac{d^2y(t)}{dt} + a\frac{dy(t)}{dt} + y(t) = f(t)$$

wherein $f(t)$ is specified and $y(t)$ is sought:

(a)   Draw a flow-graph representation containing ideal differentiators and showing $f(t)$ as a source-node signal.

(b)   Now draw the "s-domain" flow graph, in which the branch transmissions are elementary system functions and the node signals are the exponential transforms of $f(t)$, $y(t)$, and the derivatives of $y(t)$.

(c)   From the graph (b), find the transmission function $T(s) = Y(s)/F(s)$.

(*d*) Discuss the "successive approximations" type of solution of the differential equation, for which

$$y_{k+1}(t) = f(t) - a\frac{d}{dt}[y_k(t)] - \frac{d^2}{dt^2}[y_k(t)]$$

In particular, draw a suitable *s*-domain flow graph showing the node signals $Y_1(s)$, $Y_2(s)$, $\cdots$. Assume $Y_0(s) = 0$ to start the successive approximations process. Relate this graph to that in (*b*), making use of the series expansion $(1 - x)^{-1} = 1 + x + x^2 + x^3 + \cdots$.

(*e*) Repeat the entire problem, starting with a graph (*a*) containing ideal integrators, rather than differentiators, and making appropriate changes in the other parts of the problem.

7.60 One way to accomplish "frequency multiplication" is by use of a "class C" amplifier, in which the plate current is cut off during all but a small portion of the operating cycle. Consider a grounded-cathode vacuum-triode amplifier with a parallel-resonant circuit serving as the plate load. The input voltage at the grid is $v_1(t) = V_1[(\cos \omega_1 t) - 1]$, where V_1 is many times larger than the number of negative input volts required to cut off the tube. Making suitable models and approximations, carry through a preliminary design of the circuit aimed at producing an output (plate) a-c voltage which is nearly sinusoidal and which has three times the frequency of the input signal. Discuss the effect of loss in the inductance element of the resonant circuit upon the amplitude of the output sinusoid.

7.61 Formulate and sketch, with significant dimensions, the phase curve $\theta(\omega)$ associated with the *n*-pole low-pass flat (Butterworth) transmission function. Repeat for the corresponding band-pass function, assuming a pass band that is narrow in comparison with the mid-band frequency.

7.62 A typical stage of an IF amplifier, such as those used in standard broadcast receivers, is shown in Fig. P7-30(*a*). The purpose of this problem

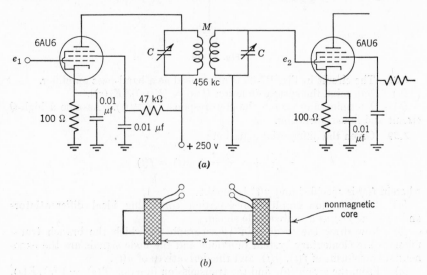

Fig. P7-30

is to study the transmission through a single stage, $E_2(\omega)/E_1(\omega)$. Assume that the self-inductance of each coil, L, is 1 millihenry. The capacitors tune each coil to resonance at 456 kilocycles. The Q of each coil is 100 at 456 kilocycles, and the capacitors may be taken to be lossless.

(a) A possible arrangement of the coils is shown in Fig. P7-30(b). The spacing x is adjustable at the time of manufacture of the amplifier. In a particular application, a maximally flat (Butterworth) transfer function is desired. Compute the value of M, the mutual inductance, to which the coil pair should be adjusted experimentally by varying x.

(b) With the value of M found in part (a), calculate the bandwidth between the 3-decibel points on the plot of $|H(j\omega)|$ versus $\log \omega$. Sketch $|H(j\omega)|$ versus $\log \omega$.

(c) In another application, extreme selectivity is desired rather than a maximally flat transfer function. How should x be adjusted to achieve this narrow bandwidth? What is the limit on the minimum bandwidth between the 3-decibel points? Sketch $|H(j\omega)|$ versus $\log \omega$ for this case.

(d) A third designer requires a maximum bandwidth but specifies that $|H(\omega)|$ shall not vary more than ± 1.5 decibels in the pass band. How should x be adjusted to achieve this characteristic? With this value of x, what is the bandwidth between 3-decibel points? Sketch $|H(j\omega)|$ versus $\log \omega$.

7.63 A linear system function $H(s)$ has n poles located along a *vertical line* lying to the left of the $j\omega$ axis in the s-plane. There are no zeros in the finite s-plane. At high frequencies the system function approaches the form

$$H(s) \rightarrow Ks^{-n}$$

where K is a preassigned constant. If we desire a frequency response $H(j\omega)$ whose magnitude is (1) as large as possible and (2) as flat as possible over the range $|\omega| < \omega_0$, how should the poles be located? Observe that the answer to this problem is not unique, because (1) and (2) are, to a certain extent, opposing desiderata.

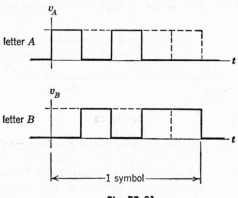

Fig. P7-31

7.64 A teletypewriter signal consists of five pulse positions per symbol transmitted, with each position exhibiting either a so-called "mark" or a "space." Figure P7-31 shows the codes for the letters A and B. The duration of a mark or space is about 40 milliseconds for 60-word-per-minute transmission.

(a)   Find the correlation functions $\psi_{AA}(\tau)$, $\psi_{BB}(\tau)$, and $\psi_{AB}(\tau)$.

(b)   Approximately what frequency bandwidth would be needed for the transmission of letter A or B without undue distortion of the signal?

(c)   Suggest a random process which might serve as a rough model for continuous teletype transmission and discuss the problem of sufficient bandwidth in the transmission system.

7.65   Design a three-stage vacuum-tube or transistor amplifier whose transmission function has a third-order zero at the origin and six poles elsewhere in the complex s-plane. The frequency-response curve is to be flat, in the Butterworth sense, over a mid-band frequency region whose upper and lower half-power frequencies are in the ratio of 4 to 1.

7.66   A driving-point impedance has open-circuit natural frequencies $s = -2$ and $s = -4$ and short-circuit natural frequencies $s = -1$ and $s = -3$. The impedance is unity at infinite frequency. Draw a flow graph relating the voltage and current, $e(t)$ and $i(t)$, at the terminals of this impedance.

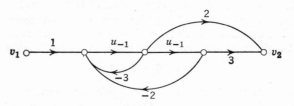

Fig. P7-32

7.67   Write the transfer function for the flow graph in Fig. P7-32 and reduce it to the canonical form of equation (7.64). Draw the flow graph corresponding to equation (7.64). If $v_1(t) = u_1(t)$, what is $v_2(t)$?

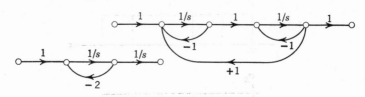

Fig. P7-33

7.68   (a) Find the transmission function of the flow graphs in Fig. P7-33.

(b)   For these two transmission functions, find the impulse response, the pole-zero pattern, and the log-log gain versus frequency plot.

7.69   Find $H(s) = [E_2(s)]/[E_1(s)]$ for each of the networks in Fig. P7-34 and plot the pole-zero locations in the s-plane. In Fig. P7-34(g) the ideal amplifier is unilateral and has zero input admittance, zero output impedance, and constant forward voltage amplification A.

7.70   The most general ordinary differential equation relating the response

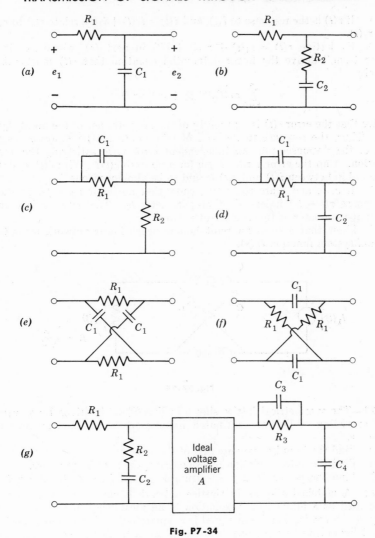

Fig. P7-34

$r(t)$ of a lumped linear network to an input $i(t)$ is of the form

$$\sum_{k=0}^{n} a_k(t) r^{(k)}(t) = \sum_{k=0}^{m} b_k(t) i^{(k)}(t) + c(t)$$

where the parenthetical superscript indicates the order of a derivative and where $a_k(t)$, $b_k(t)$, and $c(t)$ are independent time functions not related to $i(t)$.

(a) Is the equation a linear differential equation? Why?

(b) If $r_1(t)$ is the response to an input $i_1(t)$ and if $r_2(t)$ is the response to $i_2(t)$, is $r_1(t) + r_2(t)$ the response to $i_1(t) + i_2(t)$? If not, what condition must be satisfied in order that superposition will hold?

(c)   If $r(t)$ is the response to $i(t)$, and $i(t) = i_1(t) + i_2(t)$, relate $r(t)$ to $r_1(t)$ and $r_2(t)$.

(d)   By letting $r(t) = r_1(t) + r_2(t) + \epsilon(t)$ in part (c), where $\epsilon(t)$ is an "error term," derive the linear differential equation that $\epsilon(t)$ must satisfy, namely

$$\sum_{k=0}^{n} a_k(t)\epsilon^{(k)}(t) + c(t) = 0$$

Notice that the error $\epsilon(t)$ is a property of the network, not of the input signal $i(t)$. Thus, the response to the sum of two inputs can be expressed as the sum of the responses plus an independent error term satisfying the above equation. Can the error term vanish for a nonzero $c(t)$? With $c(t) = 0$, the relationship between $i(t)$ and $r(t)$ is said to be "homogeneous."

(e)   If a, b, and c are constants, show that an input $i(t - t_0)$ produces a response $r(t - t_0)$ independent of parameter t_0. The network is then a constant-parameter or time-invariant network.

(f)   Show that a time-invariant homogeneous linear network leads to a *rational* system function $H(s)$.

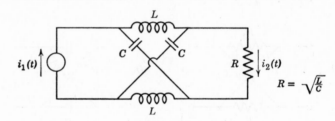

Fig. P7-35

7.71   The symmetrical lattice shown in Fig. P7-35 is driven by a current $i_1(t)$ consisting of Poisson-distributed impulses of area α and average frequency ν.

(a)   Find the impulse response $h(t)$ of the system.

(b)   Find the autocorrelation function ψ_{hh} of the impulse response.

(c)   Find the power-density spectrum $\Phi_{22}(\omega)$ of $i_2(t)$ for the given $i_1(t)$.

7.72   A matched all-pass LC lattice network having n lattice sections is to be used as a lumped approximation of an ideal-delay line. The desired delay is T seconds. The input signal is a square pulse of duration t_0 and the output signal is to be a reasonable facsimile of the input pulse shape. Discuss the quality of the output pulse shape as a function of the parameters n, T, and t_0.

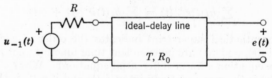

Fig. P7-36

7.73   For the transmission-line circuit in Fig. P7-36:

(a)   Sketch $e(t)$ if $R = R_0$.

(b)   Sketch $e(t)$ if $R > R_0$.

(c)   Sketch $e(t)$ if $R < R_0$.

7.74   The noise voltage $v(t)$ and noise current $i(t)$ are measured at one point on a uniform lossless transmission line and are found to have the correlation functions $\phi_{vv}(\tau)$, $\phi_{ii}(\tau)$, and $\phi_{vi}(\tau)$.   Let both the characteristic impedance and velocity of traveling wave propagation on the line equal unity, for simplicity.

(a)   Find the power-density spectra associated with waves traveling to the right $\Phi_{RR}(\omega)$ and with waves traveling to the left $\Phi_{LL}(\omega)$.

(b)   Give a physical interpretation of the complex power-density spectrum $\Phi_{vi}(\omega)$ associated with the crosscorrelation function of $v(t)$ and $i(t)$.

(c)   What can you say about the manner in which the various power-density spectra change as the observation point is moved to a new location along the line?   In particular, can you calculate $\Phi_{vi}(\omega)$ at one point on the line, given the spectra $\Phi_{vv}(\omega)$, $\Phi_{ii}(\omega)$, and $\Phi_{vi}(\omega)$ at some other point on the line?

(d)   Repeat the entire problem for the special case in which $\phi_{vv}(\tau)$, $\phi_{ii}(\tau)$, and $\phi_{vi}(\tau)$ are all sinusoids of the same frequency.

7.75   Discuss the reduction of light reflection from a pane of glass by the addition of suitable transparent (lossless) coatings on each surface.   Assume that each coating is many wavelengths thick, so that the "phase shift" through each coating, like that through the glass pane itself, may be treated as a completely random variable.

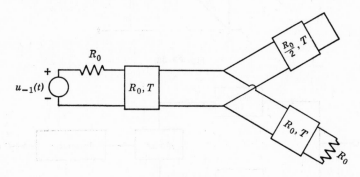

Fig. P7-37

7.76   If the ideal-delay-line configuration in Fig. P7-37 is excited with a unit step, as shown, how long does it take the system to reach a steady state?

7.77   (a) What should be the impulse response, $h(t)$, of a homogeneous linear filter which will deliver each of the responses $y(t)$ in Fig. P7-38, if the excitation $x(t)$ is, in each case, a square pulse of unit duration starting at $t = 0$?

(b)   Synthesize each of the impulse responses as a flow graph containing elementary branches such as integrators and ideal delays.

7.78   For the linear system in Fig. P7-39, sketch and dimension the pole-zero pattern of $H(s) = E_2/E_1$.

7.79   In Fig. P7-40(a) each branch of the linear signal flow graph is labeled

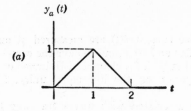

(a)

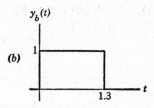

(b)

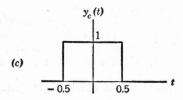

(c)

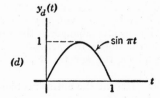

(d)

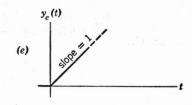

(e)

Fig. P7-38

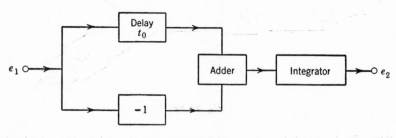

Fig. P7-39

with its impulse response. A unit impulse $v_1(t) = u_0(t)$ is applied at node 1.

(a) Sketch and dimension the other node signals $v_k(t)$.

(b) Sketch and dimension the pole-zero pattern of the transmission $T(s) = V_5/V_1$.

(c) For what values of a and b is the system stable? Explain your answer in terms of the results in both parts (a) and (b).

For the flow graph in Fig. P7-40(b), whose branches are labeled with their impulse responses, the input signal $v_1(t)$ at node 1 is a unit impulse.

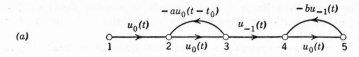

(a)

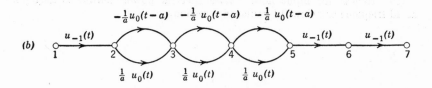

(b)

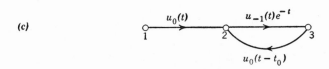

(c)

Fig. P7-40

(d)   Sketch and dimension the other node signals, $v_2(t)$ through $v_7(t)$.

(e)   Sketch and dimension the pole-zero pattern of the transmission $T(s) = V_7/V_1$.

(f)   Discuss the results of parts (d) and (e) in the limit of small a.

The flow graph in Fig. P7-40(c) has branch impulse responses indicated near each branch.

(g)   Discuss the transmission properties of the system.

(h)   What is the behavior of the signal at node 2 long after the application of a unit impulse at node 1?

(i)   To what does the transmission from 1 to 3 reduce for $t_0 = 0$?

7.80   An n-stage pulse amplifier has a per-stage impulse response $h(t) = u_{-1}(t) \exp(-\alpha t)$. The impulse response of n stages can be approximated by

$$h_n(t) = A^n e^{-\frac{1}{2}\left(\frac{t-nT}{\sigma\sqrt{n}}\right)^2}$$

(a)   Find A, σ, and T to give a good approximation for large n and discuss the quality of the approximation for small n.

(b)   For what general class of per-stage impulse responses $h(t)$ would you expect such an approximation to hold for large n? Does it hold for an $h(t)$ containing impulses? Does it hold for an $h(t)$ having zero net area? Discuss the rule of thumb that "The delay through a pulse-amplifier chain increases in proportion to the number of stages but the step-response rise time (say, the time between the 10 and 90 per cent points on the *step* response) increases only as the square root of the number of stages." This rule of thumb is considered safe for an amplifier whose one-stage step response is monotonic (free of "overshoot"). Why?

(c)   Design a four-stage pentode pulse amplifier having a gain of 80 decibels and estimate its delay and rise time.

7.81. The input to a linear system consists of a pulse signal $v_1(t) = tu_{-1}(t) \exp(-t)$ plus stationary random noise whose autocorrelation function is $\phi_1(\tau) = \exp(-|t|)$.

(a) Design the linear system for a maximum quotient of peak output-signal power and average output-noise power.

(b) Repeat for input noise whose spectral power density is negligible at all frequencies below 0.1 radian per second.

Nonlinear

and

Time-Varying Linear Systems

8.1   Introduction

In a linear system, superposition applies; the output signal due to two simultaneously applied inputs is the sum of the outputs due to each input acting alone. To say the same thing another way, the component response of the system to each input signal is independent of the presence of other inputs. Such is not the case in a nonlinear system. When nonlinearities are present, the application of an auxiliary input signal may completely change the character of the response to a primary input signal.

The modification of one signal by another (really the modification of properties of the system through which the first signal is being transmitted) is usually called *modulation*. In its simplest form modulation involves the multiplication of one signal $v_a(t)$ by another $v_b(t)$ to produce a third signal $v_a(t)v_b(t)$. The practical purpose of modulation is to convert an information-carrying signal $v_a(t)$ to an alternative form $v_a(t)v_b(t)$, in which form the transmission or processing of the information becomes more convenient.

Nonlinearity provides the actual mechanism for modulation but a system in which modulation occurs can often be represented as a *time-varying linear* system, as we shall see. Hence many of the analytic methods so useful in the treatment of linear systems apply to the study of modulation systems.   In particular, the effect of a modulation process upon the spectrum of the signal is often the key to an understanding of the process.

Even when a time-varying linear model is not suitable, the methods of signal analysis growing out of linear systems theory are still extremely useful.   For example, the transmission properties of the nonlinear

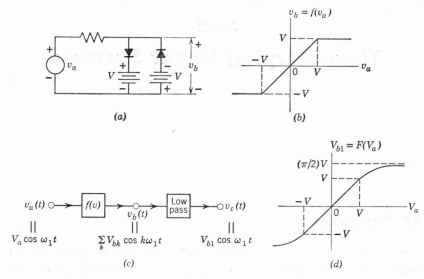

Fig. 8-1.   Nonlinear transmissions.

system in Fig. 8-1 (a) are completely described by the transfer curve (b). Now suppose that the input signal $v_a(t)$ is a pure sinusoid and suppose also that the output $v_b(t)$ is subjected to low-pass filtering which allows only the fundamental frequency ω_1 to appear in the final output $v_c(t)$, as indicated in Fig. 8-1(c).   The appropriate transfer curve relating the input and output steady-state amplitudes is shown in (d).   The construction of this curve entails Fourier analysis of $v_b(t)$ to find the fundamental component V_{b1}.   In the limit of large V_a the signal $v_b(t)$ approaches a square wave of amplitude V, so that the fundamental amplitude approaches $(4/\pi)V$.   The point is that, although Fourier analysis involves resolution of a signal into *additive* components and is therefore especially suitable for representation of signals in *linear* systems, nevertheless such resolution is exceedingly useful for many nonlinear systems problems.

In this chapter we shall begin with a consideration of elementary nonlinear systems, proceed to time-varying linear models of systems, describe the principal forms of modulation employed in practice, and conclude with some remarks about general properties of nonlinear systems containing memory.

8.2 Multiplication of Signals in a Nonlinear System

The multiplication of signals in a nonlinear system can be illustrated by the two elementary examples in Figs. 8-2 and 8-3. The basic "limiter" circuit in Fig. 8-2(a) is described by the transfer curve (b). For the input signal components $v_a(t)$ and $v_b(t)$ shown in (c) and (d), the total input signal $v_1(t)$ applied to the limiter is alternately positive or negative (e), in accord with the variations of $v_b(t)$. Hence the output $v_2(t)$, shown in (f), is identifiable as the *product* of $v_a(t)$ and a hypothetical signal $v_s(t)$, in (g), having the same waveform as $v_b(t)$. A system of this type is sometimes called a "chopper"; the signal $v_a(t)$ is said to be "chopped" by the rectangular signal $v_b(t)$. A chopper system operates like an on-off switch controlled by an auxiliary "chopping" or "modulating" signal, in this case $v_b(t)$.

Figure 8-3(a) shows another elementary system in which multiplication of signals occurs. Here, however, the nonlinearity is less violent. Assuming a square-law relationship (b) between v_1 and v_2, and the signals $v_a(t)$ and $v_b(t)$ shown in (c) and (d), we find $v_2(t) = (v_a + v_b)^2 = v_a^2 + 2v_av_b + v_b^2$. If, in comparison to $v_a(t)$, $v_b(t)$ is a slowly varying time function, then the addition of a high-pass RC filter removes $v_b(t)$ and gives an output $v_c(t) = v_a^2 + 2v_av_b$. If, in addition, the amplitude of $v_a(t)$ is small in relation to $v_b(t)$, then the term v_a^2 may be ignored and we are left with $v_c(t) \approx 2v_av_b$, as indicated in (e) and (f).

The extraction of the cross-product term from the square of a signal sum can be accomplished without a frequency filter and without restrictions on relative signal amplitudes, provided we are willing to assume the existence of a perfect square-law device, Fig. 8-4(a), together with a matched twin, as shown in (b). The difference of the squares of the sum and difference of two signals is proportional to their product. Such "balanced modulators" have found great practical use and more will be said about them later in the chapter. The point here is that the operation of multiplying two signals can be accomplished through the mechanism of nonlinearity, and that choppers and square-law modulators are two basic categories of "multipliers."

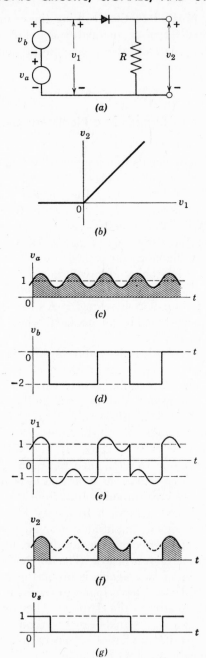

Fig. 8-2. An elementary "chopper."

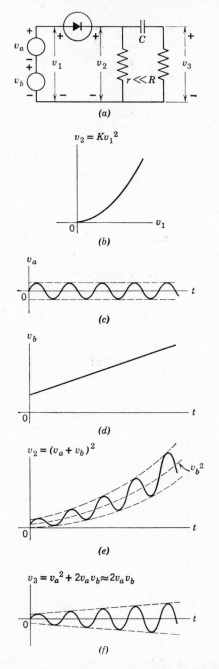

Fig. 8-3. An elementary square-law modulator.

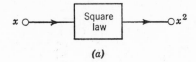

(a)

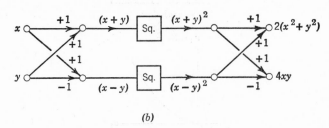

(b)

Fig. 8-4. A balanced multiplier employing two ideal squaring elements.

8.3   The Pentode as a Modulator

The pentode circuit shown in Fig. 8-5(a) is another example of a modulator. At least qualitatively, the curves in Fig. 8-3(c) through (e) are representative of this pentode circuit. The incremental control-grid-to-plate transconductance (g_m) of the pentode is a function of the screen-grid voltage, $g_m = f(v_b)$. The incremental output voltage is given by

$$v_2(t) = g_m v_a(t) \tag{8.1}$$

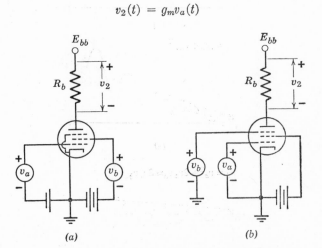

Fig. 8-5.   Multiplication of signals in a pentode circuit.

provided, of course, $v_a(t)$ is not too large. Thus

$$v_2 = f(v_b)v_a \tag{8.2}$$

Now, for a suitable choice of the origin on the v_b scale, the function $g_m = f(v_b)$ may be approximated as $g_m \approx Kv_b$ over some range of v_b and we have, once more, a signal product $v_2 \approx Kv_av_b$.

For use as a chopper (or "gate," or "switch") the pentode indicated in Fig. 8-5(b) is convenient. Here the suppressor grid is connected to an externally available terminal, permitting the application of a chopping or gating signal $v_b(t)$. The waveforms of Fig. 8-2(c), (d), and (f) are representative in this case. The suppressor grid is more convenient for chopping than the screen grid, since a suppressor grid at zero or negative potential (relative to the cathode) draws negligible current.

The vacuum triode, the transistor, the cryotron, and, in fact, any other nonlinear electrical device may be employed as a modulator or chopper simply by driving the device into nonlinear operation. The choice among them for a given application depends upon such practical considerations as noise, gain, rapidity of response, cost, and reliability.

8.4   Elementary Systems Containing Multipliers

We have seen how a nonlinear element in a system, that is, a nonlinear relation between two physical variables, can be exploited to produce effective multiplication of two signals. Since multiplication is a realizable operation, the "ideal multiplier" shown in Fig. 8-6(a) may be treated as a basic system element, along with such linear elements as the ideal amplifier and the ideal integrator. The potentiometer in Fig. 8-6(b), often used in low-frequency control systems to multiply a position signal x by a voltage signal v_1, is one example of a device that achieves multiplication directly, rather than by indirect exploitation of a nonlinear two-variable constraint. Whether synthesized directly or indirectly, multiplication of signals is a fundamental operation and the symbol in Fig. 8-6(a) is very useful as a building block for the construction of system diagrams.

In Fig. 8-4, we used "squares" to produce multiplication. Now we can turn the problem around and employ a multiplier to produce squaring, as shown in Fig. 8-7(a). Just as a nonlinear curve $v = f(i)$ was our original starting point in the "design" of a multiplier, we can now connect multipliers as suggested in Fig. 8-7(b) to approximate an arbitrary (single-valued) nonlinear curve.

One very important point to be made here is the following. The presence of a multiplier in a system diagram does not necessarily mean that the system is nonlinear. To be sure, the transmission system in Fig. 8-7 (a), having an input x and an output x^2, is obviously nonlinear.

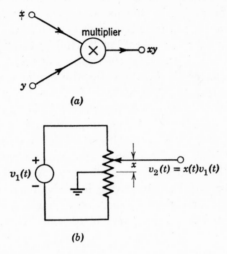

(a)

(b)

Fig. 8-6. (a) The ideal multiplier and (b) one possible physical realization.

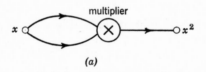

(a)

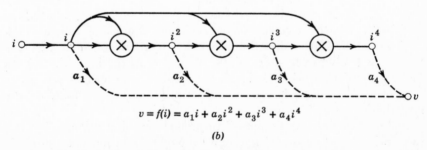

$$v = f(i) = a_1 i + a_2 i^2 + a_3 i^3 + a_4 i^4$$

(b)

Fig. 8-7. Synthesis of a nonlinear function $v = f(i)$ approximated by a polynomial.

On the other hand, if one input arm of the multiplier is driven by a *preassigned independent* signal $f(t)$, as indicated in Fig. 8-8, then the other input arm and the output arm form a *linear transmission system*. Linearity is assured by the validity of superposition. The output,

$f(t)[x_1(t) + x_2(t)]$, due to the simultaneous application of two inputs, $x_1(t)$ and $x_2(t)$, is the sum of the two outputs, $f(t)x_1(t)$ and $f(t)x_2(t)$, due to each input acting alone. In this case (Fig. 8-8) the other multi-

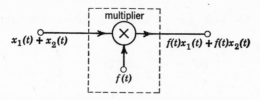

$$x_1(t) + x_2(t) \qquad f(t)x_1(t) + f(t)x_2(t)$$
$$f(t)$$

Fig. 8-8. An elementary time-varying *linear* system.

plier input arm, together with its *independent* and *unalterable* signal $f(t)$, is to be treated as a *part of the system*, as suggested by the dashed line in the figure. Thus the system is linear, but its properties vary with time. Many practical modulation systems fall into this category.

8.5 Power Amplification in a Time-Varying System

A time-varying *resistance*, such as $x(t)$ in Fig. 8-6(*b*), produces modulation. A linear circuit with a time-varying *energy-storage* element can produce not only modulation but also power amplification. To justify this statement we shall show that a time-varying capacitance (or inductance) can behave as an active element, that is, as a source of power controlled by an applied signal.

For simplicity, assume that the capacitor in Fig. 8-9(*a*) has plane parallel plates with variable spacing x. If the maximum spacing is small compared to the plate diameter, we can neglect fringing effects and express the capacitance as K/x. For convenience let K be unity.

Let us now assume that the spacing between plates is varied sinusoidally by mechanical means, so that

$$x(t) = 1 - \delta \sin \omega_0 t \tag{8.3}$$

Also, let the applied current be $\cos t$. For a variable capacitance, the terminal relation is

$$\frac{d}{dt}(Cv) = i \tag{8.4}$$

Integration yields

$$Cv = \int i \, dt = \sin t \tag{8.5}$$

Solving for v and substituting $x(t)$ for $1/C$, we have

$$v = (1 - \delta \sin \omega_0 t) \sin t \tag{8.6}$$

The product of v and i is therefore

$$
\begin{aligned}
vi &= (1 - \delta \sin \omega_0 t) \sin t \cos t \\
&= (1 - \delta \sin \omega_0 t)\tfrac{1}{2} \sin 2t
\end{aligned}
\tag{8.7}
$$

Adjusting ω_0, we find, for $\omega_0 = 2$, a negative time-average power. Specifically,

$$
\langle vi \rangle = -\frac{\delta}{2} \langle \sin^2 2t \rangle = -\frac{\delta}{4}
\tag{8.8}
$$

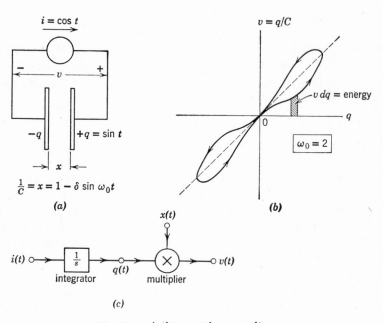

Fig. 8-9. A time-varying capacitance.

For the reference directions used in Fig. 8-9(*a*), negative power implies the properties of a source; hence the time-varying capacitance can deliver power to a resistive load or amplify a signal. At a signal frequency half that of the capacitance variation, the element behaves like a *negative resistance*. However, it should be apparent that the "negative resistance" was obtained as a result of a judicious choice of the phase relationship between the current and the mechanical drive. A positive sign in the expression for $x(t)$ would yield a positive value for the average product $\langle vi \rangle$. For a more general result, a phase angle should be included in one of the two time functions. As the phase angle is adjusted, the average power varies from positive to negative.

Physical reasoning leads very simply to the conditions necessary for obtaining power from the variable capacitance. To simplify the discussion let us assume a square-wave variation of the capacitance, that is, $x(t)$ alternates between two fixed values. Regardless of the polarity of v the force between the plates is one of attraction. Increasing x requires mechanical work which must appear in the system as electrical energy. Thus, *separation* of the plates should take place at positive or negative maximum values of v. If we move the plates together when $v = 0$, no mechanical work is involved, hence no electrical energy is lost. From these considerations we see directly the requirement for $\omega_0 = 2$ and the necessity for a specific phase relation or timing of the capacitance variation. The availability of power is a consequence of the fact that the variable capacitance is an electromechanical transducer (a variable resistance is not).

For another interpretation of the effect, let us plot the locus of operation in the voltage-versus-charge plane, as shown in Fig. 8-9(*b*), for a sinusoidal variation of the spacing x. With the phase and frequency of $x(t)$ and $q(t)$ propitiously adjusted, the locus encloses the propeller-shaped area, encircling both blades of the propeller *counterclockwise*. The product of voltage and charge is energy, so that the enclosed area represents *negative energy absorbed* or *positive energy released* by the capacitance per cycle of the applied current. Doubling the amplitude of the current evidently quadruples the energy released per cycle, so that, as with a negative resistance, the source of available power is under control of the applied signal.

In some specially constructed semiconductor junction diodes, the effective capacitance of the junction can be conveniently varied by the application of a large-amplitude "pumping" voltage. A simultaneously applied small-amplitude signal whose frequency is chosen to be half the "pump" frequency* can then be made to control the power flow from the apparent negative resistance to produce useful signal amplification at relatively high frequencies with relatively low noise. Such circuits are usually called parametric amplifiers. Magnetic amplifiers, employing saturable inductors and usually operating in a switching or chopping mode, are useful at high power levels and relatively low frequencies.

From the systems viewpoint, the variable capacitance may be represented by the diagram in Fig. 8-9(*c*). Observe that the only difference between the diagram and the "system" diagram of a variable resistance (Fig. 8-6) is the addition of an integrator to convert the current signal $i(t)$ to a "charge signal" $q(t)$.

---

* Other submultiples can also be used. In fact, if resonant circuits are included, the pump frequency need not be integrally related to the signal frequency.

8.6   General Representation of a Time-Varying Linear System

A *time-invariant* linear system is characterized by its impulse response $h(\tau)$, and the response v_2 to an arbitrary input v_1 is given by

$$v_2(t_2) = \int h(\tau)v_1(t_2 - \tau)\, d\tau \qquad (8.9)$$

where t_2, τ, and $t_2 - \tau$ are respectively the output time, the memory time, and the input time. In a *time-varying* linear system the response to a unit impulse depends not only upon how long ago (τ) the impulse was applied, but also upon the time of the observation (t_2). Hence $h(\tau)$ must be generalized to the form $h(\tau, t_2)$. Thus for an arbitrary (time-varying) linear system,

$$v_2(t_2) = \int h(\tau, t_2)v_1(t_2 - \tau)\, d\tau \qquad (8.10)$$

where $h(\tau, t_2)$ is the response at time t_2 to an impulse applied τ seconds ago.

It is convenient to postulate a system whose properties vary periodically with the time so that $h(\tau, t_2)$ is a periodic function of t_2. The Fourier-series expansion of this periodic function is

$$h(\tau, t_2) = \sum_k h_k(\tau)e^{jk\omega_1 t_2} \qquad (8.11)$$

where ω_1 is the basic frequency of the variation. The Fourier coefficients h_k are, of course, functions of τ. Substitution of (8.11) into (8.10) yields the expression

$$v_2(t_2) = \sum_k e^{jk\omega_1 t_2}\int h_k(\tau)v_1(t_2 - \tau)\, d\tau \qquad (8.12)$$

The exponentials are independent of τ and therefore can be removed from the integral, as shown.

For each value of k the integral in (8.12) can be interpreted as the response function of a time-invariant linear system. Multiplication of each response by the appropriate periodic time function yields one component of the output voltage. Summation of these components yields the total output as indicated by the system diagram in Fig. 8-10. Thus, an *arbitrary periodically time-varying linear system can be realized by means of multipliers and ordinary time-invariant linear systems*. For an actual physical realization, of course, we can group the subsystems in pairs to obtain a similar diagram in which the time-invariant impulse responses are all real and the modulator signals are real sines and cosines instead of complex exponentials. Figure 8-9(c) is an elementary example.

The main point is that *any* operation that can be accomplished by a periodically time-varying linear system can be explained in terms of ordinary (time-invariant) linear system elements coupled to modulators

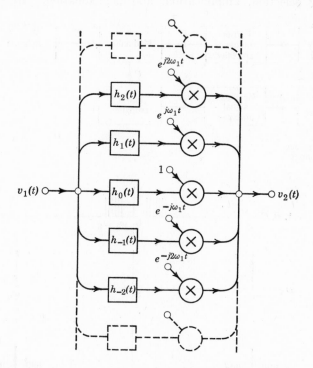

Fig. 8-10. Synthesis of an arbitrary periodically time-varying linear system by means of linear time-invariant filters and periodically excited multipliers.

of the simplest type, that is, ideal multipliers. Such a representation contributes to our intuition about the properties of modulation systems, and it is often a practical form for synthesis.

8.7 Amplitude Modulation

In communication systems, the modulation process is used to translate the message frequencies to a frequency range sufficiently high for convenient transmission over wire or through space. A simple function diagram for an amplitude-modulated radio transmitter is shown in Fig. 8-11 together with qualitative spectra of the electrical signals encountered at various points in the system. In the modulator, the time signals C and D are multiplied, and their spectra are therefore convolved to produce the spectrum E.

Reception of a high-frequency amplitude-modulated signal involves frequency selection, amplification, and demodulation. In the con-

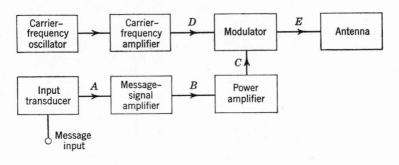

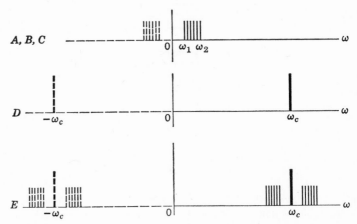

Fig. 8-11. Amplitude-modulation transmitter system.

ventional superheterodyne receiver, the process of frequency selection and amplification involves modulation. As shown in Fig. 8-12, the received signals pass through a tunable amplifier, then through a modulator (usually called a mixer) where a locally generated signal is introduced. The local oscillator is tuned to a frequency differing from the tuned-amplifier frequency by a fixed amount so that further amplification occurs in a fixed-frequency amplifier, called the intermediate-frequency amplifier. After detection there may be further amplification at message frequencies (in the range ω_1 to ω_2).

The fixed intermediate-frequency amplifier and the tunable amplifier must each pass a bandwidth of $2\omega_2$ centered at ω_d and ω_c respectively.

The band-pass filter characteristics of the amplifiers serve the important function of eliminating undesired modulation products. For example, the frequency ω_d can be formed by a carrier frequency $\omega_c = (\omega_0 - \omega_d)$ as shown in Fig. 8-12 or by a frequency $(\omega_0 + \omega_d)$. The tunable ampli-

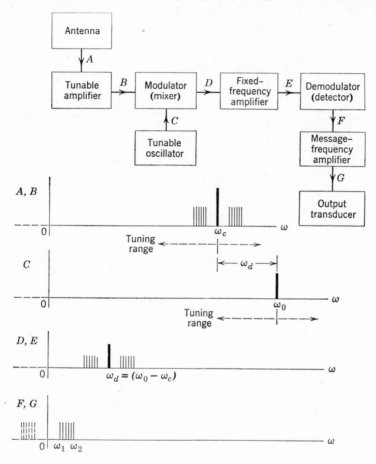

Fig. 8-12. Amplitude-modulation receiver system.

fier eliminates the latter possibility. The fixed-frequency amplifier with pass band centered at ω_d rejects incoming signals with frequency components differing from ω_c by more than the amplifier pass band. The message-frequency amplifier, following the detector, provides gain and sometimes additional frequency selectivity.

In addition to the filtering provided by the frequency-selective amplifier, unwanted frequency components can be eliminated by exploiting symmetry. To illustrate this point, let us consider the mixer in the receiver diagram of Fig. 8-12. A simple mixer is indicated diagrammatically in Fig. 8-13(a). We shall assume the center frequencies ω_c, ω_0, and ω_d are separated sufficiently to warrant the model shown in (b). This model implies that the impedance of each circuit is high at its

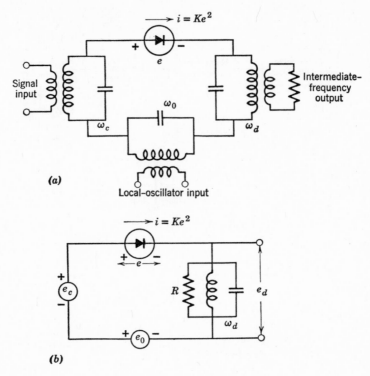

(a)

Signal input

$i = Ke^2$

ω_0

ω_c ω_d

Intermediate-frequency output

Local-oscillator input

(b)

$i = Ke^2$

e_c e R e_d ω_d e_0

Fig. 8-13. Square-law mixer.

own resonant frequency and negligibly small near the other two frequencies. Thus the signal voltage e_c at frequency ω_c and the local-oscillator voltage e_0 at frequency ω_0 appear across the diode. Assume for simplicity that the diode has a square-law curve over the range of currents and voltages involved so that

$$e_d \approx RK(e_c + e_0)^2 = RK(e_c^2 + 2e_ce_0 + e_0^2) \qquad (8.13)$$

If e_0 and e_c are sinusoids, each of the square terms yields a d-c component and a double-frequency component ($2\omega_0$ and $2\omega_c$), all of which are filtered from the output. The product term yields components at frequencies ($\omega_0 + \omega_c$) and ($\omega_0 - \omega_c$) = ω_d of which only the latter appears in the output.

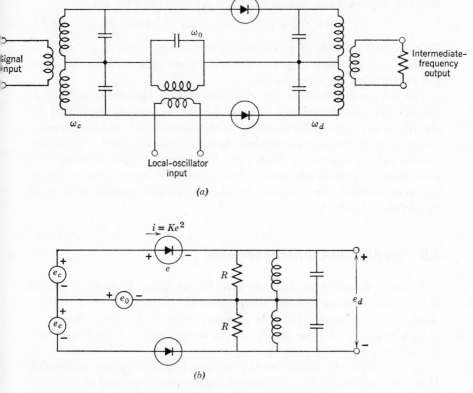

Fig. 8-14.   Balanced square-law mixer.

Since the amplitude of the product $e_c e_0$ is proportional to the local-oscillator voltage, it is advantageous in receiving weak signals to use a local-oscillator voltage much larger than the signal voltage.   Now let us examine the effects of noise modulation of the local oscillator.   The effect of noise modulation will be a low-amplitude noise spectrum on either side of ω_0.   Noise components at frequencies $(\omega_0 + \omega_d)$ and $(\omega_0 - \omega_d)$ will mix with the strong component at ω_0 to produce an output of frequency ω_d.   Such a noise output limits the sensitivity of the receiver.

A balanced mixer such as the one shown in Fig. 8-14(a) can be used to reduce the amount of local-oscillator signal present in the output. The simplified model is indicated in (b).   If the circuit is perfectly symmetrical, the source e_0 produces no output.   Thus, regardless of the filtering provided by the circuit tuned to ω_d, the frequency ω_0 is completely absent from the output because of symmetry.   Also, any noise modulation components due to the oscillator are canceled in the output.

Without the filter this circuit would be a multiplier with output

$$e_d \approx RK[(e_0 + e_c)^2 - (e_0 - e_c)^2] = 4RKe_0e_c \qquad (8.14)$$

This product consists of a component at frequency $(\omega_0 + \omega_c)$ and one at $(\omega_0 - \omega_c)$ of which only the difference term appears across the output circuit with the filter present.

The balanced circuit of Fig. 8-14 has several variations and fulfills several different functions. The particular operation performed by the circuit depends on the character of the input signals and the presence or absence of frequency-selective circuits. An idealized model containing perfect square-law diodes performs the multiplier function with a minimum of extraneous terms. A more realistic power series representation of the diode curve yields additional terms to be filtered or canceled by circuit symmetry.

8.8 Suppressed-Carrier Modulation

Suppressed-carrier modulation and demodulation is often employed in automatic-control systems to circumvent the problem of amplifying slowly varying signals. In many common systems, the carrier frequency is in the vicinity of 60 or 400 cycles per second and the signal spectrum lies between zero and a few cycles per second.

In Fig. 8-15, the inputs to the balanced modulator are sinusoidal. If we assume square-law diodes and small resistances, and also assume that e_0 is much smaller than e_m or e_c, then the circuit is a good approximation to a multiplier. The output time function is therefore the product of the carrier and modulating voltages, and the frequency spectrum of the output is the convolution of the two input spectra. The output spectrum includes components at frequencies $(\omega_c + \omega_m)$ and $(\omega_c - \omega_m)$ but the carrier frequency has been suppressed. The spectrum of the modulated signal is centered at the carrier frequency ω_c instead of the origin.

Now suppose the output signal e_0 of Fig. 8-15 is used as the input signal of a similar multiplier circuit as shown in Fig. 8-16. The other input is a sinusoid at the original carrier frequency ω_c. The convolution of E_0 and E_c yields the spectrum of the output voltage. This spectrum includes the spectrum of the original modulating signal $(\pm\omega_m)$ along with other components. Capacitances included in the circuit (as shown by the dashed lines) can be used to remove the components near $2\omega_c$, leaving only the modulating signal. Thus the balanced modulator, with a minor variation, serves also as a balanced demodulator. Demodu-

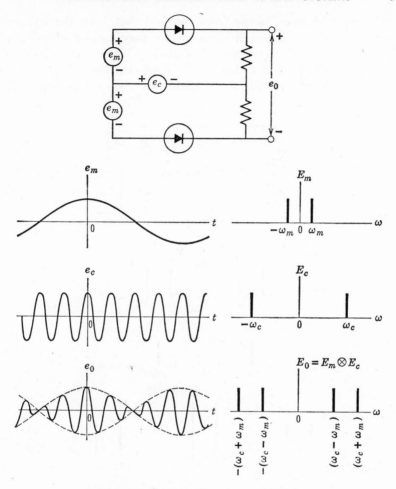

Fig. 8-15. Suppressed-carrier modulation.

lation of a suppressed-carrier signal by mixing it with the original carrier is called *synchronous detection*.

The suppressed-carrier system provides a means of avoiding the zero-set drift problems that plague d-c amplifiers. The so-called "chopper-stabilized d-c amplifier," widely used in control systems, is really not a d-c amplifier. It consists of a suppressed-carrier modulator which shifts the narrow-band signal spectrum from the vicinity of zero frequency to the vicinity of the carrier frequency. The modulated signal can then be amplified in an a-c amplifier and synchronously demodulated, as indicated in Fig. 8-17.

The term "chopper" arose from the fact that both the balanced modulator and the balanced demodulator may consist of vibrator-driven synchronous switches instead of diodes. The carrier is therefore a square wave instead of a sine wave. Replacing the sine wave by a square wave merely repeats the spectrum for each component of the

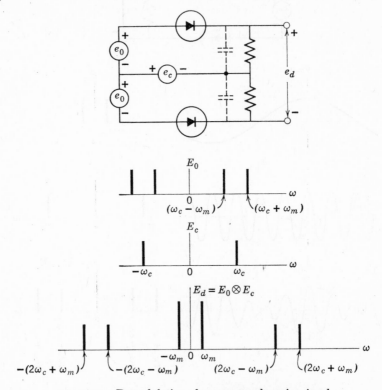

Fig. 8-16. Demodulation of a suppressed-carrier signal.

square wave. The band-pass curve of the amplifier can be chosen to remove all but the components near the fundamental frequency.

Phase sensing is an important use of the balanced-modulator circuit that arises as a special case when the signal and carrier have the same frequency. Their product contains a d-c signal with an amplitude that is a measure of the phase difference between the two signals. High-frequency output components can be eliminated by the capacitances across the resistances, as shown in Fig. 8-18. The functional form of the phase dependence varies with the nonlinear law of the diodes and with the relative signal amplitudes. For square-law diodes the output

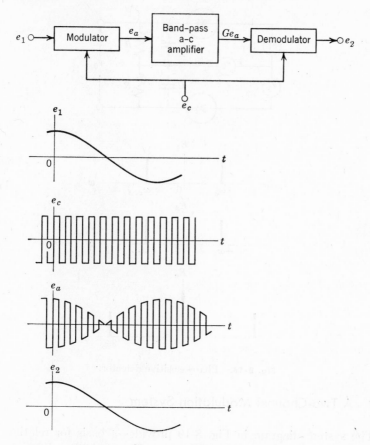

Fig. 8-17. Chopper-stabilized d-c amplifier.

is the product of e_1 and e_2. The d-c term is a simple function of the phase difference. Thus

$$e_0 = e_1 e_2 = (\cos \omega t + \phi)(\cos \omega t) \qquad (8.15)$$

which can be recast in the form

$$e_0 = e_1 e_2 = \tfrac{1}{2} \cos (2\omega t + \phi) + \tfrac{1}{2} \cos \phi \qquad (8.16)$$

With capacitances across the output, the high-frequency variation can be removed, leaving

$$e_0 \sim \cos \phi \qquad (8.17)$$

In the vicinity of $\phi = \pi/2$, the output e_0 is a sensitive measure of the phase angle ϕ.

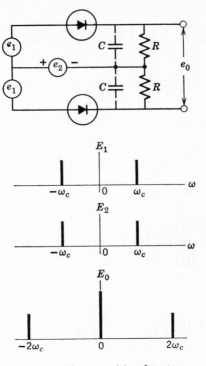

Fig. 8-18.   Phase-sensitive detector.

8.9   A Two-Channel Modulation System

The system diagram in Fig. 8-19 provides a basis for relating conventional amplitude modulation, suppressed-carrier modulation, and phase modulation.   Furthermore, this generalized modulation system illustrates the method used for color-channel combination and separation in color-television transmission and reception.   Two modulating signals, A_1 and B_1, are applied to orthogonal carriers, $\cos \omega_c t$ and $\sin \omega_c t$, having the same carrier frequency.   After transmission over a single path, synchronous detection with the same orthogonal carriers resolves the signal once more into two parts.   Assume signals $A_1(t)$ and $B_1(t)$ to have spectra at frequencies low compared to the carrier frequency. The transmission path passes frequencies in the vicinity of ω_c and the low-pass filters F pass only the low-frequency signal spectra.

Multiplication of the two input signals by orthogonal carrier components and summation of the result yield $S_1(t)$, the total signal to be transmitted:

$$S_1(t) = A_1(t) \cos \omega_c t + B_1(t) \sin \omega_c t = \left| C_1(t) \right| \cos \left[\omega_c t - \phi_1(t) \right] \quad (8.18)$$

The resultant amplitude of the signal is

$$|C_1(t)| = \sqrt{[A_1(t)]^2 + [B_1(t)]^2}$$ (8.19)

and the associated phase angle is

$$\phi_1(t) = \tan^{-1}\left[-\frac{B_1(t)}{A_1(t)}\right]$$ (8.20)

Complex vector representation is convenient for signals of this type. For example, we can express (8.18) as follows:

$$S_1(t) = \text{Re}\,[C_1(t)e^{j\omega_c t}]$$ (8.21)

where Re means "the real part of," and wherein

$$C_1(t) = A_1(t) - jB_1(t)$$ (8.22)

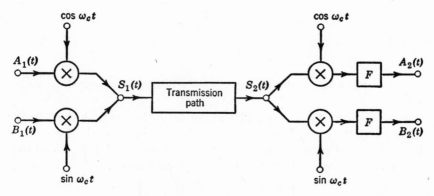

Fig. 8-19. Two-channel system.

The vector diagram in Fig. 8-20 depicts this complex expression for the envelope at a particular instant. The entire diagram must be rotated counterclockwise at angular carrier frequency ω_c and the vector amplitudes must be varied appropriately in order to generate the signal $S_1(t)$. The concept of a rotating vector whose amplitude and relative phase vary with time is a convenient concept, provided such variations are slow in comparison to the basic angular frequency ω_c.

The signal $S_2(t)$ received via the transmission path in Fig. 8-19 is a modified version of $S_1(t)$. The character of $S_2(t)$ depends on $S_1(t)$ and on the properties of the transmission medium. Let us suppose for simplicity that the transmission path can be represented by a noiseless, ideal, band-pass filter that introduces a finite time delay but has no other effect on $S_1(t)$. At the receiver we must separate and demodulate the combined signal in order to recover the two messages applied at the input. To perform these functions we require orthogonal carrier components at the same frequency ω_c as that used for modulation. Further-more, the phase of the demodulating carriers, relative to that of the modulating carriers, must be properly maintained.

The time delay experienced by $S_1(t)$ in passing through the trans-mission path can be expressed in terms of carrier phase shift and will usually amount to many radians. For convenience let this phase

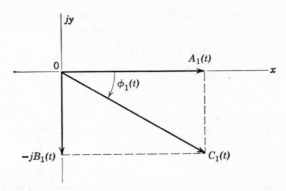

Fig. 8-20. Vector representation of a two-component signal.

shift correspond to an integral number of cycles so that $S_2(t)$ is the same as $S_1(t)$ except for the delay. Then, in general, the carriers inserted at the receiver are $\cos(\omega_c t + \theta)$ and $\sin(\omega_c t + \theta)$. The out-puts of the two demodulators are therefore as follows:

$$S_1(t) \cos(\omega_c t + \theta) = \left[\frac{A_1(t)}{2} \cos\theta - \frac{B_1(t)}{2} \sin\theta\right]$$
$$+ \left[\frac{A_1(t)}{2} \cos(2\omega_c t + \theta) + \frac{B_1(t)}{2} \sin(2\omega_c t + \theta)\right] \quad (8.23)$$

and

$$S_1(t) \sin(\omega_c t + \theta) = \left[\frac{A_1(t)}{2} \sin\theta + \frac{B_1(t)}{2} \cos\theta\right]$$
$$+ \left[\frac{A_1(t)}{2} \sin(2\omega_c t + \theta) - \frac{B_1(t)}{2} \cos(2\omega_c t + \theta)\right] \quad (8.24)$$

In each case the output of the low-pass filter is the first bracket in the trigonometric expansion. The double-frequency terms in (8.23) and (8.24) are removed by the filters.

Now, if the carrier phase at the receiver can be adjusted so that θ

is zero, the outputs of the two low-pass filters reduce to

$$A_2(t) = \frac{A_1(t)}{2} \tag{8.25}$$

$$B_2(t) = \frac{B_1(t)}{2} \tag{8.26}$$

These results demonstrate the possibility of transmitting two independent message signals by means of a single carrier wave. If the transmission path is a radio link, the variability of the troposphere or the ionosphere results in a fluctuating delay time. Under these conditions the orthogonal carriers at the receiver must be phase-locked to a received carrier.

8.10 Illustrations of Different Types of Modulation in Terms of the Two-Channel System

Since $A_1(t)$ and $B_1(t)$ are independently specifiable, Fig. 8-19 is effectively a two-channel system. However, if $A_1(t)$ and $B_1(t)$ bear appropriate relations, the same diagram is convenient to show the analytic similarities and differences between several common types of single-channel modulation systems. For example, conventional *amplitude modulation* can be obtained by imposing the following restrictions on $A_1(t)$ and $B_1(t)$:

$$A_1(t) \geq 0 \tag{8.27}$$

$$B_1(t) = KA_1(t) \tag{8.28}$$

The inequality stated in (8.27) implies that $A_1(t)$ has a direct component exceeding the instantaneous peaks of the a-c component. This means that vector $C_1(t)$ in Fig. 8-20 maintains the same orientation and never reverses direction. The proportionality expressed by (8.28) makes $\phi_1(t)$ a constant. The factor K could be set equal to zero since a single-channel modulation system is adequate to produce and demodulate amplitude modulation, in which case $\phi_1(t)$ is zero and the envelope vector $C_1(t)$ for sinusoidal modulation is

$$C_1(t) = A_1(t) = (1 + m \cos \omega_m t) \text{ where } m \leq 1 \tag{8.29}$$

To obtain *suppressed-carrier modulation* we need only remove the direct component so that

$$C_1(t) = A_1(t) = m \cos \omega_m t \text{ where } m \leq 1 \tag{8.30}$$

Multiplication of (8.29) by the carrier yields the carrier plus upper and lower side bands. When (8.30) is multiplied by a carrier, only the sum and difference frequencies are obtained. For suppressed-carrier modulation we note that vector $C_1(t)$ reverses direction twice per cycle. At each reversal of $C_1(t)$ the envelope amplitude is zero and the carrier phase changes abruptly by 180°. Demodulation of either conventional amplitude modulation or suppressed-carrier modulation amounts to a frequency translation from ω_c to zero.

The two-channel system can be used to generate *single-side-band modulation* if the modulating signal applied to one channel is also applied to the second channel after a 90° phase shift. Thus, for one modulation frequency ω_m we have

$$A_1(t) = \cos \omega_m t \tag{8.31}$$

and

$$B_1(t) = \sin \omega_m t \tag{8.32}$$

Using these signals to modulate quadrature carrier components yields

$$S_1(t) = (\cos \omega_m t \cos \omega_c t + \sin \omega_m t \sin \omega_c t) \tag{8.33}$$

This expression reduces to

$$S_1(t) = \cos (\omega_c - \omega_m)t \tag{8.34}$$

If we replace $B_1(t)$ by its negative, the result is

$$S_1(t) = \cos (\omega_c + \omega_m)t \tag{8.35}$$

In either case we have a single term at the sum or difference of carrier and modulation frequencies. Referring to Fig. 8-20 we see that $C_1(t)$ becomes a rotating vector, turning counterclockwise at angular frequency $+\omega_m$ to generate the upper side band $(\omega_c + \omega_m)$ or clockwise $(-\omega_m)$ to generate the lower side band $(\omega_c - \omega_m)$.

Demodulating (8.35) by means of two quadrature carrier components, we have

$$\cos (\omega_c + \omega_m)t \cos \omega_c t \tag{8.36}$$

and

$$\cos (\omega_c + \omega_m)t \sin \omega_c t \tag{8.37}$$

These yield sum and difference frequency terms as follows:

$$\tfrac{1}{2} \cos (2\omega_c + \omega_m)t + \tfrac{1}{2} \cos \omega_m t \tag{8.38}$$

and

$$\tfrac{1}{2} \sin (2\omega_c + \omega_m)t - \tfrac{1}{2} \sin \omega_m t \tag{8.39}$$

After filtering with low-pass filters we have $A_2(t)$ and $B_2(t)$, which include only the terms at frequency ω_m. The negative sign in (8.39) can be made positive by reversing the phase of the $\sin \omega_c t$ carrier in (8.37) or by a polarity inversion at the output of the B channel.

Vector representations for the complete signal $S_1(t)$ are shown in Fig. 8-21 for the several kinds of modulation discussed above. In each

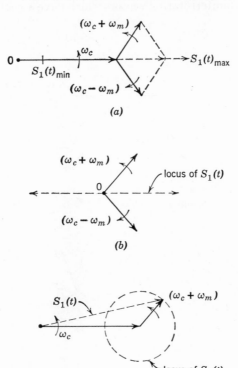

(a)

(b)

(c)

Fig. 8-21. Vector representation of modulated sine waves. (a) Conventional amplitude modulation. (b) Suppressed-carrier modulation. (c) Single-side-band modulation.

case the carrier vector has unit amplitude and the modulation vector has amplitude m. Demodulation amounts to stopping the carrier vector rotation and subtracting ω_c from the rotational velocity of the other vectors. Note that for single-side-band modulation the resultant vector $S_1(t)$ is modulated both in amplitude and in angular velocity or phase.

To produce phase modulation more nearly free of amplitude modulation, two side-band frequencies are required. The vector diagram in Fig. 8-22(a) shows these side bands to be counterrotating vectors with a vector sum that is orthogonal to the carrier vector. Only for very small phase excursions is the resultant vector independent of amplitude. For larger phase deviations, the resultant vector has the same amplitude as the carrier twice during each modulation cycle and grows to a larger amplitude twice per cycle. This slight amplitude modulation can be represented by counterrotating vectors which have a vector sum in phase

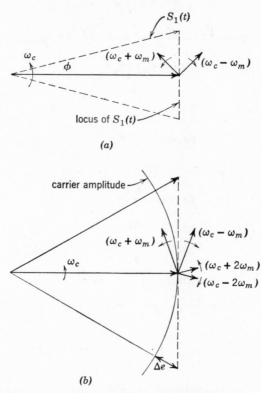

Fig. 8-22.   Vector representation of phase-modulated sine wave.   (*a*) Small deviation.   (*b*) Large deviation.

with the carrier and a frequency $2\omega_m$ as illustrated in Fig. 8-22(*b*). The amplitude-modulation side bands at $\pm2\omega_m$ leave a residual phase error that can be corrected (almost) by additional small phase-modulation side bands. Thus, except for very small phase deviations, phase modulation of a carrier by a single modulating frequency results in a whole family of side bands (at frequencies $\pm\omega_m, \pm2\omega_m, \pm3\omega_m, \cdots$). The vector representation is cumbersome if the phase deviation is large enough to require more than two pairs of side bands for adequate specification of the resultant signal vector.

8.11   Phase and Frequency Modulation

If the phase deviation is many radians, the resultant envelope vector in Fig. 8-22 alternately spins clockwise and counterclockwise at modulating frequency ω_m. Adding the fixed counterclockwise rotation of the entire diagram at carrier frequency ω_c to the alternating rotation of the envelope vector amounts to speeding up and slowing down the signal vector. Even for large deviations, the process is called *phase modulation* if the amplitude of the modulating signal determines the peak phase deviation; it is called *frequency modulation* if the modulation amplitude determines the peak frequency deviation. In the latter case, the peak phase deviation varies inversely with the modulating frequency and the spectrum width is very nearly independent of modulating frequency. In phase modulation, the maximum phase deviation is independent of modulating frequency but the spectrum width (maximum frequency deviation) is approximately proportional to the modulating frequency.

Interpretation of frequency modulation requires an extension of the "fixed-frequency" concept that pertains to sine waves. In terms of the vector representation, alternate speeding up and slowing down of the signal vector indicates a variation of the "instantaneous" frequency. Since the argument of $\sin \omega t$ is an angle, the angular frequency ω is the rate at which phase increases. Thus a constant phase rate corresponds to a constant angular frequency, and a time-varying phase rate can be interpreted as a varying frequency. By defining frequency as rate of change of phase, we generalize the frequency concept to include the time-varying case. We shall now apply these ideas to an elementary frequency-modulated wave. Let

$$v(t) = \sin [\theta(t)] \tag{8.40}$$

where

$$\frac{d\theta(t)}{dt} = \omega(t) \tag{8.41}$$

Also, let

$$\omega(t) = \omega_c + \omega_1(t) \tag{8.42}$$

Integration yields

$$\theta(t) = \int_0^t \omega(t)\, dt = \omega_c t + \int_0^t \omega_1(t)\, dt \tag{8.43}$$

For simplicity, we shall assume a single-frequency modulating signal $E_m \cos \omega_m t$. The frequency modulator must generate a frequency proportional to the modulating signal so that

$$\omega_1(t) = K_m \cos \omega_m t \tag{8.44}$$

where K_m has the dimensions of radians per second. Then

$$v(t) = \sin\left(\omega_c t + \frac{K_m}{\omega_m} \sin \omega_m t\right) \tag{8.45}$$

Note that the peak modulating voltage E_m is proportional to the peak frequency deviation K_m but that the peak phase deviation K_m/ω_m varies inversely with the modulating frequency ω_m. The quantity K_m/ω_m is called the *modulation index.*

Expansion of the trigonometric expression (8.45) leads to an infinite series of side bands. The amplitudes of the side bands are governed by the modulation index, which appears in each term of the series as the argument of a Bessel function of the first kind.* Thus, letting $K_m/\omega_m = m$, we have

$$
\begin{aligned}
v(t) = \quad & J_0(m) \sin \omega_c t \\
& + J_1(m) \left[\sin(\omega_c + \omega_m)t - \sin(\omega_c - \omega_m)t\right] \\
& + J_2(m) \left[\sin(\omega_c + 2\omega_m)t + \sin(\omega_c - 2\omega_m)t\right] \\
& \quad\vdots \\
& + J_n(m) \left[\sin(\omega_c + n\omega_m)t \pm \sin(\omega_c - n\omega_m)t\right] \\
& \quad\vdots
\end{aligned}
$$

In the general term, the positive sign is used for n even and the negative sign for n odd. If m is zero, only the carrier exists because $J_n(0)$ is unity for $n = 0$ and is zero for $n \neq 0$. For small values of m only the first pair of side bands is significant, and as m increases additional terms become significant. Since the Bessel functions are oscillatory, the carrier or any pair of side bands may disappear from the spectrum for certain values of m.

With a fixed-frequency deviation K_m, the modulation index is small for large values of ω_m. The spectrum then consists of only the first few pairs of side bands but, since ω_m is large, these are widely spaced. For small values of ω_m, the ratio m is large and the spectrum consists of many closely spaced side bands. Thus the total spectrum width is nearly independent of ω_m.

The spectra of frequency-modulated signals are further complicated

---

* See Appendix A for plots of $J_n(m)$.

by the fact that the process is nonlinear. When two or more modulating frequencies are present, the spectrum is not the sum of the separate spectra as in amplitude modulation. The relative amplitudes of all terms in the spectrum are affected by the inclusion of more modulation frequencies. The side bands at frequencies $(\omega_c \pm k\omega_{m1})$, $(\omega_c \pm k\omega_{m2})$, $\cdots$, are analogous to those obtained in the single-frequency case but with relative amplitudes influenced by the modulation index for each frequency.* In addition, there are terms at frequencies $(\omega_c \pm k\omega_{m1} \pm n\omega_{m2})$, $\cdots$.

Square-wave modulation is a special case in which the spectrum analysis of a frequency-modulated signal becomes relatively simple. Consider, for example, a signal that is alternately at frequency $\omega_1 = (\omega_c + K)$ and $\omega_2 = (\omega_c - K)$ for intervals $T/2$, where T is the period of the square wave. The signal therefore consists of alternate segments of sine waves at different frequencies. In this case, the spectrum of a square-wave modulated sine wave of frequency ω_1 can be added to a similar spectrum for a square-wave modulated sine wave of frequency ω_2 with the modulation envelope of one shifted by an interval $T/2$ relative to the other. Square-wave frequency modulation is an idealization of the frequency-shift keying system used in radiotelegraphy and radio-teletype transmission.

A frequency-modulated wave can be produced by controlling the frequency of an oscillator with a variable reactance. In the case of frequency-shift keying an increment of capacitance is switched in and out of the oscillator tuned circuit. For continuous modulation such as speech or music, an electrically controlled reactance is needed. A reactance-tube circuit can be used to add a small component of reactive current to a tuned circuit. For example, suppose the plate-cathode circuit of a pentode is connected in parallel with the tuned circuit of an oscillator. The grid-to-cathode voltage is obtained from the same source as the plate-to-cathode voltage but is phase shifted 90° by an RC circuit. Since plate current is proportional to grid voltage, it bears a 90° phase relation to the plate voltage and hence appears to be a reactive current. The phase-shift network can be chosen to make the plate current inductive or capacitive. The modulating signal is applied to the grid circuit to control the magnitude of the plate current. For a small percentage change in capacitance or inductance the corresponding frequency shift is quite linear.

---

* For systems in which nonsinusoidal modulation occurs, a quantity δ, called the *deviation ratio*, is defined as the ratio of the maximum frequency deviation to the maximum modulating frequency. For sinusoidal modulation δ is the same as m.

Demodulation of a frequency-modulated wave can be accomplished by any detector circuit that has a linear voltage-versus-frequency transfer curve. Such a circuit is essentially a "frequency meter" or, as it is more commonly called, a frequency discriminator. A rudimentary discriminator is merely a tuned circuit adjusted so that the entire frequency deviation of the frequency-modulated signal lies on one side of the resonance curve. For current-source excitation, the voltage across the circuit will be very nearly proportional to frequency because the reactance varies nearly linearly with frequency over a small range. Rectification and smoothing of the voltage across the reactance completes the demodulation process. Some discriminator circuits utilize a balanced combination of two resonant circuits, one tuned above and the other below the center frequency, and operate on the difference of the two resonance characteristics.

To eliminate the effects of signal fading, an FM radio receiver includes an amplitude limiter which provides a constant-amplitude FM input to the frequency discriminator.

8.12 Frequency Multiplexing

When more than two channels of information are to be transmitted, we can use several sinusoidal carriers differing in frequency sufficiently to permit convenient frequency separation (filtering). Radio and television broadcasting and reception provide familiar examples of channel selection on the basis of frequency. The various transmitters normally operate independently, but we could conceivably use the modulated carriers of several stations as modulating signals—all of which are to be transmitted by a much higher carrier frequency. Multiple-channel communication systems use this double-modulation technique to achieve frequency multiplexing.

The block diagrams in Fig. 8-23 indicate the general operations that must be accomplished in the transmission and reception of frequency-multiplexed signals. We assume here that the input-signal frequencies are much lower than the subcarrier frequencies $\omega_1, \omega_2, \cdots$, which are in turn considerably smaller than the carrier frequency ω_c.

After combination of signals $1, 2, \cdots, n$ in the transmitter and before separation in the receiver, system linearity is important. Nonlinear distortion is undesirable because it results in unwanted modulation or "cross talk" between channels.

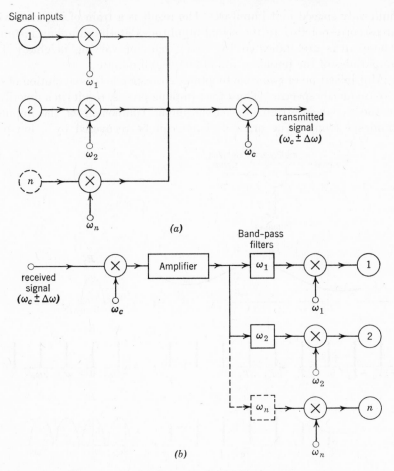

Fig. 8-23. Frequency-multiplex system. (a) Transmitter. (b) Receiver.

8.13 Pulse-Amplitude Modulation

The sampling theorem, discussed in Article 6.27, provides the theoretical basis for pulse-modulation systems. The theorem shows that a band-limited signal can be reconstructed from brief samples of the signal taken at regular intervals, provided these sampling intervals are shorter than the half-period of the maximum signal frequency. In terms of frequency, signal reconstruction requires a sampling-pulse repetition frequency greater than twice the maximum signal frequency.

The impulse modulator in Fig. 8-24 is the idealization of a sampling circuit. The signal to be sampled is multiplied by a continuous train of uniformly spaced unit impulses. The result is a train of impulses with areas corresponding to the signal amplitudes at the sampling instants. These areas are indicated by heavy bars of varying heights. The amplitudes of the impulses are, of course, all infinite.

Multiplication of two time functions corresponds to convolution of the two frequency spectra. Thus, the sampling process results in a repetition of the signal spectrum at each harmonic component of the impulse-train spectrum. The original signal can be recovered by a low-pass

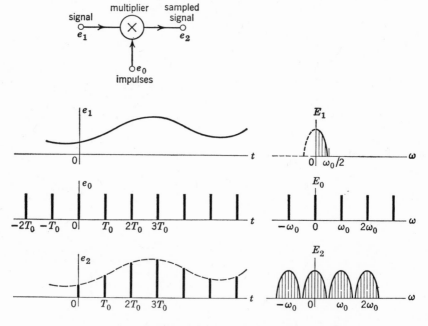

Fig. 8-24. Impulse modulator (ideal sampling circuit).

filter with cutoff at $\omega_0/2$. From the spectra in Fig. 8-24 we can deduce the requirements imposed by the sampling theorem. If the spectrum of the band-limited signal falls within $\pm\omega_0/2$, the repeated spectra are separate and the original signal can be fully recovered. If the signal spectrum extends beyond $\omega_0/2$, the sampling process will produce replicas that overlap, and the recovered signal will be distorted.

A pulse-amplitude modulator circuit is shown in Fig. 8-25. The pulses applied to the circuit at the transformer secondary should have a total effective amplitude greater than the maximum signal excursion. The transformer windings are polarized to make the pulse voltages additive; hence during each pulse the diodes conduct and effectively connect the output to the input. Thus e_2 equals e_1 during each pulse. Between pulses the diodes have reverse voltage applied as a result of the charges on the capacitors. The output is therefore isolated from the input during the intervals between pulses. The resulting waveform $e_2(t)$ is a pulse train, amplitude-modulated by the signal. These amplitude-modulated pulses are, in turn, samples of the signal waveform.

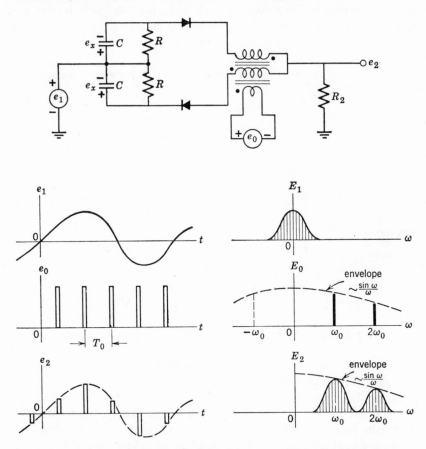

Fig. 8-25. Pulse-amplitude modulator (sampling circuit).

Pulse-amplitude modulation is used in microwave communication, in radio telemetry and in data-processing systems. When used for wire or radio communication the modulated pulses usually appear as a sub-carrier modulating a high-frequency or microwave sinusoidal carrier. The carrier might be amplitude-, phase-, or frequency-modulated by the pulse subcarrier. The simplest of these three is an amplitude-modulation system, commonly designated PAM/AM. A rudimentary block diagram of such a system is shown in Fig. 8-26. The main carrier frequency ω_c is assumed to be much greater than the pulse repetition frequency ω_0. This frequency in turn must exceed $2\omega_m$, where ω_m is the maximum frequency present in the signal. Assume for simplicity that the signal is a sine wave of frequency ω_m and the subcarrier is a train of rectangular pulses recurring at frequency ω_0. Then ω_m produces side bands $\pm\omega_m$ from each pulse-spectrum component, $\omega_0, 2\omega_0, 3\omega_0, \cdots$. This entire spectrum appears on either side of the carrier frequency ω_c.

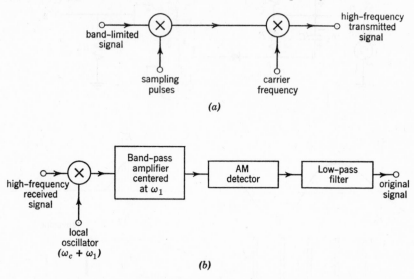

Fig. 8-26. Pulse-amplitude modulation (PAM/AM system).

Frequency modulation of the carrier is more common than amplitude modulation because the effects of signal fading due to the transmission path can be more readily eliminated. Minor modification of Fig. 8-26 will convert the PAM/AM system to PAM/FM. In the transmitter, shown in (a), the carrier-frequency multiplier must be replaced by a frequency modulator or by a phase modulator and frequency multipliers. In the receiver, shown in (b), the amplitude-modulation detector is replaced by a frequency discriminator.

8.14   Time Multiplexing

Pulse-amplitude modulation (PAM) is only one of several means of modulating a uniform pulse train in order to convey information. Other possibilities are pulse-duration modulation (PDM), pulse-position modulation (PPM), and pulse-code modulation (PCM). In each case the resulting pulse train can be used to modulate the amplitude or frequency of a high-frequency sinusoidal carrier for radio transmission.

In a single-channel system, the brief pulses that represent sample values of the signal to be transmitted may be separated by relatively long time intervals. The possibility therefore exists for interleaving pulses that represent signals from other channels provided the pulses can be separated appropriately at the receiver. Thus, we can use several signals on a time-sharing basis to modulate a single carrier. If, in a given system, we have n time-multiplexed channels on each of m frequency-multiplexed carriers, the total number of channels is nm. The total number of available channels is an important consideration in many applications, such as radio telephony. However, for a frequency spectrum of fixed width, an increase in the number of channels reduces the bandwidth available per channel.

A time-multiplexed PAM system is shown in Fig. 8-27. Electronic switches or commutators, controlled by precise timing circuits, provide the multiplexing of channels. In the transmitter, the signal inputs from channels 1 through n are sampled in sequence at a sufficient rate to satisfy the limitations imposed by the sampling theorem. For example, suppose we are dealing with voice communication and that we wish to transmit frequencies up to 3 kc (kilocycles per second). The required sampling rate then must exceed 6 kc. A typical practical value for this sampling rate is 8 kc. The basic commutating rate is then at least $8n$ kc. If there are to be n active channels, a rate of $8(n+1)$ or $8(n+2)$ may be used in order to include a synchronizing signal. The synchronizing signal can take many different forms. The only real requirement on the synchronizing signal is recognition at the receiver. If either channel pulses or noise pulses confuse the synchronizing circuits, the system becomes inoperative.

For simplicity, consider the synchronizing signal in Fig. 8-27 to be a pulse of greater duration than the channel pulses as shown in Fig. 8-28. A pulse-width discriminator can then be used to find this pulse in each frame of channel signals. Recognition of a synchronizing signal can be achieved in a variety of other ways, but width discrimination is a suitable example.

The transmitter block diagram in Fig. 8-27 (a) indicates the general process of time multiplexing. The commutator connects the channels to the sampling circuit in sequence at the basic repetition rate established by the timing circuits. Position s on the commutator indicates the fact that one pulse interval has been set aside for synchronization.

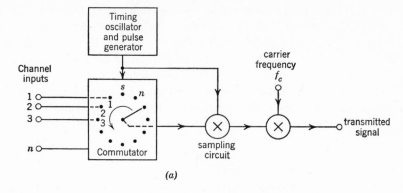

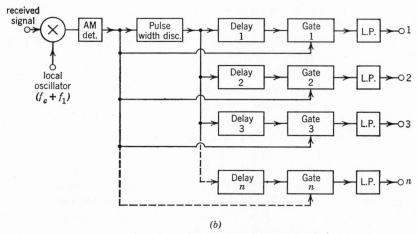

Fig. 8-27. Time-multiplexed PAM system (n channels).

The incoming channel signals are usually such that amplification is required. An audio-amplifier in each of the n channels provides one solution. However, if the commutator can switch low-amplitude signals without distorting them or introducing undesirable frequency components, it is possible to perform the amplification after sampling, thereby substituting a single pulse amplifier for n audio amplifiers.

In the receiver block diagram shown in Fig. 8-27(b) the signal is amplified in an intermediate-frequency amplifier, and then detected. As indicated by the waveforms of Fig. 8-28, the pulse-width discriminator must isolate the synchronizing signal. The synchronizing signal initiates time delays corresponding to the channel positions relative to the synchronizing pulses. Each gate circuit receives all pulses at one input; a gating pulse for a specific channel is applied at the other input. The output of each gate circuit is a sequence of samples for a single channel. A low-pass filter recovers the original information.

The system just outlined illustrates one method of establishing time-multiplexed communication channels. Several variations of the method are used in pulse-communication systems.

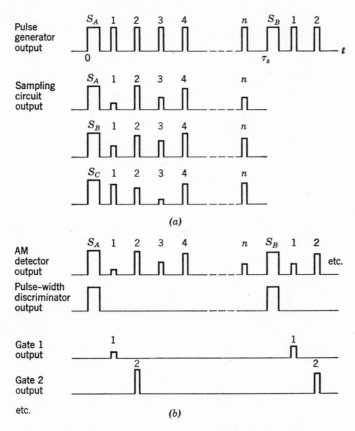

Fig. 8-28. Waveforms in the time-multiplexed PAM system.

Time multiplexing of channels can be carried out in similar fashion for other types of pulse modulation such as PDM or PPM. Duration-modulated pulses are shown in Fig. 8-29(a). The modulator to produce these pulses can be a coincidence circuit that generates a time interval proportional to a voltage-sample amplitude. With constant pulse amplitude, the area of each channel pulse is proportional to the sampled value; hence the original signal can be recovered by means of a low-pass filter as in the case of PAM.

For a multichannel PDM system each channel pulse can be started at a fixed position relative to the synchronizing pulses and the trailing edges of the pulse can be modulated. When these pulses are used to modulate a high-frequency carrier, the power transmitted is proportional to the pulse duration. Actually, the trailing edges of the channel pulses are

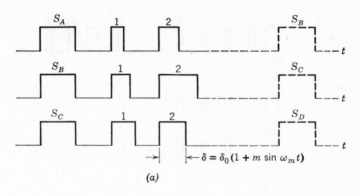

(a)

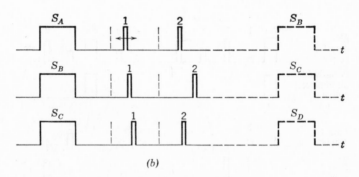

(b)

Fig. 8-29. PDM and PPM pulses.

conveying the signal variation. Advancing the leading edge of all pulses by a fixed amount is equivalent to adding a d-c component to the modulating signal. Moving the leading edge to the right subtracts from the d-c component and reduces the average carrier power to be transmitted. Assuming sinusoidal modulation, we find that the pulse duration from one frame to the next takes on discrete values that satisfy the relation

$$\delta = \delta_0(1 + m \sin \omega_m t) \tag{8.46}$$

where m must be less than unity. If only the trailing edges of the duration-modulated pulses are transmitted in the form of very brief pulses, the signal samples are represented by pulse positions. The waveforms for PPM are shown in Fig. 8-29(b) for convenient comparison with the PDM waveforms in (a).

When we observe successive frames of PPM waveforms, it is apparent that the average power remains constant. In a receiver that recognizes the synchronizing pulses and separates the channel pulses by appropriately positioned gates, as in Fig. 8-27(b), a low-pass filter will yield only a d-c component since the average power in each set of channel pulses is constant. The same general form of receiver can be used to demodulate PPM waveforms provided the gate circuit in each channel is designed to convert the PPM to PDM. The conversion can be accomplished in the following way. Let the gate circuit for the kth channel trigger a bistable circuit at a time fixed relative to the synchronizing pulse, after the latest possible arrival time of the pulse for the $(k-1)$th channel, and prior to the earliest arrival of the kth channel pulse. If the kth channel pulse then resets the bistable circuit, a duration-modulated output is available for demodulation by the low-pass filter.

8.15 Pulse-Code Modulation

In a pulse-code modulation system, the input signal is sampled and each sample value is transmitted as a "code word" consisting of a pattern of pulses. A simple illustration of PCM is the transmission by Morse code of weather information, say frequent barometer readings. The important feature of PCM, which makes possible the discrimination against certain kinds of interference, is that demodulation (extraction of the original message) requires only a decision as to the presence or absence of the pulse in each possible pulse position of the code word. Thus *slight* fluctuations of pulse height or width introduce *no error*.

The exploitation of PCM can be explained in terms of a specific numerical example. A signal v_0 consisting of marks (pulses) and spaces (absences of pulses) is to be sent from Washington to New York. At New York the signal is received, amplified, and the result v_1 is retransmitted to Boston, where a second reception and amplification take place to give the final output v_2. Signal v_0 takes either the value 6 volts (a mark) or 0 volt (a space). In each of the two legs of the Washington-to-Boston transmission, 1 volt rms of independent Gaussian noise n is added to the signal. Thus, for a space, $v_0 = 0$, $v_1 = n_1 = 1$ volt rms, $v_2 = n_1 + n_2 = \sqrt{2}$ volts rms. Since the addition of independent noises produces convolution of their amplitude probability-density

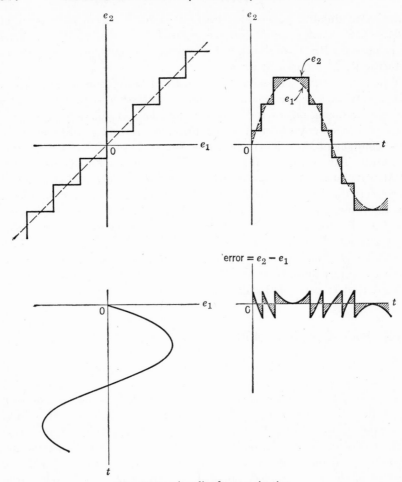

Fig. 8-30. Amplitude quantization.

functions, we have $P_0(v) = u_0(v)$, $P_1(v) = (1/\sqrt{2\pi}) \exp(-v^2/2)$, $P_2(v) = (1/\sqrt{4\pi}) \exp(-v^2/4)$. In Boston, we sample each pulse position once and record a *mark* if voltage v_2 is *above* 3 and a *space* if voltage v_2 is *below* 3. For $v_0 = 0$, the probability of making an error (recording a mark in Boston) is $\int_3^\infty P_2(v)\, dv \approx (0.020)$. Thus we can expect about 20 errors per 1000 decisions, because of the $\sqrt{2}$ volts rms of noise appearing in Boston. Now let us replace the linear "repeater" amplifier in New York by a simple nonlinear operation just like the one in Boston. In New York we record a mark for v_1 greater than 3 and a space for v_1 less than 3, and then transmit the recorded result to Boston.

For $v_0 = 0$, the probability of an error at New York is $\int_3^\infty P_1(v)\, dv \approx$
(0.0015), or about 1.5 errors per 1000 pulses. For low error rates, the errors in the second leg (New York to Boston) are not likely to be coincident with those in the first leg. Hence there will be about $1.5 + 1.5 = 3$ errors per 1000 pulses at Boston. The point is that the error rate has been reduced from 20 to 3 by the introduction of a nonlinear

Decimal number	Binary equivalent $2^3\ 2^2\ 2^1\ 2^0$				Pulse-code waveforms $2^0\ 2^1\ 2^2\ 2^3$
0				0	
1				1	
2			1	0	
3			1	1	
4		1	0	0	
5		1	0	1	
6		1	1	0	
7		1	1	1	
8	1	0	0	0	
9	1	0	0	1	
10	1	0	1	0	
11	1	0	1	1	
12	1	1	0	0	
13	1	1	0	1	
14	1	1	1	0	
15	1	1	1	1	

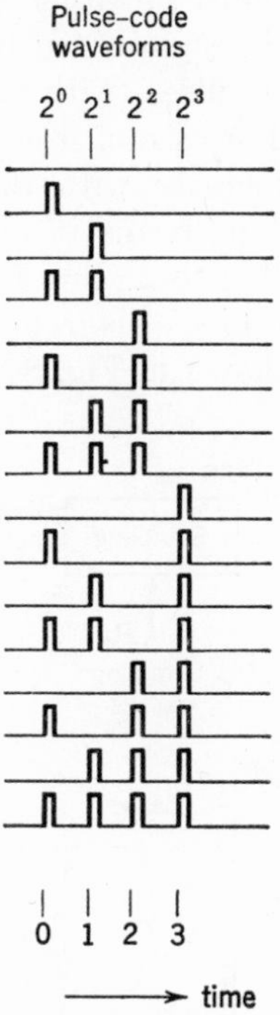

Fig. 8-31.   Binary numbers and pulse waveforms.

"yes-or-no" repeater in place of the original linear repeater at New York. Thus, depending upon the character of the signal and the noise, system nonlinearity (which we usually think of as a source of additional "error" or "noise") may actually improve the system performance. As the signal-to-noise ratio is increased in the foregoing example, or as more legs are added to the transmission path, the improvement obtainable with nonlinear repeaters becomes more striking.

The operations required to generate a PCM signal are sampling, quantization, and coding (conversion of a signal voltage to a train of pulses representing a binary number). To recover the modulation, a decoder is required to convert the group of pulses to a voltage. Over the dynamic range of the modulating signals a quantizer has a stepwise transfer curve as shown in Fig. 8-30. The more levels for a given range of voltage the smaller the "round-off" error, but in any case the signal is effectively replaced by a stepwise approximation; each value of the input signal is replaced by the nearest constant value permissible in the quantizer output. With only a finite number of possible levels at the output, each can be assigned a binary number. In a binary number, each digit must be either a 0 or a 1, and these two possibilities can be conveniently represented by the absence or presence of a pulse. Thus a train of n pulses (with some omitted) can represent an n-digit binary number. For ease of decoding, the weights assigned to successive digit positions increase with time, as indicated in Fig. 8-31. With units normalized in terms of the pulse-repetition interval, we have $t = 0$ corresponding to 2^0, $t = 1$ to 2^1, and so on.

A simple block diagram, indicating the basic steps in the coding of a signal, is shown in Fig. 8-32. As in other pulse systems, the sampling

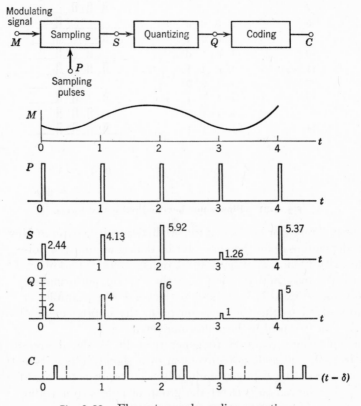

Fig. 8-32. Elementary pulse-coding operations.

rate must be at least twice the maximum modulating frequency to permit recovery of the original signal. Thus the basic pulse rate must be at least n times the sampling rate, where n is the number of digits in the binary number representing each sample.

The modulating signal M is assumed to be compressed or limited so that the range of variation remains within the dynamic range of the available quantization levels. The sampled signal in this example is quantized in eight levels. Using the numbers 0 through 7 to represent these levels, we require a three-digit code for each sample. On the waveform of coded pulses C the missing pulses in each code group are shown as dashed lines. Thus the sequence of binary numbers is 010, 100, 110, 001, and 101, corresponding to decimal numbers 2, 4, 6, 1, and 5. Note that the waveform C is delayed relative to the others by an interval δ, sufficient to perform the coding operation.

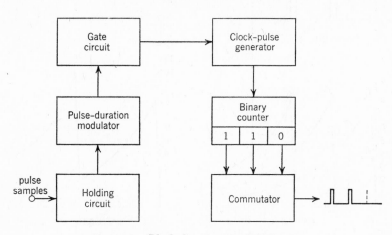

Fig. 8-33. Block diagram of a PCM coder.

Pulse coding can be performed in a variety of ways with fairly conventional circuitry or by means of special-purpose cathode-ray coding tubes. A block diagram of one form of coding circuit is shown in Fig. 8-33. Here the pulse samples are applied to a holding circuit; that is, the pulse amplitude is stored in a capacitor. The pulse-duration modulator produces a pulse with a duration proportional to the sample amplitude. This pulse is used to gate the output of a clock-pulse generator, thus controlling the number of pulses applied to a binary counter. The duration of the gate pulse is not necessarily an integral number of repetition intervals of the precisely timed clock pulses; hence the signal fed to the binary counter may consist of m pulses plus the leading edge of a pulse. This "portion of a pulse" will either have sufficient duration to trigger the counter or not.   Thus the samples have been quantized, since a definite integer number is stored in the counter after the gate pulse ends.   Each bistable stage of the counter now effectively stores a 0 or a 1 for the digit it represents (binary 011 or decimal 3 shown). An electronic switch or commutator samples the 2^0, 2^1, 2^2 digit positions

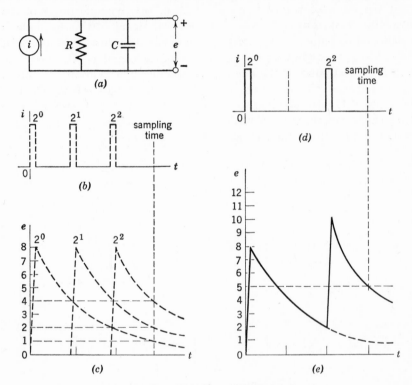

Fig. 8-34.   Decoding a PCM signal.

in sequence and transmits a 0 or 1 in accordance with the state of that stage.   The holding circuit must of course be discharged and the counter reset to 0 before the next sample is coded.

Decoding PCM is relatively simple.   We can use a current source to apply the pulse code to an RC circuit as shown in Fig. 8-34(a).   The time constant of the RC circuit must be 1.44 times the interval between pulses in the code group.   This value permits the capacitor charge from one pulse to decay to half its original value by the time the second pulse arrives and hence to one-fourth by the time the third arrives.   The response to each of the three pulses in Fig. 8-34(b), considered separately, is shown in (c). These responses belong respectively to binary numbers 001, 010, and 100 corresponding to decimal numbers 1, 2, and 4. The peak amplitude of the response and the sampling time have been chosen to make these individual responses correspond to the decimal value of the voltage. Since superposition applies in a linear circuit, any binary number involving two or three pulses will produce a total response obtained by adding the individual ones. Thus in (d) we have the binary number 101 (decimal 5) and in (e) the total response at sampling time is 5. The sampling time is not critical because the choice of time constant relative to pulse interval assures binary weighting of the three digit positions at any instant of time.

8.16 Some General Remarks about Nonlinear Systems

The systems described in the preceding several articles indicate the variety of possibilities that can be achieved with nonlinear systems. There *seems* to be no end of combinations and permutations of the elementary signal operations. Nevertheless, it is possible to show that a very large class of nonlinear systems can be synthesized by a cascade of three subsystems; namely, a nonlinear amnesic (memoryless) system, followed by a linear system exhibiting time delay, followed by a second nonlinear amnesic system. Let us begin by devising a general model for a *linear* system.

The flow graph in Fig. 8-35(a) is an approximate model for an arbitrary *linear* system. The heavy branches represent ideal delays. The constant branch transmissions are expressed as the products of constants h_k and the delay parameter δ. This notation will prove convenient in the subsequent discussion. By inspection of the flow graph (a), we have, for an arbitrary input $x(t)$,

$$y(t) = h_0 x(t)\delta + h_1 x(t - \delta)\delta + h_2 x(t - 2\delta)\delta + \cdots$$
$$+ h_k x(t - k\delta)\delta + \cdots + h_n(t - n\delta)\delta \tag{8.47}$$

or

$$y(t) = \sum_{k=0}^{n} h_k x(t - k\delta)\delta \tag{8.48}$$

In the limit of small δ and large n, three things happen. First, the specific *pulse* input shown in (b) approaches a unit impulse. Second, the step curve in (c) becomes an arbitrarily close approximation to any desired impulse-response function $h(t)$, merely by proper choice of the constants h_k. Third, the summation in (8.48) approaches (and, in fact,

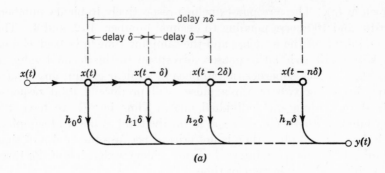

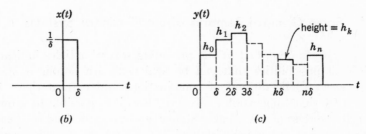

Fig. 8-35. Synthesis of a step approximation to an arbitrary pulse-response function.

defines) the integral

$$y(t) = \int_0^\infty h(\tau) x(t - \tau) \, d\tau \qquad (8.49)$$

which is recognizable as the superposition integral relating the input and output signals of a linear time-invariant transmission system.

Thus, we have synthesized an arbitrary linear transmission in the form of a tapped delay line, a set of ideal amplifiers ($h_k\delta$), and an ideal adder (the output node in Fig. 8-35). Replacement of the amplifiers and the adder by a more general amnesic operation yields the *nonlinear* system shown in Fig. 8-36. The *linear* system occurs as a special case when the computer is programmed to yield a *linear* combination of the memory samples x_k. The computer may be thought of as a look-up table or "dictionary." A specific set of values of the "letters" x_k determines a "word" $x_0, x_1, x_2, \cdots, x_n$ which can be located instantaneously in the "dictionary," thereby "translating" that word into a specific instantaneous output value $y_0 = y(t)$. For the linear case, the amnesic part of the process is equivalent to a "projection" of the "vector" $x_0, x_1, \cdots, x_n$ upon a certain direction in the associated "vector space."

A large class of signal-processing operations can be synthesized as the model shown in Fig. 8-37, an interconnection of a *linear* system (L) with an *amnesic* system (A). The linear system provides memory and displays the past history of the input as a spatial array of numbers. The

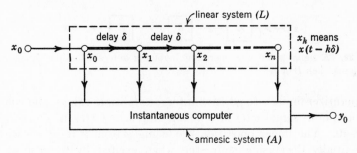

Fig. 8-36. Synthesis of a nonlinear transmission function $y_0 = f(x_0, x_1, x_2, \cdots, x_n)$.

amnesic (memoryless) system then acts instantaneously upon these numbers to give the output

$$y_0 = f(x_0, x_1, x_2, \cdots, x_n) \tag{8.50}$$

or

$$y(t) = f[x(t), x(t - \delta), x(t - 2\delta), \cdots, x(t - n\delta)] \tag{8.51}$$

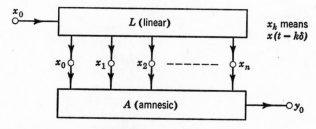

Fig. 8-37. Synthesis of a signal-processing operation as an interconnection of one single-input multiple-output linear system and one multiple-input single-output amnesic system.

For signals x that can be represented arbitrarily closely by their sample values x_k, the function (8.51) allows us to describe and synthesize a general class of (nonlinear) time-invariant signal-processing operations for which the output is an arbitrary (single-valued) function of the past history of the input.

The fact that a general process can be separated into linear and amnesic subprocesses is important, for it means that the study of linear systems and the study of memoryless nonlinear systems are not mere exercises preliminary to the understanding of more general systems; they are integral parts of general systems theory.

The synthesis of a signal-processing operation can be carried out in a modified form which involves *only single-input single-output L and A systems*, as indicated in Fig. 8-38. The details are shown in Fig. 8-39.

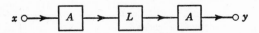

Fig. 8-38. A signal-processing operation involving only single-input single-output subsystems, each L or A.

The quantizer limits x to positive-integer amplitude values, and converts the continuous signal $w(t)$ into a stair-step signal $x(t)$, as illustrated in Fig. 8-40. The linear operation producing y from x responds with an exponentially decreasing stair step when excited by a pulse of unit width. This response can be synthesized by means of delay feedback, as in Fig. 8-41. Each circulation around the loop produces unit delay and multiplication by one-tenth.

The decimal shift due to the delay and attenuation is illustrated by the histories of x and y in Table 8-1. (Assume that x vanishes for all

Table 8-1.   An Example of Histories of x and y

k	$x(t-k)$	$y(t-k)$
7	0	0.000000
6	7	7.000000
5	7	7.700000
4	3	3.770000
3	2	2.377000
2	5	5.237700
1	9	9.523770
0	8	8.952377

$k > 7$.) The digits of $y(t)$ shift to the right and the most recent value of x is added at the left (replacing the previous value). Here the information about the history of the input is stored in the decimal places of $y(t)$. The last box in the system is effectively a look-up table in which any desired set of output values may be assigned to the various possible sets of amplitude-quantized input data describing the different possible input histories. The output z is an arbitrary function of the quantized input-history samples,

$$z(t) = f[x(t), x(t-1), x(t-2), \cdots] \tag{8.52}$$

Thus, we have a rather general signal-processing operation, Fig. 8-39,

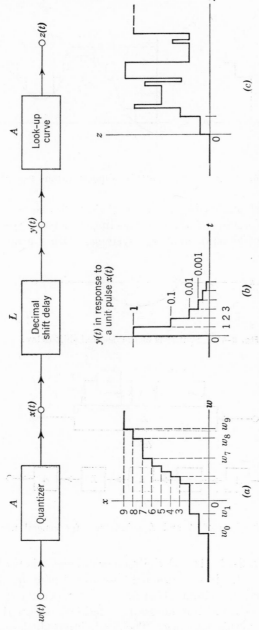

Fig. 8-39.   An *ALA* system consisting of a quantizer, a decimal shift delay, and a look-up curve.

that can be described in terms of three simple curves, that is, three single-input single-output systems each of which is either linear (L) or amnesic (A).

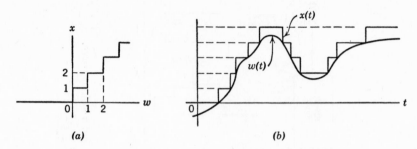

Fig. 8-40. Quantization of $w(t)$ by a uniform stair-step curve.

The cascade of three subsystems (ALA) is only one of many possible combinations of nonlinear amnesic and linear memory systems leading to a synthesis of general nonlinear systems. Other arrangements are

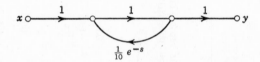

Fig. 8-41. Synthesis of the decimal shift delay.

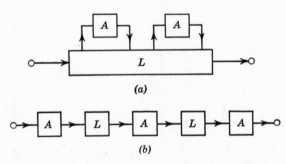

Fig. 8-42. Combinations of A and L subsystems for general nonlinear system synthesis.

suggested in Fig. 8-42. In (a) the memory element is used to provide feedback whereas (b) is an extended cascade without feedback. Both (a) and (b) include the simple ALA cascade as a special case.

Practical systems are not necessarily designed as an ALA cascade but many fall into this category. The single-input single-output A and

L systems are recognizable as abstractions of the circuit models treated in elementary electronic circuit theory.

We can of course use a binary instead of a decimal relation in Fig. 8-40. This leads to a binary shift delay which relates directly to the PCM system discussed in Article 8.15. In PCM systems, as in general non-linear systems, the significant memory length (number of digits) is limited by the accuracy of the quantizer and by noise considerations.

In conclusion, it should be pointed out that an alternative approach to the representation of nonlinear transmission systems involves the choice of linear time-invariant filters and ideal multipliers as basic system building blocks. Much recent work on the theory of nonlinear systems has taken this line. In particular, if the outputs of a bank of filters, such as those in Fig. 8-10, are multiplied together in various combinations to produce the final output signal, the resulting arrangement of filters and multipliers is a very general and flexible model of a nonlinear process.

PROBLEMS

8.1 The two strain-gauge networks shown in Fig. P8-1 can be used to measure small deflections. In practice, the resistors are attached to a machine part, or airplane structural member, or other body whose elastic deformation then changes the shape or size of the resistor with a consequent small change

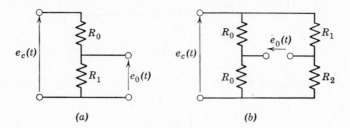

(a)   (b)

Fig. P8-1

in the resistance. Let $e_c(t) = V_c \cos \omega_c t$, $R_1 = R_0 + r(t)$, and $R_2 = R_0 - r(t)$.

Compare the two circuits as modulators when $r(t) \ll R_0$. In particular, what is the advantage of the balanced circuit (b) over the unbalanced form (a)?

8.2 The inputs to an ideal multiplier are

$$f_1(t) = e^{-\frac{1}{2}(t/5T_0)^2}, \qquad F_1(\omega) = 10\pi e^{-\frac{1}{2}(5T_0\omega)^2}$$

and

$$f_2(t) = \sum_{k=-\infty}^{+\infty} u_0(t - kT_0)$$

(a) Sketch and dimension the output time function $f_3(t)$ and spectrum $F_3(\omega)$.

(b) Devise a simple system to recover $f_1(t)$ from $f_3(t)$.

(c) The time function $f_3(t)$ determined in part (a) is applied to a network with an impulse response

$$h(t) = u_{-1}(t)u_{-1}(T_0 - t)$$

Sketch the output time function $f_4(t)$.

8.3 An input signal v_1 is applied to a square-law amplifier $(v_2 = av_1^2)$. If $v_1 = E_c(\cos \omega_c t)(1 + m \cos \omega_m t) + K$:

(a) What is the magnitude of the component at frequency ω_m? Of $2\omega_m$?

(b) Without working out the details, state what other frequency components are present.

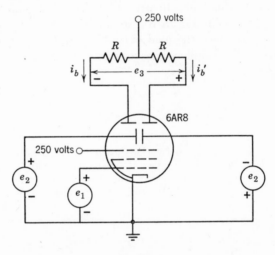

Fig. P8-2

8.4 The multiplier tube in Fig. P8-2 has the following characteristics:

$$i_b = (I_0 + g_m e_1)(\tfrac{1}{2} + Ke_2)$$

$$i_b' = (I_0 + g_m e_1)(\tfrac{1}{2} - Ke_2)$$

Plot the spectrum of e_3, showing the amplitude and frequency of each component, for

$$e_1 = -1 + \cos \omega_m t$$

$$e_2 = \sin \omega_c t$$

8.5 Given voltage $v(t) = A_0 + A_1 \sin(\omega_1 t + \beta) + A_2 \sin 2(\omega_1 t + \beta)$:

(a) Draw a block diagram of an analog computer (using time delay, multiplier, and integration blocks) which could be used to measure the autocorrelation function of $v(t)$.

For each of the following items *discuss briefly what the required quantities mean physically*. Include physical dimensions.

(b)   Determine the autocorrelation function $\phi(\tau)$.   Interpret the calculation graphically.   Sketch and dimension $\phi(\tau)$.

(c)   Has any information about $v(t)$ been lost in obtaining the autocorrelation function?   What do you think of the prospects for recovering $v(t)$ from the autocorrelation function?

(d)   How are $\phi(\tau)$ and its value for $-\tau$ related?

(e)   What is $\phi(0)$?   Can $\phi(\tau)$ exceed $\phi(0)$?   Explain.

(f)   What is the average of the autocorrelation function (the average with respect to τ)?

(g)   Determine the Fourier coefficients in the Fourier series for $\phi(\tau)$.

(h)   The time function $v(t)$ is also a Fourier series.   Show how the voltage line-spectrum (Fourier-series) coefficients are related to the power spectrum coefficients found in part (g).

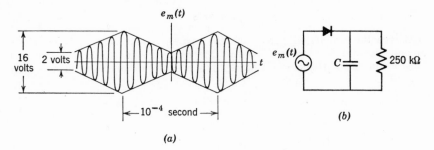

(a)

(b)

Fig. P8-3

8.6   A modulated signal $e_m(t)$, as indicated in Fig. P8-3, with a triangular envelope, is applied to a detector circuit.   If $R = 250$ kilohms, determine the maximum value C can have in order that there be no distortion; that is, the diode is closed once each cycle.   Assume the diode is ideal and the period of the carrier frequency is much smaller than 10^{-4} second.

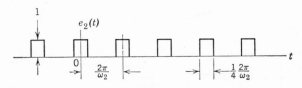

Fig. P8-4

8.7   Consider an amplitude-modulated signal $e_1(t) = E_1 (\cos \omega_1 t)(1 + m \cos \omega_m t)$ and the periodic pulse signal $e_2(t)$ shown in Fig. P8-4.   Assume ω_1 is much greater than ω_m.   Draw a simple block diagram of a system having inputs $e_1(t)$ and $e_2(t)$ and an output consisting of amplitude modulation on a carrier ($\omega_1 - \omega_2$).   What is the amplitude of the output signal?

8.8   We are given a nonlinear device whose output is $y = ax + bx^2$, where x is the input.   An ideal band-pass filter, whose frequency response is that shown in Fig. P8-5(*a*), is also available. Draw a block diagram of a modulator that will use the signal spectrum shown in (*b*) to modulate a carrier signal, $\cos \omega_c t$.

Define restrictions on ω_1, ω_2, and ω_c in terms of ω_3.

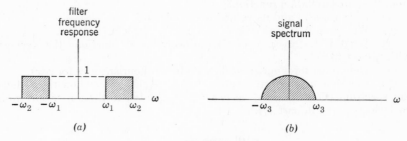

(*a*)   (*b*)

Fig. P8-5

Given the modulated signal, and the carrier, $\cos \omega_c t$, show by means of a block diagram how we can recover the original signal, allowing only d-c distortion (zero frequency). More than one of the nonlinear devices may be used.

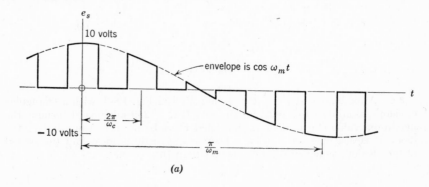

(*a*)

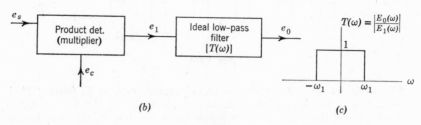

(*b*)   (*c*)

Fig. P8-6

8.9 Figure P8-6(*a*) depicts the waveform of a chopper-modulated sinusoid. This waveform is to be detected by the system (*b*). If $e_c = 10 \cos (\omega_c t + \phi)$, and $e_1(t) = e_s(t)e_c(t)$ at the output of the product detector:

(a) Sketch $E_1(\omega)$, the spectrum of $e_1(t)$, for $\phi = 0°$.

(b) If $\omega_c = 10^4$ radians per second, $\phi = 0°$, and ω_m may assume values from 1 to 100 radians per second, what is the permissible range of values for the filter cutoff frequency, ω_1, that will allow only ω_m to appear in e_0? What is the magnitude of e_0?

(c) If $\phi = \pi/2$, what is the magnitude of e_0, using the same filter as in part (b)?

8.10 A switch modulator can be visualized as a device which multiplies a low-frequency wave, say a sine wave, by a high-frequency square wave. Find by convolution the output spectrum of the modulator, using a frequency ratio of 5 to 1 between the square-wave fundamental and the sine wave.

8.11 Referring to Fig. 8-18 in the text, determine and plot e_0 versus ϕ, where ϕ is the phase difference between the input sine waves at frequency ω_c. Let the diodes be ideal and assume $RC\omega_c \gg 1$. Do this for (a) equal input amplitudes and (b) an amplitude ratio of 5 to 1.

8.12 In Fig. P8-7(a), signals $v_1(t)$ are identical square waves of fundamental frequency 1 megacycle. Signal $v_2(t)$ is of the form $f(t) \cos \omega_2 t$, where $\omega_2/2\pi$ is 100 kc and $f(t)$ has the spectrum indicated in (b). Resistances r are

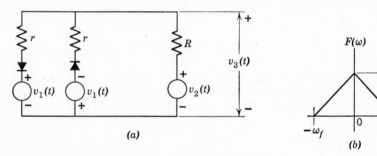

(a)

(b)

Fig. P8-7

very small in comparison with R, and the amplitude of $v_2(t)$ is approximately the same as that of $v_1(t)$. Plot the frequency spectrum of $v_3(t)$, assuming that $\omega_f/2\pi$ is 100 kc. What is the maximum value of ω_f for which the signal $f(t)$ is recoverable from $v_3(t)$ by a simple filtering and detection scheme? Suggest a scheme.

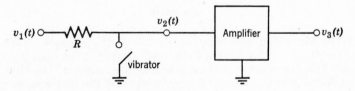

Fig. P8-8

8.13 In Fig. P8-8, $v_1(t)$ is a signal whose spectrum is restricted to frequencies below 10 cycles per second. The vibrator switch operates periodically at a repetition frequency of 100 cycles per second, and remains closed during one-half of each period. The input impedance of the amplifier is effectively infinite.

(a) If the amplifier passes only frequencies *above* 75 cycles per second, sketch $v_2(t)$, $v_3(t)$, and their spectra, illustrating the relationship to a typical $v_1(t)$.

(b) Repeat for an amplifier that passes only frequencies *between* 75 and 125 cycles per second.

(c) Repeat for an amplifier that passes only frequencies *below* 75 cycles per second.

8.14 In the modulator circuit of Fig. P8-9, the diodes can be assumed to be ideal. Let $e_2 = E_2 \cos \omega_2 t$ and assume e_1 to be an arbitrary waveform

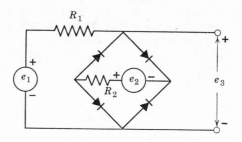

Fig. P8-9

subject to a restriction on peak value ($E_1 \ll E_2$) and on maximum frequency ($\omega_{1\max} \ll \omega_2$). Express e_3 in terms of e_1 and a multiplying function $m(t)$. Sketch and dimension $m(t)$. What is e_3 for the specific input $e_1 = E_1 \cos \omega_1 t$?

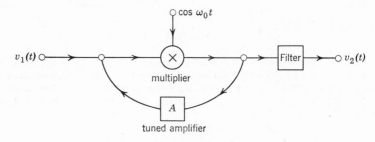

Fig. P8-10

8.15 In Fig. P8-10, the input $v_1(t)$ is an audio-frequency signal. The carrier frequency ω_0 lies far above the audio range. The high-Q amplifier is tuned to the frequency ω_0 and has a gain A at resonance. The filter passes only audio-frequencies. Discuss the performance of the transmission system.

8.16 Signal $f(t)$ is a unit-amplitude square wave having a period equal to 2, and is known to be an odd function. Signal $v_1(t)$ is periodic with a period equal to 1, and is known to be an even function. The system shown in Fig. P8-11 is at rest for negative t. You are allowed to observe the output

$v_2(t)$ only at the times $t = 1, 3, 5, 7, \cdots$. You are also allowed to change the amplifier gain A from one real value to another, but such changes must be made only at the times $t = 0, 2, 4, 6, \cdots$. Under these restrictions, what can

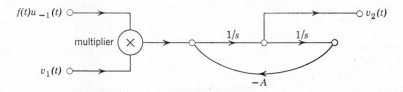

Fig. P8-11

you find out about $v_1(t)$? In particular, how would you control A so that the observed values of $v_2(t)$ are simply related to the Fourier series coefficients of $v_1(t)$?

8.17 The signal $v_1(t)$ in Fig. P8-12 has a spectrum that is appreciable only for $|\omega| \le \omega_1$ and the same is true of the spectrum of $n(t)$, amplifier noise. The amplifier pass band is flat and extends up to $10\omega_1$. The filter pass band is flat and covers the range $|\omega| \le \omega_1$.

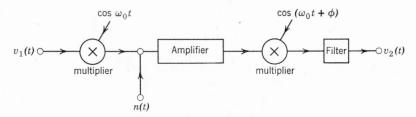

Fig. P8-12

(a)   Discuss the choice of ω_0 to make $v_2(t)$ a faithful reproduction of $v_1(t)$.

(b)   What is the phase of $v_2(t)$ relative to $v_1(t)$ for the special case in which $v_1(t)$ is a sinusoid?

8.18   In Fig. 8-19 of the text, signals $A_1(t)$ and $B_1(t)$ have low-frequency spectra, compared to ω_c. The transmission path passes frequencies in the neighborhood of ω_c. The filters pass only low frequencies.

(a)   How are $A_2(t)$ and $B_2(t)$ related to $A_1(t)$ and $B_1(t)$?

(b)   How would you choose $A_1(t)$ and $B_1(t)$ to illustrate:

    (1)   Ordinary amplitude modulation and detection?

    (2)   Phase modulation and detection?

    (3)   Suppressed-carrier transmission?

    (4)   Single-side-band transmission?

8.19   A 100-megacycle carrier is frequency-modulated by an audio-frequency signal. The frequency deviation is proportional to the signal amplitude (maximum deviation is ± 75 kc corresponding to the maximum amplitude of the modulating wave). Sketch the appearance of the frequency-modulated spectrum (see Appendix A) for each of the following conditions:

(*a*) Modulation frequency 5 kc. Modulation amplitudes 1/15, 1/5, 1/3, and 2/3 of maximum value.

(*b*) Modulation amplitude 1/15 of maximum value. Modulation frequencies 0.1, 0.5, 1.0, 2.0, 3.0, 4.0, 5.0 kc.

(*c*) Modulation amplitude at maximum value. Modulation frequencies 0.1, 1.0, and 5 kc.

8.20 A high-frequency carrier is frequency-modulated by a sinusoidal modulating signal. Choose significant values of the modulation index (see Appendix A) and sketch a series of spectra for each of the following conditions:

(*a*) Assume a constant modulating frequency ω_1 and let the modulation amplitude vary so that the modulation index ranges from 0 to 10.

(*b*) Assume a constant amplitude and let the modulation frequency vary so that the modulation index ranges from 0 to 10.

8.21 Describe the frequency spectrum of a square-wave-modulated frequency-modulated wave. Specifically, the signal is a sinusoid of frequency ω_1 for a time interval $T/2$ and then becomes a sinusoid of frequency ω_2 for the next time interval $T/2$, so that the variation repeats with period T.

8.22 In many oscillator circuits the resonant frequency of a tuned circuit determines the oscillator frequency. Hence, frequency modulation of the oscillator output can be accomplished by varying the inductance or capacitance

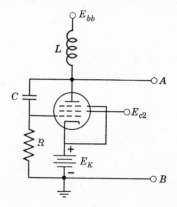

Fig. P8-13

of the tuned circuit. Figure P8-13 shows a "reactance-tube" circuit whose parameters can be adjusted to produce the appearance of effective incremental inductance or capacitance at the terminals AB. The value of this artificial inductance or capacitance can be made to vary by changing the grid bias or by the application of any other auxiliary signal that alters the effective transconductance of the tube. Analyze the reactance-tube circuit and suggest a design for a frequency modulator employing this circuit.

8.23 Compare the basic half-wave rectifier circuit with the full-wave rectifier circuit for frequency multiplication. In each case assume ideal diodes and a resistive load.

8.24 Frequency multiplication can be achieved by distorting a sine wave in a nonlinear circuit to generate harmonics. A band-pass filter tuned to the

nth harmonic produces the desired output. Consider a pentode amplifier with parallel RLC plate load tuned to a frequency $n\omega$, and with a grid input signal $e_1 = -E_0 + E_1 \sin \omega t$. Assume a source resistance R_1 and a grid-cathode resistance r_g for $e_c > 0$.

(a) Determine the effect on the nth harmonic output of E_1 and E_0 (or of E_1 and E_1/E_0) if e_c is restricted to negative values. Make suitable simplifying approximations.

(b) Compare the results of part (a) with those obtained by letting E_1 and E_0 assume values that make $e_c > 0$ during part of the cycle.

(c) Determine the value of Q required to suppress adjacent harmonics $(n \pm 1)$ by a factor M relative to the desired harmonic (n).

8.25 A certain "linear" demodulator consists of a multiplier driven by an input signal $v_1(t)$ and a carrier signal $v_c(t)$. The multiplier output $v_2 = v_1 v_c$ is passed through a frequency filter to obtain the system output signal $v_3(t)$. The input-signal spectrum is $V_1(\omega) = F(\omega + \omega_c) + F(\omega - \omega_c)$ and the desired output spectrum is $V_3(\omega) = F(\omega)$. Discuss the choice of a suitable filter when $v_c(t)$ is:

(a) A square wave of period $2\pi/\omega_c$.

(b) A periodic train of impulses which alternate in sign (with period $2\pi/\omega_c$ and impulse spacing π/ω_c).

8.26 A modulating signal $e_m(t) = 1 + m \cos \omega_m t$ and a carrier consisting of a train of unit impulses occurring at intervals $2\pi/\omega_c$ are applied to an ideal multiplier. Plot the frequency spectrum of the output $e_0(t)$.

8.27 (a) Sketch the spectrum of a train of rectangular pulses of repetition frequency 10 kc and 1-microsecond duration.

(b) Sketch the spectrum after amplitude modulation of the signal by a 1-kc sine wave.

8.28 The modulation system shown in Fig. P8-14 has a carrier signal $v_c(t)$ consisting of a periodic train of unit impulses with period T. The system function of the filter is $[1 - \exp(-sT)]/s$.

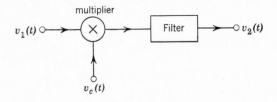

multiplier

$v_1(t)$ ○───→ ✕ ───→ | Filter | ───→ ○ $v_2(t)$

$v_c(t)$

Fig. P8-14

(a) Discuss the time-domain relationship between $v_1(t)$ and $v_2(t)$.

(b) For $v_1(t) = \cos \omega_0 t$, where $\omega_0 < 2\pi/T$, sketch the spectrum of $v_2(t)$.

(c) Repeat for $v_1(t) = \cos[\omega_0 + (2\pi/T)]t$.

(d) How would you suggest recovering the original signal $v_1(t)$ from $v_2(t)$, given that the spectrum of $v_1(t)$ contains negligible energy at frequencies equal to or greater than $2\pi/T$?

8.29 Devise a simple diode circuit to accomplish pulse-amplitude modulation.

8.30 Devise a number of alternative methods of accomplishing the time-multiplexing functions indicated in Fig. 8-27. Assume a basic sampling rate of 8 kc and let $n = 12$. Consider, for example, sine-wave phasing networks, pulse-delay networks, and time-delay generators (such as multivibrators and sawtooth generators) followed by voltage-coincidence circuits.

8.31 Figure 8-30 shows linear amplitude quantization with the discrete amplitude levels equally spaced. Alternatively, the levels may be chosen to give a fixed percentage change from one level to the next. Treating the quantization error (the difference between the quantizer input and output signals) as a noise, compare the "noisiness" of the two quantizers for selected illustrative signals having various waveforms and amplitudes. Try to draw a few simple conclusions from these examples.

8.32 The impulse response $h(t)$ of an amplifier is a rectangular pulse of unit height and duration T. The input is the sum of two components: a step signal $v_1(t) = u_{-1}(t)$, and broad-spectrum noise $n_1(t)$ whose spectral power density may be taken as a constant N_1.

Discuss the choice of the pulse duration T for maximum output signal-to-noise *power* ratio at a *specified* time t_0. What is the ratio?

The Negative-Feedback Concept

9.1 Introduction

A feedback loop is a closed chain of dependency, a closed path of signal flow in a system diagram. Since the relationships among the signals in a given *physical* system may be represented as any one of a number of different system diagrams, some containing feedback loops and some not, it can be argued that the presence or absence of "feedback" in the "system" is more a matter of viewpoint than of physical reality. Nevertheless, many physical systems are, by the very philosophy of their design, strongly associated with diagrams containing loops, and in such cases we find it comfortable to speak of the physical arrangement itself as a "feedback system." It should be remembered, however, that all of our thinking is carried out in terms of models; the circuit diagram of an electronic amplifier is an abstract model of the hardware. Similarly, at least from the analysis standpoint, a signal flow graph representing the circuit equations is a further abstraction, a model arising from one's own interpretation of the physical behavior of the system.

From the synthesis or design standpoint, the signal flow graph or block diagram is the starting point, the basic expression of process. If we ask a system designer to draw a "picture of the system," he is likely to sketch, not the hardware, but a block diagram of the pertinent cause-and-effect relationships. It is in this sense that one speaks of a feedback system, usually having in mind a block diagram in which feedback loops are purposely introduced to obtain better system performance or a more economical design. The term "negative feedback" refers to the fact that certain desirable signal-transmission characteristics can be realized by imbedding an imperfect transmission element in a feedback loop whose loop transmission is a large negative number.

As we shall see, feedback may be used to reduce the effects of undesirable disturbances such as noise or nonlinearity, and to make circuit or system performance less dependent on variations of device properties due to manufacturing tolerances or aging. In return for these improvements in performance we are faced with a stability problem. Canceling a distortion at one frequency may yield reinforcement and spontaneous oscillation at some other frequency. We shall first consider systems in which there are no unwanted phase shifts, thus temporarily ignoring the stability problem. Simple examples of such systems are resistive circuits. When energy-storage elements are included and unwanted phase shifts exist, we not only introduce stability problems but impose bandwidth limitations. In the design of a feedback system, gain, bandwidth, and stability are closely related. If the gain is fixed, we can trade bandwidth for increased stability. If we fix the margin of stability, some juggling of gain and bandwidth is possible, but the product of gain and bandwidth has an upper limit. If the system response calls for a given bandwidth, we must select the stability margin and the gain that yield the most suitable design.

9.2   Automatic Control by Means of Negative Feedback

The philosophy underlying the automatic control of transmission characteristics can be explained in terms of Fig. 9-1. The input signal is v_1 and the *desired* value of the output is K_0v_1. Suppose that an amplifier capable of delivering the required output power to the specified load is available and suppose also that its voltage amplification K can be adjusted to the desired value K_0. In this case the two solid-line branches in Fig. 9-1 represent a suitable system design. However, the voltage amplification of an electronic circuit (or the ratio of speed to excitation current in a motor, or the transmission constant of any other powerful system element) may not be sufficiently dependable or reliable for the task required. In this case we must either choose a better amplifier or else devise a means of controlling the cheaper but less reliable one to meet the design specifications.

The dashed-line branches in Fig. 9-1 show a possible means of controlling the transmission. The output v_2 is combined with the input v_1 to produce an "error signal" v_ϵ proportional to the difference between the actual output v_a and the desired output $K_0 v_1$. In effect, the *actual output* is *measured* and *compared* with the *desired output*. The information obtained from this comparison is then *fed back* to the input of the unreliable element, where it adds to the input signal v_1 to produce a "corrected input signal" v_c.

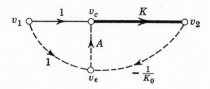

Fig. 9-1. Automatic control of a transmission.

If K is less than the nominal value K_0, the error signal v_ϵ becomes positive and the correction $A v_\epsilon$ is obviously of the proper polarity to lift the output signal closer to the desired value. Hence a negative loop transmission $(-KA/K_0)$ is necessary in order to achieve the desired control. Moreover, the larger the value of A, the tighter the control. For a very large A, the slightest difference between actual and desired output will produce an appreciable correction signal $A v_\epsilon$, and the system may therefore be expected to behave like a dependable amplifier of voltage amplification K_0.

The success of the entire scheme is based, of course, upon the tacit assumptions that (1) the sensing and feedback elements (the dashed-line branches) are dependable but relatively inexpensive, since they need not operate at high power levels, (2) the transmission element to be controlled (K) is powerful and relatively expensive, but imperfect or undependable, and (3) a sufficiently dependable transmission element, of the same power-handling capacity as K, would be considerably more expensive than K. In short, the matter is ultimately one of economics, as are all design problems.

By inspection of Fig. 9-1, the transmission is

$$\frac{v_2}{v_1} = \frac{(1+A)K}{1+(AK/K_0)} \tag{9.1}$$

and for large A

$$\frac{v_2}{v_1} \approx K_0 \left[1 + \frac{1}{A}\left(1 - \frac{K_0}{K}\right) \right] \tag{9.2}$$

demonstrating that the transmission becomes essentially independent of K for sufficiently large A. Notice also that for K close to K_0 the transmission approaches K_0 more quickly as A increases.

Figure 9-2(a) shows the basic negative-feedback diagram, a simplified form of Fig. 9-1 obtained by omitting the original signal-injection

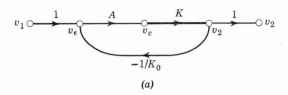

(a)

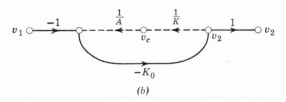

(b)

Fig. 9-2. A linear negative-feedback system.

branch between v_1 and v_c. Here the input to the transmission element K consists entirely of the correction signal Av_ϵ. The transmission is given by

$$\frac{v_2}{v_1} = \frac{AK}{1 + (AK/K_0)} \tag{9.3}$$

For large A we have

$$\frac{v_2}{v_1} \approx K_0\left(1 - \frac{K_0}{AK}\right) \tag{9.4}$$

and in the limit

$$\frac{v_2}{v_1} \to K_0, \quad \text{as } A \to \infty \tag{9.5}$$

This result can be shown explicitly by inverting the feedback loop to obtain the equivalent graph in Fig. 9-2(b). For large A the dashed-line branches in (b) may be ignored, leaving a simple path whose transmission is K_0 (increasing the transmission of the original loop to infinity decreases that of the inverted loop to zero). The character of relationship

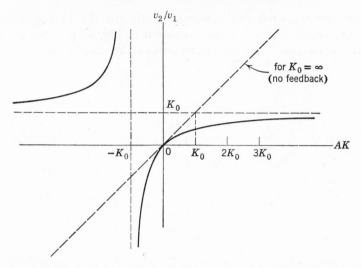

Fig. 9-3. Transmission with feedback (v_2/v_1) as a function of transmission without feedback $(v_2/v_\epsilon = AK)$.

(9.3) is indicated in Fig. 9-3. For large AK, say $10K_0$ or more, the transmission ratio v_2/v_1 becomes relatively insensitive to variations in K.

9.3 Control of a Nonlinear Transmission

Let us now examine the effects of feedback around a nonlinear amplifier described by the transfer curve $v_2 = f(v_c)$, as illustrated in Fig. 9-4(a) and (b). Without feedback $(K_0 = \infty)$, the nonlinearity of the amplifier characteristic will cause appreciable distortion of waveforms having output amplitudes larger than about $V/2$.

One's first thought might be to increase the linear range of the amplifier by altering the saturation level to a higher value. However, the saturation level of a power stage is closely related to cost. For example, in a vacuum-tube or transistor amplifier the saturation level is governed by supply voltages which are in turn limited by the allowable power dissipation ratings of the circuit components. We may find it more economical to extend the linear dynamic range of v_2 by the addition of feedback and the introduction of relatively inexpensive low-power-level linear preamplification A.

The equations of the system are

$$v_2 = f(v_c) \tag{9.6}$$

$$v_c = Av_1 - (A/K_0)v_2 \tag{9.7}$$

The second equation (9.7) plots as a straight line of negative slope K_0/A in the v_2 versus v_c plane, as shown in Fig. 9-4(c), and the intersection with (9.6) at point p represents the simultaneous graphical

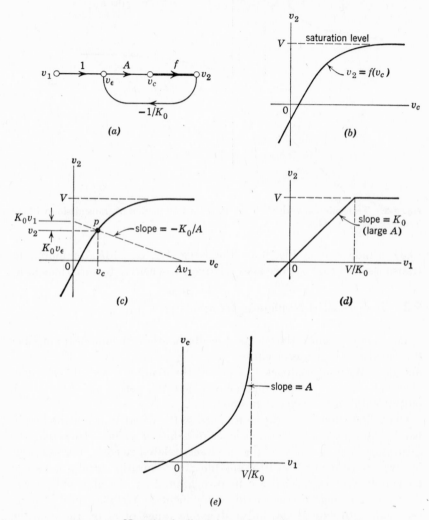

Fig. 9-4. Negative feedback around a nonlinear element f.

solution of the two equations. As "parameter" v_1 varies, the "feedback line" (9.7) moves parallel to itself, generating various pairs of values of K_0v_1 and v_2. It is apparent from the graphical construction that K_0v_1 and v_2 are very nearly equal for large A, provided K_0v_1 does not exceed the saturation level V. Any attempt to drive the output v_2 beyond this level results only in an increased error signal v_ϵ and a sharp saturation of the over-all transmission characteristic, v_2 versus v_1, as indicated in Fig. 9-4(d). However, within the upper bound imposed by saturation, the application of preamplification and negative feed-

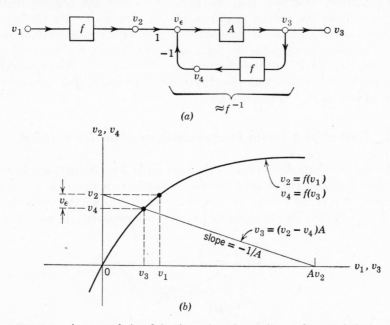

Fig. 9-5. An example involving inversion of a nonlinear characteristic f.

back has, in effect, *linearized* the original nonlinear characteristic and has therefore extended the useful dynamic range of the system. To say the same thing another way, for a fixed output signal amplitude the preamplification and feedback have reduced the amount of *distortion* suffered by the input signal waveform.

If v_c, rather than v_2, is visualized as the system output signal, then the nonlinear element f becomes part of the feedback path around the forward amplification element A. Just as the appearance of $1/K_0$ in the feedback path tends to produce an over-all transmission proportional to its reciprocal K_0, so the appearance of a nonlinearity in the feedback path tends to produce inversion of that nonlinear relationship in the over-all characteristic, as illustrated by the v_1-to-v_c transfer curve in Fig. 9-4(e). For sufficiently large A, the function $v_c = g(K_0v_1)$ is essentially the inverse of $v_2 = f(v_c)$, which is another way of saying that $v_2 = f[g(K_0 v_1)]$ is nearly linear. With the amplifier curve (v_2 versus v_c) convex upward, the "control characteristic" (v_c versus v_1) must be convex downward if we are to have the system transfer curve (v_2 versus v_1) nearly linear.

Figure 9-5 offers another illustration of the inversion of a feedback characteristic. Suppose that we wish to recover the original input signal v_1 from the output v_2 of a nonlinear element f. By placing a replica of that element in the feedback path of a second system and cascading the second with the first, as in Fig. 9-5(a), we can produce an output v_3 which is a nearly faithful reproduction of v_1. The graphical construction (b) shows that the error v_ϵ becomes small, and v_3 therefore approaches v_1, as A is made large.

9.4   Control of a Linear Frequency-Dependent Transmission

In the previous discussion of the system in Fig. 9-2(a), the transmission K was treated as a parameter, subject, perhaps, to random variations over an ensemble of systems or to predictable variations such as a decline due to aging of physical components. It was shown

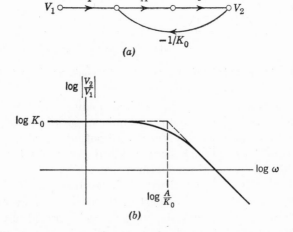

(a)

(b)

Fig. 9-6. Influence of negative feedback upon frequency response.

that preamplification and negative feedback discriminated against the effects of such variations. Since the system was linear, the same conclusions may be expected to apply to a frequency-dependent transmission $K(s)$.

To begin with a simple example, assume that K is an ideal integrator, as shown in Fig. 9-6(a). The system transmission is

$$\frac{V_2}{V_1} = \frac{A/s}{1 + (A/K_0 s)} = \frac{K_0}{1 + (K_0/A)s} \tag{9.8}$$

and this leads directly to the steady-state ($s = j\omega$) frequency-response curve (b). As the preamplification A is allowed to increase, the bandwidth of the system (A/K_0) becomes large. In the limit of infinite A, the system transmission is the same (K_0) at all frequencies. Thus

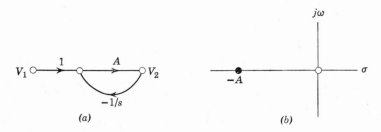

Fig. 9-7.   Approximate differentiation by integration in the feedback path.

preamplification and frequency-independent feedback tend to produce a frequency-independent transmission within that frequency range where the loop transmission remains large compared to unity.

Just as a nonlinear characteristic in the feedback path appears inverted in the system transmission characteristic, so does a feedback-path frequency function. Figure 9-7(a) shows the synthesis of an approximate differentiator by means of feedback through an ideal integrator. The system transmission

$$\frac{V_2}{V_1} = \frac{A}{1 + (A/s)} = \frac{s}{1 + (s/A)} \tag{9.9}$$

has a zero at the origin and a pole at $-A$ in the complex s-plane, Fig. 9-7(b). Hence the system may be expected to perform accurate differentiation upon any input signal whose spectrum is restricted to frequencies safely below A, say $|\omega| < A/5$. As A increases without limit, the transmission approaches that of an ideal differentiator, s.

Figure 9-8(a) shows a scheme that has found use in the design of high-Q voltage amplifiers (for transmission of a very narrow band of frequencies). The feedback transmission $[(s^2 + 1)/(s + 1)^2]$ has simple zeros on the $j\omega$ axis, as depicted in (b), and the system transmission is

$$\frac{V_2}{V_1} = \frac{A}{1 + A[(s^2 + 1)/(s + 1)^2]} = \frac{A(s + 1)^2}{(s - s_1)(s - s_2)}\left(\frac{A}{A + 1}\right) \quad (9.10)$$

where s_1 and s_2 are the poles shown in Fig. 9-8(c). As the forward amplification A is increased, the Q of the system transmission becomes

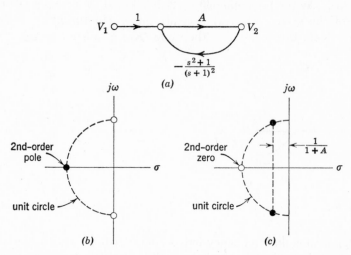

(a)

(b)

(c)

Fig. 9-8. Realization of a high-Q frequency response by means of a selective null response in the feedback path. (a) The system. (b) The pole-zero pattern of the feedback path. (c) The pole-zero pattern of the system.

arbitrarily large. In practice, a feedback transmission with zeros on the $j\omega$ axis can be synthesized as a relatively simple passive RC circuit, such as a "twin-T" filter [the double pole in (b) must then be replaced by two separate simple poles on the negative real axis]. Hence, the feedback system in Fig. 9-8(a) may be more economical, more convenient or more dependable than a straightforward design employing a resonant circuit in the forward path and no feedback. Notice that for large A the nearness of the poles to the $j\omega$ axis is not an extremely sensitive function of the value of A, so that severe tolerances on A are not required in the design.

Figures 9-7 and 9-8 illustrated the approximate inversion of a transmission function by placement of that function in the feedback path of a negative-feedback system. The scheme is workable *provided the resulting system is stable*. Consider, for example, the proposal to produce negative time delay by placing ideal positive delay, exp $(-s)$, in the feedback path, as shown in Fig. 9-9(a). (This scheme is in the same category as the perpetual motion machine; the foundations of science would rock if ideal negative delay, that is, ideal *prediction*, were possible.) Here the answer is simple; the system transmission is

$$\frac{V_2}{V_1} = \frac{A}{1 + A \exp(-s)} \qquad (9.11)$$

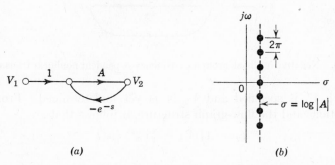

$$(a) \qquad\qquad\qquad (b)$$

Fig. 9-9. Failure, due to instability, of an attempt to produce negative delay by placing ideal positive delay in the feedback path.

and this transmission becomes unstable (has poles in the right-half s-plane and hence a forever-growing impulse response) when the magnitude of A exceeds unity, as indicated by the pole pattern in Fig. 9-9(b). Negative delay, that is, the transmission function $\exp(s)$, can be approximated closely over a restricted frequency band, but the ideal is unattainable.

9.5 Control of a Nonlinear Frequency-Dependent Transmission

When the loop of a feedback system contains both nonlinear elements and frequency-dependent linear elements, the general rule, suggested by the preceding examples, still holds; namely, a "large amount of negative loop transmission" tends to produce a system transmission proportional to the inverse of the feedback transmission, provided stability is maintained.

Although quantitative solution of the general analysis or synthesis problem is difficult, many special cases are tractable. The system in Fig. 9-10 is one example. Let us assume a sinusoidal input signal, a low-pass preamplification function $A(j\omega)$ that passes the fundamental frequency with an amplification A_1 but blocks all higher harmonics, and a nonlinear element f that can be approximated by a pure cubic. Thus,

$$v_1 = V_1 \cos t \tag{9.12}$$

$$v_2 = V_2 \cos t \tag{9.13}$$

$$v_3 = v_2{}^3 = V_2{}^3 \cos^3 t = V_2{}^3(\tfrac{3}{4}\cos t + \tfrac{1}{4}\cos 3t) \tag{9.14}$$

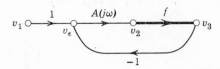

Fig. 9-10.   Negative feedback around a frequency-dependent nonlinear transmission.

in which V_1 is specified and V_2 is as yet undetermined. From the assumptions and the flow-graph structure, it follows that

$$v_2 = A_1(V_1 - \tfrac{3}{4}V_2{}^3)\cos t \tag{9.15}$$

whence

$$V_1 = \frac{1}{A_1}V_2 + \tfrac{3}{4}V_2{}^3 \tag{9.16}$$

Now, if A_1 is large, we have

$$V_1 \approx \tfrac{3}{4}V_2{}^3 \tag{9.17}$$

and

$$v_2 \approx (\tfrac{4}{3}V_1)^{\frac{1}{3}}\cos t \tag{9.18}$$

$$v_3 \approx \tfrac{4}{3}V_1 \cos^3 t = V_1 \cos t + \tfrac{1}{3}V_1 \cos 3t \tag{9.19}$$

$$v_\epsilon \approx -\tfrac{1}{3}V_1 \cos 3t \tag{9.20}$$

Observe that the amplitude of the output $v_3(t)$ is proportional to the input amplitude V_1, an evidence of linearization produced by feedback at the fundamental frequency. However, the feedback loop is effectively broken at the frequency of the third harmonic. The error signal $v_\epsilon(t)$ stands ready to provide opposite distortion in $v_2(t)$ which would reduce the third-harmonic distortion in the output, but this action is blocked by the postulated frequency selectivity of $A(j\omega)$.

For smaller values of A_1, the cubic equation (9.16) must be solved for V_2 in terms of V_1. In practice, the nonlinear function relating the fundamental-frequency amplitudes of v_2 and v_3 may be available as an experimental curve, whence the solution, for any A_1, can be obtained graphically by exactly the same type of construction as that in Fig. 9-4(c). To summarize, if filtration in the loop is such that the nonlinear element is excited by a single sinusoid, then the problem reduces in principle to that of an amnesic (frequency-independent) loop, and the significant nonlinear curve is one relating the fundamental-frequency components at the input and output of the nonlinear element.

9.6   Reduction of Noise and Distortion

The appearance of noise in a transmission system can be accommodated by a model such as that in Fig. 9-11(a). In electronic systems, noise arises from thermal agitation of electrons in a resistor (thermal noise), from the discrete nature of charge in an electron current (shot

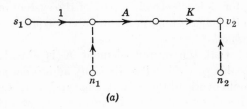

(a)

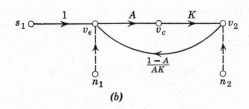

(b)

Fig. 9-11. Representation of a noisy system as a noiseless system plus auxiliary noise generators.

noise), from random fluctuation of the apparent "conductivity" of a hot cathode or a semiconductor (flicker noise), or from any other physical process that contributes an independent random component to the signal.

The signal-to-noise ratio at the output of the system is a significant measure of the quality of the system, for too much noise obviously interferes with our recognition of the signal. If the signal and the noise have non-overlapping frequency spectra, the noise can be removed by simple filtration. However, in a region of spectral overlap, there are only two ways to improve the signal-to-noise ratio: (1) increase the signal, and (2) reduce the noise.

Figure 9-11(a) shows a linear transmission system in which noise is unavoidably added at both the input and the output portions of the system. The input signal is s_1 and the output, containing both signal and noise, is given by

$$v_2 = AK(s_1 + n_1) + n_2 \qquad (9.21)$$

The output signal-to-noise power ratio, assuming n_1 and n_2 are orthogonal to each other and to the signal, is

$$\frac{(A^2K^2)\overline{s_1}^2}{(A^2K^2)\overline{n_1}^2 + \overline{n_2}^2} \qquad (9.22)$$

By increasing the preamplification A we can discriminate against n_2 but not against n_1, for n_1 is effectively a part of the system input $(s_1 + n_1)$. The discrimination against n_2 is a simple consequence of the *increase* in the output *signal*.

Suppose now that the output element K is already operating at maximum allowable power level, so that any additional preamplification of the signal would overload the output stage and either exceed the rating or produce undue distortion. In this case we can call upon feedback to maintain the desired output level as the preamplification A is increased. The feedback parameter $(1 - A)/AK$ in Fig. 9-11(b) is here a function of A, specifically chosen to make the transmission from s_1 to v_2 independent of A. From the signal-flow graph we find, after simplification of the expressions,

$$v_2 = K(s_1 + n_1) + \frac{1}{A} n_2 \qquad (9.23)$$

$$v_c = s_1 + \left(\frac{1 - A}{AK}\right) n_2 \qquad (9.24)$$

For large positive A these expressions reduce to

$$v_2 \approx K(s_1 + n_1) \qquad (9.25)$$

$$v_c \approx s_1 + n_1 - \frac{1}{K} n_2 \qquad (9.26)$$

Notice the appearance, in v_c, of an opposite noise $(-n_2/K)$ just sufficient to cancel the n_2 injected at the output, so that the only noise appearing in v_2 is Kn_1.

When properly interpreted, the foregoing analysis applies to distortion as well as to noise. Distortion due to nonlinearities can be visualized as a "noise" that is dependent upon the output signal level of a nonlinear element. Thus if the output amplifier in Fig. 9-11(b) is nonlinear, we may represent it as a linear model K plus a distortion generator n_2, as shown. Both noise and distortion represent "contamination" of the signal and both can be accounted for by an auxiliary generator injecting the contamination into an otherwise linear homogeneous model. The "distortion-generator" representation is, of course, mainly useful when the amount of distortion is not too large, for then the distortion-generator signal remains much the same as the parameter A in Fig. 9-11(b) is varied.

The representation of an incipient nonlinearity by a linear model containing a "contamination generator" brings the results of linear feedback theory to bear upon systems that are actually nonlinear. A feedback design that reduces the sensitivity of the system transmission to changes in the transmission of a linear element may be expected to discriminate against distortion when that element becomes nonlinear. The particular result of interest here is that negative feedback reduces the distortion by a factor equal to the return difference (unity minus the loop transmission), provided preamplification is introduced to maintain a fixed output signal level. In Fig. 9-11(b) the loop transmission is $1 - A$ and the return difference is therefore A. In the linear calculation of loop transmission we assume that K is, in some reasonable sense, the "best linear approximant" to the actual nonlinear element, perhaps that approximant which leads to the smallest mean-square value of the contamination-generator signal.

The amount of feedback is often conveniently expressed in decibels. By definition, the number of decibels of feedback is $F_{db} = -20 \log_{10} |1 - L|$, where L is the loop transmission. "Negative feedback" occurs when F_{db} is negative and "positive feedback" when F_{db} is positive. For a single-loop diagram with a single forward path transmission P and a loop transmission L, the over-all transmission T therefore can be expressed in decibels as $T_{db} = P_{db} + F_{db}$.

9.7 Sensitivity

The sensitivity of system performance to variations in components is an important design consideration. In feedback systems, sensitivity considerations are doubly important, particularly when stability margins are close and a small drift in the component may produce spontaneous oscillations.

A rudimentary flow-graph manipulation will help us to formulate the effects of changes in a specific system element upon the over-all transmission. Figure 9-12(a) shows an arbitrary flow graph with one particular branch g placed in evidence. All other branches and nodes (except the input and output nodes) are inside the box. We may introduce an interior node in branch g by replacing g with a cascade of two branches (1 and g) whose transmission product is g, as shown in (b).

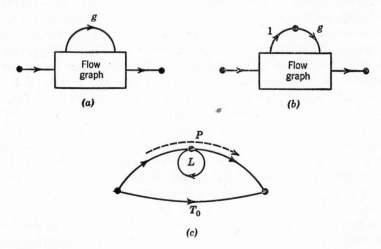

Fig. 9-12. Reduction to a basic graph that places in evidence the effect of changes in a specified branch transmission g.

Now, absorption of all other nodes (except the source and the sink) gives the general residual form (c). The transmission is

$$T = T_0 + \frac{P}{1 - L} \qquad (9.27)$$

Quantities P and L contain g as a factor but T_0 does not. (T_0 is just the value taken by T when g is set equal to zero.) From (9.27) we can compute the sensitivity of T with respect to changes in g. The *sensitivity* is defined as

$$S_g(T) = \frac{\partial \log (T)}{\partial \log (g)} = \frac{\partial T/T}{\partial g/g} \qquad (9.28)$$

Sensitivity S_g is a measure of the *percentage* change in T produced by a small *percentage* change in g. We can also define the *relative sensitivity*

$$S_g(T - T_0) = \frac{\partial \log (T - T_0)}{\partial \log g} \qquad (9.29)$$

The relative sensitivity measures the effect of g on that part of T which vanishes when g vanishes.

Substitution of (9.27) into (9.29), and use of the fact that P and L

each contain g as a factor, gives

$$S_g(T - T_0) = \frac{\partial \log [P/(1 - L)]}{\partial \log (g)} = 1 + \frac{L}{1 - L} = \frac{1}{1 - L} \quad (9.30)$$

Now, since $T - T_0 = P/(1 - L)$ and

$$\frac{\partial \log (T - T_0)}{\partial \log (T)} = \frac{T}{T - T_0} \quad (9.31)$$

we may divide (9.30) by (9.31) to obtain

$$S_g(T) = \frac{1 - (T_0/T)}{1 - L} \quad (9.32)$$

There are two ways to make T insensitive to changes in g. One is to design the system so that T is equal to T_0, but this is a trivial solution. With T equal to T_0, the transmission is independent of g; the branch g is effectively disconnected from the remainder of the system, as is, for example, the impedance of the detector arm in a balanced bridge circuit. The other way to reduce sensitivity is to insist upon a *large negative* loop transmission L around the element g. If g represents an undependable but powerful element, utilized for power gain in the main transmission path of the system, the addition of negative feedback around g reduces the sensitivity from unity to a lower value.

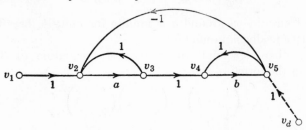

Fig. 9-13. The use of positive local feedback and negative over-all feedback for suppression of distortion or noise injected at the output point.

For a system consisting of two or more stages in cascade, such as a and b in Fig. 9-13, it is sometimes convenient to add *positive local* feedback around each stage and *negative over-all* feedback around the complete forward path. In Fig. 9-13, the graph has been normalized to make the desired operating values of a and b both equal to unity. Now let us examine the effects of changes in a and b upon the transmission.

$$T = \frac{v_5}{v_1} = \frac{ab}{1 - a - b + 2ab} \quad (9.33)$$

Transmission T is a function of a and b

$$T = f(a, b) \tag{9.34}$$

By inspection of (9.33)

$$f(1, 1) \equiv 1 \tag{9.35}$$

$$f(a, 1) \equiv 1 \tag{9.36}$$

$$f(1, b) \equiv 1 \tag{9.37}$$

$$f(0.9, 0.9) = 0.988 \tag{9.38}$$

For $a = b = 1$ the transmission is the same as it would be without feedback. (Positive feedback increases the transmission, negative feedback reduces it, and in this case the effects cancel.) However, the sensitivity to changes in a and b is obviously much less than it would be without feedback. In particular,

$$S_a(T) = \frac{1}{1 - a + [ab/(1 - b)]} \tag{9.39}$$

and

$$S_a(T) = \frac{1 - b}{b}, \qquad \text{for } a = 1 \tag{9.40}$$

$$S_a(T) \equiv 0, \qquad \text{for } b = 1 \tag{9.41}$$

The loop transmission around a is infinite for unity b, because of the local positive feedback around b.

From another viewpoint, the transmission equation (9.33) can be rewritten in the form

$$\left(\frac{1}{T} - 1\right) = \left(\frac{1}{a} - 1\right)\left(\frac{1}{b} - 1\right) \tag{9.42}$$

The function $(1/T) - 1$, plotted as a surface above the $(1/a) - 1$ versus $(1/b) - 1$ plane, exhibits a saddle point at the origin, a neighborhood where the surface is flat. The flatness of the saddle point is another interpretation of the insensitivity of $(1/T) - 1$, and therefore of T, to changes in a and b about the value unity.

In Fig. 9-13 a distortion or noise source is shown injecting a signal at the output point v_5. By inspection of the graph,

$$\frac{v_5}{v_d} = \frac{1 - a}{1 - a - b + 2ab} = 0, \qquad \text{for } a = 1 \tag{9.43}$$

$$\frac{v_2}{v_d} = -\frac{1}{1 - a - b + 2ab} = -1, \qquad \text{for } a = b = 1 \tag{9.44}$$

Thus noise or distortion generated in the final stage is suppressed by the feedback and appears, not at the output, but rather as a correction signal at the point v_2.

9.8 Control of Impedance

The general expression (9.27) exhibiting the effect of a specific branch g upon the transmission T can be placed in a more convenient form when the transmission happens to be a *driving-point impedance* or a *driving-point admittance*. Figure 9-14(a) depicts a circuit having a driving-

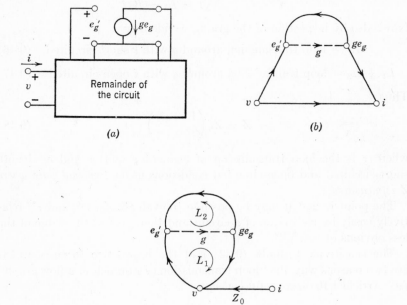

(a)

(b)

(c)

Fig. 9-14. Formulation of a flow graph appropriate for driving-point impedance evaluation.

point impedance v/i and containing a transconductance parameter g, here shown as an external element connected to the remainder of the circuit. For definition or interpretation of the branch transmissions in the flow graph (b) it is convenient to ignore (temporarily) the transconductance constraint g relating the grid voltage e_g' and the current source ge_g. Thus the remainder of the circuit is (temporarily) driven by two *independent* sources, v and ge_g. The associated responses are

$e_g{'}$ and i as specified by the four solid-line branches in (b). Now, to reconstitute the constraint $(e_g = e_g{'})$ we add branch g to give the complete graph. Note that the graph in Fig. 9-14(b) is essentially the same as that in Fig. 9-12(c) and reduces exactly to 9-12(c) if either node $e_g{'}$ or node ge_g is absorbed.

Inversion of the branch from v to i in Fig. 9-14(b) gives the alternative formulation (c), more convenient for the discussion of driving-point impedance. In graph (c), the branch transmission Z_0 is recognizable as the value of impedance v/i when g is set equal to zero. From the graph,

$$\frac{v}{i} = Z = Z_0 \left(\frac{1 - L_2}{1 - L_1 - L_2} \right) \tag{9.45}$$

Now, also by inspection of the graph, we identify

$$L_1 = \text{loop transmission around } g \text{ with } v \text{ short-circuited} \tag{9.46}$$

$$L_1 + L_2 = \text{loop transmission around } g \text{ with } i \text{ open-circuited} \tag{9.47}$$

Thus,

$$Z = Z_0 \left(\frac{1 - \tau^{sc}}{1 - \tau^{oc}} \right) \tag{9.48}$$

where τ is the loop transmission of element g and sc and oc denote short-circuited and open-circuited conditions *at the terminal pair where Z is measured.*

The point is that it may be possible to evaluate Z_0, τ^{sc}, and τ^{oc} relatively easily by inspection of a circuit and thereby find the value of the less obvious quantity Z.

The sensitivity formula (9.32) and the impedance formula (9.48) are two reasons why the "loop transmission of a branch in a flow graph" (see Article 4.10) is a useful concept.

9.9   Stability Considerations

To obtain large negative loop transmission in a feedback system it is sometimes necessary to use several stages of amplification in the forward path. Each stage of an electronic amplifier contains unavoidable reactance, such as interelectrode capacitance, which causes phase shift at frequencies above the transmission band. Similarly, RC coupling between stages produces phase shift at frequencies below the transmission band. Since the total phase shift is the sum of the stage phase shifts, it is easily possible to have a negative real loop transmission within the desired frequency band and a positive real transmission (180° additional phase shift) at some frequency outside that band. If the magnitude of the positive real loop transmission exceeds unity we may expect the system to be unstable. More precisely, if the loop transmission $L(s)$ takes on the value unity anywhere on the $j\omega$ axis or in the interior of the right-half s-plane, then the system is unstable, for the "unity points" of the loop transmission are the poles of the system transmission.

Fortunately, it is not necessary to examine the entire right-half s-plane. Instead, as the following example will illustrate, we can

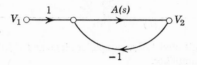

Fig. 9-15. A feedback amplifier diagram.

express the loop transmission $L(s)$ as the product of a steady-state frequency-response function and a real scale factor; *if a feedback system is stable for small values of the loop scale factor, and if the steady-state complex locus of the loop transmission $L(j\omega)$ sweeps across the point $+1$ as the scale factor is increased from zero to its nominal value, then we know that a pole of the system transmission has moved across the $j\omega$ axis into the right-half s-plane, making the system unstable. This is the so-called Nyquist stability criterion.*

Figure 9-15 shows the linear flow graph for a negative-feedback system in which the forward transmission $A(s)$ is a function of frequency. Suppose that

$$A(s) = \left(\frac{K}{s+1}\right)^4 \tag{9.49}$$

The flow graph and the function (9.49) may arise, for example, from the feedback amplifier model in Fig. 9-16(b), each of whose stages has the circuit model shown in (a). For simplicity (and without loss of generality) we have set $\omega_0 = 1$ in (9.49). The system transmission or system function is given by

$$\frac{v_2}{v_1} = H(s) = \frac{A(s)}{1 + A(s)} \tag{9.50}$$

Hence

$$H(s) = \frac{K^4}{(s+1)^4 + K^4} \tag{9.51}$$

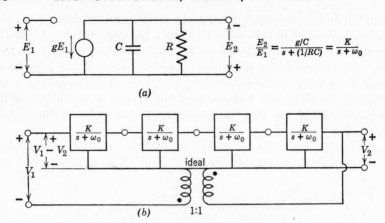

$$\frac{E_2}{E_1} = \frac{g/C}{s + (1/RC)} = \frac{K}{s + \omega_0}$$

(a)

(b)   1:1

Fig. 9-16. (a) A circuit model of an amplifier stage and (b) the schematic model of a four-stage feedback amplifier.

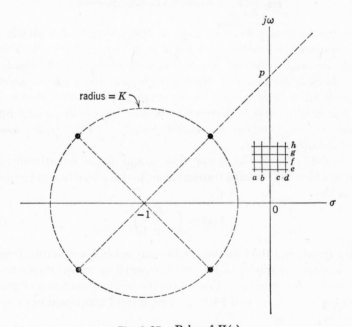

Fig. 9-17. Poles of $H(s)$.

We are interested in the location of the poles s_p of the system function, at which the loop transmission is unity and $A(s)$ is therefore -1,

$$H(s_p) = \infty \tag{9.52}$$

$$A(s_p) = -1 \tag{9.53}$$

In this particular example the equation (9.53), although a quartic in s_p, is so simple that the poles can be located directly by solution of (9.53) for s_p,

$$s_p = -1 + (-1)^{1/4} K \qquad (9.54)$$

Figure 9-17 indicates the pole locations in the complex s-plane. By inspection of the figure we see that the system is unstable for $K \geq \sqrt{2}$, which means that the magnitude of the low-frequency loop transmission (K^4) must be restricted to values < 4.

The same conclusion can be reached without solving for the precise pole locations. Figure 9-18(a) shows the complex locus of $A(j\omega)$ as ω

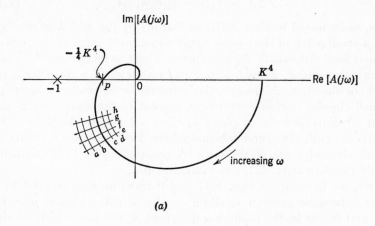

(a)

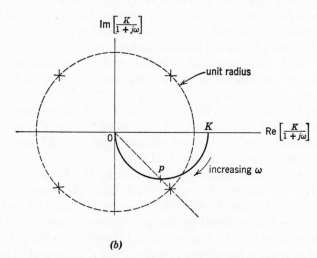

(b)

Fig. 9-18. Frequency loci of (a) $A(j\omega)$ and (b) $[A(j\omega)]^{1/4}$.

proceeds from 0 to $+\infty$. This locus, usually called a Nyquist plot, is the A-plane "map" of an s-plane curve, namely, the positive half of the $j\omega$ axis. Since the function $A(s)$ is analytic, we may express it as a Taylor series about some point s_0,

$$A(s) = a_0 + a_1(s - s_0) + a_2(s - s_0)^2 + \cdots \qquad (9.55)$$

For a small displacement

$$\Delta s = s - s_0 \qquad (9.56)$$

the higher-order terms are small and the corresponding displacement of A is

$$\Delta A = A(s) - a_0 \approx a_1 \Delta s \qquad (9.57)$$

Thus, as indicated in Figs. 9-17 and 9-18(a) by the grid lines $abcd$ and $efgh$, a small patch of the s-plane maps into a small patch of the A-plane without *local* distortion. Such mapping is said to be *conformal*. Under conformal mapping, a small square becomes a small square, not a rectangle or rhombus. Moreover, the mapping never produces inversion; a small circular *clockwise* motion of a point in the s-plane maps as a small circular *clockwise* A-plane motion, *not* counterclockwise. The relative magnification and rotation of the local map are fixed by the magnitude and angle of the complex constant a_1 in (9.57), which is simply the derivative $dA(s)/ds$ evaluated at s_0.

Now, let us compare Figs. 9-17 and 9-18(a) as K is allowed to increase. Imagine yourself standing on the $j\omega$ axis at point p in Fig. 9-17 and facing in the positive-ω direction, a direction which we shall call north. As K increases, a pole of $H(s)$ approaches from the southwest, skitters between your feet, and recedes toward the northeast. In Fig. 9-18(a), you map as an observer located at point p and facing along the Nyquist plot in the positive-ω direction, which we shall again call north. As K increases, point p moves with the expanding Nyquist plot. From the standpoint of the moving observer, the critical point (-1) appears to approach from the southwest, pass at point p, and recede toward the northeast. In fact, we could have plotted the Nyquist diagram of $A(j\omega)/K^4$, rather than $A(j\omega)$, in which case the plot would be fixed as K increases and the new critical point, $-1/K^4$, would move in from the left along the negative real axis.

Figure 9-18(b) shows another way of making the Nyquist plot, convenient when all stages of amplification have the same frequency function. Here the fourth root of $A(j\omega)$ is plotted and the single critical point (-1) is replaced by the four different fourth roots of -1. The transformation $y = x^{\frac{1}{4}}$ is analytic and therefore conformal, so that an observer at point p has similar experiences as K is allowed to increase.

Incidentally, it is also possible to plot the loop transmission $(-A)$, for which the critical point is $+1$, or the return difference $(1 + A)$, whose critical point is the origin. In any case, the result is that conformality leads to a Nyquist stability criterion, and the steady-state frequency response of the loop transmission contains the desired informa-

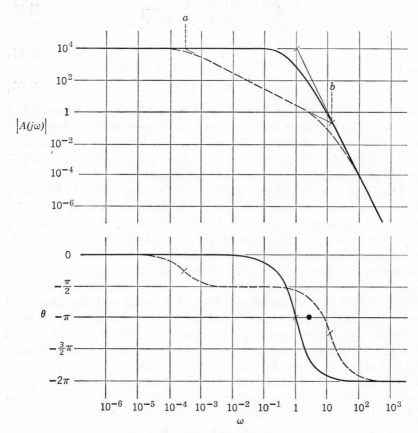

Fig. 9-19. Gain and phase curves.

——————— $K^4/(s + 1)^4$

- - - - - - - $K^4/(s + a)\,(s + b)^3$, $a < b$, $ab^3 = 1$

tion about system stability, *provided* the system is known to be stable when the feedback constant is small.

The solid-line curves in Fig. 9-19 show the gain and phase of $A\,(j\omega)$ for $K = 10$. As ω increases, the phase θ reaches $-\pi$ *before* the magnitude $|A|$ drops to unity. The Nyquist plot therefore spans the critical point and the system is unstable.

If we must insist upon keeping K at the value 10, then frequency bandwidth must be sacrificed in order to retain stability. One way to accomplish this is to alter the frequency characteristics of one of the four stages of amplification. Let the new function be

$$A'(s) = \frac{K^4}{(s + a)(s + b)^3} \tag{9.58}$$

where

$$a < b \tag{9.59}$$

and

$$ab^3 = 1 \tag{9.60}$$

In terms of Fig. 9-16, the change from $A(s)$ to $A'(s)$ can be accomplished by increasing the shunt resistance R of one stage and decreasing that of the other three, keeping the over-all low-frequency amplification (K^4/ab^3) fixed. The parameter K is the "gain-bandwidth product" g/C of a single stage and is assumed to be fixed.

The Nyquist plot and pole pattern of $A'(s)$ are shown in Fig. 9-20, for a considerably smaller than b. As ω increases from zero, the vector r_a in (b) becomes nearly vertical before vector r_b departs markedly from the horizontal. Accordingly, the Nyquist plot (a) sweeps rapidly around an approximate semicircle before phase shift due to r_b begins to accrue. Comparison of Figs. 9-18(a) and 9-20(a) emphasizes the effect. On the gain-phase curves, Fig. 9-19, the dashed lines show the initial gain-decay of one stage, beginning at a, and the associated $\pi/2$ phase lag, which are continued until $|A|$ drops to unity. Thereafter, at b, the three remaining stages may be permitted to break. Since the phase θ reaches $-\pi/2$ *after* the magnitude drops to unity (a point indicated by the heavy dot), the system is stable.

The maximum allowable a for a given K can be calculated approximately, as follows. Let n be the number of stages and ω_1 the frequency at which $|A| = 1$. Assuming $a \ll \omega_1 \ll b$, we have, from (9.58),

$$1 \approx \frac{K^4}{\omega_1 b^{n-1}} = \frac{K^4 a}{\omega_1} \tag{9.61}$$

With r_a and r_b not too far away from vertical and horizontal, respectively, in Fig. 9-20(b), and with $\omega = \omega_1$, we can write

$$-\theta = (\text{angle of } r_a) + (n - 1)(\text{angle of } r_b) \tag{9.62}$$

$$-\theta \approx \frac{a}{\omega_1} + (n - 1)\frac{\omega_1}{b} \tag{9.63}$$

Ignoring the small term (a/ω_1), setting $\theta = -\pi$, eliminating ω_1 with the

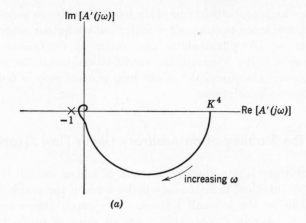

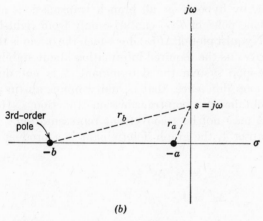

Fig. 9-20. (a) Frequency locus and (b) pole pattern of $A'(s)$.

aid of (9.61), and remembering that $ab^{n-1} = 1$, we find

$$K^{n-1}a \approx \left[\frac{\pi}{2(n-1)}\right]^{\frac{n-1}{n}} \tag{9.64}$$

Hence, in this particular example, the allowable bandwidth a of the loop transmission is nearly inversely proportional to the magnitude (K^n) of the loop transmission at low frequencies. The approximation (9.64) is conservative for small n or small K. The value of a indicated in Fig. 9-19 is roughly that given by (9.64).

No matter what the exact scheme for modifying the loop-transmission characteristics, the general result will be some effective gain-bandwidth limitation imposed by stability requirements, provided the high-frequency asymptotic behavior of the loop transmission is determined by parasitic reactance or some other factor not under our control.

If unavoidable phase shifts also occur at frequencies below the transmission band, then similar modifications must be made in the low-frequency characteristics of the loop transmission in order to avoid low-frequency oscillations.

9.10   The Stability of an Arbitrary Linear Flow Graph

An arbitrary linear flow graph, each of whose branch transmissions is a stable function, is stable only if the zeros of the graph determinant $\Delta(s)$ all lie in the left-half s-plane. The graph transmission is $T = \sum P_k \Delta_k / \Delta$, wherein P_k, Δ_k, and Δ are all sums of products of branch transmissions. If, by hypothesis, all branch transmissions are stable, then right-half-plane poles of $T(s)$ can arise only from right-half-plane zeros of $\Delta(s)$. A Nyquist plot of $\Delta(j\omega)$, for which the origin is the critical point, therefore gives us the required information about stability.

For a multiple-loop system the determinant Δ is not directly interpretable as a loop difference, that is, unity minus an (in principle) experimentally obtainable loop-transmission function. Hence the Nyquist plot of Δ may not be a convenient representation. However, as defined in Chapter 4, the graph determinant is a product of return differences

$$\Delta = \Delta_1{}' \, \Delta_2{}' \, \Delta_3{}' \, \cdots \, \Delta_n{}' \tag{9.65}$$

$$\Delta_k{}' = 1 - \tau_k{}' \tag{9.66}$$

where

$\tau_k{}'$ = loop transmission of node k, as measured with all higher-numbered nodes split or erased $\tag{9.67}$

Each of these "partial" return differences, $\Delta_k{}'(s)$, is physically interpretable and also, happily, a simpler function to plot than $\Delta(s)$. The set of Nyquist plots for $\Delta_1{}'$, $\Delta_2{}'$, $\cdots$, $\Delta_n{}'$ contains the desired information about the stability or instability of the system, as we shall now show.

First we must recognize that the Nyquist plot of any rational analytic function $F(s)$ specifies the *difference* between the number of right-half s-plane *zeros* and the number of right-half s-plane *poles*. In Fig. 9-21 the $j\omega$ axis, C, maps into the F-plane as the Nyquist plot C'. We assume here that $F(s)$ has no poles or zeros on the $j\omega$ axis. If such poles or zeros exist we can treat $F(s)$ as a limiting form in which poles or zeros are allowed to approach, but not touch, the $j\omega$ axis. Poles or zeros at infinity can be replaced by poles or zeros in a remote portion of the s-plane, say far out on the negative axis. Let us now draw any simple curve A' from the origin to infinity in the F-plane. Curve A' maps back into the s-plane as a set of curves A, each running *from* a zero *to* a pole. This follows from the fact that the roots of the equation $F(s) = A'$ vary continuously with parameter A', approach the zeros of $F(s)$ for small A', and approach the poles of $F(s)$ for large A'. Any

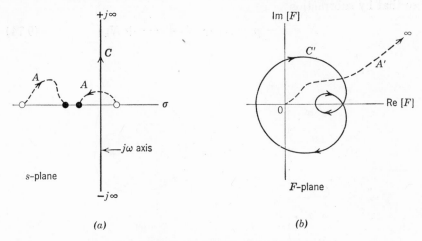

(a)   (b)

Fig. 9-21. Mapping properties of the function $F(s)$.

and all intersections of A with C in the s-plane necessarily appear *conformally* as intersections of A' with C' in the F-plane. Thinking of the curves A, C, A', C' as one-way streets, we can say that a motorist entering C from A in Fig. 9-21(a) must turn right. Conformality then requires a matching right turn from A' onto C' in (b). The conclusion is that

$$N = z - p \qquad (9.68)$$

where

N = number of *clockwise* crossings of an infinite radial curve (A') by the Nyquist plot $F(j\omega)$ as ω increases from 0 to $+\infty$ and then from $-\infty$ back to 0 (9.69)

z = number of right-half s-plane zeros of $F(s)$ (9.70)

p = number of right-half s-plane poles of $F(s)$ (9.71)

Multiple-order poles or zeros are, of course, to be counted according to their order, and curve A' should be chosen to avoid the point $F(\infty)$.

Parts (a), (b), and (c) of Fig. 9-22 illustrate the fact that the result (9.68) is independent of our guess about the precise structure of the reverse map A.

Now let us associate N, z, p with Δ and N_k, z_k, p_k with $\Delta_k{}'$, in expression (9.65). Evidently

$$z = z_1 + z_2 + \cdots + z_n \tag{9.72}$$

$$p = p_1 + p_2 + \cdots + p_n \tag{9.73}$$

so that by subtraction

$$N = z - p = N_1 + N_2 + \cdots + N_n \tag{9.74}$$

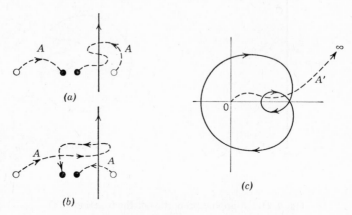

Fig. 9-22. Alternative interpretations of the mapping.

The postulated flow graph has stable branch transmissions. Its determinant Δ, made up of a sum of products of stable functions, is itself stable and therefore free of right-half-plane poles. Hence any poles p must be canceled by coincident zeros, leaving

$$N = \textit{net} \text{ number of right-half-plane zeros of } \Delta(s) \tag{9.75}$$

A given $\Delta_k{}'$ may have a right-half-plane pole, but such a pole originates from a zero of some earlier-numbered $\Delta_k{}'$, and the zero cancels the pole in the product (9.65). Thus

$$N = N_1 + N_2 + \cdots + N_n \tag{9.76}$$

together with (9.75), gives us the desired result, relating the stability of the system to the Nyquist plots of the partial return differences $\Delta_k{}'$. The system is stable for $N = 0$ and unstable for $N > 0$. A negative N is, of course, impossible.

9.11 Illustrative Examples of Feedback in Electronic Circuits

The following examples are intended (1) to bring out the general flavor of that category of circuits usually called "feedback amplifiers," and (2) to illustrate further the use of linear signal flow-graph techniques for practical calculations of amplification and impedance.

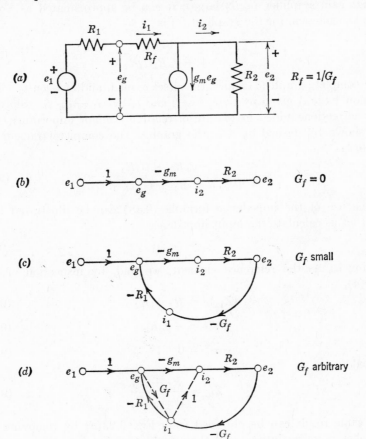

Fig. 9-23. Plate-to-grid negative feedback.

The incremental circuit model in Fig. 9-23(a) permits us to study the effect of plate-to-grid admittance in a plate-loaded triode or pentode amplifier. With a resistive feedback element R_f, as shown, the circuit is sometimes called an "anode follower." If R_f is replaced by a capacitance, we have the Miller integrator. Parts (b), (c), and (d) of Fig. 9-23 indicate the formulation of the graph by successive approximations. If we begin with $G_f = 0$ as in (b), we have the conventional plate-loaded amplifier with transmission

$$e_2/e_1 = -g_m R_2 \qquad (9.77)$$

For a small value of G_f, the effect of current i_1 is to modify e_g by causing a voltage drop in resistance R_1, as indicated in (c). Since $e_2 \gg e_g$ for a high-gain amplifier ($g_m R_2$ large), i_1 can be approximated as $-G_f e_2$. The transmission for the graph in (c) is

$$\frac{e_2}{e_1} = \frac{-g_m R_2}{1 + g_m R_2 G_f R_1} \qquad (9.78)$$

The complete graph (d) shows the effect e_g on i_1 and of i_1 on i_2. Thus we now have i_1 given by $G_f(e_g - e_2)$ and i_2 by $(i_1 - g_m e_g)$. Since the two corrections added in (d) are of relatively minor importance, they are shown by dashed lines in the graph. The complete transmission for (d) is

$$\frac{e_2}{e_1} = \frac{-g_m R_2 + G_f R_2}{1 + g_m R_2 G_f R_1 + G_f R_1 + G_f R_2} \qquad (9.79)$$

The use of the impedance formula (9.48) can be illustrated here. First let us calculate the input impedance

$$Z_{\text{in}} = e_g/i_1 \qquad (9.80)$$

Taking g_m as the reference element, we find, by inspection of Fig. 9-23(a),

$$(Z_{\text{in}})_0 = R_f + R_2 \qquad (9.81)$$

$$\tau^{oc} = -g_m R_2 \qquad (9.82)$$

$$\tau^{sc} = 0 \qquad (9.83)$$

so that

$$Z_{\text{in}} = \frac{R_f + R_2}{1 + g_m R_2} \qquad (9.84)$$

The same result can be obtained from Fig. 9-23(d) by removing the branches pointing into e_g and then evaluating the transmission i_1/e_g, which is the reciprocal of Z_{in}.

The output impedance "faced by" R_2 is

$$Z_{\text{out}} = -e_2/i_2 \qquad (9.85)$$

as measured with $e_1 = 0$ and with R_2 replaced by a current or voltage source. By inspection of the circuit,

$$(Z_{\text{out}})_0 = R_1 + R_f \qquad (9.86)$$

$$\tau^{oc} = -g_m R_1 \tag{9.87}$$

$$\tau^{sc} = 0 \tag{9.88}$$

Remember that oc and sc now refer to the output terminals. The result is

$$Z_{out} = \frac{R_1 + R_f}{1 + g_m R_1} \tag{9.89}$$

This can be verified by inspection of Fig. 9-23 (d); with branch R_2 erased, the transmission from e_2 to i_2 is the negative reciprocal of Z_{out}.

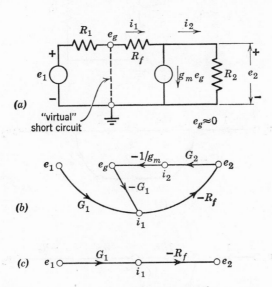

Fig. 9-24. A "virtual" short circuit produced by negative feedback.

The fact that e_g remains very small leads to the concept of a "virtual" short circuit as indicated in Fig. 9-24 (a). A virtual short circuit is an open circuit across which the voltage is known to remain negligibly small. Since the same current flows in R_1 and R_f, the virtual short circuit in Fig. 9-24 (a) acts as a "voltage fulcrum." If e_1 goes up R_1 volts, e_2 must go down R_f volts. The effect is placed in evidence by inverting the main loop of Fig. 9-23 (c) to obtain the graph of Fig. 9-24 (b). As the gain of the inverted loop approaches zero, e_g approaches zero and the transmission, given by (c), becomes

$$\frac{e_2}{e_1} = -G_1 R_f = -\frac{R_f}{R_1} \tag{9.90}$$

Another simple "feedback" circuit is the common-emitter transistor amplifier. In this circuit additional negative feedback can be introduced by an emitter load R_e, as in Fig. 9-25(a). The transistor incremental model used here neglects collector conductance ($r_c = \infty$) but includes the dependent current source ai_e or $[a/(1-a)]i_b$ and the

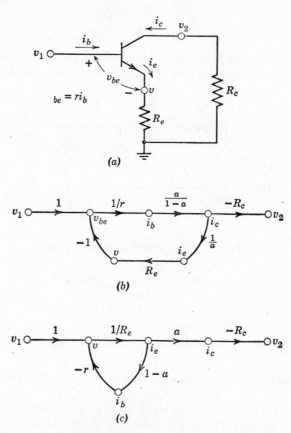

Fig. 9-25. Negative feedback due to emitter loading in a common-emitter transistor amplifier.

common-emitter resistance $r = r_b + [r_e/(1-a)]$. The graphs in (b) and (c) represent two different formulations of the circuit transmission to show the effects of R_e. Note that in (b) the feedback loop opens as R_e approaches zero and the effective current gain is the large value $a/(1-a)$. This formulation is therefore useful in emphasizing factors important in determining a-c gain. For the formulation in (c), the loop transmission decreases as R_e increases and the over-all transmission approaches that of a common-base circuit. This condition is desirable for stabilization of the d-c operating point. In fact, the common-emitter circuit is usually designed with a series impedance whose d-c resistance is large but whose a-c impedance is small. The transmission of the graph in Fig. 9-25(b) is

$$\frac{v_2}{v_1} = \frac{-\dfrac{R_c}{r}\left(\dfrac{a}{1-a}\right)}{1 + \dfrac{R_e}{r}\left(\dfrac{1}{1-a}\right)} \tag{9.91}$$

while that obtained from (c) is

$$\frac{v_2}{v_1} = \frac{-a\,\dfrac{R_c}{R_e}}{1 + \dfrac{r}{R_e}(1-a)} \tag{9.92}$$

The equivalence of these two forms is readily verified; multiplication of numerator and denominator of (9.92) by $R_e/r(1-a)$ yields (9.91).

The circuit in Fig. 9-26(a) is a two-stage RC-coupled amplifier with plate-to-plate negative feedback. An incremental model is shown in (b) and the flow graph is formulated in (c). Again, branches of secondary importance are shown dashed. Ignoring these, we have the approximate transmission

$$\frac{e_3}{e_1} = \frac{(g_{m1}R_1)(g_{m2}R_2)}{1 + g_{m2}R_2G_fR_1} \tag{9.93}$$

As might be expected, this is the same as (9.78) multiplied by the gain $g_{m1}R_1$ of the first stage. The complete expression for the transmission is

$$\frac{e_3}{e_1} = \frac{(g_{m1}R_1)(g_{m2}R_2) + g_{m1}R_1G_fR_2}{1 + g_{m2}R_2G_fR_1 + G_fR_1 + G_fR_2} \tag{9.94}$$

For sufficiently large $g_{m2}R_2$ the transmission approaches

$$\frac{e_3}{e_1} \approx \frac{(g_{m1}R_1)(g_{m2}R_2)}{g_{m2}R_2G_fR_1} = g_{m1}R_f \tag{9.95}$$

which demonstrates the insensitivity of the amplifier to changes in g_{m2}, an insensitivity produced by negative feedback around the second stage, which also makes the output impedance small.

The amplifier shown in Fig. 9-27(a) is sometimes called the "Schmitt trigger circuit." The linear incremental model for the first stage (b) can be represented as the flow graph (c). The voltages and currents in

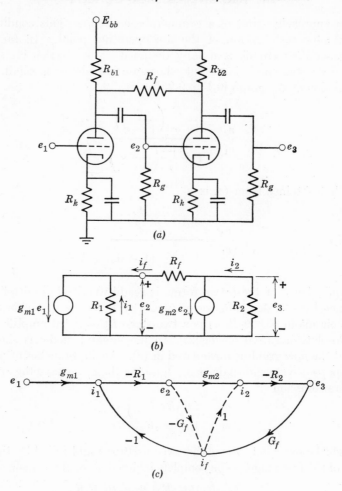

Fig. 9-26. Plate-to-plate negative feedback.

(a) are total quantities whereas those in (b), (c), and (d) are incremental. The dependence of v_1 upon e_1 and e_k can be simplified somewhat by absorption of node e_{g1}. Similarly, the internal potential v_2 of the second stage can be expressed directly in terms of e_2 and e_k, as indicated in the complete graph (d).

The major loop, from e_2 to e_k and thence back to e_2, has a positive transmission. Hence, for a certain value of the voltage-divider parameter k we may expect the incremental amplification (e_3/e_1, as found from the flow graph) to become infinite. The incremental amplification is the slope of the transfer curve in Fig. 9-28 measured in the intermediate

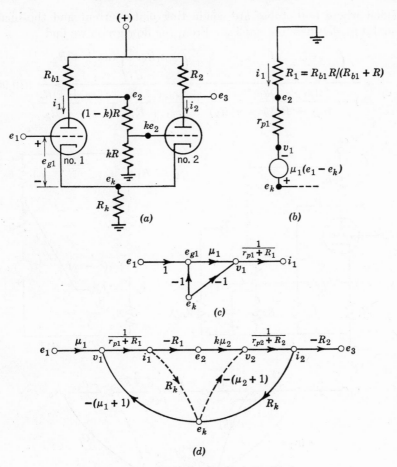

Fig. 9-27.   Cathode-to-cathode feedback.

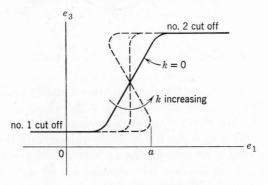

Fig. 9-28.   Transfer curves for an amplifier with cathode-to-cathode feedback.

region where both tubes are conducting plate current and the incremental model therefore applies. From the flow graph we find

$$\frac{e_3}{e_1} = \frac{\left(\dfrac{\mu_1 R_1}{r_{p1} + R_1}\right)\left(\dfrac{k\mu_2 R_2}{r_{p2} + R_2}\right) + \left(\dfrac{\mu_1 R_k}{r_{p1} + R_1}\right)\dfrac{(\mu_2 + 1)R_2}{r_{p2} + R_2}}{1 - \dfrac{(\mu_1 + 1)k\mu_2 R_1 R_k}{(r_{p1} + R_1)(r_{p2} + R_2)} + \dfrac{(\mu_1 + 1)R_k}{r_{p1} + R_1} + \dfrac{(\mu_2 + 1)R_k}{r_{p2} + R_2}} \qquad (9.96)$$

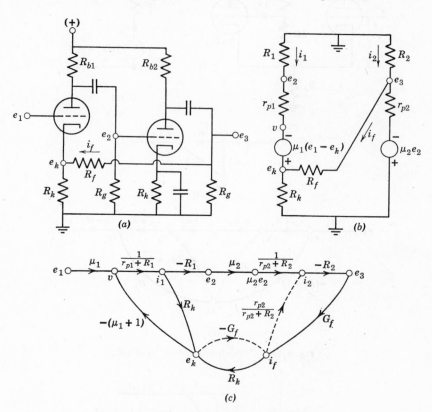

Fig. 9-29. Plate-to-cathode negative feedback.

By adjusting k to make the denominator of (9.96) vanish, we obtain the intermediate transfer curve in Fig. 9-28, whose central region is nearly vertical. For larger k the slope becomes negative in the central region, the function $e_3 = f(e_2)$ is multiple-valued, and the circuit then operates as a trigger or switch. As e_1 is increased continuously from zero, plate current in the first tube remains cut off until e_1 reaches the critical value a, at which time the first tube suddenly "switches on" (conducts) and the second tube cuts off. A subsequent continuous decrease in e_1 brings us to a new critical point, at the upper knee of the curve, and the circuit then switches back to its original state. With $k = 0$, the circuit becomes a cathode-coupled amplifier. The transmission from e_1 to e_k is then recognizable as the gain of a cathode follower with cathode load R_k in parallel with the input impedance at the cathode of the second stage (the right-hand loop of the flow graph accounts for this additional loading in parallel with R_k). The transmission from e_k to e_3 is the amplification of a grounded-grid stage. (For this calculation branches R_k may be erased, since e_k is given and therefore acts as a source node.) The over-all incremental amplification e_3/e_1 is the product (e_k/e_1) (e_3/e_k), but it is just as simple, in this case, to evaluate e_3/e_1 directly from the graph.

The circuit of Fig. 9-29(a) is a two-stage RC-coupled amplifier with negative feedback obtained by coupling from the plate of the second stage to the cathode of the first stage. In the a-c linear incremental model, (b), R_1 and R_2 are the a-c loads, consisting of R_{b1} or R_{b2} in parallel with R_g. To formulate a flow graph, we might begin with the feedback resistor R_f removed and arrive at a graph like that of Fig. 9-29(c), but without the four branches which touch node i_f. These four branches may then be added to account for the dependence of i_f upon e_k and e_3, and the influence of i_f upon e_k and i_2. Once again the branches contributing to minor effects are shown as dashed lines.

The transmission of the main loop is negative and large, having both $\mu_1 + 1$ and μ_2 as factors. The complete expression for the transmission is

$$\frac{e_3}{e_1} =$$

$$\frac{\left(\dfrac{\mu_1 R_1}{r_{p1} + R_1}\right)\left(\dfrac{\mu_2 R_2}{r_{p2} + R_2}\right)(1 + G_f R_k) + \dfrac{\mu_1 R_k G_f r_{p2} R_2}{(r_{p1} + R_1)(r_{p2} + R_2)}}{1 + \dfrac{(\mu_1 + 1)R_1 \mu_2 R_2 G_f R_k}{(r_{p1} + R_1)(r_{p2} + R_2)} + \dfrac{(\mu_1 + 1)R_k}{r_{p1} + R_1} + \dfrac{G_f R_2 r_{p2}}{r_{p2} + R_2}}$$

$$+ G_f R_k + \dfrac{(\mu_1 + 1)R_k G_f r_{p2} R_2}{(r_{p1} + R_1)(r_{p2} + R_2)} \tag{9.97}$$

If we ignore certain minor terms arising from the dashed-line branches, then

$$\frac{e_3}{e_1} \approx \frac{\left(\dfrac{\mu_1 R_1}{r_{p1} + R_1}\right)\left(\dfrac{\mu_2 R_2}{r_{p2} + R_2}\right)(1 + G_f R_k)}{1 + \dfrac{(\mu_1 + 1)R_k}{r_{p1} + R_1} + \dfrac{(\mu_1 + 1)R_1}{r_{p1} + R_1}\left(\dfrac{\mu_2 R_2}{r_{p2} + R_2}\right)G_f R_k} \tag{9.98}$$

Further simplification results if the major loop transmission is the dominant term in the denominator and if $\mu_1 \gg 1$,

$$\frac{e_3}{e_1} \approx \frac{1 + G_f R_k}{G_f R_k} = \frac{R_f + R_k}{R_k} \qquad (9.99)$$

Relation (9.99) is evidence of the fact that e_k is very nearly equal to e_1 for large negative feedback, and i_1 is small, so that approximately the same current flows in R_k and R_f. Thus the series combination of R_k and R_f is effectively a potentiometer or voltage divider, automatically controlled in such a way that the "error signal" $(e_1 - e_k)$ remains small. The potentiometer ratio is

$$\frac{e_k}{e_3} = \frac{e_1}{e_3} = \frac{R_k}{R_f + R_k} \qquad (9.100)$$

which verifies the approximation (9.99).

As a final example, let us analyze a two-stage transistor feedback amplifier, whose *incremental* model is shown in Fig. 9-30(a). In the transistor models used here we have again ignored collector admittance, so that base and emitter resistances can be accounted for by a single resistance $r = r_b + [r_e/(1 - a)]$, the effective "common-emitter" input resistance of the transistor.

Formulation of the flow graph (b) begins with the simplifying assumption that $r = 0$, after which the branch $-r$ may be added to complete the graph. The formulation is purposely aimed at a graph in which v_1 and i_2 appear as source nodes, since the amplifier has high forward-voltage gain, high input impedance, and low output impedance, and is therefore conveniently described by the standard forward-voltage-transmission flow-graph form, to which (b) reduces after absorption of all nodes other than sources and sinks. Graphs (c) and (d) are in that form. Graph (d) shows that for large negative feedback the input admittance $(1/b_1 b_2 R_1)$, the output impedance (R_2/b_2), and the reverse current transmission $(-1/b_1 b_2)$ are all small, so that the circuit approaches the performance of an ideal "voltage amplifier" with amplification $(R_1 + R_2)/R_1$. Resistance R_2 cannot be made indefinitely large, of course, because too large a value would violate the assumption that the collector admittance of the second transistor (effectively in shunt with the output) is negligible. However, R_2 can be made much larger than R_1, thereby producing a respectable amount of voltage amplification. By inspection of the graph in Fig. 9-30(b), the exact expression is

$$\frac{v_2}{v_1} = \frac{1 + \left(1 + \dfrac{R_2}{R_1}\right) a_1 b_1}{1 + \dfrac{r(1 - a_1)}{R_1} + a_1 b_1} \qquad (9.101)$$

The transistor amplifier can be viewed as an automatic control system containing a voltage divider $(R_1 + R_2)$ whose current is controlled to maintain a small "error signal" $(v_1 - v_2)$. For i_1 negligible compared to i_f and for $(v_1 - v)$ small, the voltage-division ratio is

$$\frac{v_2}{v_1} \approx \frac{v_2}{v} = \frac{R_1 + R_2}{R_1} \qquad (9.102)$$

Hence, as in (9.100), the feedback produces a transmission function which is relatively independent of the properties of the power-amplifying

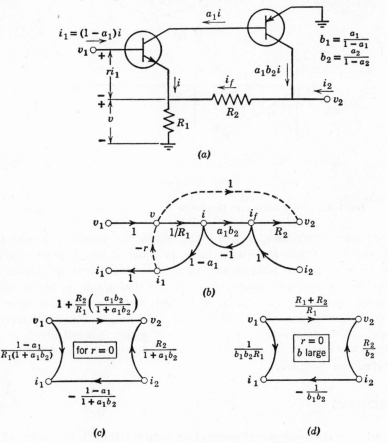

Fig. 9-30. A transistor feedback amplifier.

device, that is, the tube or transistor. Figure 9-31(a) shows an alternative flow graph designed to emphasize the "error-signal" interpretation of $(v_1 - v)$. Here the quantity $R_1/(R_1 + R_2)$ appears explicity as a factor in the main feedback path.

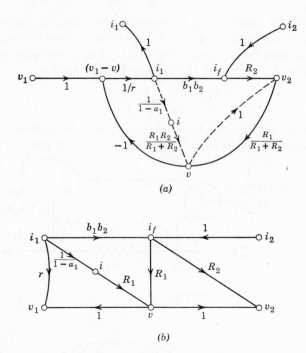

(a)

(b)

Fig. 9-31.   Alternative flow graphs for the transistor feedback amplifier.

Another alternative, Fig. 9-31(b), shows the result of formulation on the open-circuit impedance basis, in which i_1 and i_2 are the source nodes, v_1 and v_2 are sink nodes, and all source-to-sink transmissions are therefore open-circuit impedances. Notice that graph (b) has no loops. Hence one could claim (if he so wished) that the amplifier is not a feedback amplifier. However, the graph in Fig. 9-31(a) is probably a more satisfactory representation of the situation, since it places in evidence the concept on the basis of which the circuit was probably conceived and designed.

PROBLEMS

9.1   Using a nonlinear element whose output voltage is the square of the input voltage, design a feedback circuit whose output voltage approximates the square root of the input voltage. Assume that a high-gain linear voltage amplifier is available.

9.2 Relate Fig. 9-4 to the cathode-follower circuit, treating the cathode-to-grid voltage e_g as the error v_ϵ.

9.3 A high-gain voltage amplifier and a vacuum diode, whose plate current is an exponentially decreasing function of negative plate voltage, are available. Design a feedback amplifier whose output voltage is approximately the logarithm of the input voltage.

9.4 In Fig. P9-1, the amplifier A has infinite input impedance, zero output impedance, and an amplification $A = e_b/e_a$. A unit step voltage is applied at the input e_1. Find the values of A and k such that the step response

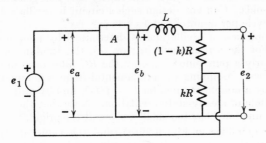

Fig. P9-1

at e_2 has the same final value as, but is ten times faster than, the step response which would be obtained with $k = 0$ and $A = 1$. Relate this result to the steady-state frequency-response characteristics of the system.

9.5 A "low-pass" signal, v_1, whose spectrum has negligible energy above some frequency ω_0, is passed through a nonlinear amnesic filter f. The distorted result, v_2, is then sent through a linear low-pass filter L which tends to block frequencies above ω_0. It is claimed that the low-pass output signal, v_3, contains all of the information present in v_1 and that v_1, or possibly a delayed replica of v_1, can be recovered from v_3 by suitable processing. Consider and discuss a recovery scheme such as that in Fig. 9-5(a), with both f and L in the feedback path. What about stability of the system?

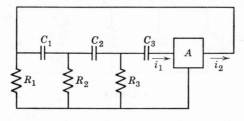

Fig. P9-2

9.6 The system in Fig. P9-2 is usually called a "phase-shift oscillator." The transistor current amplifier A has negligibly small input impedance, high output impedance, and a current amplification $i_2/i_1 = -A$, where A is a positive constant. In practice, $C_1 < C_2 < C_3$ and $R_1 > R_2 > R_3$, but for the purposes of this problem let $C_1 = C_2 = C_3 = C$ and $R_1 = R_2 = R_3 = R$.

(a) Draw a suitable flow graph.

(b) Plot the Nyquist diagram of the loop transmission.

(c) Find the critical value of A for which the circuit oscillates.

(d) Calculate the frequency of oscillation.

(e) Now interchange the positions of R_1 and C_1, R_2 and C_2, and R_3 and C_3, and repeat the analysis. Does arrangement (e) have any practical advantages over the original arrangement shown in Fig. P9-2?

(f) Suggest a design based upon a voltage amplifier rather than a current amplifier.

(g) Phase-shift oscillators are convenient for the generation of low-frequency sinusoids. Can you design such a circuit to oscillate at 1 cycle per second? at 1 cycle per minute? at 1 cycle per day?

(h) The amplitude of oscillations is determined by nonlinearities in the amplifier A. For the arrangement in part (e), the amplifier input signal is likely to be nearly a pure sinusoid, since the RC filter discriminates against higher frequencies. Assuming the fundamental-frequency amplitudes I_1 and I_2 are related by a nonlinear function $I_2 = f(I_1)$, find by graphical construction the amplitude of steady-state oscillation. Note that the circuit will not oscillate if the function f has too small a slope at the origin.

9.7 For the amplifier in Fig. 9-29(a), find the value of R_f required to produce 0.01 sensitivity of e_3/e_1 to changes in μ_2. Insert practical numerical values for the circuit parameters.

9.8 In Fig. 9-23, find the sensitivity of the voltage amplification to changes in g_m. Insert practical numbers and calculate the value of R_f required for a sensitivity equal to $\frac{1}{10}$.

9.9 Suppose that the system in Fig. 9-2(a) has $K = 1/(\tau s + 1)^n$ and $K_0 = 100$. Quantity A is a positive real parameter.

(a) Sketch the Nyquist plots of the return difference (1 minus the loop transmission) for $n = 1, 2, 3$, and 4. For what critical value of A/K_0 does the system become unstable for $n = 1, 2, 3$, and 4? In each case, at what frequency does the system oscillate when A/K_0 reaches the critical value?

(b) Now let $K = 1/(\tau s + 1)^2 (10\tau s + 1)$. Sketch the Nyquist plot and find the critical value of A/K_0. Compare with the results for $n = 3$ in part (a).

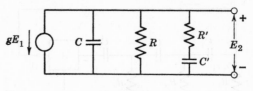

Fig. P9-3

9.10 To trade bandwidth for increased low-frequency loop gain in the amplifier of Fig. 9-16, consider the modification of *two* of the stages as shown in Fig. P9-3. Assume $R' \ll R$ and $C' \gg C$, so that the poles of the modified stage are located approximately at the points $s = -1/R'C$ and $s = -1/RC'$. There is, of course, a zero at $s = -1/R'C'$.

(a)   Sketch the gain and phase curves, and also the Nyquist plot, of the loop transmission, with R' and C' chosen to maintain a reasonable stability margin for a low-frequency loop transmission whose magnitude is 10^4.

(b)   Does it help to allow different R' and C' values for the two modified stages?

(c)   Discuss the results of identical modification of all four stages. In this case the system is "conditionally stable"; the system can be made stable only for some *intermediate* range of values of the loop scale factor.

9.11   The oscillator circuit shown in Fig. P9-4 can be used as a frequency modulator, provided the modulating signal e_m has only frequency components lying well below the frequency at which the circuit oscillates. The

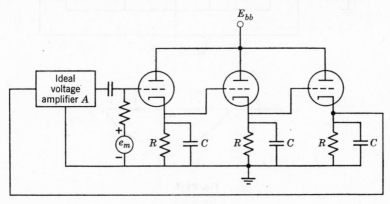

Fig. P9-4

pole location of each cathode-follower stage varies as a function of e_m, because e_m changes the operating point of the tube, and hence alters g_m. For large R, the pole of each stage is located approximately at $s = -g_m/C$.

What is the value of amplification A required to make the circuit oscillate? Assume the d-c amplification of the cathode followers to be unity. What is the frequency of oscillations in terms of g_m/C?

9.12   A negative-feedback control system is designed, built, and turned on. It oscillates at 10 cycles per second. To stop the oscillations, someone suggests inserting a 10-cycle-per-second rejection filter into the loop. This suggestion is carried out, whereupon the system no longer oscillates at 10 cycles per second but at a new frequency f_1. Someone else suggests the insertion of an additional rejection filter to block frequency f_1. What is going on here, anyhow?

9.13   In Fig. 9-23(a), replace R_f by a capacitance C and plot the Nyquist diagram of the loop transmission of branch g_m in the flow graph (d). Is the system stable? Find the input and output impedances as functions of frequency.

9.14   Under certain simplifying assumptions, the circuit in Fig. P9-5(a) can be represented approximately as the flow graph (b). Carry through the details. Find e_2/e_1 for $k = 0$ and for $k = 1$, and compare the bandwidth, gain, and output impedance in the two cases.

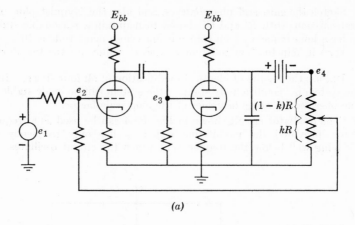

(a)

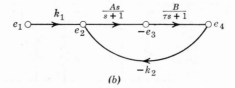

(b)

Fig. P9-5

9.15 For the amplifier in Fig. 9-30(a) calculate the sensitivity of v_2/v_1 to changes in b_2. Choose practical values for all circuit parameters except R_1 and R_2 and discuss the choices of R_1 and R_2 for large v_2/v_1 and small sensitivity. Design the amplifier, including d-c polarizing voltages not shown in the incremental model. What are the numerical values of input and output impedance?

9.16 For the system in Fig. 9-13, let $a = 1.5/(s + 1)$ and $b = 0.4/(s + 1)$. Determine the stability or instability of the system by examining the Nyquist plots of the partial return differences at nodes 2, 3, 4, and 5 (see Article 9.10). Verify the result by direct location of the poles of the transmission v_5/v_1. Is the system stable with branch b erased?

9.17 In the circuit of Fig. 9-30(a), we can say that "r_1 should be several times larger than the apparent impedance at the emitter of the first stage, for otherwise the feedback current i_f would be effectively shunted to ground and the loop transmission would be small." We also know that "with v_1 applied, the amplifier produces a v nearly equal to v_1, so that i is considerably smaller than i_f and approximately the same current flows in R_2 and R_1." Are these two statements contradictory? Explain. First give a physical interpretation of the loop transmission of node i_f in the flow graph, Fig. 9-30(b).

9.18 For the amplifier in Fig. 9-23(a), choose practical numerical values for all parameters and carry out a quantitative analysis of the circuit.

(a) Calculate such quantities as amplification, input impedance, output impedance, and loop transmissions around those principal elements that are likely to produce distortion or drift in the actual physical circuit.

(b) Discuss possible sources of instability, if any.

9.19 Repeat Problem 9.18 for the circuit in Fig. 9-25(a).

9.20 Repeat Problem 9.18 for the circuit in Fig. 9-26(a).

9.21 Repeat Problem 9.18 for the circuit in Fig. 9-29(a).

9.22 Repeat Problem 9.18 for the circuit in Fig. 9-30(a).

9.23 Calculate the impedance faced by R_k in the circuit of Fig. 9-27(a). Do this from the given flow graph, after suitable slight modification of the graph.

9.24 For the circuit in Fig. 9-27(a), choose practical numerical values for all parameters except k and then calculate the value of k required to make the incremental voltage amplification infinite.

9.25 Discuss the frequency response of the amplifier in Fig. 9-26(a). In particular, how is the bandwidth changed by the addition of feedback? (Ignore the reactances of the cathode bypass capacitances and concern yourself with coupling capacitances and with parasitic plate-to-cathode shunt capacitances.)

9.26 For the amplifier in Fig. 9-30(a), give an explanation for the low output impedance. In particular, interpret the circuit as an automatic control system and discuss the control action taking place in response to a change in the externally injected current i_2.

9.27 For the amplifier in Fig. 9-30(a), give an explanation for the low input admittance. In particular, interpret the circuit as an automatic control system that tends to maintain v nearly equal to v_1.

Bessel Functions of the First Kind

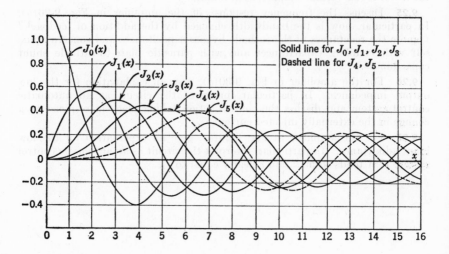

I N D E X

Almost-periodic signals, 184
Alternating component, 190
Amnesic system, 549
Amplification in a time-varying system, 511
Amplifiers, flow-graph analyses of, 157–172
Amplitude modulation, 515
  receiver, 517
  transmitter, 516
Amplitude quantization, 544
Analytic continuation, 377, 378
Analytic function, 337
Autocorrelation, 218
Automatic control, 566
Average signal power, 184

Balanced square-law mixer, 519
Band-pass transmission, 428
Binary numbers, 545
Binomial delay system, 466
Butterworth function, 426

Carrier delay, 366
Cascode amplifier, 170
Cathode-coupled amplifier, 169
Cathode follower, 37
Characteristic resistance, 443
Circle diagram, 392
Circuit analysis, flow-graph, 127
  matrix, 6
  topological, 54

Coder for PCM, 547
Complex exponential signals, 335
Complex power, 41, 42
Components, direct and alternating, 190
  even and odd, 193
  real and imaginary, 194
Content, of a signal, 237
Contour integration, 376
Convolution, 215
  algebra, 326
  equations, 330
  flow graphs, 331
Correlation coefficient, 198–204
Correlation efficiency, 200
Correlation function, 206–213
Correlation of input and output signals, 343
Crosscorrelation, 212
  of spectra, 279

D-c amplifier, chopper-stabilized, 523
Decibels, 359
Decilogs, 358
Decoder for PCM, 548
Delay, of carrier and envelope, 366
Determinant, 14
  expansion of, 16
  in loops, 110
  factorable, 111
  of flow graph, 107
  of matrix, 14
  partial factoring of, 56

613

Direct component, 190
Distortion reduction, by means of feed-
    back, 577

Energy signal, 181
Ensemble average, 187
Envelope delay, 366
Equations, cause and effect form of,
    94, 127
Even component, 193
Exponential transforms, 369
    properties of, 373

Feedback amplifier, 585, 595, 598, 600,
    601, 602, 605
Floating admittance matrix, 27, 31, 36
Flow graph, branch inversion, 117
    determinant of, 107
    loop inversion, 115
    path inversion, 115, 116
    reversal of, 122
    transmission of, 99, 104, 114
Flow graph for, cascaded network, 137
    reciprocal circuit, 134
    transistor model, 157
    triode model, 157
    unistor network, 155
Fourier, integral, 232, 242
    representation, completeness of, 249
    series, 222, 242
        exponential, 227
        properties of, 231
        trigonometric, 222
    transforms, 235
Frequency-modulation spectrum, 532
Frequency multiplexing, 534

Gain and phase, 358, 365, 589
Gain-bandwidth product, 357
Gaussian pulse, 181, 182
Graph transmission, 100
Gyrator, 71
Gyristor, 71

Hilbert transformation, 360-364

Ideal delay, 440, 464
Idealization of circuits and signals, 311
Imaginary component, 194
Impulse, modulator, 536

Impulse, response, 318
    signal, 181
Integrator, 3, 38, 396

Laplace transforms, 369
Linear systems, 310
    definition of, 318
    superposition in, 320
Loop, 101
Loop-current analysis, 145
Loop transmission, 101
    of a branch, 105
    of a node, 105
Low-pass transmission, 422
Lumped attenuator, 450

Matched signals, 347
Matrix, 6
    column, 7
    diagonal, 7
    element, 7
    equations, 13
    floating admittance, 27
    hermitian, 43-45
    inversion, 12, 17
    multiplication, 9
    nodal admittance, 20
    nodal impedance, 24
    operations, 8
    rectangular, 7
    row, 7
    square, 7
    triangular, 7
Miller integrator, 3, 38, 396
Mixers, square-law, balanced, 519
        unbalanced, 518
Modulation, amplitude, 515
    frequency, 531
    phase, 531
    pulse, 535
    single-side-band, 528
    suppressed-carrier, 520
Modulators, balanced, 508
    "chopper"-type, 506
    pentode, 508
    square-law, 507
Multiplexing, frequency, 534
    time, 538
Multiplication of signals, 505
Multiplier, 508, 510

Negative feedback, cathode-to-cathode, 601
  control of impedance by, 583
  control of transmission by, 569, 572, 575
  plate-to-cathode, 602
  plate-to-grid, 595
  plate-to-plate, 600
Nepers, 358
Network, determinant, 55
  models, 132
  path, 57
  tree, 55
  two-terminal-pair, 129
Nodal, admittance matrix, 20
  impedance matrix, 24
Node, absorption of, 81, 98
  splitting, 105
Node-voltage analysis, 145
Noise reduction by means of feedback, 577
Nonlinear systems, 503
  synthesis, 549
Normalization of branch transmission, 120
Nyquist plot, 588, 590, 591

Odd component, 193
One-pole all-pass transmission, 436
One-pole transmission, 385
  characteristics of, 391
  circle diagram, 392
Orthogonal components, 195

Paley-Wiener criterion, 361
Path, 101
Path transmission, 101
Paths and loops, flow graph, 100
Pentode amplifier, 172
Periodic signals, 182
  and spectra, 261–269
Pole, 376
Polynomial approximation of nonlinear system, 510
Probabilistic system, 471
Probability density, 186
Pulse-amplitude modulation (PAM), 535, 538
Pulse-code modulation (PCM), 543
Pulse-duration modulation (PDM), 542

Pulse-forming line, 460
Pulse-position modulation (PPM), 542
Pulse signals, 180
  and spectra, 251–261

Quality factor Q, 420

Random-phase transmissions, 458
Random process, stationary, 188
Random signals, 185
  and spectra, 269–279
Rational transmissions, 432
RC circuit analysis, 386
RC circuit frequency response, 404
Real component, 194
Real part integral, 354
Realizable frequency-response function, 350
Reflection coefficient, 447
Reflection of waves, 444
Residue of a pole, 376
Resonance in an RC feedback circuit, 418
Resonant two-pole transmission, 406

Sampling circuit, 536
Scattering coefficients, 455
Self-loop, 96
Sensitivity, 579
Signal analysis, 178–287
Signal components, direct and alternating, 190
  even and odd, 193
  real and imaginary, 194
Signal flow graph, 93
Signals, almost-periodic, 184
  form constants of, 237
  matching of, 345
  periodic, 182
  processing of, 2
  pulse, 180
  random, 185
  transmission of, 2
Singularity signals, 310
  differentiation of, 311–313
  symbols for, 316
Source node, 95
Spectrum bounds, 237
Square-law mixer, 518
Stability, 584
  of a linear flow graph, 592

Stable system, 324
Stationary random process, 188
Superposition integral, 320
  correlation interpretation of, 324
  forms of, 322
  graphical interpretations of, 321, 323
Suppressed-carrier, demodulation, 522
  modulation, 520
System function, 340
Systems, linear, 310
  nonlinear, 503
  time-varying linear, 503

Time average, 187
Time-varying, capacitance, 512
  linear system, general model, 514
Topological analysis, 54
  transmission law, 59, 66, 76
Transforms, exponential, 369
  properties of, 373

Transmission, automatic control of, 566
  nonlinear, 569
  one-pole, 385
  two-pole, 399
Transmission law, topological, 59, 66, 76
Tuned circuit, 413
  flow graphs for, 416
Two-channel modulation system, 524
  vector representation of, 526
Two-pole transmission, 399

Unilateral constraints, 153
Unistor, 62
  analysis, 68, 69

Variation of a signal, 237
Vectors, 195

Wave launching, 449
Wiggliness of a signal, 237